AFRICA

A New Geographical Survey

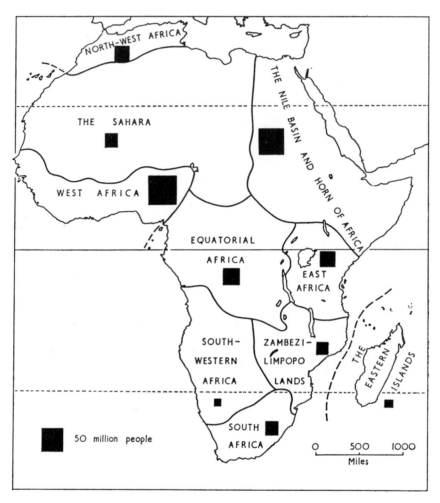

Figure 1 *The divisions of Africa as used in the text.* The total population of each is shown for comparison

AFRICA

A New Geographical Survey

ALAN B. MOUNTJOY

and

CLIFFORD EMBLETON

With a contribution by
W. B. MORGAN

FREDERICK A. PRAEGER, *Publishers*

NEW YORK • WASHINGTON

BOOKS THAT MATTER

Published in the United States of America in 1967
by Frederick A. Praeger, Inc., Publishers
111 Fourth Avenue, New York, N.Y. 10003

The original edition of this book
was published in 1966
by Hutchinson Educational, London
as *Africa: A Geographical Study*
This edition has been greatly revised
and brought up to date by the authors

Library of Congress Catalog Card Number: 67–11686

Printed in the United States of America

Contents

Maps and Diagrams

Plates

Preface

There is a great need for up-to-date texts on Africa incorporating the multitude of recent political, economic and social changes, and the more detailed information that has become available in these post-war years. It is hoped that this book will go some way to fill the gap, and will help to illuminate and give deeper understanding to many of the problems that are being, and have yet to be, resolved in Africa. The text is so presented that emphasis falls upon the variety of social and economic changes that are taking place in contemporary Africa.

For ease of treatment the continent has been divided into a number of Parts (Fig. 1) and the physical geography of each Part is presented first as a base for the subsequent consideration of the political units it contains. The regional approach has been adopted, although the treatment is not stereotyped and is adjusted to suit the varying character of different countries and the reliability and availability of information. Since neither of the authors is familiar with West Africa, they sought the aid of Dr. W. B. Morgan, formerly of University College, Ibadan, and it is with gratitude they record that he is responsible for most of the material on that part of the continent.

The spelling of African place and tribal names varies between different authorities. Here, where there seemed any doubt, *The Times Atlas of the World,* Vol. IV (mid-century edition), has been followed. Quantities are expressed in metric tons unless stated otherwise.

The last few years have seen the founding and growth of universities in many African countries. A marked increase of interest in African studies by scholars in the United States and Britain is indicated by the establishment of special schools at various universities and by the founding, in 1957, of the African Studies Association of the United States and, in 1963, of the African Studies Association of the United Kingdom. One consequence of these moves is increasing research into African problems and a growing list of related publications. These developments are underlined, and it is hoped to encourage further reading by the inclusion of a selected list of mainly recent books and articles appended to each Part.

We acknowledge with pleasure the help and encouragement of a number of our colleagues at Bedford College, particularly Professor Gordon Manley and Professor B. C. King for helpful comments on the climatic and geological sections respectively; Dr. Brenda Turner for advice on Part VII on East Africa, and the ever-helpful staff of the College Library.

April, 1967   A.B.M.

                                                                              C.E.

For better or for worse the old Africa
is gone and the white races must face
the new situation which they have
themselves created.

Jan Christiaan Smuts

Introduction

The great compact land-mass of Africa is second only in size to Asia. This is not widely appreciated, perhaps because the fact is somewhat disguised by the projections frequently used for world maps. In fact, the area of 11,700,000 sq. miles is four times the size of the United States, and the variations and diversity within Africa are far greater than in North America. Africa is also the most tropical of continents: it is almost bisected by the equator and 9 million sq. miles of Africa lie within the tropics. This is one of the factors that delayed discovery and penetration and now retards economic development. From the Mediterranean to the Cape it is 5,000 miles, and from Dakar to Cape Gardafui on the Horn of Africa 4,600 miles. This sheer size of Africa aggravates the problems posed to those seeking to outline its geography, for no longer do we agree with Jonathan Swift that:

> . . . geographers, in Afric maps,
> with savage pictures fill their gaps,
> And o'er unhabitable downs
> Place elephants for want of towns.

An ever-growing body of literature is now available to enlarge and enrich our knowledge of the continent. Certainly, our real knowledge of Africa is very recent: a hundred years ago the course of the Congo had not been defined. However, no longer is Africa the 'Dark Continent', for, while there is much still unknown, in recent years governments, both colonial and independent, and international organisations such as UNO and UNESCO have made public the results of many scientific, social and economic surveys and have prepared much statistical material of increasing reliability.

Most of the data is basic and economic in character: numbers of people, where they live, how they live, their standards of living and plans for the future. It underlines the dominant fact that Africa is largely an undeveloped continent, the bulk of its inhabitants among the poorest on the earth. The last two decades have seen the emergence of a world conscience much disturbed by the great and growing differences in the wealth of nations. Strong support and help is now being given to measures designed to raise the national income of the world's poorer countries. Thus world attention has become focussed on economic development in Africa and upon the economic and political significance of the rising nationalism that has marked the end of the colonial era over most of the continent.

Economic development and political development both involve change. Contemporary Africa is a continent of change: economies are being transformed, social structures and ideologies modified and aspirations lifted. We are, however, by now aware of stale clichés that no longer have impact: 'Africa is awake, on the march, in a ferment.' Perhaps they have been overdone, but we must not overlook the fact that in Europe the series of technological and social revolutions, developing one from the other, were spread over at least two centuries, but in Africa they have come together. The continent is now passing through agricultural, industrial, technological, social and political revolutions all at once. At no other time in history have dynamic forces of such magnitude racked the societies of this or any other continent. Peoples recently self-sufficient and living in relative isolation are being swept into the complexities of a Western commercial way of life, into close contact with other tribes and faiths and into new social and political groupings.

In the decade 1954–64 the number of independent African states more than quintupled: a staggering fact. With fifty divisions (ignoring microscopic enclaves) the average area of African states is still high (234,000 sq. miles), but the population is low (av. 5 million). Here lies the root of many economic difficulties—an excess of area and a deficiency of population: 'The average African state is a pygmy staggering in an outsize robe' (Hamdan). The weaker a state, the greater its need of friends and assistance; one consequence of this excessive fragmentation is being demonstrated in attempts to play off Western democracies against Eastern communist states in the seeking of aid.

It is a new Africa we are studying. For good or ill, colonial Africa is practically finished: a new chapter in Africa's long but little recorded history is beginning. A geographical study of Africa today is fascinating and exciting, for in relation to the diversity and limitations of the African environment it gives us a fuller understanding of the explosive dynamism of the African economic and social scene.

PART I

The Physical Basis

In terms of physique, as in other aspects of its geography, Africa is a continent of extremes. Its land surface ranges from 440 feet below sea-level to nearly 20,000 feet above sea-level; lofty mountain ranges and majestic volcanic cones contrast sharply with endlessly undulating plains and plateaux. The rocks of Africa, yielding most of the world's diamonds and uranium, and two-thirds of the world's gold, include both the youngest and the most ancient known on earth. The continent possesses the world's largest desert, and at the same time, high rainfall areas such as Mount Cameroon with 400 inches annually. Africa is the most tropical of continents, yet it embraces snow-clad peaks standing almost on the equator, and whole regions in the Atlas have been known to be isolated by snow for weeks at a time. Its vegetation ranges from tropical rain forest and mangrove swamp to mountain tundra, its soils from tropical red earths to podsols. Africa contains many of the world's largest rivers—the Nile, flowing for over 4,000 miles, is claimed as the world's longest—but the continent bears no major tracts of river alluvium to compare with those, for instance, in south or east Asia. Although it lacks great mountain barriers on the scale of the Himalaya or the Cordillera of the Americas, it possesses in the Rift Valley one of the greatest fractures in the earth's crust, and, in the Drakensberg, one of the most magnificent of escarpments.

I

Geology and Structure

The larger part of the continent of Africa consists of a great continental shield, stretching between the Atlas in the north and the Cape Ranges in the south, and comparable in form and origin with the Brazilian or Laurentian shields. Since the end of the Pre-Cambrian this shield area has acted as a relatively rigid block; it has been subjected to vertical movements and has been fractured, but it has suffered only slight folding. Yet it must not be thought that the structure of this area is a simple one; it is becoming increasingly clear that the rocks of the African shield bear the impress of several periods of ancient (Pre-Cambrian) earth-movement, though there is now little or no topographic manifestation of these old structures, because of subsequent denudation. But around the north-western and southern extremities of the African shield there are examples of later folding—the Atlas and Cape Ranges—where the present land-forms are still related to the orogenic structures.

THE GEOLOGICAL RECORD (Fig. 2)

Over vast areas the basement rocks of Pre-Cambrian age may be seen, and it is these ancient basement rocks, sometimes referred to as Archaean, which underlie virtually the whole continent. Geological maps do not always agree precisely over the surface outcrops of these and other rocks, for in addition to the fact that many areas are still incompletely surveyed, the rocks in the tropical regions are often deeply weathered and surface exposures of solid rock may be infrequent. There are also large tracts where recent deposits conceal the solid geology (e.g. the Kalahari). However, even the most conservative estimates indicate that Pre-Cambrian rocks outcrop over one-third of the total surface area of the continent. They are particularly extensive over West Africa and the Sudan, throughout much of East Africa, and in Rhodesia, and it is in the upper Pre-Cambrian rocks that many valuable minerals, such as gold, copper, chrome and manganese, are located. The Pre-Cambrian formations consist not only of igneous and metamorphic rocks (Archaean) but also include in places very great thicknesses of unfossiliferous sediments.

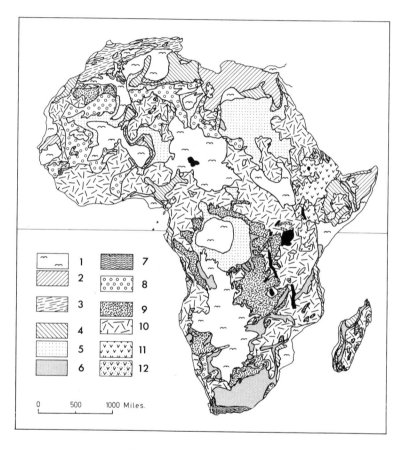

Figure 2 *The geology of Africa*

1. Quaternary (undifferentiated) and continental Tertiary (unfolded). 2. Marine Tertiary (unfolded). 3. Atlas folded zone. 4. Marine Mesozoic (unfolded). 5. Continental Mesozoic other than Karroo (unfolded). 6. Karroo (unfolded). 7. Cape folded zone. 8. Palaeozoic (other than Karroo). 9. Younger Pre-Cambrian. 10. Older and undifferentiated Pre-Cambrian. 11. Post-Jurassic lavas. 12. Other igneous

Following the Pre-Cambrian period there is usually a great gap in the geological record, representing the first of many long intervals of erosion to which Africa has been subjected. Over the whole of southern Africa, for instance, outcrops of Lower Palaeozoic sediments are very restricted in extent, and the next major rock series belongs mainly to the Devonian. Devonian sandstones and shales form the Cape Ranges, packed into folds around the Pre-Cambrian basement by Permo-Triassic earth-movements. In northern Africa the record of Lower Palaeozoic sedimentation is more complete, though still patchy; in West Africa and parts of the Sahara shallow seas have left limestones, sandstones and shales.

We now come to the most important series of sedimentary rocks in central-southern Africa. It is known as the *Karroo System*, made up of rocks varying in age from Carboniferous to Lower Jurassic, and originally covered most of the south-central parts of the continent, from the Cape to the Congo Basin. It has since been denuded from some regions, but still attains a thickness of 25,000 feet in South Africa. Resting with marked unconformity on the older rocks, the Karroo System consists entirely of continental sediments, apart from some volcanic rocks near the top of the series; these sediments accumulated under conditions varying from glacial to arid, and are the products of prolonged erosion of the Pre-Cambrian basement. Economically, they are exceedingly important, for they contain in South Africa and the Rhodesias the only significant coal seams in the whole continent.

Broadly comparable in age with the Karroo System are certain continental formations in the Sahara. First, there is the series of *Nubian Sandstones* in Libya and parts of the Sudan, where sediments accumulated in broad basins from the Carboniferous to the early Cretaceous. Secondly, in the western Sahara there is the *Continental Intercalaire*, consisting of sandstones, conglomerates and clays of Jurassic and Cretaceous age.

The only significant marine formations in Africa are of Jurassic and later age. In northern Africa sagging of the continent allowed shallow flooding of extensive areas by Cretaceous and Eocene seas which left limestones and sandstones; parts of West Africa were similarly invaded. South and central Africa, in contrast, remained a land area, and marine formations are only to be found in the coastal regions, where down-warping allowed great thicknesses to accumulate locally.

The Tertiary period saw the gradual withdrawal of the sea from northern Africa. The newly exposed portions were again subject to sub-aerial denudation, and the continental weathering products of the later Tertiary and Quaternary once again accumulated in basins, many of which have no outlet for drainage. In southern Africa, apart from continued marine deposition on the coastal margins, the deposits of the Tertiary and Quaternary represent sub-aerial denudation of the interior, and in the Kalahari reach a thickness of about 500 feet.

From this brief review of the geology of Africa a number of important points emerges. In the first place, the part played by the Pre-Cambrian basement must be stressed. It not only provides the foundation of almost the whole continent but also possesses a wealth of mineral resources. Secondly, it must be noted that the geological record is very incomplete, and that many areas have for long periods been subject only to erosion. Thus it is not surprising to find that many of the landscape features are of considerable antiquity. A study of the geomorphology of Africa in fact provides much evidence on the evolution of the continent at those times when gaps appear in the geological record. Thirdly, of all the sedimentary formations of Africa south of the Atlas, the continental Karroo System and its Saharan equivalents, the Nubian Sandstone and Continental Intercalaire, are the most extensive and significant. The Karroo System contributes much to the scenery of South Africa in particular, where it also contains about 97 per cent of Africa's coal resources. In the Sahara the Nubian Sandstone and Continental Intercalaire are the major water-bearing formations beneath the desert surface. Lastly, it will be observed that there are relatively few areas of marine sediments in Africa south of the Sahara, which is why this part of the continent is generally lacking in oil resources, a fact that adds greatly to the significance of the Karroo coal-bearing deposits. In the north of the continent, on the other hand, the great potential oil resources contained in the marine formations of the Sahara, West Africa and Suez are only just being appraised.

THE STRUCTURAL EVOLUTION OF THE CONTINENT

It is believed by many geologists that the Pre-Cambrian block of Africa was once united with the other southern continents of the globe in one great land-mass to which the name Gondwanaland has been attached (Fig. 3). The evidence for the former union of the southern continents comes from many varied sources; there are some remarkable similarities in their geological records, there are biological links, and, most important, portions of all the southern continents were subjected to extensive glaciation in the Carboniferous period, which is exceedingly difficult to explain if these portions were not at that time joined closely together. At some stage in the Mesozoic era it has been suggested that Gondwanaland gradually separated into blocks resembling the present southern continents (though without some of their present major fold ranges); most geologists now agree that this separation occurred by 'continental drift'.

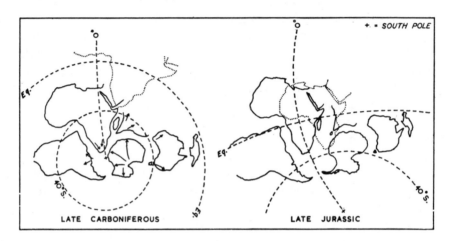

Figure 3 *Reconstructions of Gondwanaland according to L. C. King.* In each case, the outline of Africa in its present position is indicated by dots. In the late Carboniferous, ice movement is shown by arrows; the gaps between the continents are occupied by continental shelves and sub–oceanic ridges (oblique stereographic projections)

L. C. King[1]* has put forward the view that the present continent of Africa was born in the early Cretaceous period with the final dismemberment of Gondwanaland, and he contends that portions of the Gondwana land surface are still recognisable in the present landscape in the form of extensive planation surfaces generally at altitudes of over 4,000 feet. He also argues that some of the present major features of Africa were initiated with the break-up of the Gondwana land-mass. First, a new coastline not dissimilar to the present-day one was created; subsequent modifications to the outline of the continent south of the Sahara have been mainly concerned with the addition of new areas of land by deposition. Secondly, because the interior surface of Gondwanaland probably rose to 2,000 feet above its original distant margins, fracturing of this land-mass produced escarpments of considerable size towards

* Figures in the text = references at the end of each part.

its centre. Thus Africa, most of which lay near the centre of Gondwana-land, emerged as a continent with a high interior plateau in the centre and south, bounded with steeply rising sides. Subsequently, erosion has pushed back these bounding escarpments from their original coastal position, but in places they are still today features of great magnitude. The escarpment of the Natal Drakensberg (Plate 10) rises to over 10,000 feet, though a great part of this height is due to later uplift in the Cretaceous and Tertiary periods.

The third major result of the fracturing of Gondwanaland was the dismemberment of the existing river systems. In the African block, many rivers were deprived of their former lower courses, and made their exit abruptly to the new coastline. As a result of resistance by the rocks in many cases, these rivers are far from having readjusted their profiles; the effect has been greatly accentuated by later uplift of the continental interior. Thus the present major rivers of Africa possess waterfalls or cataracts of considerable size in their lower or middle courses, while their upper portions in the heart of the continent, not yet affected by this rejuvenation, are usually more mature in aspect.

Since the supposed disruption of Gondwanaland and the birth of Africa, earth-movements have continued to affect the continent. Apart from the fold belt of the north-west, these movements have been of an epeirogenic nature and, excepting the coastal margins, have been princi-pally of uplift. Indeed, it appears that such movements have been charac-teristic of this land-mass throughout its known geological history: it can often be demonstrated that axes of warping and lines of faulting follow ancient trends, in some cases dating back to the Pre-Cambrian.

Unequal uplift and differential faulting have between them produced some of the major features of present-day Africa (Fig. 4). The interior of Africa is characterised by the existence of a series of great basins, separated by gently rising uplands or plateaux. These basins represent areas which have lagged behind in the general uplift of the interior and have become the repositories for erosion products worn off the surround-ing rises. The age of the basins varies considerably. The Congo Basin, for instance, must have been initiated in the Palaeozoic era as a downwarp in the Pre-Cambrian floor, since it contains sediments of Karroo age, and this applies to other basins of southern Africa. In fact, the presence of softer Karroo sediments in some of the basins has enabled the river systems to expand easily within the basins, and in some cases (e.g. the lower Zambezi) to maintain an outlet from the basin in spite of further uplift of the basin rim. There are other basins in Africa which, however, are of much more recent origin; thus the Chad Basin is due to Quaternary downwarping, and Lake Victoria occupies a gentle crustal sag associated with the later phases of rift valley evolution.

Throughout southern Africa there has been a general tendency for the

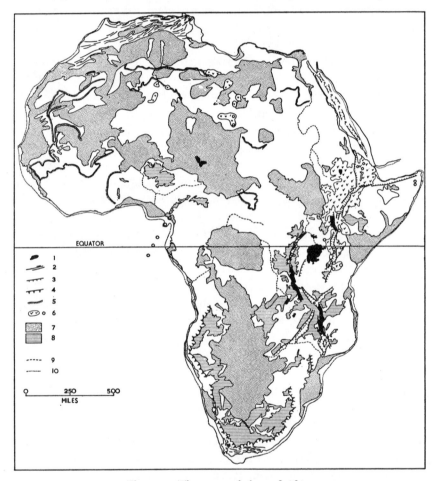

Figure 4 *The geomorphology of Africa*

1. Lakes. 2. Fold Mountains. 3. Faults of the East African Rift Valley System. 4. The Great Escarpment of Southern Africa. 5. Erosion scarps in Northern Africa. 6. Post-Jurassic Volcanics, and associated volcanic cones. 7. Tertiary and Quaternary sediments. 8. Erosion surface remnants ascribed to the Gondwana and African cycles by L. C. King. 9. Major rivers (only part shown for reference). 10. 100-fathom line of the sea floor

rim of the continent to rise intermittently since Karroo times, due to the existence of a great monoclinal flexure running parallel with the coast, which was initiated in the early Jurassic. It is of great structural importance in Natal, where the Karroo beds have been tilted in its vicinity at angles up to 45 degrees to the east and south-east. It probably continues through the Cape region, curving north into South-West Africa. On the seaward side of this flexure the downwarping has allowed the accumulation of great thicknesses of Jurassic-Tertiary marine sediments, while in the interior the zone of maximum elevation has been along the Drakensberg and Rhodesian highlands and to a lesser extent along the South-West African highlands. The Kalahari Basin in the centre has, however, risen more slowly than these surrounding uplands. From recent gravity surveys it appears that the Natal monocline at least is still tectonically active.

The East African Rift Valleys

The effects of faulting on the African block are demonstrated on an immense scale in the rift valleys of East Africa (Fig. 4). Recent work by Dixey[2] indicates that here also the structures may be of great age, possibly originating in the Pre-Cambrian, though very recent (Plio-Pleistocene) movements are more obvious in their topographic effects. The rift valley system includes the Red Sea trough and extends as far north as Syria; its other extremity in Africa lies south of Lake Malawi (formerly Lake Nyasa). Apart from the Red Sea section, the width of the rift valleys is remarkably consistent, usually averaging 25 to 30 miles; in East Africa the sides rise frequently to heights of over 6,000 feet, whilst the floor of Lake Tanganyika, for instance, lies 2,150 feet *below* sea-level. But undoubtedly the most imposing feature of the rift valleys is the great horst of Ruwenzori, situated between Lakes Albert and Edward, standing in the rift valley yet rising to 16,800 feet and capped with snowfields and glaciers. Though there are several areas of extinct volcanoes (as in Ethiopia or in the region of Mount Kenya and Kilimanjaro) and one area of active vulcanism (west of Lake Victoria) associated with the rift valleys, there are also some parts, surprisingly, where there are no signs of volcanic activity at all.

Various hypotheses have been put forward in an attempt to explain the origin of the rift valleys. J. W. Gregory (1921)[3] thought that initial compression of the crust produced an arch, and that an axial section of this arch collapsed downwards when the pressure was released and replaced by tension; but there are many objections to this notion. In the first place, unless there was an empty space for the 'keystone' of this crustal arch to fall into (which is manifestly absurd), one would expect a great deal of molten material to be displaced from below: yet, as we have noted, vulcanism is absent from many parts of the rifts. Secondly, gravity surveys carried out in 1933-4 by an expedition under E. C. Bullard showed that in general there is an excess of light matter under the rift floors; thus, they would tend to rise in order to re-establish isostatic equilibrium, but in fact must be held down by some stronger force. This is incompatible with Gregory's suggestion of crustal tension allowing the free collapse of the arch. And, thirdly, it is impossible to account for the existence of Ruwenzori on this hypothesis, where a section of the African plateau has been thrust up 10,000 feet above its normal elevation in this area.

E. J. Wayland (1921)[4] brought forward an ingenious alternative to Gregory's hypothesis in suggesting that compression of the African plateau produced major thrust faults and forced sections of the crust downwards (rifts) or upwards (horsts). This hypothesis is compatible with Bullard's gravity surveys, and also with the absence of volcanic activity in some areas, for the faults would remain tightly closed. Furthermore, Bullard has used this hypothesis to explain why the width of the rift valleys is so constant. But there are still many unsolved problems. Structures typical of crustal compression are hardly ever seen; in contrast, some very large normal faults are known to exist. Further gravity surveys have shown the existence of areas where the rift floors must be underlain by relatively dense matter (as in the Red Sea), or where departures from isostatic equilibrium are very small (e.g. near Nairobi). And, most important, it is abundantly clear that the rift valleys are not new features of the African continent but have a long and complex history. Some sections of the rifts contain great thicknesses of Mesozoic and Tertiary sediments which, being relatively light, might explain by themselves the results of Bullard's gravity surveys. It is also known that sections of the rift valleys have at one time been partially infilled with such sediments and later exhumed, so that the steep sides seen today in such cases are really ancient fault-line scarps, possibly rejuvenated by more recent faulting.

The Fold Mountain Systems

Thus the African block has suffered faulting and differential uplift on a gigantic scale, together with extensive warping. Very different structures are to be found at its northern and southern extremities, however (Fig. 4). In the north-west the Atlas fold mountains stretch for about 1,500 miles from southern Morocco to Tunisia, and possess peaks of more than 13,000 feet. Details of their configuration and structural history are complex, and can only be outlined here. Essentially the Atlas region lies between the Mediterranean area, the site of an old land-mass of which only fragments now remain (Corsica, Sardinia, etc.), and the main African continental shield. Between these two land-masses a geosyncline of varying dimensions, known as the Tethys, existed since the Jurassic, and in it accumulated great thicknesses of sediments, including massive limestones. The folding and uplift of these sediments, together with portions of the African shield, were accomplished by pressure between the two land-masses, directed mainly from the north. The most important folding occurred in the mid-Tertiary. Since the pressure came from the north, the area of most intense folding is that of the Rif, now flanking the Mediterranean Sea. Farther south, the folds of the High Atlas and Saharan Atlas are more open, since the sedimentary rocks here rest on the African shield.

In South Africa the Cape Ranges are also of folded structure, though less complex and of more ancient formation. They attain heights of almost 8,000 feet. The folds follow two different trends: generally north-south in the western Cape Province, but east-west along and behind the south coast. In the area of the Hex River Mountains the two fold directions cross and produce locally complex structures. Most of the folding took place in the late Triassic, with pressure presumably coming from that part of Gondwanaland which then lay to the south.

2

Landforms

Though Africa south of the Atlas is entirely lacking in recent fold mountains, it is not without its high peaks and plateaux. There are in fact five distinct areas of the continent outside the Atlas where the land rises to over 10,000 feet (Fig. 6). In the Sahara the isolated mass of Tibesti attains a height of 11,204 feet, while to the south-west, in the Sudan, the highland of Darfur reaches 10,073 feet. The high peaks of Tibesti are extinct volcanic cones, and in many other parts of Africa we find similarly that volcanic activity has been responsible for the highest elevations. The Cameroon Mountain (13,350 feet) is a volcano which has recently shown signs of activity and is high enough to experience occasional snow. Volcanic rocks in Ethiopia reach a height of over 15,000 feet; continuing southward into East Africa there are no less than six mountain masses of over 13,000 feet, four of these being volcanic in origin, and one (Kilimanjaro), the highest point of Africa, rising to 19,340 feet. Finally, in Lesotho, where the Drakensberg Escarpment is capped with Karroo lavas, the maximum altitude so far surveyed is 11,425 feet.

The contribution of volcanic activity to the morphology of Africa is thus impressive. There are, however, some high mountains of non-volcanic origin, notably in the High Atlas (maximum 13,664 feet), and also in the region of the rift valleys (e.g. Ruwenzori 16,794 feet) where earth-movements have thrust up portions of the African block to abnormal levels. It must be remembered, too, that the volcanic cones or lavas in east and south Africa rest on relatively high portions of the continental shield: thus the base of Kilimanjaro stands on the East African plateau at about 5,000 feet.

The greater part of Africa consists of plateaux, renowned for their extent and for their uniformity of level over large areas. About 62 per cent of the continent lies at over 1,200 feet; while if we take Africa south of the equator the equivalent figure is nearly 80 per cent, and the proportion of land over 3,000 feet no less than 47 per cent. The highest plateaux of Africa are found in the east of South Africa at 4,000 to 6,000 feet, rising still further in Lesotho* to the edge of the Drakensberg, in Rhodesia and Zambia at 3,500 to 5,000 feet, and throughout much of East Africa (up to 6,000 feet in the vicinity of the rift valleys). On the opposite side of the continent the greater part of the Angola plateau lies between 3,000 and 5,000 feet. As one proceeds north of the equator, however, the general levels of the plateaux decrease. Throughout the territories formerly known as French Equatorial Africa the land lies mainly between 1,500 and 3,000 feet; in West Africa only restricted areas exceed 2,000 feet, and the most common elevation is 1,000 to 1,500 feet. The Sahara desert, though still strictly a plateau, rarely rises above 1,000 feet except where it is traversed from west-north-west to east-south-east by the Ahaggar-Tibesti highlands.

Sunk into the plateau surfaces of Africa are the great basins (Fig. 5), whose structural origins have been indicated in the preceding chapter. Nearly all these basins have very restricted outlets to the sea, and portions of several possess only inland drainage. El Juf, in the west of the Sahara, sinks in its centre to below 500 feet and in this part is completely arid; farther south, the Upper Niger enters from the Guinea highlands, and only just succeeds in maintaining its flow in the dry season around the great bend near Timbuktu before making its exit in a south-easterly direction. The Chad Basin, except for a small corner which is tapped by the Benue river, is a true interior drainage basin, though Lake Chad does not occupy the hydrographic centre, since it drains underground to the Borkou oases farther north-east. In southern Africa parts of the Kalahari are basins of inland drainage. The Cubango (Okovango) and other rivers drain southward into the Okovango swamp and neighbouring pans; farther west there is the separate Etosha pan; while in the south the Molopo river drains in flood-time to the Abiquas Puts. In contrast with these basins of interior or limited drainage the well-watered Congo Basin possesses an integrated river system in the heart of the continent, its floor lying 1,000 to 1,500 feet above sea-level. Its outlet, however, is still very restricted where it cuts through the plateau rim.

Because of the general plateau nature of the continent, coastal lowlands are not extensive. Nowhere have the great rivers built up wide alluvial

* Formerly Basutoland.

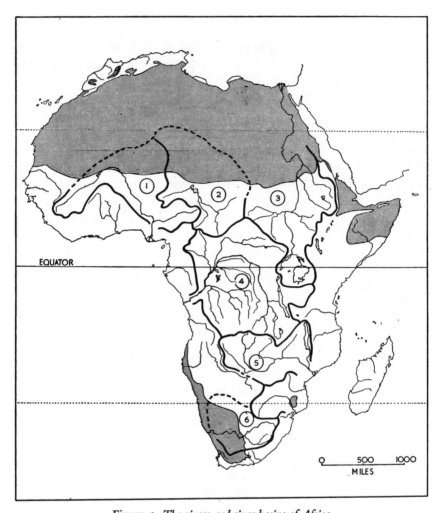

Figure 5 *The rivers and river basins of Africa*
1. Niger. 2. Chad. 3. Nile. 4. Congo. 5. Zambezi. 6. Orange. Areas with
less than 10 inches of rainfall annually are shaded

plains in their lower courses, since these courses are either entrenched or ungraded. The largest single delta in Africa is that of the Niger (about 16,000 sq. miles). True coastal plains occupying larger areas than this are limited to the following:

(i) the Moçambique plain
(ii) the coastal belt of Somalia and part of Kenya
(iii) the coastal plains of Mauritania and Mali.

The Nile delta, though supporting nearly 60 per cent of Egypt's population, occupies less than 10,000 sq. miles.

The coastline of Africa south of the Atlas region is characterised by a lack of major indentations or peninsulas. The total length of coastline is 17,000 miles, compared with 36,000 miles for Asia, which is one and a half times the size of Africa. It is true to say that in no other continent have there been such difficulties in finding approachable and protected harbour sites. Frequently the shoreline is unbroken by any sizeable inlets for hundreds of miles. Furthermore, the river mouths, with one exception, are either deltaic or blocked by sand-bars. The Congo is the only major river possessing a deep-water estuary. Several of the most important ports in Africa have been enormously expensive to construct as a result of the lack of naturally protected deep-water sites. Takoradi and Tema in West Africa are entirely artificial ports; that of Beira in Moçambique has proved very costly to maintain and improve in what can only be described as a mediocre situation.

It should also be noted that the continental shelf of Africa is relatively narrow, and in a few places virtually non-existent. The 100-fathom line approximating to the edge of the shelf usually lies within 15 or 20 miles of the coast; in some stretches (e.g. Angola, Somalia or southern Natal) it approaches within 3 miles. The only two areas of more extensive shelf are off Cape Agulhas in South Africa (where the shelf edge at 130 fathoms lies 130 miles from the coast at its most distant point), and off the coasts of Portuguese and former French Guinea (up to 120 miles from the coast to the 100-fathom line). The lack of extensive shelf areas means that the feeding grounds for fish are limited.

PLANATION SURFACES AND ESCARPMENTS

One of the most characteristic elements of African morphology is the planation surface.* It was emphasised in discussing the geology of Africa that there have been many gaps in the stratigraphical record, representing long intervals of time when processes of erosion were dominant over vast areas. Throughout the whole history of the evolution of Africa there appear to have been many occasions when these processes of erosion were able to continue until a surface of subdued or negligible relief was produced. These planation surfaces thus represent the end-

* This term is preferred to that of 'erosion surface', since the latter does not imply bevelling of the landscape.

products of individual cycles of erosion. They frequently bear little relation to the underlying rock structures, bevelling the various rocks indiscriminately. The continent of Africa is renowned for the extent and perfection of form of its planation surfaces; lying at various levels now, it is these surfaces which give rise to the general plateau nature of the continent.

The development of planation surfaces has also been helped by the general stability of the Pre-Cambrian basement, which, though affected by epeirogenic movements, has nowhere suffered sharp folding since early Pre-Cambrian times. Furthermore, only in northern Africa have more than limited areas been affected by periods of marine submergence and deposition. Some planation surfaces are in fact generally recognised as being of great age; examples are known which date from the Jurassic and have never since been covered by any extensive deposits. Still farther back in geological history, planation surfaces are known to have been covered by later deposits, and are now in process of being 'exhumed' as the deposits are again stripped off by recurrent erosion. Partially exhumed surfaces can theoretically be traced laterally to a point where they become geological unconformities, and thus their age can be determined; but in other cases complete exhumation may make it impossible to differentiate such an ancient surface from one of more recent formation.

The exact processes which lead to the formation of extensive planation surfaces in Africa (and other continents) are still in dispute. They are certainly sub-aerial, and intimately related to the drainage system. The surfaces are usually separated by scarps, which may vary in height from a hundred feet or so to as much as 4,000 feet, and it is these bounding scarps which provide much vital evidence on the origin of the surfaces they serve to separate. It is by 'retreat' or erosion of the scarps that the surfaces expand in size. On small-scale maps the scarps may appear as linear features, but viewed closely they consist of a series of gorge-like re-entrants, the deepening and widening of which results in overall scarp recession. There is little evidence that, once a planation surface is bevelled, it continues to be lowered in altitude by general denudation. W. M. Davis's views on the overall down-wearing of peneplains are not generally accepted. Once such a surface is formed, there is no appreciable process at work causing it to be further lowered, and it can only be destroyed by recession of its bounding scarps and entrenchment of any rivers crossing it as a result of rejuvenation; alternatively, it may be buried by later deposits. Thus it becomes possible for a whole series of planation surfaces to co-exist in a landscape which has suffered intermittent uplift, each being destroyed slowly by retreat of the scarp separating it from the next lower surface, but in the meantime preserving its original bevelling. The size of the planation surface will vary according to the length of time available for its formation; thus examples are known in Africa of surfaces which are almost continental in extent, whilst at the other extreme more recently cut surfaces occur within the lower parts of the major river valleys, witnessing smaller intervals between periods of rejuvenation. The rate of recession of the bounding scarps seems to be very variable, relating first and foremost to local rock structure and character of the drainage pattern.

The ages of the various planation surfaces in Africa are often matters for considerable controversy. In a few cases a surface may be overlain, for example, by later fossiliferous deposits or volcanic rocks whose age can be ascertained, but it is still not known how long before such deposition the planation of the surface was achieved. Attempts have been made to trace an individual surface to coastal regions with the hope of correlating it with some local marine unconformity but, once again, the method often breaks down in practice. Correlation of separate fragments of a planation surface is made much more difficult, too, by the differential faulting and warping which have affected many parts of Africa, so that correlation from one region to another by absolute altitude of the surface is unlikely to be valid. Nevertheless, the distribution and approximate age of the major African planation surfaces are now becoming generally clear.

We may mention first of all a surface mainly important in southern Africa. This is known as the *sub-Karroo surface*, which represents the gradual exhumation of large parts of the unconformity at the base of the Karroo System. Wherever Karroo rocks are found, the surface is obviously still buried. Because of its great age it has undergone much warping and tilting in places, and has been dislocated by Karroo or post-Karroo faulting.

Secondly, L. C. King has recognised a *Gondwana surface*, which he claims was bevelled some time before the disruption of Gondwanaland (Fig. 4). It now lies generally at altitudes of 4,000 feet and over in southern Africa. Other workers prefer to use less specific terms, and refer to it as the early Cretaceous surface. There is, in fact, evidence that more than one surface of this age exists. Various other Cretaceous surfaces have been claimed, but the next major one has been named the *African* or *Great Miocene surface*, bearing witness to a cycle of erosion which destroyed large parts of the so-called Gondwana surface. The African surface varies in southern Africa from 2,000 feet near the coasts to as much as 5,000 feet inland as a result of warping. Later still, the End-Tertiary surface was produced; in the Zambezi valley, the recession of the Victoria Falls represents this cycle cutting into the higher African surface. More recent phases of erosion (Plio-Pleistocene) have been studied in the lowest parts of the African river valleys.

All these surfaces fall steadily in altitude as they are traced into northern Africa. At the same time, the vertical intervals separating them also become reduced, so that on the southern margins of the Sahara the various surfaces are almost impossible to distinguish. Farther north they disappear beneath Cretaceous or Tertiary deposits. These facts show clearly that the continent of Africa has been affected by greater total uplift in the south than in the north.

3

African River Systems

Each of the five major African rivers for some part of its course flows through, and receives drainage from, one or more of the great structural basins of the continent (Fig. 5). There is a tendency for drainage to be concentrated towards the centre of each basin, and for there to be only one outlet from the basin. The evidence available generally indicates that the drainage lines within each basin are of considerable antiquity, whilst the present outlet in several cases is of comparatively recent origin. The following accounts of the development of the main river systems are inevitably generalised; many more field studies are necessary before the precise evolution of river-courses in Africa can be established. Five main river systems will be discussed: those of the Nile, Niger, Congo, Zambezi and Orange (Fig. 6).

It is thought that in the mid-Tertiary period the early Nile had its source about latitude 18–20°N, and from there flowed northward to the sea in accordance with the slope of the various planation surfaces. One of its headstreams may have been the present River Atbara. In the Sudd region south of Khartoum there existed an enclosed drainage basin, containing an immense lake, which received drainage not only from the adjacent uplands but also from the northern rift valley (Lakes Albert and Edward). At a later stage (about 25,000 years ago) Lake Victoria developed a new outlet through the tilting of the East African plateau, and also sent its waters to Lake Sudd. The level of Lake Sudd gradually rose, and overflowed into the Atbara-lower Nile stream at a point named Sabaloka (50 miles north of Khartoum). The overflow waters cut down rapidly, and Lake Sudd was drained (about 21,000 years ago), thus unifying the drainage from Lake Victoria to the Mediterranean.

The evolution of the Niger's course also involves the formation of a

temporary inland lake. In the mid-Tertiary the upper Niger was a
headstream of the Senegal river, until increasing accumulations of sand
and gravel in the region north of Bamako forced the river to flow north-
eastward into the centre of the Timbuktu Basin. At times in the late-

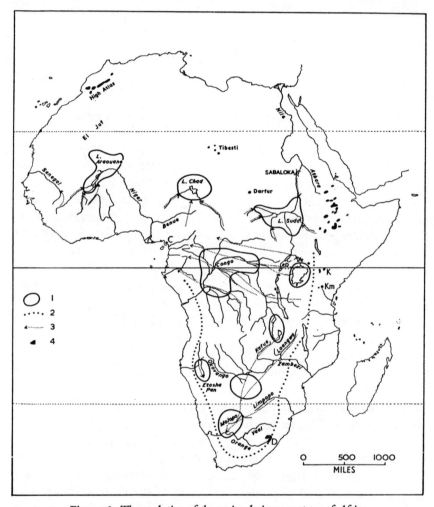

Figure 6 *The evolution of the major drainage systems of Africa*

1. Present and former basins of inland drainage (south of the Sahara).
2. Former watershed representing the 'rim' of southern Africa. 3. Former
drainage lines. 4. Land over 10,000 feet

C Cameroon Mountain, K Mount Kenya, R Ruwenzori, D Drakensberg,
Km Kilimanjaro

Tertiary and Quaternary a lake formed here (named Araouane after the village north of Timbuktu) when the flow of water from the upper Niger was in excess of evaporation. Deposits in the lake, however, rapidly built up until the lake basin was virtually infilled; and during one of the wetter periods of the Quaternary it seems that drainage began to escape eastward from the basin at Tosaye (160 miles east of Timbuktu) into the valley of what is now the lower Niger. Headward erosion of the Lower Niger, facilitated by soft sediments flooring this section of its valley, may have hastened this diversion.

The early history of the Congo is somewhat obscure. An initial outlet into the Chad Basin has been suggested and, later, an outlet across the Cameroun Republic to the Gulf of Guinea. It is quite certain, however, that the present outlet of the basin, from Leopoldville to Matadi, is of very recent origin. It appears that earth-movements blocked up the early outlets of the Congo Basin, forcing the waters to accumulate in a vast lake. This lake is known to have existed until early post-Glacial time on archaeological evidence, for there is a fascinating story of the migration of early lake-side settlements up the hill slopes as the lake-level rose. Eventually the lake spilled over just west of Leopoldville, and the cutting of the great gorge seen now in the present lower course of the Congo began. Today only swamps and restricted lakes bear witness to the existence of Lake Congo in the interior.

The story of the Zambezi and Orange river systems is less well known, though it seems that their evolution is inseparably linked together. The early drainage of southern Africa appears to have been directed into the Kalahari Basin, including the upper Zambezi, the present Okovango, the Vaal and upper Orange rivers. There is evidence, too, that the lower Limpopo and lower-middle Zambezi troughs did not at this time exist; that the Loangwa in Zambia also drained south-westward to the Kalahari; and that the upper Limpopo also flowed to the Kalahari in a direction opposite to its present one. In the early Tertiary the rising rim of Africa (Fig. 6) emphasized the basin structure of the Kalahari, and possibly resulted in a decrease of rainfall in the interior. At times evaporation losses may have accounted for all the water entering the Kalahari by the above-mentioned rivers. In any case, the rivers brought heavy loads of sand and alluvium into the basin, thereby raising its floor-level, and enabling an outlet to be formed for any excess drainage in the neighbourhood of the present lower Orange river. It is now necessary to refer to the opposite side of the continent where, in Cretaceous times, the island of Madagascar was split off from the east coast. It is believed that this was related to the disruption of Gondwanaland. At the same time, trough-faulting occurred along what are now the lower Limpopo and lower-middle Zambezi valleys. Powerful, steeply graded streams developed draining east into the new Moçambique Channel now separating Madagascar, and extended headwards along the fault-troughs, capturing in turn the Loangwa, Kafue and upper Zambezi rivers, and also reversing the Limpopo drainage. This deprived the Kalahari Basin of much of its drainage, and the Orange-Vaal system soon ceased to receive any water from the north. In this southern part of the Kalahari several dry gorges can be seen, and the present width of the Orange gorge below Aughrabies Falls may be due to the former greater volume of the lower Orange. In dry winters the Orange river now fails to reach the sea.

In these examples of river development in Africa it can be seen that a number of common factors have operated. In each case it is likely that the basins now traversed by the rivers were at certain stages basins of inland drainage, where the inflow of water was either accounted for by evaporation or stored temporarily as a lake. Three main factors appear to have been responsible for the formation of outlets from these basins to the sea:

(i) if a lake was present the water-level rose until the lake spilled over at the lowest available point. Thereafter, downcutting of the spillway drained the lake.

(ii) deposition of alluvium raised the floor-level of the basin until its altitude equalled or exceeded that of the lowest point of the basin rim; drainage could then escape from the basin at this point.

(iii) the basin was tapped by the cutting-back of a powerful river, thus capturing the inland drainage. This hypothesis must be used with care; it is unlikely to apply where the coastlands outside the basin are arid.

Thus, whilst one can legitimately argue that the lower Zambezi cut back from the Moçambique coast and captured the Loangwa and upper Zambezi, it is absurd to suggest that the lower Orange cut back from the west coast to capture the Kalahari drainage, for the west coast here is a desert one; there would be no river at all here at a time when the Kalahari was totally an area of inland drainage.

Today some other basins of inland drainage are in process of being tapped by powerful external streams, these streams deriving their power from the recent uplifts of the continent. Thus the Benue is gradually extending into the Chad Basin, and recession of Victoria Falls on the Zambezi will at some distant date capture some of the Okovango drainage.

THE LONG PROFILES OF THE GREAT RIVERS

Comparison of the five profiles drawn to the same scale on Fig. 7 reveals the well-known fact that all are ungraded in their lower courses. The Congo drops nearly 1,000 feet in the last 250 miles of its course; the Niger possesses falls at Jebba, 450 miles from the sea; the Aughrabies Falls (480 feet high) on the lower Orange are within 350 miles of the coast; whilst the Zambezi possesses many natural interruptions in its lower-middle course, culminating in the 350-foot-high Victoria Falls. The cataracts on the Nile between Aswan and Khartoum are less spectacular, but again lie in the lower half of the river. The first cataract at Aswan is 500 miles upstream from the head of the delta. These water-falls are all primarily the result of rejuvenation following uplift; they are large-scale knick-points, sometimes held temporarily at a resistant rock barrier, but otherwise gradually migrating upstream, and cutting into the next higher surface. Even in the case of the Nile cataracts the existence of rock bars is of secondary importance; the rock outcrops have merely arrested the recession of knick-points resulting from rejuvenation.

The rivers therefore reflect clearly this one aspect of the evolution of Africa: that the continent has suffered intermittent uplift on an immense scale, but that each uplift was preceded and followed by periods of relative stability. The waterfalls and cataracts (knick-points) were initi-ated at or near the coast by uplift, and have receded inland for distances which are a measure both of local rock-resistance and of the length of time that has elapsed since the initiation of the knick-points. In addition, the fact that Africa has been gradually tilted to the north has meant that the knick-points on the lower Nile are of smaller dimensions than those on the more southerly rivers.

Between the various falls and rapids there are stretches of more gentle gradient. The Congo between Kinshasa and Kisangani* has an aver-age slope of less than 4 inches per mile; the White Nile in the Sudd region from Juba to Khartoum falls only 1 inch in every 2 miles on average. These sections represent the alluvial floors of the old lake basins; in such parts the rivers wander through swamps and split up into a maze

* Formerly Stanleyville.

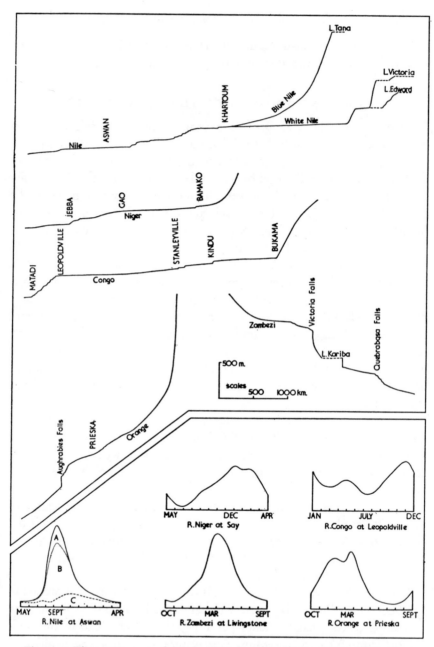

Figure 7 The upper part of the diagram shows the long profiles of the five
principal rivers of Africa. Note that within 400 miles of the sea, all are
interrupted by falls or cataracts. The lower part of the diagram gives the
régimes of each of these rivers at selected points. The vertical scale showing
discharge is not the same for each. In the case of the Nile, the portions lettered
A, B, C, show respectively the proportion of water contributed by the Atbara,
Blue Nile and White Nile

of channels, and their main work is in deposition, in contrast to the active erosion of the steeply graded sections.

The Orange river has the steepest overall gradient of the five main rivers; it rises at 10,800 feet in the Drakensberg, and at no point on its course does the gradient drop below 1½ feet per mile. It also has the distinction of being the only African river to rise on one side of the plateau and flow to the opposite coast.

THE RÉGIMES OF THE GREAT RIVERS

The variations in discharge of the rivers throughout the year are dependent on climate. Since the climate of Africa has not yet been considered, the river régimes can only be discussed briefly here and in general terms. It is, however, valuable at this stage to compare the régimes of the five great rivers, so that a comprehensive picture of the African river systems may be built up.

The graphs in Fig. 7 show the mean annual variations in discharge at one point on each of the five rivers:

> Lower Nile (Wadi Halfa)
> Middle Niger (Say)
> Lower Congo (Kinshasa)
> Middle Zambezi (Livingstone)
> Middle Orange (Prieska)

In some cases the mean monthly discharge is plotted; at others, the mean monthly water-level. The points of gauging on the Nile, Congo and Orange are chosen to illustrate the behaviour of the trunk stream below the confluence of the main tributaries. On the Zambezi a point is chosen above the Kariba Dam, whilst on the Niger a clearer picture is obtained of the river's behaviour by studying its régime just after it emerges from the Timbuktu Basin.

Four of the graphs show a simple variation between one period of low water and one of high water each year. The April maximum on the Zambezi at Livingstone reflects the summer rainfall of the upper Zambezi Basin. The October maximum on the Nile at the Egyptian border results from monsoon rains in the Ethiopian highlands feeding the Blue Nile. The December-March season of high water on the Niger at Say is also caused by monsoon rains, this time in the Guinea highlands.

The régime of the middle Orange appears at first sight to possess double maxima, but this is solely due to irregularities of flow within the twenty-five-year recording period. The season of high water from November to April reflects in the first month or so the melting snows of the Basuto-land Mountains, and subsequently the summer rainfall of the High Veld. In this season it becomes a raging muddy torrent, equal in magnitude to the highest floods on the Zambezi, whilst at the other end of the year its flow diminishes to a mere trickle.

The régime of the lower Congo is more complex, with two maxima, in May and December, because of the many large tributaries which the Congo possesses, gathering water from $1\frac{1}{2}$ million sq. miles of land. Over this vast area the rainfall maxima occur in different months, so that the various rivers contribute floodwaters at different times. The net result on the lower Congo is a régime for which no simple explanation can be given but which shows smaller differences between high and low water than any other major river of Africa.

With the exception of the Congo, then, all the major rivers of Africa have markedly seasonal régimes. In the case of the lower Nile the mean maximum discharge is 13 times the mean minimum discharge. The corresponding factor for the middle Zambezi is 11, and for the middle Orange over 14.

THE HISTORICAL AND ECONOMIC SIGNIFICANCE OF THE GREAT AFRICAN RIVERS

The three most important uses for rivers in Africa are navigation, irrigation and power generation. The first is nowadays the least important, but in the past the navigability of sections of the great rivers was vital in enabling the interior of the continent to be penetrated and developed. However, the existence of the great falls never very far from the coast on the rivers south of the Sahara was to a large extent responsible for the relatively slow penetration of parts of the continent in the nineteenth century. For long, the existence of great navigable stretches in the middle and upper reaches of the rivers lay unsuspected. Nowadays, river transport is becoming less and less significant; the difficulties of navigation, the fluctuations of level and the frequent interruptions of falls and rapids mean that traffic is being increasingly taken over by road and railway.

The use of river water for irrigation agriculture is of vital importance in Africa, for one-third of the continent receives less than 10 inches of rain per annum (Fig. 5). Furthermore, the greater part of the continent lies within the tropics, which means that evaporation losses are high and the 'effectiveness' of the rainfall greatly reduced. The great rivers, however, all tap areas of high rainfall, and four of them carry this water surplus to semi-arid or arid regions. Unfortunately the régimes are such that expensive control works are necessary to regulate the flow; as we have just seen, the discharge in the dry season may be less than one-tenth that of the flood-time. Annual discharge may also vary unpredictably, necessitating the construction of reservoirs capable of holding two or three years' supply. Finally, the areas topographically suitable for irrigation agriculture in Africa are distinctly limited. Nowhere does Africa contain gently sloping alluvial lowlands such as those of India and Pakistan.

So far as the availability of water power is concerned, several authorities affirm that Africa has the highest potential in the world. Zimmermann quotes a figure of 40 per cent of the world's total, for example. This tremendous reserve of water power to some degree offsets the general lack of coal outside southern Africa, and of oil south of the Sahara. On the other hand, schemes to harness the great rivers have to be undertaken on an immense scale, with enormous capital outlay, partly because of the size of the flood discharge and the irregularity of régime from one year to the next. Moreover, many of the most suitable sites for power generation are impossibly distant from the main centres of demand for electricity, and many are unsuitable for the establishment of local industry. It is estimated, for instance, that more than half of Africa's potential water-power resources is locked up in the Congo Basin—mostly at its outlet—but so far no major hydro-electric scheme has been developed in this area.

Africa possesses some of the largest river systems in the world, yet their economic value is in every respect offset by grave disadvantages. For this, the climate and morphology of the continent are together responsible.

4

Climatology

Because of its position, Africa is a continent which experiences mainly tropical and sub-tropical conditions. In only a few areas of high altitude does the climate approximate to the temperate or cool climates of higher latitudes. The point in Africa farthest from the equator lies in latitude 37° 21′N (Cape Blanc in Tunisia). In the southern hemisphere Cape Agulhas does not quite reach latitude 35°. Between these extremes the continent covers 11¼ million sq. miles (excluding islands), and roughly two-thirds of this lies between the tropics. The greatest width of the continent, about 4,600 miles, is to be found in latitude 12°N (from Guinea to Somalia).

Comparisons with the neighbouring continent of South America are instructive. As a whole, Africa lies much farther north than South America, and attains its greatest width in latitudes where the Americas dwindle to a narrow isthmus. The Atlas lands are equivalent in latitude to part of the Cotton Belt of the United States; whilst no part of Africa extends south of the latitude of Buenos Aires. It is also worth noting that whereas South America is separated from Antarctica only by the relatively narrow Drake Strait, Africa is cut off from Antarctica by over 2,000 miles of open ocean.

The absence of any continuous or lengthy mountain chains in Africa allows a virtually unhindered circulation of air over the land. As a result, the changes of climate from place to place often occur very gradually, and in few areas is it possible to define precisely the limits of any climatic region. There are no great physical weather divides such as affect the circulation of air over South America, North America or Eurasia. On the other hand, the elevated plateaux of much of east, central and south Africa considerably moderate the local temperatures; this is one of the principal reasons why much of the permanent white settlement in the continent has taken place in these plateau regions.

Large stretches of the Atlantic coasts of Africa are washed by relatively cool waters (Fig. 13). In the northern hemisphere, the Canaries current has a mean temperature of 60–70°F, affecting the coast between Morocco and Cape Verde. In the southern hemisphere the Benguela current between Cape Town and Cape Lopez generally has a temperature of 55–65°F. The low temperatures are the result not only of mass transfer of water from high to low latitudes but also of the upwelling of cold water from the ocean depths as the local winds push the surface waters obliquely away from the coast (as in the case of the Peruvian current off western South America). Between Cape Verde and Cape Lopez, but with the notable exception of the eastern Ghana-Togo strip, the coast of West Africa is in contact with relatively warm waters (temperature usually about 80°F).

On the eastern seaboard of the continent only a small portion of coast is affected by relatively cool ocean waters, and then only in the northern solstice season. At this time the prevailing south-west monsoon blowing over Somalia has the effect of pushing the warm surface waters of the Indian Ocean here to the east, whilst their place is taken by cooler waters from below, with temperatures below 70°F. The rest of the coast of eastern Africa, from Natal to the Red Sea, is in contact with relatively warm waters all the year, varying from 65°F in the south to 85°F near Aden. Parts of the Red Sea reach temperatures of over 90°F in July.

Lying along the north of Africa, the Mediterranean Sea is relatively warm for its latitude. Continual evaporation in excess of the inflow of river water results in high salinity. Over the Gibraltar 'sill', which is relatively shallow (1,200 feet), the saline Mediterranean water slides out into the Atlantic, leaving room only for a 400-foot layer of warm surface Atlantic water to enter in order to replenish the Mediterranean Sea. The temperature of the Mediterranean is maintained generally above 55°F (February) and may exceed 75°F in August.

TEMPERATURES OVER AFRICA (Fig. 8)

By any standards, Africa is the hottest of all the continents. It is, for example, the only continent where the 50°F sea-level isotherm never appears. Cape Town, at the southern extremity, records a July mean temperature of 55°F; in the case of Algiers, in the north, the January mean is 53°F. At higher elevations, of course, lower temperatures are to be found, but even Johannesburg, at 5,500 feet, has a June mean of

50°F. In parts of the continent some very high temperatures have been experienced, such as the world record of 136°F in Tripolitania on 13th September 1922. Insalah, in Algeria (latitude 27°), has a July mean of 99°F and an average daily maximum for this month of 117°F. Largely because of the much more extensive ocean in the southern hemisphere and the smaller land area, no part of southern Africa is subject to such extremely high temperatures, though many places in the vicinity of the lower Orange river have January mean temperatures of over 85°F, and

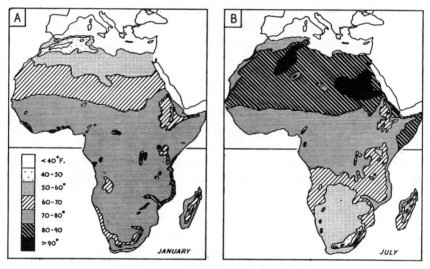

Figure 8 *Actual mean temperatures over Africa in January and July*

in the central Kalahari, below 3,000 feet, the thermometer may at times register over 100°F.

The equatorial parts of the continent do not have such high temperatures as those parts nearer the tropics, nor do they experience any great difference of temperature through the various seasons of the year. The seasonal range is usually less than 10°F in the Congo, along the Guinea coast and on the East African plateaux. Moving to higher latitudes, the annual range of temperature increases steadily to 15°F or 20°F in South Africa, and as much as 45°F in the dry air of the interior parts of the Sahara, where night temperatures may fall below freezing-point. On the coastlands the annual range is much less—Algiers 25°, Alexandria 23°—because of the moderating influence of the sea.

Since the relatively low-lying Saharan-Arabian land-mass in summer is the hottest part of the continent, it develops its own temporary low-pressure system, resulting from the strong convection off the hot land surface. In the winter this heat low disappears and surface pressure rises. In southern Africa former notions of a surface low-pressure system in summer over the interior have been shown to be wrong; in reality there are persistent anticyclonic conditions here, merely weaker in summer than in winter.[5] Flanking the continent on its western side are the two permanent anticyclonic cells of the North and South Atlantic, centred approximately over latitudes 30°. The pressure and circulation of each of these becomes intensified in the local winter, and somewhat reduced at the opposite end of the year. To the east of Africa, pressure conditions are further complicated by the presence of the Asian land-mass. Over the south Indian Ocean, centred again about latitude 30°, high-pressure conditions generally exist throughout the year, though there may be no stable or permanent anticyclonic cell such as exists over the North or South Atlantic. Over Arabia, Persia and the Indian desert a powerful low-pressure system builds up through land heating in the summer; in the local winter these areas come under the influence of anticyclonic conditions which now extend from North Africa right across to central Asia.

THE GENERAL WIND-FLOW PATTERN

Figs. 9 and 10 attempt to show the general circulation of the air for the two opposite seasons of the year, resulting from the pressure distribution just described. Such maps must be accepted with caution, for as well as being oversimplified, there are many parts of Africa for which adequate wind-flow data are not yet available. The actual wind-flow on any individual day of the year will be far more complicated in relation to the local meteorological conditions.

In the southern solstice season the strong circulation over North and West Africa is induced by the intensification of the North Atlantic (Azores) anticyclonic cell. A similar flow from the central Asian high-pressure areas dominates the rest of the Sahara, the Sudan and Arabia. This air travels south across the equator as far as Botswana,* as the

* Formerly Bechuanaland.

prevailing anticyclonic conditions over the South African plateau weaken. The margins of South-West Africa and Angola come under the influence of southerly winds from the South Atlantic anticyclonic cell.

In the northern solstice season a strong north-westerly air-flow sweeps across the Mediterranean and North Africa on its way towards Arabia and the Indian desert. These are the well-known Etesian winds. It is interesting to note that, over Egypt, the wind-flow is from the north or north-west at both seasons of the year, and hence it is nearly always

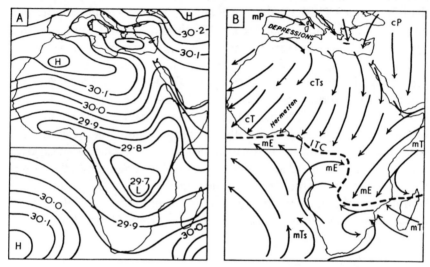

Figure 9 A. Mean atmospheric pressure over Africa in January. Pressure in inches, reduced to sea-level. B. Mean circulation at lower levels over Africa in January. ITC—Inter-Tropical Convergence

possible to sail *up* the River Nile. In the southern hemisphere stronger anticyclonic conditions prevail at this (winter) season; a strong air-flow passes northward across the equator drawn towards the Arabian-Indian low-pressure areas. This is the south-west monsoon, which affects areas from West Africa to the Ethiopian highlands and beyond. It should be observed that the general direction of wind-flow along eastern Africa from Ethiopia to Moçambique is reversed twice each year.

AIR-MASSES

Involved in the general circulation just described are many different air types. These will be separated into five broad groups for simple discussion, though it must be borne in mind that innumerable transitional types and local variations exist:

Continental Polar	cP
Maritime Polar	mP
Continental Tropical	cT
Maritime Tropical	mT
Maritime Equatorial	mE

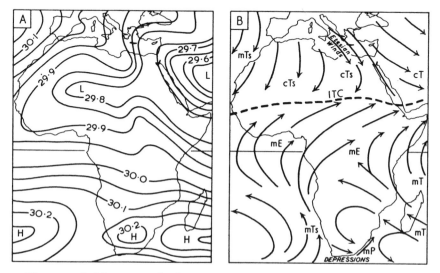

Figure 10 A. Mean atmospheric pressure over Africa in July. Pressure in inches, reduced to sea-level. B. Mean circulation at lower levels over Africa in July. ITC—Inter-Tropical Convergence

This classification is based on the characteristics of the areas from which the air has recently travelled.

Since Africa lies in relatively low latitudes, tropical air-masses are of most importance, and polar types need only be mentioned briefly. cP air is rare even in the extreme northern parts of Africa, and is unknown in the southern half because of the great expanse of sea dividing Africa from any possible source of cP air in Antarctica. In the north cP air from Asia and eastern Europe in winter may arrive in north-east Africa with relatively low temperatures; moisture acquired in passage over the Mediterranean has been known to cause snow showers in Cairo and in El Golea (Algeria). MP air is more common, and affects much of North Africa in the winter, its associated depressions bringing the winter rains of the Mediterranean. This air type has travelled from the North Atlantic, so that by the time it reaches North Africa it has become much warmer and moister than the mP air which so commonly afflicts the British Isles. mP air, again greatly modified, also reaches Cape Province in the southern winter, and produces the characteristic winter rains of this 'Mediterranean' corner of South Africa. Travelling east, the mP air brings winter rain to the Knysna-Port Elizabeth district, and occasionally continues to skirt Natal, adding a little winter precipitation there. On the high ground of Lesotho* it gives rise to snow, which is occasionally experienced also on the High Veld.

The three tropical types of air-mass (cT, mT, mE) have a very much wider distribution in Africa, and all parts of the continent are liable to be affected by at least one of them at certain times. cT air originates in the upper levels of the atmosphere above the Sahara and Kalahari all the year. It is very dry and stable, and in its descent to ground-level becomes warmer and even drier. It is responsible primarily for the arid conditions in these areas; over West Africa in the local winter the strong outflow of dry cT air from the Sahara is known as the Harmattan.

mT air varies greatly in its characteristics; it originates in similar latitudes to cT air, but over the sea. Its source regions are in the eastern sectors of the Azores and South Atlantic anticyclonic cells. Initially it is warmer higher up than in its lower levels—in other words, a temperature inversion is present, usually at 2,000 to 3,000 feet, with an associated stratus layer. This is partly caused by the relatively cold ocean waters present in these regions (the Benguela and Canaries currents) and, in the case of South-West Africa, by the outward movement of warm cT air from the heated plateau at a high level to overlie the cool maritime air. Near its source regions the mT air is thus highly stable; it is this type of air which controls the climate of the coastlands of South-West Africa and southern Angola, and of Mauritania and Morocco throughout the year, and is the cause of the aridity which prevails in these areas. A similar type of air dominates the Somalia coastlands.

As the mT air moves outward from its source regions its subsident characteristics gradually disappear with heating from below, and absorption of moisture if it continues to move over the sea. In order to show these changes in the character of the mT air it is sometimes designated mTs in its source regions, and mTn (= neutral) at the point when warming from below has destroyed its temperature inversion. Further

* Formerly Basutoland.

heating and humidification will complete the transition to the highly unstable mE type of air. Thus, as the mTs air off South-West Africa and Angola is drawn northward in the northern solstice season, it passes over increasingly warm seas, so that it reaches the Guinea coast as a thoroughly moist and unstable air-mass (mE), producing much rain of a thundery nature. If mE air is, in addition, subject to orographic lifting, very large quantities of rain may be released, as for example on Cameroon Mountain with over 400 inches annually. Maritime equatorial air travelling across the Congo Basin eventually encounters the Ethiopian highlands and there produces the intense monsoon rains of the northern solstice season.

FRONTS

Well-marked frontal phenomena resulting from the meeting of different types of air-mass are common throughout the Mediterranean in the winter season, when modified polar air meets the tropical air of North Africa. The weather situations are broadly similar to those encountered in north-west Europe, and are often very complex. Most of the winter rain in the Mediterranean area is associated with frontal disturbances. In the Cape region of South Africa, and at times along the coasts of eastern Cape Province and Natal, weaker frontal phenomena are common in winter.

The most important frontal phenomena in Africa are those associated with the Intertropical Convergence Zone (ITC; see Figs. 9, 10). This is the zone in which tropical air-masses originating in different hemispheres meet; there is frequently a well-defined discontinuity surface or 'front' between these different air-masses (e.g. when the hot dry air from the Sahara meets and overruns the humid and slightly cooler air from the south). Partly because of the lack of controlling relief features in Africa, the ITC varies considerably in position from one season to another. It has been known to reach the Tibesti highlands (in 1936) and Merowe on the Nile. At the other extreme it may touch the Limpopo valley and southern Moçambique. Between these limits lies that part of Africa regularly crossed by the ITC in its northward and southward migrations. But the movements and positions of the ITC are not readily predictable; it does not move steadily from one extreme to the other throughout the year, and sometimes it fails to reach a region normally affected by it. This is of great importance climatically, for behind certain sections of the ITC, rain-bearing air-masses (mE or mTn) prevail, and failure of the ITC to reach an area may result in a disastrous drought. Furthermore, in its more distant positions from the equator, the ITC is associated with intense weather disturbances, producing much rainfall. The varying position of the ITC is therefore of cardinal importance in

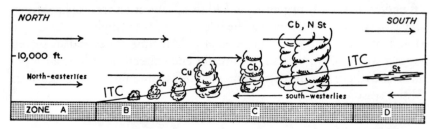

Figure 11 *A section through the Intertropical Convergence (ITC) north of the equator in summer.* Hot dry air from the north (Sahara) overruns slightly cooler and humid air of maritime origin from the south. Zone A—dry, with clear skies; B—moister air but little precipitation: light cumulus; C—as the moist air increases in depth, more continuous rainfall sets in, heralded by line squalls. Development of massive cumulo-nimbus; D—lighter rain and development of stratus

the climate of Africa. As a final consideration, it should be noted that frequently the actual contact of the main ITC front with the ground is a dry zone, and that precipitation from moist air behind the front only occurs when the layer of moist air is of sufficient thickness; this may be as much as 200 miles from the line of ground contact (see Fig. 11).

5

Major Climatic Regions

Sixty years ago A. J. Herbertson put forward a scheme for the division of the world's land-masses into 'major natural regions', which possessed 'a certain unity of configuration, climate and vegetation'.[6] In Africa he recognised five such regions: western margin with winter rain (Mediterranean type), eastern margin with summer rain (China type), tropical deserts (Sahara type), inter-tropical tablelands (Sudan type) and equatorial lowlands (Amazon type). It is now evident, in the light of more recently acquired data on the climate and vegetation of Africa, that this scheme is too simple, and, even more important, that it assumes that climate and vegetation are entirely interdependent. Many textbooks on the geography of Africa have used a division of the continent on a climatic-vegetation basis, merely elaborating Herbertson's scheme. But climate is only one of many factors which influence the present pattern of vegetation. Savanna grassland is not merely the product of a tropical climate with summer rain. Soils, drainage and man's activities are equally important in determining the nature of the plant cover. It should be borne in mind that in many parts of Africa it is no easy matter even to determine or to delimit the major vegetation types. Many changes have occurred in the last century as agriculture has been extended and, for countless years before, the inhabitants have been at work clearing the forests and adapting the land for various forms of cultivation or pastoralism. Practices such as shifting cultivation, bush-burning or overgrazing have been very destructive of the flora, and it is often difficult to distinguish between primary and secondary growth. Moreover, there are still many areas whose vegetation has never been studied in detail. Nevertheless, studies of present vegetation are often very useful indicators of potential land use.

In this and the succeeding chapter a firm distinction will be made between climatic and vegetation regions. The former will be based on

purely climatic criteria—precipitation, evaporation and temperature—
while the vegetation regions will be based on the principal characteristics
of the present flora. In both cases it should be remembered that although
there are certain features of climate or vegetation typical of each region,

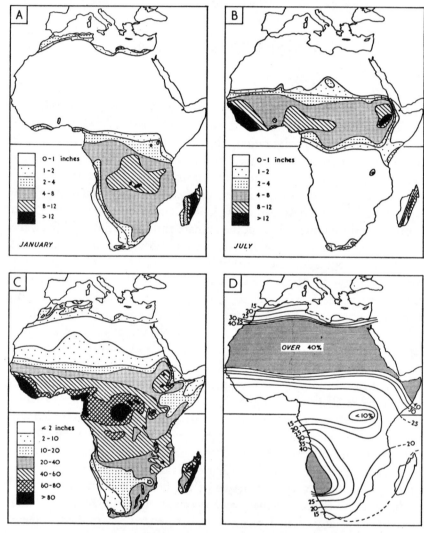

Figure 12 A, B. Mean monthly precipitation over Africa in January and July.
C. Mean annual precipitation over Africa. D. Rainfall variability in Africa:
Figures are percentages, representing the expected deviation from the mean
annual precipitation (highly generalised owing to lack of sufficient data)

there are usually no rigid boundaries in nature between the regions but only varying rates of transition. It is nevertheless useful to indicate regional boundaries on maps; those on Figs. 13 and 14 are, of course, highly generalised.

Climatic interest in Africa centres on rainfall rather than on temperature. The amount of moisture and its seasonal distribution (Fig. 12) are the primary criteria employed in the description of climatic regions which follows. With the exception of the highest parts of Ethiopia, Lesotho and certain isolated peaks, all the climates of Africa may be classed as tropical or warm temperate. The climatic regions (Fig. 13a) are based on Trewartha (1961).[7] The map of 'moisture regions' (Fig. 13b)

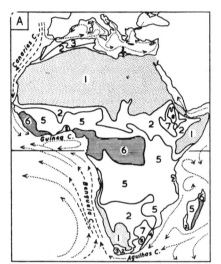 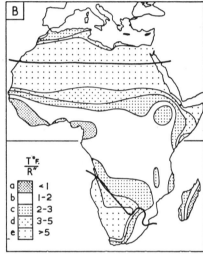

Figure 13 A. *Climatic regions of Africa.* 1. Arid. 2. Semi-arid. 3. Dry summer sub-tropical. 4. Humid sub-tropical marine. 5. Tropical wet-and-dry. 6. Tropical humid. 7. Warm temperate uplands with summer rain. 8. Cool temperate highlands

Ocean currents are shown for January; broken lines indicate cold currents, dotted lines indicate warm currents

B. *Moisture regions of Africa* (after A. Miller, 1951). a. Perhumid. b. Humid. c. Sub-humid. d. Semi-arid. e. Arid

Since the effectiveness of rainfall is partly dependent on evaporation loss, a simple index of aridity or humidity can be obtained by dividing temperature (degrees Fahrenheit) by rainfall (inches)

The part of Africa lying between the heavy black lines experiences a hot climate with no mean monthly temperatures below 64°F., except in certain highland regions takes into account both the actual amount of precipitation reaching the ground and the potential amount of moisture lost by evaporation and transpiration, and is based on Thornthwaite's system. The similarity between the two maps should be noted, and also the extent of arid and semi-arid conditions in the continent. In no other continent does the desert of the northern hemisphere approach the equator so closely.

1. Arid

The truly arid parts of the continent consist of the vast expanse of the Sahara, the world's most extensive area of intense aridity, reaching from the Red Sea to the Mauritanian coastlands; of the much more restricted Namib and western Kalahari deserts in the southern hemisphere; and of the Somalia coastlands. The aridity of the central and eastern Sahara is due to its domination by cT air all year, air which is continually descending from the upper levels of the atmosphere where, in these latitudes, anticyclonic conditions are permanent. The rare and isolated rain showers which are known in parts of the Sahara are caused chiefly by incursions of unstable mP air from the north-west or the occasional penetration of moist equatorial air from the south. Average rainfall figures for such regions mean little, for rainfall is very erratic. BILMA, to the west of Tibesti, has an annual average of 0·8 inches. The aridity of the Namib desert and the Mauritanian coastal strip results from the prevailing mTs air in these regions. Temperatures are lower here than in the interior of the Sahara or in the Kalahari, for cool ocean waters wash the shore, and the resulting temperature inversion is marked by a cloud layer, usually at about 1,500 to 2,000 feet, cutting off much insolation. Surface fogs over the cool coastal waters are also common. The lowest precipitation apparently coincides with the actual coast. WALVIS BAY (South-West Africa) has 0·3 inches annual average rainfall, though its occurrence is very erratic, and the warmest month has an average of only 66°F. Equivalent figures for PORT ETIENNE on the Mauritanian coast are 1·0 inches of rain, and 69°F.

Along the Somalia and Gulf of Aden coasts the lack of rainfall is due primarily to two factors: that these areas lie in the rain shadow of the Ethiopian highlands in the season when the latter are being bombarded with mE air from the south-west, and that in the other season they are exposed to the cT airstream from Arabia which absorbs only a negligible amount of moisture in crossing the Gulf of Aden. BERBERA on the hot

Gulf of Aden coast has a total of only 2·5 inches; the six months of the northern solstice season here have virtually no rain. Mean temperatures vary from 76°F in January to 97°F in July and August, when the south-west winds are descending from the interior highlands. The Somalia coast is much cooler in the south-west monsoon season, when the off-shore winds promote an upwelling of cool water along the coast, conducive to mist or fog formation.

2. Semi-arid

As would be expected, a semi-arid fringe borders the deserts; in places the fringe is narrow, but there are three larger areas of semi-arid climate: namely, the southern margins of the Sahara, parts of Somalia and eastern Ethiopia and a considerable portion of South-West Africa, Botswana and the eastern Kalahari. The southern margins of the Sahara are just reached in normal years by the ITC (see previous chapter) and the moist air-masses behind it. Thus KHARTOUM in the east has a total average rainfall of 6·5 inches, of which 5 inches fall in the two-month period July–August when the ITC arrives. Similarly, GAO on the Niger (latitude 16°) has just over 9 inches on average each year; of this, 5·5 inches fall in July and August. At Khartoum the mean monthly temperature varies from 69°F in January to over 91°F in May and June before the rains.

A large area of southern Africa qualifies for inclusion in this semi-arid zone. For much of the year this area is, like the Sahara, under the influence of local cT air, but the weakened anticyclonic conditions of the summer allow a greater and more frequent penetration of moist air-masses, of both tropical and mid-latitude origin. UPINGTON on the Orange River has a rainfall of 6 inches, of which three-quarters falls in the five months December–April. WINDHOEK, at 5,500 feet in the South-West African highlands, has an average of 14·3 inches, 8 inches of this falling in January, February and March.

The third sub-region of semi-arid climate lies in eastern Ethiopia and adjacent parts of Somalia. The lack of rainfall is due to the same basic factors that promote the desiccation of the Somalia coast, but the rise in elevation inland contributes to the slightly higher frequency of rain showers. The increase in temperature of the coastal waters from Mogadiscio southward also plays its part: Mogadiscio itself has 17 inches annually, of which most falls between April and July when the ITC passes north.

3. Dry summer sub-tropical

The typical conditions associated with a 'Mediterranean' climate—namely, warm dry summers and cool moist winters—are encountered in two relatively small areas of Africa: the northern parts of Morocco, Algeria and Tunisia on the one hand, and the south-western Cape of South Africa on the other. Both areas come under the influence of subsiding anticyclonic air in the local summer, and of modified mP air with associated frontal disturbances in the local winter. One of the best criteria for delimiting the north-west African area of Mediterranean climate is the distribution of the olive, which will only flourish under these particular conditions which guarantee winter moisture and little chance of any serious frost. ALGIERS on the north African coast shows the effect of the subsiding tropical air in summer: mean temperature for July, August and September ranges between 75°F and 78°F, while the total rainfall for the four months from June to September is only 2 inches. In winter, however, the mean monthly temperature falls to 53°F (January), and in the six months from October to March 24 inches of rain fall.

CAPE TOWN, which is actually 3° nearer the equator, has a somewhat more equable climate; it experiences mainly south-easterly winds in the summer, sometimes strong, blowing over a cooler sea than the Mediterranean at Algiers, and producing the 'tablecloth' or white cloud on Table Mountain. The mean temperatures for January, February and March vary between 68° and 70°F; the coolest month is July (55°F). Rainfall shows the same distribution seasonally as at Algiers, but the total is 25 inches compared with 30 inches at Algiers. Over three-quarters of the rainfall at Cape Town comes in the six-month period April-September.

4. Humid sub-tropical marine

The only part of Africa which qualifies for inclusion under this heading lies along part of the south and east coast of South Africa, from approximately Mossel Bay to the north of Natal. Due to a maritime position, range of temperature is moderate (Port Elizabeth 11°, Durban 13°), but conditions are much cooler in the southerly parts than towards the north. PORT ELIZABETH has six months below 62°F, while DURBAN has no month below 64°F and a mean temperature of 77°F in February. There is also a change in seasonal rainfall distribution, for whereas the Natal coastlands experience a relatively dry winter (only 14 per cent of Durban's 43 inches falls in the four months May-August), the southern coastlands between Port Elizabeth and Mossel Bay enjoy a remarkably evenly distributed rainfall. KNYSNA (28 inches) has the following allocation of rainfall for the four quarters of the year: 22, 21, 25 and 32 per cent.

5. Tropical wet-and-dry

A tropical climate with a marked concentration of rainfall in the summer season is to be found over two-fifths of inter-tropical Africa. This type of climate provides a transition from the tropical arid and semi-arid areas on the one hand to the humid tropical areas with rainfall in every month. The transition is effected both by an increase in total rainfall and by a gradual shortening of the dry season as one passes from tropical to equatorial latitudes. Another important characteristic of the tropical summer rain areas is that they are exposed to regular overhead passages of the ITC. The following examples will illustrate this point:

At VICTORIA FALLS, near the southern limit of the tropical wet-and-dry climate in the interior, the ITC passes overhead about November, remains just to the south for about three or four months and returns northward about the beginning of March. Between November and March 25 inches of rain fall on average, from the northerly mE airstream and from disturbances associated with the actual front zone when this is in the neighbourhood. For the remaining eight months of the year drought conditions prevail, with but 1·5 inches of rain for the whole of this period.

MWANZA, on the south-east shore of Lake Victoria, lies in latitude 2°30'S at an elevation of about 4,000 feet. The mean monthly rainfall figures in inches are:

J	F	M	A	M	J	J	A	S	O	N	D	Total
2·5	3·2	6·5	8·7	3·3	1·9	0·1	1·5	1·8	3·1	5·1	4·9	42·6

Here there are only four months of the year with dry conditions, i.e. less than 2 inches in any one month. The rainy season, occupying eight months, has two distinct maxima (the wettest months are underlined above). The ITC passes south over Mwanza usually in October, and returns north about April or May; between October and April, then, the area is under the influence of moist mE air.

KANO in northern Nigeria is on the northern margin of the tropical wet-and-dry climate (latitude 12°N) and has an average of 34 inches of rain annually. The dry season lasts for seven months (compare Victoria Falls), and over 32 inches of the annual rainfall comes in the period May to September. The ITC passes north in May and returns south in September. mE air from the south reaches the area between these two months.

It should be emphasised that the various figures quoted above for rainfall are average figures, representing the mean recordings over periods of many years. In any one year or month, however, the rainfall may differ considerably from the average; rainfall variability, arising from unpredictable changes in the weather, is a serious obstacle to agricultural development. Weather forecasting in the tropics is often very difficult owing to the wide area in which there occur very feebly defined movements of air-masses charged with moisture. Generally, the variability of the rainfall becomes greater towards the drier margins of the tropical wet-and-dry zone. A second notable point is that as the rainfall comes mainly in summer, it falls in the season when potential evaporation losses are highest; in other words, the effectiveness of the rainfall is greatly decreased by its concentration in the warmer part of the year. At Kano, for instance, the mean monthly temperatures of the rainy season vary from 69° to 75°F. And everywhere the rainfall effectiveness is reduced by the manner in which it falls. It is usual for rain in the tropics to fall in sporadic showers of high intensity, often with associated thunder. There is thus less opportunity for percolation into the ground, and more for surface run-off, which can consequently promote flooding or erosion in certain circumstances.

Many of these rainfall characteristics also apply to other climatic zones in tropical and sub-tropical Africa, especially to the semi-arid zone and to the uplands of South Africa, where variable summer rainfall is the general rule.

6. Tropical humid

Parts of Africa which experience a rainfall of more than 50 inches annually, and continuously high temperatures (no month below 68°F), comprise the Congo Basin below 2,000 feet; most of the neighbouring Congo Republic (Brazzaville), Gabon and the southern Cameroun Republic; and the southernmost parts of West Africa from Sierra Leone to the Cameroun border, excepting only the drier section between Takoradi and Porto Novo. In all these areas the rain is brought by convectionally unstable mE air. The heaviest falls are found where orographic obstacles force this already unstable air to rise, as in the Cameroun or Futa Jallon highlands. Cameroon Mountain, with about 400 inches annually, is the wettest place in Africa. It is important to note, however, that this rainfall is by no means equally distributed throughout the year, and certain months often have surprisingly little rainfall. CONAKRY in West Africa has a total of 169 inches, but of this only 2 inches fall between December and April inclusive. The thundery character of the rainfall is pronounced: 6 inches or more in a day is not uncommon. The thunder showers are not only caused by random thermal convection but also by frontal disturbances and by inward surges of moist air from the south-west.

The examples in Table 1, p. 68, illustrate the range of variation within this climatic zone.

The humid tropical climate is characterised by a limited range of temperature both seasonal and diurnal. Apart from the usually short dry seasons, the climate is monotonous and the relative humidity often unpleasantly high. Variability of rainfall is as marked in some places as in the drier parts of Africa: POINTE NOIRE, with an annual average of 51 inches, received only 6 inches in 1958, but 54 inches in 1959.

Eastern Malagasy may be considered to possess a form of humid tropical climate. It lies more than 12° from the equator, and therefore has a more pronounced seasonal range of temperature. TAMATAVE, on the coast, is coolest in July (68°F) and warmest in February (81°F). Its rainfall amounts to 131 inches, and no month has less than 3 inches, whilst nine months have more than 8 inches each.

7. Warm temperate uplands with summer rain

Much of the eastern plateau of South Africa lies between 4,000 and 6,000 feet above sea-level. This is the area known as the High Veld, where climate is akin in some respects to parts of the tropical wet-and-dry zone, since the rainfall comes mainly in summer, but where temperatures are greatly moderated by altitude. Westward, as the land drops in elevation, there is a gradual transition to semi-arid conditions in the Kalahari. On the east rise the highlands of Lesotho and the Drakensberg. BLOEMFONTEIN, at 4,500 feet, has mean monthly temperatures ranging

Table 1

Station	Alt. (feet)		J	F	M	A	M	J	J	A	S	O	N	D	Year	Temp. range
Douala	26	Temp. °F	80	80	80	80	80	78	75	75	77	76	78	79	77	4
		Rain in.	1·8	3·7	8·0	9·1	11·8	21·2	29·2	27·3	20·9	16·9	6·1	2·5	158·5	
Libreville	115	T.	80	80	81	81	80	78	76	77	78	78	78	79	79	5
		R.	9·8	9·3	13·2	13·4	9·6	0·5	0·1	0·7	4·1	13·6	14·7	9·8	98·8	
Kinshasa	1,066	T.	79	80	80	80	80	75	73	74	77	79	79	78	78	7
		R.	5·3	5·7	7·7	7·7	6·2	0·3	0·1	0·1	1·2	4·7	8·7	5·6	53·3	

from 47°F in June to 73°F in January. Rainfall totals 22 inches, of which only 2 inches fall in the four-month period June to September. In winter then, there are relatively cool dry conditions, with frost liable to occur between May and September.

North of the equator, the less-elevated parts of the Ethiopian highlands possess a warm temperate climate, with a strong concentration of precipitation in the summer months. On the higher ground (over 8,000 feet), temperatures are reduced further, even though the region is within 15° of the equator. The higher peaks (up to 15,000 feet) experience occasional snow. The annual range of temperature is very small, characteristic of places at high altitudes. HARAR, at 6,000 feet, has mean monthly temperatures varying from 65° to 69°F; ADDIS ABABA at 8,000 feet has corresponding figures of 52° to 56°F. The climate of Ethiopia is of particular significance in view of the fact that the Blue Nile rises here; its floods provide the bulk of the water for irrigation in Egypt and the northern Sudan. The rainfall at Addis Ababa (elevation 8,038 feet) will serve to illustrate the seasonal variations in climate:

	J	F	M	A	M	J	J	A	S	O	N	D	Total
R. ins.	0·5	1·5	2·6	3·4	3·4	5·4	11·0	11·8	7·5	0·8	0·6	0·2	48·7

The outstanding feature is the monsoon rain, brought by mE air from the south-west between April (when the ITC moves north) and September (when it returns south). For most of the rest of the year Ethiopia is affected by dry cT air from Arabia.

8. Cool temperate with summer rain

The higher parts of Ethiopia strictly qualify for inclusion here, though the salient features of their climate were outlined in the previous section.

In South Africa the Lesotho highlands form a major area of cool climate with mainly summer precipitation. As the elevation ranges from 5,000 to more than 11,000 feet, there are large areas which experience severe winters and prolonged snow cover. Even on the lower parts, monthly temperatures drop to less than 45°F in June and July. The maximum precipitation (on the Drakensberg crest) is over 75 inches, but in most places is below 40 inches. It is predominantly summer rain brought by moist air from various sources, frequently from the north, but most winter months show a trace of precipitation, often as snow.

6

Vegetation

The term 'natural vegetation' is purposely avoided, as much of the present plant cover is not natural because of man's interference. The map (Fig. 14) indicates only the present vegetation, not the presumed climax types. At the small scale of the map, and in the general terms used in this description, areas of cultivation cannot be dealt with.

The first comprehensive study of African vegetation was that of Marbut and Shantz (1923).[8] Excluding Madagascar, they calculated that forest covered 18 per cent of the continent, grassland 42 per cent and desert 39 per cent. These broad categories were, of course, subdivided and included transitional types. Thus, they showed that 'forest' varied from evergreen rain forest through open deciduous woodland to thorn scrub, generally reflecting the moisture available. That grassland should occupy a larger area than either of the other two basic types we now know to be the result not solely of climate or other physical controls but also of the destruction of original forest by fire and by grazing animals. Under the heading 'desert', Marbut and Shantz included semi-desert shrub and grass, and whilst this occupies a very large part of Africa, their figures show how limited is the truly barren desert area—8 per cent.

The work of Marbut and Shantz has now been amplified and modified in a new map of African vegetation south of the Tropic of Cancer.[9] Over 260 different sources were used in its compilation. Naturally, the reliability of the map varies—from countries which have only generalised small-scale maps available, to others, such as South Africa, where some relatively detailed studies have been made. The published map is at a scale of 1 : 10 million; Fig. 14 is a further reduction and generalisation. At such scales the intricate patterns of vegetation in highland regions, and even the effects of relief and drainage on the flatter areas, cannot be shown. Furthermore, as in the case of climatic regions, the boundaries must not be thought of as precise. Two of the descriptive terms to be used need brief preliminary explanation. 'Savanna', which unfortunately has in the past been applied to a supposed climatic-vegetation zone, is here used to describe areas of perennial grasses which exceed 3 feet in average height and which are subject to fairly regular burning. 'Steppe' refers to the shorter grass areas associated with drier conditions and less affected by burning.

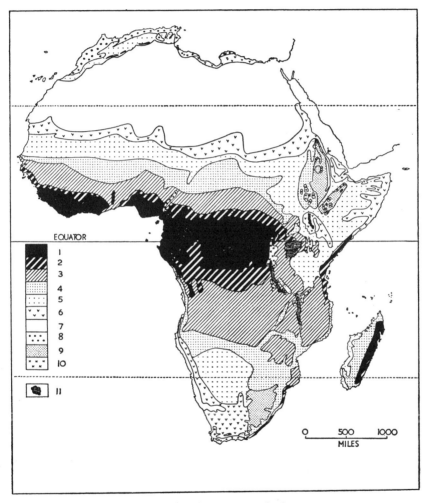

Figure 14 *The vegetation of Africa*

1. Tropical rain forest. 2. Forest-savanna mosaic. 3. Wooded savanna. 4. Dry savanna. 5. Wooded and grass steppe. 6. Dry steppe, sahel, Karroo. 7. Desert. 8. Maquis. 9. Temperate and sub-tropical grassland. 10. Montane. 11. Lakes.

It is important to realise that the present vegetation pattern is neither static nor stable. In terms of centuries or longer periods, slow climatic change has its effects. Since the last pluvial period of the Quaternary (more or less contemporaneous with the last Glacial period of higher latitudes) African rainfall has diminished considerably, while there have also been less-pronounced shorter-term fluctuations. Neolithic man was able to cross the Sahara and inhabit parts of it that have since become desiccated. Then it must be remembered that the vegetation of much of Africa, particularly between the tropical rain forest and the desert, changes remarkably from season to season. Where the grass has been burnt off and the majority of the trees are leafless, the savanna may appear as a semi-desert waste; but seen after the rains, with tall lush grass and trees in full leaf, it resembles an open forest with rich undergrowth.

1. *Tropical rain forest*

This is undoubtedly the climax vegetation of those humid tropical areas possessing no marked or lengthy dry season. The characteristic features of the true rain-forest vegetation have often been described, but not always accurately. Generalisations have too readily been made from limited studies, and exaggerated claims advanced. The mature rain forest consists of tall evergreen or partly evergreen trees, an abundance of other woody plants and little undergrowth except along river banks. The trees may attain great heights—150 feet is common, and some specimens of 300 feet have been recorded. The forest contains a great many species, so that commonly each tree differs from its neighbour. The dense canopies supported by the trees, often at two or more distinct levels, permit only a little sunlight to filter through to the ground, so that undergrowth is not dense except where clearings or rivers break up the forest. As a result of the continuous heat and heavy rain there are no obvious seasonal changes, except in some areas where a well-marked dry season occurs; flowering and fruiting can and do occur all year round. It is often claimed that the rain forest is impenetrable, but this notion of dense jungle areas arose mainly because the forest was viewed from a river traversing it. The forest is obviously more difficult to pass through than, say, savanna country, but 'it is the slippery clay soil and the abundance of fallen logs and branches which make progress in the forest slow and laborious, rather than the thickness of the vegetation'.[10]

The extent of the true rain forest has often been exaggerated. Even within those regions shown on the map there are areas of lighter tropical forest and patches of wooded savanna often associated with highly laterised soils, of swamp and of land cleared for cultivation.

2. Forest-savanna mosaic

Largely forming a fringe on the north or south of the rain forest, this consists of patches of rain forest surrounded by tall-grass savanna. The distribution of the forest or savanna bears no direct relationship to physical conditions. It is generally agreed that the savanna in this mosaic has been derived by burning of the rain forest. Most parts of the savanna are fired annually, so that only fire-tolerant trees and shrubs survive.

3. Wooded savanna

Within the tropical regions of Africa subject to a long and severe dry season in winter and a rainy season in summer the larger part is occupied by various forms of vegetation collectively included in the conventional term 'savanna'. The climax vegetation is thought to be closed woodland with little grass, though on level poorly drained areas, or on lateritic soils possessing a ferruginous hardpan, tree growth has naturally been inhibited. Tree growth also becomes more restricted towards the bordering dry savanna and semi-arid regions, principally because of the lengthening of the dry season. The latter in the wooded savanna zone varies from three to seven months in most cases. But grassland is dominant mainly because of fire. The 'bush' is burned regularly in the dry season, to clear the land for cultivation, or perhaps to hunt out animals. The trees remaining today in the savanna are fire-tolerant to a greater or lesser extent. The density of tree cover depends not only on physical conditions but on the frequency and severity of human interference and thus indirectly on population density. In parts of West Africa, for instance, alteration of the vegetation has been particularly rapid and radical due to repeated clearing for cultivation. In sparsely populated country, on the other hand, the trees of the savanna may form a light canopy and grow in height to 60 or 70 feet, and if there is both sufficient moisture and protection from fire, shrubby undergrowth may develop. The grasses of the savanna are adapted to the annual climatic rhythm, presenting a varied picture throughout the year. When the rains are plentiful they grow rapidly to heights of 6 to 12 feet, but in periods of drought they are either burned off or die right down to their roots, remaining in this dormant condition until the next rains.

4. Dry savanna

With increasing aridity and higher summer temperature there is a gradual transition from tall-grass savanna to short-grass steppe, with scattered deciduous or drought-resistant trees and shrubs. Much of the 'bushveld' of the northern Transvaal and Limpopo valley falls in this category, as well as areas around the Angola – South-West Africa border and from Senegal to the southern Sudan.

5. Wooded and grass steppe

A further stage in the transition to semi-desert is provided by areas of short grass, acacia scrub and thickets of thorn trees. This is characteristic of the Kalahari from the Okovango towards the Orange river, of the southern edge of the Sahara and the drier parts of Kenya and eastern Ethiopia. All species are adapted to withstand prolonged drought. Occasional thorn trees may reach 10 or 20 feet. Grasses are generally sparse and wiry, growing in tussocks, and provide only meagre grazing for nomadic pastoralists. On the upper parts of the South-West African highlands, however, the slightly cooler and moister conditions produce rather better pasture.

6. Dry steppe, sahel and karroo

The plant cover becomes discontinuous, with many bare patches of ground. There are a few low perennial shrubs; annuals, including grasses, flourish for only a few weeks after rain. Tree growth is only found along water-courses.

7. Desert

Vegetation is very sparse, though not entirely absent—except in some areas of rock or mobile dunes. Plants have either adapted themselves in some way to the lack of water, or consist of varieties which, when a shower of rain falls, are able to grow, flower, set fruits and seeds, and then die down when all moisture has evaporated, the seeds only remaining till the next rain. Occasional perennial low herbs, or shrubs such as tamarisk, may appear. In the oases the familiar date-palms are cultivated, often providing shade for other crops.

8. Maquis

This is the well-known Mediterranean sclerophyllous flora composed of evergreen species. The long summer drought promotes the development of plants protecting themselves by various devices (shiny leaves, spines, etc.) against loss of moisture by evaporation. In parts of north-west Africa, where the rainfall is above average, more substantial tree growth may occur; this consists of evergreen species of cork oak, cedar, pine, olive, juniper and many others according to the nature of the locality. Cedars are mostly found on the slopes of the Tell Atlas above 3,000 or 4,000 feet where conditions are cooler. In the south-west Cape region various forms of scrub vegetation, rarely attaining heights of more than 10 or 12 feet, are most characteristic. There are, in fact, few trees here now compared with north-west Africa, except on some of the higher Cape ranges such as the Cedarberg, where the trees are less accessible and the rainfall greater. Farther inland the maquis scrub degenerates still further into the dry steppe and karroo vegetation.

In both these areas of Mediterranean climate the vegetation has frequently been removed or altered. Goats in particular have proved very destructive, especially in the hilly parts, where erosion is all too easily provoked by removing the cover of vegetation. Excessive cutting of the cork oak and other forests in north-west Africa, of the cedars and cypresses of the Cape, and the pasturing of too large flocks of sheep and goats, have resulted in great depletion and alteration of the natural flora.

9. Temperate and sub-tropical grassland

From about 3,500 to 9,000 feet in South Africa there is almost pure grassland. Apart from the occasional acacias it extends monotonously for hundreds of miles on the High Veld. The grasses vary considerably: in the better areas, as regards climate and soil, grass may reach 2 to 3 feet in height, but it never attains the luxuriance of some of the savanna grasses. Since the rainfall in summer is subject to heavy evaporation losses, with temperatures in the seventies, and as it also falls in sporadic downpours, the Veld often presents a parched appearance at this time of the year. The spring is the only season of growth when the landscape appears green, before the temperatures rise too high. Winter frost is a factor in restricting tree growth to a minimum.

On the Ethiopian plateaux and highlands, from roughly 6,000 to 10,000 feet, various forms of grassland predominate. Trees are abundant up to 8,000 feet in the wetter parts but disappear rapidly at higher altitudes due to the lower temperatures. Above 10,000 feet, as in Lesotho, the grassland bears some resemblance to Alpine pasture.

10. Montane communities

It is impossible here to deal with all the diverse types of plant community which occur on the mountains of Africa. Above certain altitudes, depending on size, position of the mountain and the kind of slope, distinctive montane species and assemblages appear. Evergreen forest, bamboo thicket, Alpine grassland and woodland consisting of tree-ferns and giant heathers are amongst the great range of peculiar floristic communities to be found. Tundra-like vegetation appears on the highest parts of Lesotho and Ethiopia, and also below the snow-line on the East African mountains.

7

Soils

Agricultural possibilities in any continent or country not only depend on the nature of the climate but also on the characteristics of the local soils. For too long the study of soils has lagged behind the study of other aspects of the physical environment, but in recent years the situation has been changing, partly as a result of the world-wide need for agricultural expansion. It is now generally recognised that a study of local soils is indispensable to the further development of agriculture. In Africa much progress has been made since Marbut in 1923 published his broad survey of African soils. The distribution of different soil types and their particular characteristics is now generally clear in South Africa, in much of West Africa and in many parts of East Africa. The publication of a soil map of Africa by Schokalskaja[11] in 1948 (reproduced as Fig. 15) showed the extent of the progress achieved since Marbut's tentative soil map of 1923. But there are nevertheless many areas of Africa whose soils have never been investigated, and it will be many years before a soil map of the continent is produced which can rank equally with maps of the geology, relief or vegetation.

Various systems for classifying soils have been devised, based on geology, climate, vegetation or other features of the environment. The Russian soil scientists, such as Dokuchaiev and Glinka, were the first to establish that on a continental scale differences of climate are most significant in determining variations in soils. Glinka's leading idea was that the degree of humidity prevailing in the soil is the principal regulator of the various soil-forming processes. Thus, rock weathering will be in general more active under a humid climate; furthermore, the upper parts of the soil may be deprived of certain minerals or compounds by the downward passage of water percolating through the soil—a process known as leaching. In drier areas, on the other hand, the predominant direction of movement of the soil water may be upwards, in conditions when evaporation

at the surface draws up water by capillary action; this will normally
result in the deposition of soluble salts at or near the surface.

Another consideration is the permeability of the soil, for if rainfall is
in excess of the amount of water that can be absorbed by the soil, surface
run-off will develop and may cause erosion of the soil. In this connection
the character of the rainfall is of great importance, for heavy downpours
not only encourage leaching but apply water to the soil in excess of its
percolation capacity, so that surface run-off and erosion are promoted.
Heavy rain may also beat down the surface of the soil, reducing its

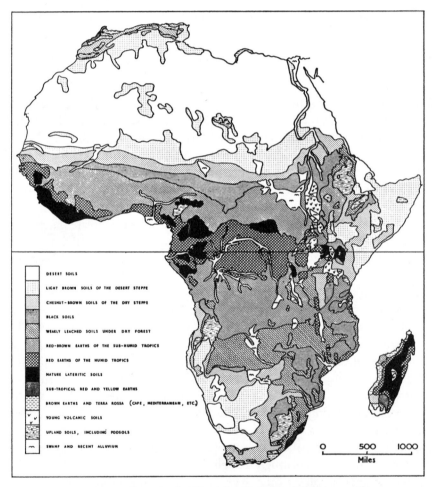

DESERT SOILS

LIGHT BROWN SOILS OF THE DESERT STEPPE

CHESNUT-BROWN SOILS OF THE DRY STEPPE

BLACK SOILS

WEAKLY LEACHED SOILS UNDER DRY FOREST

RED-BROWN EARTHS OF THE SUB-HUMID TROPICS

RED EARTHS OF THE HUMID TROPICS

MATURE LATERITIC SOILS

SUB-TROPICAL RED AND YELLOW EARTHS

BROWN EARTHS AND TERRA ROSSA (CAPE, MEDITERRANEAN, ETC.)

YOUNG VOLCANIC SOILS

UPLAND SOILS, INCLUDING PODSOLS

SWAMP AND RECENT ALLUVIUM

0   500   1000
                Miles

Figure 15 *The soils of Africa* (after S. J. Schokalskaja, 1948)

percolation capacity even further. All these conditions are frequently encountered in most parts of Africa; concentrated downpours of rain, rather than prolonged light rain, are the general rule. The seasonal distribution of the rain, too, has a great influence on soil development. In the rainy season downward leaching of minerals and organic compounds will be paramount; in the dry season some compounds may be returned to the surface layers by capillary action, possibly forming 'crusts' or 'hard pans' which will in turn affect the movement of soil water. According to the relative lengths of dry and wet seasons, a range of different soil types will be produced. Africa, with climates ranging from arid to very humid through all the intermediate zones of seasonal rain, may be expected to produce many contrasting varieties of soils on these considerations alone.

But though soil moisture and its movement are important, the effects of temperature must not be forgotten. In this connection soil temperature will be more significant than air temperature, but the latter will provide a useful guide. It is well known that, in general, the higher the temperature, the more rapidly chemical reactions proceed. In the humid tropics, which occupy much of central Africa, both rock weathering and soil formation therefore take place relatively quickly and efficiently. Even in the arid tropical regions the general lack of soil moisture is to some extent offset by the intensity of chemical reactions in high temperatures. In general, soil forms most rapidly and reaches maturity sooner in hot wet conditions, while, on the other hand, cold dry conditions (almost unknown in Africa) discourage the soil-forming processes.

Study of a soil map of Africa (Fig. 15) will show the correspondence between soils and climate. But there are other factors affecting soil development. Geology must not be ignored, relief and drainage also affect soil character and vegetation has a considerable influence. The influence of rock type on soils is most easily seen in areas where soil development is slow or has been retarded. Given sufficient time, and conditions of stability such that the soil is not affected by erosion, movement or surface deposition, the soil character will, with one exception, come to be independent of the underlying rock. It is well known that the chemical composition of all rock types, save only limestone, is basically very similar, consisting of 60–70 per cent silica, from 5–20 per cent of oxides of iron and aluminium, and numerous less-important minerals. The products of rock weathering are therefore very similar also; only in the case of limestone is the material on which the soil-forming processes set to work very different, and limestone formations are not extensive in Africa south of the Sahara.

The major part of Africa has been a region of stability since early geological times, and over large areas soil formation has gone on through long periods of time. In such areas the relatively minor differences in parent rock have become completely disguised by soil formation, provided only that there have been sufficient supplies of moisture to enable the soil-forming processes to work efficiently. It is common to find in Africa that the same rock in different climatic regions will give rise to different soils. Examples of areas in Africa where rock-type has more influence on soils are the deserts (where soil formation is retarded by lack of moisture) and regions of recent deposition (where soil-forming processes have not had time to operate).

The part played by relief and drainage in the development of various soil types has already been hinted at. Areas of free drainage help the movement of moisture through the soil; in extreme conditions of free drainage the soil may dry out, or if there is much rainfall the soil will be readily leached. On the other hand, in areas of impeded drainage, such as swamps or even some irrigated lowlands, the continuous evaporation often leads to the soil becoming excessively saline or alkaline. Relief is also of decisive importance in determining the local character of the soil. On flat areas, such as the widespread planation surfaces in Africa, soil development may proceed uninterrupted by superficial movement or significant erosion, and a soil may be able to reach full maturity—i.e. it becomes completely adapted to the local climate and hydrography irrespective of rock type. But in areas of strong relief, or wherever erosion is actively at work, the soil will always be immature, and reflect the parent rock more closely. On hillsides a whole series of different minor soil types will be found, according to degree of slope, drainage, rate of supply of weathered material from above, etc. In Africa the great planation surfaces are all uplifted; in consequence, their margins are areas of considerable dissection where no mature soils are likely to be found.

It is often thought that climate and soil largely determine the vegetation. Yet the latter has important effects on the soil in turn. It supplies the humus or organic matter to a soil; desert areas without vegetation possess only accumulations of weathered rock, which are not strictly soils. One must beware, however, of thinking that the vegetation can be used as an indicator of soil fertility. That this is a fallacy is easily shown by reference to the tropical rain forest, which, if cleared, exposes relatively poor soil. In this case it is the warm climate which encourages such luxuriant growth, the growth in turn providing its own organic nourishment. Clearing of rain forest, too, often leads to excessive leaching and surface erosion as a result of the high rainfall. One of the principal influences of all types of vegetation on the soil is to protect it. Vegetation will not only protect the surface from erosion (except under extreme conditions)—it also shades the ground from temperature changes and protects it from excessive evaporation. The roots of plants serve not only to break up the soil and therefore aid percolation but also hold it in position so that it has a better chance of mature development.

It has been pointed out that the decay of vegetable matter provides humus to enrich the soil. Humus is able to retain surprisingly large amounts of moisture, but can, of course, be removed by leaching if there is an excess of percolating water. Furthermore, humus may itself decompose, a process which is encouraged by high temperatures; over 77°F the decomposition of humus tends to outpace its formation. Many tropical soils are therefore poor in organic content.

Finally, brief mention at least must be made of man's influence on soils. Ramann in 1911 affirmed that man has the most potent effect on soil formation. Clearing of vegetation, cultivation of crops, the grazing of animals, all affect the soil. Primitive practices of shifting cultivation affect the soil, and are in turn adapted to it, for incomplete clearance helps to prevent widespread soil erosion, and temporary abandonment of a patch of land helps it to regain a little of the fertility extracted by cultivation. More modern methods of cultivation usually involve ploughing the soil; this not only breaks up and mixes the surface soil but also compacts the lower layers, thus hindering percolation and encouraging surface run-off. Removing vegetation before ploughing also leads to increased evaporation from the soil surface and exposes the soil to rainwash and erosion. In tropical areas of heavy rainfall it is essential that the land be cleared in small patches, that a temporary cover crop be employed and that ploughing should be done along the contour. Even such precautions may not be successful in preventing erosion. Intensive agriculture—repeated cash crops, for instance— quickly exhausts the natural fertility of the soil. Examples of this can be seen over many parts of Africa. All too often there is no attempt at crop rotation; in many cases manure or artificial fertilisers are not available or are too expensive.

It is impossible here to mention all the ways in which man's activities affect the soil, but it is important to bear in mind how easily and quickly a soil, built up over thousands of years, can be impoverished or destroyed by unsuitable methods of cultivation, and that once destroyed, little can be done to replace it.

THE MAIN SOIL GROUPS OF AFRICA

Five broad groups only will be discussed here. Many different factors affect local soil development, and the possible combinations of conditions and variations are almost infinite; the following descriptions of soil types are therefore inevitably generalised.

Desert soils

The lack of any significant organic content is the primary characteristic of these soils. Because of the general lack of moisture, too, the soil-forming processes operate only slowly, and the parent rock exerts considerable influence. But chemical weathering is by no means absent in deserts, as shown by the widespread occurrence of concretions and accumulation layers of certain minerals. In fact, the infrequent showers of rain, combined with the prevailing high temperatures, bring about a rearrangement of soluble minerals, and even cause silicates to weather and become mobile. Soluble salts often collect on the surface; and crusts of 'calcrete' (in limestone areas) and 'silcrete' (from silica compounds) at or just below the surface, such as the 'dorbank' of the Little Karroo in South Africa, bear witness to chemical changes in the surface layers. It is possible, however, that some of these concretionary forms relate to past periods of wetter climate, especially in the Pleistocene.

The soils of desert regions can only be utilised where irrigation is possible; and even then the lack of organic matter is a serious disadvantage, and saline or excessively alkaline conditions must be avoided.

Chestnut-brown soils of the semi-desert

On the desert margins rainfall becomes more significant and more regular, so that grass growth may appear. The soil now has a source of humus, and it is the humus which provides the brown colouring of the upper layers (lighter or darker according to the amount present). Soil moisture is in these areas sufficient also to retard the accumulation of alkali salts in the surface layers. With irrigation, these soils are more agriculturally productive than the desert soils.

Chernozems and black soils

These are now thought to be largely restricted to a zone running across Africa westward from the Sudan (where the black clays are known as the 'badob') to the middle Niger; to a few parts of East Africa; and to parts of Rhodesia, the Transvaal and the western High Veld. Whether many of the black soils in these parts of Africa can be classed as chernozems is very uncertain. It is true that there are, to some extent, similarities of climate between some of the black-soil areas of Africa and the classic chernozem areas of southern Russia, and that the soil types often are of very similar appearance, but many more detailed analyses of black soils from many parts of Africa are still needed.

The black-soil areas of Africa in general possess temperature and moisture conditions which promote rock weathering and the formation of humus, but not so extreme that much leaching or decomposition of humus can occur. The humus content, in fact, varies greatly, being rather low in the black clays of the Bushveld, for instance, whereas normal chernozems should contain a relatively high amount of humus. All the easily soluble salts are leached out from the uppermost layers of the black soils, but the less-soluble salts of calcium and magnesium are only slightly leached. These usually collect in an accumulation layer in the lower horizons of the soil, where lime concretions may be found. This accumulation of calcium takes place irrespective of the calcium content of the underlying rocks.

The black soils in Africa are always associated with areas of low relief; this, together usually with a grass cover, helps them to attain maturity. In the rainy season they become sticky and difficult to work, but often prove relatively fertile for grain crops if the necessary water requirements are satisfied.

Red tropical soils and lateritic soils

Soils of generally reddish colour are know to occur widely throughout tropical Africa and in South Africa even beyond the Tropic. This group of soils thus covers about one-third of the continent. The common characteristic of these soils is that they have been affected by a process known as 'laterisation'. In a few areas this process has been carried virtually to completion, producing in the soil a material termed laterite (see below), but over much larger areas the soils are only partly laterised. These immature tropical soils are often called 'red earths' or 'yellow earths', depending on their colour. It should be pointed out, however, that colour is not an infallible guide to the mode of development of tropical soils; for instance, if there is little or no iron in the parent rock, the lateritic soil may be greyish instead of red. Usually, however, iron compounds are widely found in the parent rocks, and it is the concentration of ferrous oxide in the upper soil layers which is responsible for the predominant red coloration of tropical soils.

A typical profile of a mature lateritic soil shows the following sequence of horizons:

A° At the surface, little or no accumulation of organic matter (humus).

A^1 Friable clay—generally 2 to 10 feet in thickness, but sometimes removed by erosion.

A^2 An iron-rich layer, several feet thick. This appears at the surface if the A^1 horizon is eroded away; on exposure it hardens to form a resistant crust that will support practically no vegetation. It is often quarried for building material, and this is in fact the origin of the term 'laterite' (Latin *later* a brick), first employed by Buchanan (1807) in India. Cases are known where the iron content has been as high as 86 per cent, and the substance is sometimes used as iron ore. Other types of lateritic crust may contain appreciable quantities of bauxite or manganese.

A^3 Beneath the iron-rich layer a red clay usually occurs, also fairly rich in oxides of iron and aluminium. Its thickness is very variable.

B   The lower horizon of the lateritic soil is pale-coloured and often very thick. Its mineral content is mainly of silicates, and it is usually soft in texture.

C   The parent rock. The total thickness of the overlying A and B horizons is often 50 feet and may attain over 200 feet in some cases.

The formation of lateritic soils is complex and not fully understood, but the essential points are these. Under conditions of high temperature and abundant moisture in the soil, silica is leached downwards to accumulate in the lower layers. The oxides of iron and aluminium remain behind in the surface layers, but also appear to be greatly enriched by the same compounds moving upwards from the lower layers during dry periods. Thus, $Fe_2 O_3$ and $Al_2 O_3$ are precipitated in the form of a crust (Buchanan's 'laterite') somewhere within the A horizon. The upward movement of these iron and aluminium compounds can only take place in dry periods and in conditions where the water table is not far below the ground surface. It is thus essential for the formation of mature lateritic soils that there should be an alternation of wet and dry seasons.

Other conditions linked with the process of laterisation are that temperatures should be sufficiently high to promote leaching of the silica, and also to prevent any significant accumulation of humus in the soil; and that the area should not be liable to erosion. The second is most effectively maintained on areas of subdued relief such as planation surfaces, and under some form of vegetative cover in the initial stages at least. The mature lateritic soil may later become so infertile that vegetation degenerates into poor scrub. Then surface erosion may expose the iron crust to transform the surface layers into a purely mineral formation.

The whole process of laterisation, as for other soil-forming reactions, covers a considerable period of time. This is another reason why lateritic formations are often associated with planation surfaces. In some areas remnants of laterite crusts can be seen at different levels and related to surfaces of different ages. Rejuvenation following each stage of planation has then lowered the water table regionally, effectively 'killing' the laterisation process, and leaving the lateritic material as a fossil substance. The occurrence of ancient laterite crusts in some semi-arid areas probably indicates a change of climatic conditions.

Mature lateritic soils are fairly permeable. The upper clay horizons are not plastic but friable, especially in dry weather, and this helps to combat erosion. The iron crust also acts in this way until it is broken through. Once broken, rapid and severe erosion may follow in the soft B horizon, removing the crust by undercutting. In part of Malagasy drainage ditches dug to help remove flood waters served to break the crust and initiate extensive erosion.

It should be emphasised again that the final product of laterisation is relatively restricted in its extent in Africa. Over vast areas reddish soils representing early stages of laterisation are to be found, but they have many characteristics in common with the mature lateritic soil. Low humus content leads to rapid soil exhaustion if lateritic soils are employed for any form of intensive agriculture. The high rainfall of the wet season leaches out many elements valuable for plant growth, such as potash, nitrogen or phosphorus. The great depth of weathered material associated with humid tropical conditions provides many opportunities for soil erosion once the vegetation is cleared on even moderate slopes; and the incipient iron crust makes it very difficult to arrest gullying once started, for the gullies rapidly enlarge themselves by undercutting the crust. Ignorance of the nature of tropical soils has frequently led to failure in attempts to use them for intensive cultivation. One of the greatest problems in tropical Africa is how to preserve the fertility of these lateritic soils. If there is adequate land, shifting systems of cultivation may represent an excellent adaptation to soil conditions, but if through population pressure the fallow period is shortened, or if attempts are made to grow cash crops year after year, these soils rapidly deteriorate and yields fall drastically.

Soils of the Atlas and Cape regions

In these two areas of Mediterranean climate the soil-forming processes have been retarded for many reasons, so that mature soils are relatively rare. Mountainous terrain has assisted greatly in this respect, preventing the accumulation of thick soils except in the valley bottoms. The generally low rainfall, except on the higher parts of the Cape Ranges, delays rock weathering, while the summer drought period restricts vegetation. Consequently there is little humus available. The fact that soil moisture is only present generally in the cool season has also retarded chemical reactions and redistribution of compounds within the weathered layer.

On areas of flatter land the soil profile indicates that podsolisation is taking place to some extent, with the accumulation of silica in the A horizon, and the gradual downward leaching of the sesquioxide minerals ($Fe_2 O_3$ and $Al_2 O_3$) to the B horizon. The colouring is generally brown near the surface if any humus is present, though on limestone areas a reddish colour is common. Nearly everywhere in these Mediterranean regions there is still a close relation between soil type and parent rock. In the Cape region, for instance, the Table Mountain Sandstone gives sandy acid soils, whereas the Bokkeveld Shales outcropping on the valley floors have weathered to produce brown clays which are agriculturally much more productive. In both the Cape and Atlas regions the best soils for agriculture are on lowlands and in valleys where weathered material has been able to accumulate and develop a soil profile in relatively undisturbed conditions.

References

1 L. C. King, 'The study of the world's plainlands', *Quart. Journ. Geol. Soc. London*, 106 (1950), 101–31
    L. C. King, *The morphology of the Earth* (Edinburgh, 1962)
2 F. Dixey, 'Erosion surfaces in Africa: some considerations of age and origin', *Trans. Geol. Soc. South Africa*, 59 (1956), 1–16
3 J. W. Gregory, *The rift valleys and geology of East Africa* (London, 1921)
4 E. J. Wayland, 'Some account of the geology of the Lake Albert Rift Valley', *Geog. Journ.*, 58 (1921), 344–59
5 S. P. Jackson, 'Air masses and the circulation over the plateau and coasts of South Africa', *S. Afr. Geog. Journ.*, 29 (1947), 1–15
    S. P. Jackson, 'Atmospheric circulation over South Africa', *S. Afr. Geog. Journ.*, 34 (1952), 48–60
6 A. J. Herbertson, 'The major natural regions: an essay in systematic geography', *Geog. Journ.*, 25 (1905), 300–12
7 G. T. Trewartha, *The Earth's problem climates* (Madison, 1961)
8 C. F. Marbut and H. L. Shantz, *The vegetation and soils of Africa* (New York, 1923)
9 Published on behalf of L'Association pour l'Etude Taxonomique de la Flore d'Afrique Tropicale (Oxford, 1959), with notes by R. W. J. Keay
10 P. W. Richards, *The tropical rain forest* (Cambridge, 1952)
11 S. J. Schokalskaja, *Die Boden Afrikas* (Berlin, 1953)

Selected Bibliography

Climatological Atlas of Africa, C.C.T.A. (Lagos/Nairobi, 1961)
M. A. Garbell, *Tropical and equatorial meteorology* (London, 1947)
W. G. Kendrew, *The climates of the continents* (Oxford, 1961, 5th ed.)
B. Willis, *East African plateaus and rift valleys* (Washington, 1936)

F. Dixey, 'African landscape', *Geog. Rev.*, 34 (1944), 457–65
F. Dixey, 'The Nyasa-Shiré Rift', *Geog. Journ.*, 91 (1938), 51–6
J. H. Jennings, 'The eruption of Mount Cameroon, 1959', *Geography*, 44 (1959), 207–8
B. C. King, 'The geomorphology of Africa', *Science Progress*, 180 (1957), 672–81, and 181 (1958), 97–107
L. C. King, 'A theory of bornhardts', *Geog. Journ.*, 112 (1948), 83–7
A. C. Veatch, 'The evolution of the Congo Basin', *Geological Society of America, Memoir No. 3* (1935)

A. H. Bunting, 'Some problems of agricultural climatology in tropical Africa', *Geography*, 46 (1961), 283–94

P. E. Lydolph, 'A comparative analysis of the dry western littorals', *Ann. Assoc. Am. Geogr.*, 47 (1957), 213–30

F. J. Simoons, 'Snow in Ethiopia: a review of the evidence', *Geog. Rev.*, 50 (1960), 402–11

M. Baldwin and J. Thorp, 'Laterite in relation to soils of the tropics', *Ann. Assoc. Am. Geogr.*, 30 (1940), 163–83

M. M. Cole, 'Vegetation nomenclature and classification with particular reference to the savannas', *S. Afr. Geog. Journ.*, 45 (1963), 3–14

H. B. Gilliland, 'Some current problems concerning the understanding of African vegetation', *Geog. Rev.*, 40 (1950), 466–8

J. Gottman, 'Laterisation in Africa', *Geog. Rev.*, 32 (1942), 319–21

PART II

Historical and Political Evolution

The significance of recent economic and political changes in Africa can only be properly assessed in the perspective of history. For many centuries, and for many reasons, Europeans have been interested in Africa, but it was not until the nineteenth century that the interior of the Dark Continent was illuminated by the efforts of explorers, missionaries, prospectors and traders. It is difficult for us to realise today that in 1850 no white man had even seen Victoria Falls, the snow-clad peaks of Ruwenzori or the great Congo river above its estuary. Since 1850 the continent has been explored and colonised; by 1910 only Morocco, Liberia and Ethiopia remained unoccupied by one or other of the European powers. But in the last ten years the situation has been dramatically reversed, so that by mid-1967 the only sizeable territories not independent of European control were Rhodesia, Angola and Moçambique.

8

Exploration

Hardly a hundred years have elapsed since the primary outlines of African physiography were finally made clear. In 1862 the riddle of the Nile was solved when Speke showed that the continent's longest river rose in Lake Victoria; in 1877 the course of the Congo to its estuary was first established. Yet the continent of Africa was almost certainly circum-navigated by Phoenician sailors, and the details of much of its coastline were known to Portuguese mariners by the early sixteenth century. It is at first sight surprising that so few attempts should have been made to penetrate the interior of the great continent before the closing years of the eighteenth century. Many things combined to delay such penetration, not least the physical geography. The coastline of much of Africa is not an attractive one to the sailor. There is a lack of major inlets providing shelter; the sea is sometimes shallow for some little distance off-shore, especially in parts of West Africa; and there are some strong currents. But once having landed on the coast, penetration inland is discouraged by other physiographical features. Most of the great rivers possess deltaic mouths and major obstructions to navigation in the form of waterfalls or rapids not far from the coast. In the tropics the coastal vegetation is frequently dense; inland, the great forested areas in West Africa and the Congo defied the efforts of explorers to depart from the lines of the rivers.

The climate of much of Africa also served as a deterrent to settlement and exploration. In the north the great Sahara desert, stretching from one side of the continent to the other, is broken only by the valley of the Nile, which is itself blocked for boats by the cataracts and by the vast swamp region of the Sudd above the cataracts. About half the Atlantic coast of Africa is arid and waterless; before the opening of Suez, and because of the occupation of most of the east coast by Arabs from the eleventh and twelfth centuries onward, this was the only coast of Africa accessible to Europeans. Other aspects of climate were also unattractive to Europeans—the heat and humidity of the tropics, and the associated insects and tropical diseases. Finally, though the native population of Africa was not large, in many instances it was definitely hostile to explorers, largely because of the activities of both European and Arab slave-traders over two and a half centuries.

But we must reckon not only with deterrents: apart from missionary activities, there was for long little incentive for penetrating the interior. It did not seem that there were any valuable minerals to be had there— a contrast with South America where the search for gold and silver led the Spaniards to some of the most inaccessible parts of the continent. The first traders in Africa were concerned with slaves and ivory, both of which could in general be obtained without leaving the coastlands. Both physical and economic factors combined, then, to retard the 'opening-up' of Africa. Until the nineteenth century Africa was a coast, not a continent.

THE EARLIEST EXPLORERS

The valley of the Nile in Egypt was the home of the oldest civilisation in Africa, and has been continuously settled for at least 6,000 years. The early Egyptians, however, knew little of the rest of Africa, apart from the coastlands of the Red Sea and the more northern parts of Ethiopia. The Sahara barred all routes to the west, and the Sudd region on the Nile prevented any expansion to the south.

In the fifth century B.C. Egypt was visited by the Greek historian Herodotus, who travelled up the Nile as far as the first cataract, recording many features of the geography of northern Africa as they were then known. It is interesting to note particularly his mention of rumours that a great river swarming with crocodiles, existed far to the south-west of Egypt. This may well be the first reference to the River Niger, and the information was possibly obtained through trading expeditions which had ventured into the Sahara.

We also have records from Herodotus of what was probably the earliest circumnavigation of Africa. It appears that Necho, who was Pharaoh of Egypt about 600 B.C., sent out an expedition, manned by carefully chosen Phoenician sailors, to determine whether Africa was surrounded by sea on the south. They set sail on the Red Sea, and after three years, during which they landed to plant corn and replenish their food supply, returned by way of the Straits of Gibraltar. Xerxes later ordered a ship to sail round Africa in the reverse direction, but the unfortunate vessel got no farther than Morocco.

Westward from Egypt, along the Mediterranean shores, a few Greek colonists attempted to establish themselves: in north-west Africa the Carthaginians were in occupation from Tripoli to Tangier, and had set up trading settlements on the Atlantic coast of Morocco. In about 500 B.C. Hanno, a Carthaginian general, pushed farther down the coast to the Senegal river and probably Sierra Leone, where he records encounters with 'hairy females' (probably apes), and a coast ablaze with torrents of fire. Some suppose from this that Hanno saw an eruption of Cameroon Mountain, but it is more likely that the fires were widespread bush-burning by the natives.

In the second century B.C. Carthage was overthrown by Rome. The Roman Empire produced its own great historians and travellers, but added little to knowledge of interior Africa. Much of the geographical description produced by Strabo and others was a compilation of existing material. But Ptolemy's map of the 'World' (A.D. 150) showed some interesting features. The Blue Nile was shown rising in a lake in Ethiopia, whilst the main Nile had its source in the snow-clad 'Mountains of the Moon', somewhere in equatorial Africa. Also plotted were interior river systems in the Sahara, one of which was labelled 'Nigir'.

THE TRAVELS OF IBN BATTUTA

Beginning in the seventh century A.D., a series of Moslem invasions swept across northern Africa from Egypt (see Fig. 16), not only conquering these lands but obliterating almost all traces of Greek and Roman influence. By 640, Egypt was conquered, and Spain was invaded from north-west Africa in 711. On the eastern side of Africa the Arabs were soon to spread much farther south, as far as Zanzibar and the mouth of the Zambezi river. The Arabs produced many eminent writers and cartographers. Itineraries and topographical descriptions were published to aid pilgrims and other travellers. One of the greatest Arab travellers was Ibn Battuta. In 1330 he sailed from Aden along the East African coast, visiting Berbera, Mogadiscio, Mombasa and Kilwa (latitude 8°S), where he met other Arabs who had reached Sofala in latitude 20°S. But his most important journey was in western Africa. In

1351 he set out from Fez to cross the Atlas and the Sahara, and succeeded in reaching the African kingdom of Mali, whose capital lay by

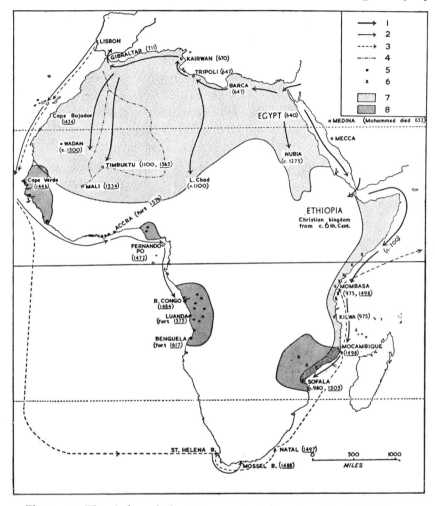

Figure 16 *The Arabs and the Portuguese in Africa, 640–1650 A.D.* (Dates relating to the Portuguese exploration and expansion are underlined; other dates relate to the earlier Arab conquest)

1. Lines of Islamic expansion, seventh to thirteenth centuries. 2. Early Portuguese explorers, 1430–86. 3. First voyage of Vasco da Gama, 1497–9. 4. The journey of Ibn Battuta, 1351–4. 5. Portuguese settlements in western Africa, fifteenth to early seventeenth centuries. 6. Arab settlements in eastern Africa, conquered by the Portuguese. 7. Moslem dominated by 1450. 8. Probable extent of Portuguese influence inland by the early seventeenth century

the upper Niger (Fig. 16). Thence he travelled to Timbuktu and Gao in 1353. The Niger, he thought, was the upper Nile. From Gao, he re-crossed the Sahara to Fez.

THE PORTUGUESE SEAMEN OF THE FIFTEENTH CENTURY

In the years 1430 to 1500 Portuguese seamen not only examined the whole Atlantic coast of Africa but also sailed round the southern Cape into the Indian Ocean for the first time for 2,000 years since the Phoenicians. Their motive was to find a way to the East which avoided the difficult overland route through Moslem and Turkish territory. The stimulus was provided by the advance of the Turks, who by 1453 had captured Constantinople. The Portuguese found it no easy matter to sail south along the west coast of Africa in search of the Cape and the sea-route to India, on account of the arid nature of the coast of the Sahara, which was the part first encountered, not to mention strong currents and fogs.

Said the mariners, this much is clear, that beyond this Cape of Bojador there is no race of men nor place of inhabitants: nor is the land less sandy than the deserts of Libya, where there is no water, no tree, no green herb—and the sea so shallow that a whole league from land it is only a fathom deep, while the currents are so terrible that no ship, having once passed the Cape, will ever be able to return.

Azurara, 1430

However, by 1434 Cape Bojador was successfully rounded, and twelve years later Cape Verde (Fig. 16). Under Prince Henry the Navigator the mariners continued to persevere, and by 1461 had reached Sierra Leone, and in 1472 the island of Fernando Poo. Along the coast, trading posts were established—the first direct commercial contacts between Europe and West Africa—and a flourishing slave trade grew up. In 1484 Diogo Cão reached the Congo estuary, whilst on a later voyage he apparently touched Walvis Bay. But still the coastline of Africa continued to extend southward, and Walvis Bay was nearly 3,500 miles from Lisbon. The Portuguese were, however, certain that a route round the southern tip of Africa would eventually be found. In 1486 Bartolomeu Dias set out on a voyage which was at last to take the Portuguese into the Indian Ocean. In one repect his venture was unique, for instead of keeping close to the coast and being held up by currents, he stood well out into the south Atlantic, only turning east in about latitude 40°S where the westerly winds prevail. Failing to sight land, he sailed north, to meet the South African coast at Mossel Bay in February 1488. After voyaging on to the mouth of the Great Fish river in longitude 27°E he returned to Lisbon. Bartolomeu Dias was followed in 1497 by Vasco da Gama, who was the first to reach India by way of the Cape of Good Hope. Relying on existing information, he took a course south-south-eastward from Sierra Leone (Fig. 16), spending three months out of sight of land, and turning east in latitude 33°S to meet the coast at St. Helena Bay north of Cape Town. After rounding the Cape he reached and named the Natal coast on Christmas Day; proceeding northward, he touched his first Arab port at Moçambique. Thence he sailed on to Mombasa and Malindi, before crossing to India using the southwest monsoon. Thus the Portuguese had achieved their object: a new route to the east had been opened, and numerous trading posts set up incidentally on the west coasts of Africa.

1500–1788: A PERIOD OF STANDSTILL IN THE EXPLORATION OF AFRICA

In the years following Vasco da Gama's voyage the Portuguese established further trading posts and ports of call on the route to India via the Cape, but made little attempt, apart from the efforts of a few missionaries, to penetrate the interior of Africa. In time Portugal declined in power, and her position was taken by other European nations in turn. English, Dutch and French sailors visited the West African coasts, and developed many lines of commerce with the native peoples, rarely attempting, however, to get at the source of the products. There existed a general fear of the 'dark interior' which was only gradually to be dispelled. We can afford for the moment to pass over the years until 1788, an important landmark in the history of African exploration, for in that year the African Association was founded in London, a body which was later to merge with the Royal Geographical Society. Its aims were not directed at the development of commerce but were to promote exploration and the advancement of knowledge of Africa.

The Niger Basin

In 1788 neither the source nor the mouth of the River Niger was known, though its middle course had been encountered more than four centuries earlier by Ibn Battuta. The African Association commissioned Mungo Park to solve the problem. In 1795 he travelled from the Guinea coast up the Gambia river (Fig 17), crossed over to the Senegal river and by a circuitous route reached the upper Niger near Segou on 20th July 1796.

> Looking forwards, I saw with infinite pleasure the great object of my mission; the long sought for, majestic Niger, glittering to the morning sun, as broad as the Thames at Westminster, *and flowing slowly to the eastward.*
>
> (Mungo Park, 1799)

He returned by proceeding *up* the Niger before crossing to the Senegal and Gambia rivers. In 1805 he set out on his fateful second expedition, in which he sailed down the Niger as far as the Bussa rapids, where he was drowned. At the time of his death he seems to have believed that the Congo estuary represented the outlet of the Niger.

His work was carried on by Clapperton and Lander; in 1830 Lander solved the problem of the Niger by showing that the great river reached the Gulf of Guinea in an immense forested delta.

The Chad Basin

The exploration of this area was a natural sequel to Mungo Park's travels. In 1823 Denham reached Lake Chad after crossing the Sahara from Tripoli. Thirty years later Barth investigated the area more thoroughly also after journeying from Tripoli across the desert (Fig. 17), but passing through Kano in northern Nigeria. From Lake Chad, Barth visited both the Benue and Niger rivers before proceeding to Timbuktu and returning to England.

South Africa

Before taking up the story of the exploration of the other major river basins in tropical Africa we must examine the penetration of the southern part of the continent. It will be recalled that the Cape region was visited by the Portuguese as early as 1486; the founding of several settlements, as ports of call on the route to the east, dates from the next few years. Present-day Port Elizabeth, for instance, stands on Algoa Bay—the name indicating the route 'to Goa' in India; Lourenço Marques on Delagoa

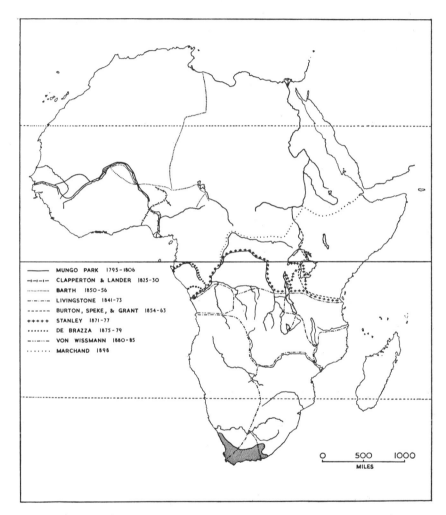

Figure 17 *A century of exploration by Europeans.* Only those explorers who made major contributions to Europe's geographical knowledge of Africa in the nineteenth century are shown. The shaded portion in the south indicates the extent of Cape Colony at the beginning of the nineteenth century

Bay ('from Goa') was sited farther north. These early settlements were temporary, and with the decline of Portuguese power left only their names behind. It was not until 1652 that the Cape region was again used for similar purposes, this time by the Dutch. Like their Portuguese predecessors, the Dutch found this part of Africa attractive, with its warm 'Mediterranean' climate, and in 1652 the decision was taken to establish a permanent port of call on the route to the Indies. Just over 300 years ago the boats of Jan van Riebeeck slid up on the beach of the hospitable bay below Table Mountain, and here he built a five-bastioned fort that became the nucleus of white settlement. He was instructed to found a self-supporting colony which could also re-victual the Dutch ships. The small colony slowly grew in size; in 1688, 164 French Huguenots landed in Table Bay, small in numbers, but to have a profound influence on the Cape. By 1770 the little colony of Dutch and French numbered about 2,000.

Attempts had already been made to penetrate the interior beyond the coastal ranges and escarpments, but the land appeared generally arid and unattractive, and most settlers remained on the coastlands and valleys.

The original native population of the Cape region was small and scattered, consisting of Bushmen and Hottentots. Neither were warlike; the Bushmen retreated into the desert, while the Hottentots, together with West Africans and Malays, were absorbed as slaves into the Dutch community. But as in later years a few of the settlers spread farther inland and north along the coast towards the Great Fish river, they came into contact with Bantu-speaking tribes such as the fierce, warlike Xhosa, who were spreading southward from East Africa in search of new lands. Meanwhile, in Europe, the Napoleonic Wars had broken out in 1795, and in 1796 the Netherlands were absorbed by France. This spelled the end of the Dutch East India Company, and the Boer settlers in the Cape were virtually abandoned. Shortly thereafter, the British, now involved in India, occupied the Cape region to safeguard the sea-route to their new colonies. The Boers in the Cape were forced to accept British military control, and later even military aid, because of increasing clashes with the Bantu natives in the east. By this time individual Boer settlers had penetrated well into the interior, beyond the arid Karroo to the grasslands of the Veld. They established small isolated farmsteads, surrounded by large sheep and cattle ranches. Much of the movement to the interior was prompted by dislike of British rule in the Cape, and also by the system of yearly leases of land in the Cape region. There was a certain amount of British immigration to the Cape lowlands, both military and colonial, so that by 1800 the white population of the whole of South Africa numbered some 26,000.

As already indicated, relations between the British and the Boers were never good; friction increased in the next few years over interference by the British in Boer land-tenure systems and other customs, but a principal cause of trouble lay over the question of African slaves, essential to the Boer social system. The British Act (1833) of freeing the slaves in the Cape was one of the events which prompted the majority of the Boers to leave the Cape region in the Great Trek of 1836. Harsh battles with such tribes as the Zulu distinguished this great migration. In the next few years the Boers occupied large tracts of the Veld, as far north as the Limpopo, subjugating the natives and setting up farmsteads. In 1852 and 1854 respectively, the two Boer colonies of the Transvaal and the Orange Free State were founded.

The Kalahari and the Zambezi lands

The outlines of the greater part of this vast area were explored by the most celebrated of all missionaries, David Livingstone. In 1841 he landed at Algoa Bay (where Port Elizabeth had been founded by the British twenty-one years previously), and trekked northward to cross the Orange river into Botswana (Fig. 17). His missionary activities en route were mush resented by the local Boers. In 1849 he reached Lake Ngami, and two years later the River Zambezi itself. A second expedition took him on up the Zambezi; in 1854 he crossed the watershed between this river and the Congo drainage, and after many trials, both through illness and hostile natives, reached the Atlantic coast at Luanda. Returning by roughly the same route to northern Botswana, he travelled on down the Zambezi, becoming the first white person to see the Victoria Falls, and eventually came to the mouth of the great river. He had thus succeeded in traversing southern Africa from Luanda to the Zambezi delta; in 1856, he wrote:

> The peculiar form of continent was ascertained to be an elevated plateau, somewhat depressed in the centre, and with fissures in the sides by which the rivers escaped to the sea.

—a correct impression of the physiography of this part of Africa.

In 1859 the indefatigable missionary-explorer set out up the Zambezi and its tributary the Shiré. His discovery of Lake Nyasa and its surrounding highlands opened up a whole new territory to British missionaries and traders. His last expedition, from which he was not to return, left Zanzibar in 1866. Following the Ruvuma river, he crossed the highlands to Lake Nyasa, and thence journeyed northward, past Lake Tanganyika (already known from other travellers), to discover first Lake Mweru and later Lake Bangweulu. After further travels in the neighbourhood of Lake Tanganyika he crossed the lake to Ujiji on the eastern shore, where took place the famous meeting with Stanley who had been dispatched to search for him. Together they visited the northern extremity of Lake Tanganyika, and showed conclusively that, since the river there flowed *into* the lake, this lake could not be the source of the Nile. In 1873 Livingstone returned alone to Lake Bangweulu, hoping there to find the source of the Nile, but on 30th April he died. Unknowingly he had visited not the Nile's headwaters but those of the Congo.

The search for the source of the Nile

The location of the source of Africa's longest river, and the cause of the annual floods in Egypt, had been the subject of speculation for centuries before the Christian era. Herodotus in the fifth century B.C. believed that the Nile rose to the south of the Atlas; it then curved eastward (here he was obviously confusing it with the Niger); and farther east, near Merowe, turned north to flow through Egypt. His theory of the Nile floods was that the reduced evaporation of winter allowed more water to flow down the river. Controversy over the cause of the floods continued in Roman times, though it was soon determined that these were brought down by the Blue Nile as a result of rains in Ethiopia. Ptolemy (A.D. 150) shows the upper Nile divided into two branches, each fed by a great lake in the region of the 'Mountains of the Moon'. In more modern times the first major contribution was by Bruce (1769), who reached the source of the Blue Nile in Lake Tana. Penetration up the White Nile was, however, completely impeded by the swamps of the Sudd region. In 1848–9 two German missionaries in East Africa reported seeing snow-capped mountains in the interior; these were thought to be Ptolemy's 'Mountains of the Moon', but were more probably Mounts Kenya and Kilimanjaro.

The first definite attempt to locate the source of the White Nile was

made by Burton and Speke. In 1857 they crossed East Africa to discover
Lake Tanganyika. They did not at the time ascertain its relation to the
surrounding drainage—Livingstone did that a few years later—and
returned to Tabora in the centre of East Africa. In 1858 Speke alone set
out from there to explore northward, and one month later arrived at
the shores of Africa's largest sheet of water, which he named Lake
Victoria. The next year the Royal Geographical Society commissioned
Speke and Grant to explore Lake Victoria further, to show if there was
any connection with the Nile drainage. In 1862 they succeeded in proving
that Lake Victoria does indeed feed the White Nile, draining north over
the Ripon Falls. The course of the river was traced downstream as far
as Gondokoro (latitude 4°50′N), where they met the explorer Baker,
who had at last, in the face of tremendous difficulties, forced a route
through the Sudd region on his way upstream from Khartoum. Baker
later travelled on up another tributary of the Nile to discover Lake
Albert. In 1877 Stanley reached the last great lake remaining undiscovered,
in East Africa—Lake Edward—and demonstrated that this too contributed
to the waters of the Nile by feeding into Lake Albert. But Stanley's
most momentous discovery was of Ptolemy's 'Mountains of the Moon',
rising on the equator to nearly 17,000 feet in Ruwenzori, capped with
snow and ice. In 1888 he was camped on the plateau west of Lake Albert
when the natives pointed out to him an apparition they had often
mentioned. Even then Stanley hesitated to believe what he saw, but the
glistening peaks reappeared as he travelled closer. The extraordinary
elusiveness of Ruwenzori results from the almost continuous cloud
cover. The first to climb the peaks was the Duke of Abruzzi in 1906.

The Congo Basin

This was the last of the major African drainage systems to be elucidated.
The mouth of the Congo had been reached by Diogo Cão in 1484;
Mungo Park three centuries later considered that this was the mouth of
the Niger. Stanley in 1877 solved the question, not by attempting to
force a way up the river past the great falls which bar it not far above
the estuary, but by following down what he thought might be one
of its head-streams in the region of Lake Tanganyika. He eventually
reached the estuary. It was left to Thompson, a couple of years later,
to show that Lake Tanganyika actually drained into the Congo system
via the Lukuga outlet.

The courses of the Congo's main tributaries and other adjacent rivers were traced out in the closing years of the nineteenth century. Mary Kingsley in 1895 explored the Ogooué river in what was afterwards to become French Equatorial Africa; later de Brazza crossed from the Ogooué valley into the Congo (Fig. 17). The Kasai tributary of the Congo was put on the map by von Wissmann, and many other great southern tributaries by Grenfell.

Thus, by the last decade of the nineteenth century the main outlines of relief and drainage in Africa had been defined. The greatest contributions were undoubtedly those of Livingstone, Speke and Stanley. In succeeding years the remaining gaps, with the exception of the heart of the Sahara, were gradually but laboriously filled in; still later decades saw the first detailed topographical maps produced. Compared with the neighbouring continent of South America, the exploration of the interior of Africa has been long delayed.

9

Colonisation and Partition

Passing references were made in the previous chapter to settlements established by various European countries around the coasts of Africa from the fifteenth century onwards. The earliest European settlements were in general of two sorts. There were in the first place 'ports of call', serving the trade routes with India and the East, such as those established in southern Africa by the Portuguese and later by the Dutch. Secondly there were the trading posts, also located on the coast, which dealt in the several commodities which Africa itself produced. Since the eastern side of the continent was far less accessible, and also because most of it was already in the hands of the Arabs (see Fig. 16), these trading posts were located mainly along the Atlantic coast, and particularly along the shores of the Gulf of Guinea, where they could tap the resources of the area south of the Sahara. The early traders were interested in a limited range of valuable products which could be obtained by barter without any need to penetrate inland: ivory, gold and spices were in great demand, and names such as the Ivory Coast and Gold Coast date from this period. But the most lucrative and extensive form of commerce was the slave trade. In this case also the trade was carried on along or near to the coasts where forts were built. In the interior the slave trade had long been under the control of the Arabs, whose influence and power extended right across the Sahara to the grasslands beyond the desert in West Africa, and who were jealous of any European attempts to penetrate from the coast and seek the slaves for themselves. Largely because of the slave trade, the Africans were hostile to any Europeans, and it was due to these and other difficulties that the exploration of interior Africa was so long delayed.

As late as the year 1880 a map of Africa (Fig. 18) shows only very limited European settlements and colonies, with the exception of the south, where the Dutch had been established since 1652 and the British since 1806. Throughout the whole of tropical Africa European settlement was confined to the coastlands. The only settlement with non-European connections was Liberia. The founding of Liberia was linked with the freeing of slaves by several countries in the early nineteenth century; American desire to help ex-slaves led to the establishment of a colony

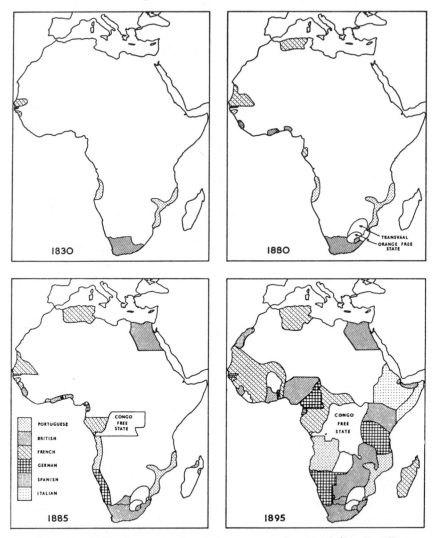

Figure 18 *The occupation of Africa by Europeans in the nineteenth century*. Few frontiers were defined before the Berlin Conference of 1884–5. No distinction is made between colonies, protectorates, or internally self-governing colonies (such as Cape Colony after 1872). British occupation of Egypt lasted from 1882 to 1936, though it was a British Protectorate from 1914 to 1922 only

for them in 1822 on Providence Island (Monrovia), and in 1847 the state of Liberia was founded. Earlier the British had also undertaken the re-settlement of slaves in parts of Sierra Leone, and it was at this time (1792) that Freetown, the present capital, received its name.

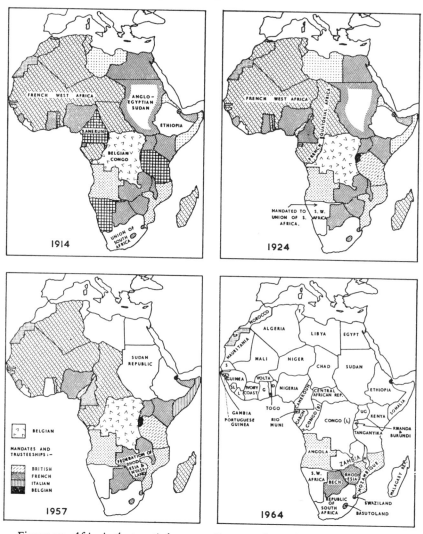

Figure 19 *Africa in the twentieth century.* By 1967, few colonies or protectorates remain. The following abbreviations are used: D Dahomey, G Ghana, L Liberia, M Malawi, S Senegal, SL Sierra Leone, SP Spanish Sahara, T Tunisia, UG Uganda

Where applicable, the same shading as for Figure 18 has been used

In the two decades between 1880 and the close of the century the greater part of the continent of Africa was divided up among six European powers. Before taking a look at the manner in which the partition was effected let us consider briefly why there should have been such a scramble for territory in Africa in these years. The second half of the nineteenth century showed a growing appreciation by European nations of the resources of Africa. It was soon realised that the most accessible source of tropical and sub-tropical products was West Africa, where such commodities as palm oil, rubber and timber were present in abundance. It was also realised that tropical Africa had considerable potentialities for the production of other commercial crops such as cotton, coffee, cacao and sugar. With the progress of the Industrial Revolution, and the other advances of the nineteenth century, raw materials and products such as these were in great demand. No longer were coastal trading posts in tropical Africa sufficient to cater for this demand; it was becoming essential to reach the sources of the raw materials in order to develop their production.

There was, secondly, a growing awareness among the industrialists of the period that the considerable population of Africa, particularly West Africa, represented an important market for the cheaper products of the Industrial Revolution; and, furthermore, the local population would provide the necessary cheap labour for the extraction of the raw materials and the development of the resources.

These, briefly, were the main economic reasons why it was desirable to 'open up' Africa. But there were also political motives. Overseas colonies served to raise the prestige of the country possessing them, and there were already several successful examples of colonies in Africa. The French had established themselves in the north since the 1830's, and the British in the Cape since 1806. Explorers of various nationalities had demonstrated the main outlines of African physiography by 1880, and had revealed the existence of resources and lands merely awaiting acquisition and exploitation.

One other event in the latter half of the nineteenth century must be mentioned: the opening of the Suez Canal in 1869. At last a direct route to eastern Africa was available, and at last Arab domination of eastern Africa and the Red Sea was broken. A new route to India was created, and as the Cape region of Africa declined in importance strategically, so the lands bordering the Red Sea and the Indian Ocean acquired a new significance.

In 1884 the first international convention to discuss the claims of various European nations to parts of Africa was held in Berlin, when it was agreed that claims to any territory must be upheld by effective occupance. The Berlin Conference was followed by a rush on the part of the six major European nations interested in Africa to extend their territorial claims inland from their original coastal footholds. A spate of treaties between various nations and with the African chiefs ensued; tracts of land changed hands for loops of beads, and boundaries were laid down rapidly and arbitrarily as each power sought to obtain the largest possible slice of territory in Africa. By 1914 most of the present political boundaries in Africa were in existence and the process of partition was virtually complete. 'Africa was a melon, and it was duly portioned out' (J. Gunther).

In south-central Africa many of the boundaries were laid down along watersheds, because the early exploration was primarily concerned with elucidating the drainage pattern. But even watersheds were not always easy to define on the ground, as in the case of the south-west frontier of the Sudan on the flat land between the Nile and the Congo drainage. Other boundaries followed rivers (e.g. the lower Congo-Ubangi), thereby disrupting the essential unity of the river basin. Some were laid down as parallels, meridians or other mathematically defined lines. No detailed maps were available at the time, so it is not surprising that in many cases boundary anomalies resulted, which paid no heed to the convenience or customs of local tribes or peoples. There were examples of frontiers which severed rivers and ports from their hinterlands (e.g. Gambia), and of frontiers which cut across tribal lands or the regularly used routes of nomads (e.g. Kenya–Somalia). Then there is the frontier which separates the Congo from Zambia, here bisecting the rich copper-mining area. Only in a few cases have such anomalies been subsequently adjusted: the cession of land from Angola to the Belgian Congo to allow for the extension of the port of Matadi and the re-alignment of the Matadi–Leopoldville railway is an exception.

THE OCCUPATION OF AFRICA BY EUROPEAN POWERS
(Figs. 18 and 19)

The story of the partition of Africa between approximately 1880 and 1920 is a complex one. So much was happening at once in different parts of the continent that a strictly chronological account would be confusing.

One can only obtain a clear picture of the events in these years by studying the activities of each European power in turn. In the following account the occupation of Africa is taken up to about 1925, with the one exception of the Italian colonies, which must be dealt with up to 1940. A separate section will consider the far-reaching changes of the period since 1950.

THE BRITISH IN AFRICA

West Africa

At the mouth of the Gambia river a British fort had been built as early as 1664. Claims to the hinterland were not, however, established till 1814, long after the original fort had been destroyed. Farther south the colony of Sierra Leone dates back to 1787, when the first attempt was made to settle slaves there. Sierra Leone became a British Protectorate in 1896. Linked with it until 1850 was the third British colony in West Africa, the Gold Coast. In the fourth colony, which, as Nigeria, was to become the largest British possession in West Africa, the slave trade continued to flourish until the 1850's. Subsequently, trading posts concerned with other commodities were established in the Niger delta region (Lagos was ceded to Britain in 1861), and in 1886 the Royal Niger Company was formed, following the Berlin Conference. Thirteen years later the Company's administration was replaced by the creation of the Protectorates of Northern and Southern Nigeria, which in 1914 were united with Lagos.

Thus the four original British coastal settlements in West Africa were enlarged and extended, but they remained separated. In this respect the British statesmen were less far-sighted than the French, who had by 1900 linked all their West African colonies together by the acquisition of territory inland, completely surrounding the smaller British possessions.

East Africa

The first important English explorers were Burton and Speke, who in 1857 penetrated into this part of Africa which had hitherto been the preserve of the Arab traders dealing in slaves and ivory. The Arabs were well acquainted with the area at least as far inland as Lakes Victoria and

Tanganyika, and had established regular caravan routes. The chief of these was from Lake Tanganyika to Dar es Salaam, via Tabora. The main centre of commerce, especially for the slave trade, was the island of Zanzibar; the Sultan of Zanzibar in fact ruled the coastal fringe of the mainland opposite. In 1869 the Suez Canal was opened, and Arab power was challenged by the British who realised the economic and strategic significance of East Africa. In 1888, the British East Africa Company was formed and extended its influence over the areas now corresponding to Kenya and Uganda. It suffered considerable financial losses, however, and was even forced to withdraw from Uganda; in 1894–5, the British Government was finally persuaded to establish Protectorates over the two colonies. Later development awaited railway construction; in 1901, Lake Victoria was linked by rail with Mombasa. Significant white settlement in the highlands of Kenya and Uganda dates from after World War I, during which German East Africa was conquered and renamed Tanganyika.

South Africa

In 1867 diamonds were discovered on the banks of the Orange river near Hopetown, and three years later at Kimberley. The year 1870 marks the commencement of the great influx of European people. The estimated European population in 1800 was only 26,000, but by 1880 the numbers of Europeans in the Cape, Transvaal and Orange Free State had risen to 411,000. Immigration to Natal (annexed in 1844) began about the same time, but included a large proportion of Indians, brought over to work the British sugar plantations. From 1867 onwards, stimulated by mineral discoveries, a network of railways was gradually built, extending inland from the ports, and reaching Kimberley in 1885 and Johannesburg in 1892. In 1886 gold was discovered in the area known as the Witwatersrand, attracting still more European settlers to South Africa. The British South Africa Company was founded in 1889 to administer the mineral resources and prospecting. By 1904 the total European population of the provinces other than Natal had reached a figure of 1,135,000. Meanwhile, friction between the British and the Boers had not been lessened by the mineral discoveries, and conflicting claims over ownership of land and investment in the mines were among the causes of the two Boer Wars of 1880–1 and 1899–1902. In 1902 the Boers were forced to surrender to British demands. In 1910 union of

the four provinces (Cape Colony, Natal, Orange Free State and Transvaal) was achieved, and South Africa emerged as a self-governing
Dominion of the British Empire. Excluded from the Union were the
territories of Basutoland and Swaziland, which together with Bechuanaland had earlier been created Protectorates, under the direct control of a
High Commissioner appointed by the Crown. The only important
subsequent political change in South Africa was in 1920, when the
Union was given a mandate over former German South-West Africa
by the League of Nations.

The Union was the area of most extensive white settlement in Africa
south of the Sahara. It should be remembered that even here, however,
the native peoples still outnumbered those of European origin by about
three and a half to one.

Central Africa

The Zambezi Basin and the Lake Nyasa region were explored by Livingstone between 1841 and 1860; penetration of these lands by British
missionaries and traders soon followed. The more precise delimitation
of the British sphere of influence here resulted from attempts by Portugal
in 1886 to link her colonies of Angola and Moçambique across central
Africa. Cecil John Rhodes, an Englishman who had amassed considerable
wealth from the gold and diamond mines of South Africa, was primarily
responsible for thwarting the Portuguese ambitions. In 1888 he negotiated
with the Matabele (the chief tribe within the area later known as Southern
Rhodesia) to obtain exclusive rights for mineral prospecting in the area,
where gold had been known to exist for some twenty years. In 1889
Rhodes established the British South Africa Company (already mentioned
in connection with South Africa) which two years later took over the
administration of the territories that were later named Northern and
Southern Rhodesia. The first British settlers had arrived in 1890, when
the town of Salisbury was founded. The first railway reached Southern
Rhodesia in 1897 (from Mafeking to Bulawayo) and by 1899 a link
had been completed between Salisbury and the Portuguese port of
Beira.

The British Protectorates of Bechuanaland and Nyasaland were
established in 1891; in Nyasaland it took six years of strenuous warfare
to crush the power of the Arab slave-traders.

Administration of the Rhodesias by the British South Africa Company ceased in 1923-4; Southern Rhodesia became a self-governing colony of the British Empire, and Northern Rhodesia a British Protectorate.

North-east Africa

Both Egypt and the Sudan have at times in the past been under British administration. Egypt was conquered by the Turks in the sixteenth century, and for nearly 300 years thereafter it remained a neglected part of the Ottoman Empire. Passing over Napoleon's temporary conquest of Egypt in 1798, the interest of European powers in this country was slight until the development of the Suez Canal project and the opening of the Canal in 1869. At this time Egyptian internal government was in a state of upheaval, and had been so since the death of the Turkish viceroy, Mohammed Ali, in 1849. Since the 1850's the French had been developing a scheme to extend their empire eastward across Africa to the Nile Basin, so that when in 1880 Egypt requested British help to restore internal order, Britain was only too ready to comply, and thus defeat the French ambitions, at any rate in the north of the Nile valley, and safeguard the Suez Canal, the route to India, at the same time. From 1882 to 1914 Egypt was effectively a British Protectorate, and was proclaimed one in 1914 shortly after the outbreak of World War I. The Protectorate lasted until 1922, when Egyptian independence was re-established, though Britain still retained responsibility for the Suez Canal.

Meanwhile, in the Sudan, Kitchener's campaign of 1896-8 succeeded in regaining control of this area after the revolt of the Sudanese against Egyptian and British rule. In 1899 the British and Egyptian governments agreed to administer the area jointly, and thus put an end finally to French territorial ambitions in the Nile Basin.

THE FRENCH IN AFRICA

North Africa

In 1830 a French military force entered North Africa, ostensibly with the motive of suppressing the Barbary corsairs, who for long had exacted dues from shipping passing through the Straits of Gibraltar. Within only four years the French claimed colonial possession of the Algerian coastlands, though fighting with the Arabs continued till 1847. Between

1848 and 1880 many attempts were made to induce French people to settle in Algeria, and considerable numbers of Spaniards and Italians also found their way into the country. The development of the interior was slow, partly because it appeared inhospitable and unproductive in comparison with French colonies in West Africa, and partly because of the hostility of the native Berbers and the Arabs. The more successful development of the coastlands, however, encouraged the French to think of extending their colonisation to other parts of the North African coast. In 1881 a Protectorate was claimed over Tunisia, and in 1904 France's interest in Morocco was recognised. In 1912 the Sultan of Morocco was forced to accept French control, though it was to be some years before French authority was extended to all parts of the territory.

West Africa

Small coastal settlements had been established here by French traders since the seventeenth century, and attempts at plantation agriculture on the lower Senegal river were made in 1820, but little came of them. It was following the success of their colonies on the coastlands of Algeria that the French were persuaded to develop their holdings in West Africa, and in the 1850's they formulated an ambitious scheme to link their various African possessions together. In 1861 an expedition penetrated up the Senegal to the middle Niger, and made direct contact with the local African kingdoms in the Sudan zone. Subsequent military expeditions drew up or imposed treaties on the Africans, and established forts at key points (e.g. Bamako in 1883). At the same time French control and occupation were extended in towards the interior from the south coast, particularly from Dahomey, so that the French territories from Senegal to Dahomey were soon linked. Only the Ivory Coast remained a separate enclave for some time, owing to difficulties with the natives and the dense forest behind the coast here. In the interior of West Africa the French continued to occupy further territory, and by 1893 were in possession of Timbuktu. In 1904 the Federation of French West Africa was proclaimed, consisting of the original coastal settlements (Senegal, French Guinea, Ivory Coast and Dahomey) and four newly defined blocks of territory linking them together in the interior—Upper Volta, Niger Colony, French Sudan and Mauritania, the last three of which were to be contiguous with the southern boundary of Algeria. Thus the great French Empire in West Africa was laid out; as noted already, the four British territories here were now completely surrounded and separated from each other by French colonies.

Equatorial Africa

French settlements on the coast of equatorial Africa to the north of the Congo estuary date from the first half of the nineteenth century; Libreville, for instance, was founded in 1848 as a settlement for freed slaves. French control was gradually extended inland, though the process was not so rapid as in West Africa. It should be noted that the territory which until 1958 was known as French Equatorial Africa actually included the Chad Basin and parts of the Sahara as far north as the Tibesti highlands, though this northerly extension was not established until after World War I. The frontier with the Anglo-Egyptian Sudan was agreed on in 1924.

East Africa

A French base was set up at Obok on the Gulf of Aden in 1883, and a Protectorate claimed (French Somaliland) some years later. This territory with its ports is of considerable strategic significance, commanding the narrow strait of Bab el Mandeb. The French were later responsible for building the only railway into Ethiopia from their port of Djibouti; the line reached Addis Ababa in 1926.

Madagascar

The island was originally discovered by the Portuguese in 1500, but the French were the first European settlers of note. In 1883 the French claimed that part of the north-west coast had been ceded to them by local native chiefs; attempts to enforce their claim led to war. Hostilities ceased in 1885, when the French gained control of the fine harbour of Diego Suarez. In 1890 Britain formally recognised a French Protectorate over Madagascar. In 1896 the ruling sovereign was deposed, and Madagascar became a French colony.

THE GERMANS IN AFRICA

The rapidity with which the Germans acquired a colonial empire in Africa is remarkable. Between 1884 (the year of the opening of the

Berlin Conference) and 1900 the Germans obtained colonies and Protectorates in Africa covering nearly 1 million sq. miles. In West Africa a
new colony of Togoland was proclaimed in 1884, separating the British
Gold Coast from French Dahomey; in the same year a Protectorate was
established in the Cameroons. The latter was greatly enlarged in the next
few years, so that by 1912 it extended from Lake Chad almost to Libreville,
a distance of nearly 900 miles. In East Africa the Germans had been active
explorers, travellers and missionaries since the 1840's; the first survey of
Kilimanjaro, for instance, was by a German in 1861–2. After 1884, German
claims on that part of East Africa now known as Tanganyika were
generally recognised. Economic development of this area in competition
with the British colonies of Kenya and Uganda proceeded rapidly;
between 1904 and 1914 the Germans completed the railway from Lake
Tanganyika to Dar es Salaam, which was designed to capture the trade
of the interior hitherto tapped only by the British line to Lake Victoria
(completed 1901). The fourth area taken over by the Germans after
1884 was South-West Africa, from the Orange river northward to
Angola. Only Walvis Bay remained in British hands.

During World War I the defeat of Germany resulted in the dismemberment of her African empire, which was distributed by the League of
Nations. Togoland and the Cameroons were each divided into two
parts, one British and the other French. East Africa was divided into
Tanganyika (under British mandate) and Ruanda Urundi (under Belgian
mandate). South-West Africa after 1920 was administered by the Union
of South Africa.

In 1945 the League of Nations mandates became Trusteeship Territories
of the United Nations, except South-West Africa, over which both
the United Nations and South Africa claim authority.

THE BELGIANS IN AFRICA

By 1877 Stanley had defined the course of the Congo and indicated the
extent of the basin which this river drains in the heart of the continent.
After Stanley's return to Europe, King Leopold II of Belgium realised
the immense possibilities for the development of this part of tropical
Africa, in competition with West Africa where commerce was already
established; he also appreciated that the Congo and its tributaries would
prove very useful lines of communication at least in the initial stages of
economic development. Leopold encouraged further exploration of

the Congo Basin and further assessment of its resources. These activities alarmed the Portuguese, who had since the fifteenth century maintained coastal trading stations, and claimed priority especially over possession of the mouth of the Congo. Matters were not settled till the Berlin Conference of 1884-5, when Leopold's right to the Congo, by virtue of his support for exploration there, was formally recognised; the area was thereafter somewhat misleadingly known as the 'Congo Free State' —it was in fact virtually one of Leopold's private possessions. Portuguese territory was delimited as Angola and Cabinda, and the Congo mouth passed into Belgian hands. Leopold was now free to undertake further development of the Congo; railway construction, essential to bypass the falls on the Congo, was pressed forward, and exploitation of the resources, particularly rubber, extended. In 1892 the rich mineralised zone of Katanga was annexed (this, however, was not tapped by railway until 1910); by 1900 a railway had been completed from the Congo estuary to Leopoldville above the great Livingstone Falls. In 1907 the Congo Free State was formally annexed by Belgium as a colony, thereafter being known as the Belgian Congo.

THE PORTUGUESE IN AFRICA

Angola

Until the mid-nineteenth century the activities of the Portuguese were confined to a few trading posts along the coast from the region of the Congo estuary southward to Benguela. Some of these had in fact been continuously occupied since about 1500 when the Portuguese mariners first charted the coast. In 1839 a rather larger colony was founded at Moçamedes, mainly by Portuguese from Brazil. But until the other European powers began dividing up Africa, Portugal took little interest in these settlements. In 1884 the dispute, already mentioned, between Portugal and Belgium over the Congo arose, as a result of which the Portuguese territory of Angola was first clearly delimited, though the precise definition of all boundaries was not completed until 1927.

Moçambique

Here again Portuguese settlement on the coast dates from the sixteenth century; the Portuguese later extended northward as far as Cape Delgado with the gradual decline of Arab power. The Portuguese aimed at control of commerce in the Indian Ocean, and in the later sixteenth and early seventeenth centuries Moçambique was closely linked with the Portuguese colonies in India; at one time it was actually governed from Goa. The only significant penetration of the interior of Moçambique was along the Zambezi river. In 1886 Portugal conceived the grandiose scheme of joining up her possessions across Central Africa from Angola to Moçambique. This scheme received a measure of support from France and Germany, but, as we have noted, was frustrated by Rhodes's operations in central Africa. The frontiers of Moçambique were delimited in 1890, and the only subsequent change was the addition of a small corner of former German East Africa in 1919.

Apart from the islands of Cape Verde, São Tomé and Principe, the only other Portuguese colony in Africa is the small territory of Portuguese Guinea, first defined in 1879.

THE SPANIARDS IN AFRICA

Spanish settlements on the coast of Morocco date from the fifteenth century and earlier, but by the Pope's edict dividing the world in 1494, Spanish interests in any part of Africa were abolished and the Portuguese were given a free hand in the continent. The present Spanish colonies therefore date from a more modern period; in 1778 Portugal ceded the area now known as Spanish Guinea (including several islands); and in 1860 the small territory of Ifni was ceded to Spain by Morocco. The Spanish Sahara (including Rio de Oro) was delimited in its present form by agreement with the French in 1912. Also in 1912 part of Morocco (the Rif), including the important port of Ceuta, was established as a Spanish Protectorate.

THE ITALIANS IN AFRICA

Her late arrival on the scene of the partition of Africa led to Italy's exclusion from all the more attractive areas of Africa by her competitors. Throughout many parts of North Africa Italian settlers were numerous in the later nineteenth century, but Italy's sphere of influence was restricted to the zone between Tunisia and Egypt. This desert region was of little use, and was retained by Italy only for prestige purposes. Actual Italian administration of this area, known as Libya, dates from 1911.

The other part of Africa in which Italy has had an interest is Ethiopia and its borderlands. Italians had settled on the southern Red Sea coast since 1869, and in 1880 Italy took over the two ports of Massawa and Assab. In 1889 the Italian Protectorate of Eritrea was proclaimed, including the hinterland of these two towns. Later, claims were extended to eastern Somaliland fringing the Indian Ocean. Attempts to invade the Ethiopian highlands were, however, defeated by the Ethiopians in 1896. Forty years later, under Mussolini, the Italians were more successful, and occupied the country for a few years, until in 1939–40 they were driven out by the British, and the Emperor of Ethiopia was returned to power.

RECENT POLITICAL CHANGES IN AFRICA (Fig. 19)

Developments in Africa since 1925, and more especially since 1945, have been proceeding at a rapid pace. The progress of settlement, the improvements in communications, and the expansion of agriculture, mining and industry, will be dealt with in the regional chapters; at the moment it is the major political changes that command attention. The period since the Second World War has seen the growth and emergence of African nationalism, which aims eventually to establish self-government by Africans throughout the continent. In 1950 the only independent states in the continent were the Union of South Africa, Egypt, Ethiopia and Liberia. By 1967 no less than 38 countries had attained independence, even though many still retained economic or defence links with the former colonial power.

First, let us examine the present status of countries within or formerly within the British Commonwealth. The Union of South Africa, independent since 1910, became a Republic in 1961. The Rhodesias and Nyasaland were linked together in a Federation from 1953 to 1963; Malawi (Nyasaland) and Zambia (Northern Rhodesia) are now self-governing and independent; Rhodesia (Southern Rhodesia) retains a minority white government and its *de facto* independence has not yet been recognised by Britain. Of the three High Commission Territories in South Africa, two achieved independence in 1966: Basutoland (renamed Lesotho) and Bechuanaland (renamed Botswana). In West Africa the former British colony of the Gold Coast was renamed Ghana and achieved independence in 1957; Nigeria received its independence in 1960, Sierra Leone in 1961, and Gambia in 1965. In East Africa, in 1963, Kenya was the last of the three territories of former British East Africa to gain independence. The year 1964 saw the Union of Tanganyika and Zanzibar in the state of Tanzania.

The French colonies in Africa were radically but unobtrusively reorganised after the Constitution of the Fifth Republic of France came into force in October 1958. Algeria and the Algerian Sahara remained initially as Departments of the French Republic under the direct control of the Prime Minister of France. French Somaliland retained its former colonial status. But the remainder of the former French colonies, with three exceptions, became independent members of the French Community. As constituted in December 1958, these are the Republics of the Ivory Coast, Dahomey, Upper Volta, Niger, Chad, Central Africa, Gabon, Congo (Brazzaville), Senegal, Sudan, Mauritania and Madagascar (renamed the Malagasy Republic). In April 1959 the Soudan and Senegal joined together in the Federation of Mali, but later split again into Mali and Senegal. The Republics of Chad, Central Africa, Gabon and Congo (Brazzaville) joined together in an economic union. Guinea, formerly French Guinea, chose not to join the French Community and has now no political links with France. The former French Trusteeship territories of Cameroun and Togo became independent Republics in 1960. In Algeria, Moslem demands for independence from France were opposed by the French settlers, with much resulting violence for a time, until in 1962 the demands were acceded to and the complete separation of Algeria from France achieved, though France still retains some rights in the Sahara.

In North Africa, apart from Algeria, Egypt became a Republic in 1953. In 1958 she joined with Syria temporarily to form the United Arab Republic, and although subsequently separated has continued the use of that title. Of the North African colonial states, Libya was the first to achieve independence (January 1952), followed by Morocco and Tunisia in 1956. On the eastern side of Africa the Anglo-Egyptian agreement to administer the Sudan was terminated in 1954; the Sudan is now an independent Republic. Somalia, formerly under Italian Trusteeship since 1950, and British Somaliland joined to become an independent Republic in 1960.

Finally, in equatorial Africa, Belgian administration of the Belgian Congo came abruptly to an end on 30th June 1960; the country was plunged into a state of chaos, with rival factions striving to gain control, and though the Leopoldville government eventually emerged as the central authority, it was some time before the secession of Katanga was ended. A Federal constitution is being established.

Selected Bibliography

J. N. L. Baker, *A history of geographical exploration and discovery* (London, 1948)

A. Boyd and P. Van Rensburg, *An atlas of African affairs* (New York, 1965)

J. D. Fage, *An Atlas of African history* (London, 1958)

R. Hallett, *The penetration of Africa: European exploration in North and West Africa to 1815* (New York, 1965)

R. J. Harrison Church, *Modern colonisation* (London, 1951)

G. H. T. Kimble, *Geography in the Middle Ages* (London, 1938)

R. Oliver and J. D. Fage, *A short history of Africa* (Baltimore, 1962)

M. Perham and J. Simmons, *African discovery: an anthology of exploration* (Evanston, Ill., 1963)

J. O. Thomson, *A history of ancient geography* (Cambridge, 1948)

E. Axelson, 'Prince Henry the Navigator and the discovery of the sea route to India', *Geog. Journ.*, 127 (1961), 145–58

K. M. Barbour, 'A geographical analysis of boundaries in intertropical Africa', in K. M. Barbour and R. M. Prothero (Eds.), *Essays on African population* (London, 1961)

F. Debenham, 'New light on Livingstone's last journey', *Geog. Journ.*, 120 (1954), 1–14

G. Hamdan, 'The political map of the new Africa', *Geog. Rev.*, 53 (1963), 418–39,

PART III

The Human Geography

Human geography is concerned with the relations of human groups to their physical environment. However, the physical background of the continent is relatively stable, whereas the human scene is far more variable, and striking changes have occurred during the last half-century. The pace of change has speeded up during recent years with newly evolving political and economic relationships between the black and white peoples. Africa of the 1960's is very different even from the Africa of the 1930's. What might have been a process of gradual change was speeded by the upheaval of World War II. This led to the growth of a world conscience regarding the poverty and plight of the underdeveloped countries and to new assessments by Europeans of Africa's resources and peoples, exemplified in new political, social and economic relationships.

Africa is the second largest continent, one and a half times the size of North America. The very size of Africa is a pitfall for generalisations and over-simplifications which, while having some substance in fact, may also mask considerable diversity. Much has yet to be learnt about both her physical and human resources: the maps of relief, hydrology, geology, soils, meteorology and land use are a long way from completion.

10

Population and Society

The density and distribution of population provide valuable signposts to the human geography of an area. Before examining the population map of Africa (Fig. 20), with this in mind, the deficiencies in our knowledge of African population in all its aspects must be emphasised. We still do not know with much precision the total population of the continent. The United Nations estimate for 1962 was 269 million, but this may be as much as 20 per cent too many or too few and several decades will pass before fairly accurate figures derived from comprehensive census-taking become available. Much of tropical Africa has still to have its first census and for these parts there are only estimates of population. Where censuses have been taken (e.g. in the former British colonies in West and East Africa and in former French West Africa) techniques are rudimentary in comparison with the sophisticated operation in most European countries. The scarcity of literate persons makes it difficult to secure sufficient enumerators and necessitates carrying out the census over a lengthy period. In some cases censuses of sample areas are taken and estimates of total population made from them, but as techniques improve the enumeration increasingly becomes extended to whole countries. Also the scope of the information sought widens from a simple counting of heads to include such data as race, age, sex, place of birth, marital status, polygamy, number of sons born and occupation. Where elements of the population are suspicious or hostile, inaccuracies are bound to occur, and since almost everywhere in Africa there is no registration of birth, age data are very unreliable. Nevertheless much progress has been made since the end of World War II in response to the urgent need for more population data in a host of former colonies where franchise is becoming extended; and plans for economic development, hinging upon improvements in education, medical and social services and public utilities, are being drawn up.

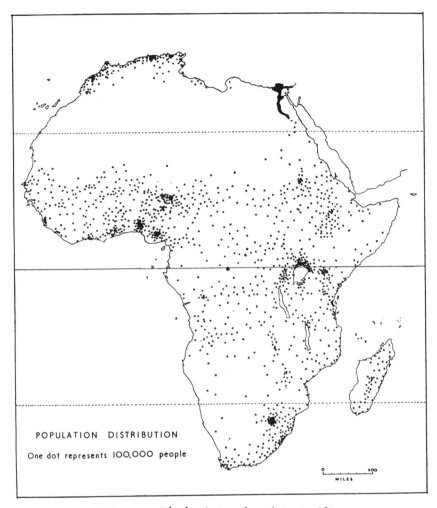

Figure 20 *The distribution of population in Africa*

The Sahara is often held to separate Africa from Europe rather than the Mediterranean, for the countries of North Africa have long connections with Europe whence, with the Middle East, their civilisation is derived. They are Mediterranean countries and closer to Greece, southern Spain and Turkey than to the countries of *Afrique Noire* to the south of the great desert. These countries of North Africa contain some 56 million, while Black Africa holds some 213 million. The greatest problem, slowly and painfully being resolved in Africa today, lies in the fact that of this vast total no more than 5 million are of European descent. These relatively few white people have a far greater importance than their puny numbers suggest. They have been the energetic leaders and innovators responsible for the economic development of the continent by bringing in ideas, techniques, capital, enterprise and organisation, and imposing law, order and stability in the process. Of these 5 million about 3 million are in the Republic of South Africa and 1 million in former French North Africa. Thus the white population over the rest of Africa is no more than 1 million—outnumbered nearly 200 to 1 and now nearly everywhere relinquishing power and privileges in face of the inevitable forces of nationalism. Black Africans are becoming more articulate and educated, and desire freedom to rule themselves with a greater say in their destinies. Other notable components of the population are Asians, probably less than 1 million and mainly Indian, but also including Syrians and Lebanese. The Indians are to be found along the east coast, particularly in Natal and East Africa, where at the turn of the century they entered as indentured labour to help on sugar plantations or in railway construction, afterwards settling, many to become traders, shopkeepers and small business men.

The average density of population for the whole continent is very low, being about 23 per sq. mile. Of the continents only Australia is less densely populated; however, as the map shows, these overall figures can be misleading, for wide variations in population density occur ranging from the irrigated Nile valley supporting in places over 2,000 people per sq. mile to the uninhabited wastes of the Sahara which cover more than a quarter of the continent. Except for the Nile valley in Egypt, the valleys of the major rivers of Africa are not densely settled, the physical conditions generally being unfavourable. If one excepts the few developed industrial and mining areas of southern Africa it will be perceived that water supply is the paramount geographical influence upon the pattern of African settlement, for most livelihood is dependent on farming or pastoral activities.

Much of Africa offers too much or too little rainfall, but aridity is the principal limiting factor. A number of favoured areas support heavy populations and in certain places overpopulation imposes increasing problems, as in parts of West Africa, the lake region of the East African highland and the Egyptian Nile valley. The sparseness of population over wide areas has far-reaching social and economic implications and is particularly noticeable in many cases where foreign (usually European) commercial and mining ventures need to overcome labour shortage by fostering labour migrations on a considerable scale. In a sense this eases the problems of many of the overpopulated areas who supply the migrant labour, but raises a number of other serious social and economic problems. Some 60 per cent of the African labour in the mines of the Republic of South Africa comes from outside the Republic, especially the High Commission territories and Moçambique. Overcrowded Rwanda and Burundi provide seasonal workers for the cotton farms of Uganda and European farms of Kenya; Malawi provides much labour for the mines and manufacturing industries of Zambia and Rhodesia. Local over-population leads to over-stocking and over-cropping of the soil, resulting in lowered soil fertility and the alteration of both the chemical and physical properties of the soil; steep slopes progressively come under cultivation with the ever-attendant danger of soil erosion. This, if in the hills near watersheds, is particularly serious, for the continent is short of water and cannot afford the destruction of catchment areas. Policies of white African governments in establishing Native Reserves which are too small and often comprise land of indifferent quality contribute to these processes.

Population structures

Our knowledge of the structure of African populations (i.e. proportion between the sexes and between the age groups) is remarkably slender. As we have said, very few countries or colonial territories have yet carried out censuses in sufficient detail to reveal age structure, and for those that have, a considerable degree of error must be accepted. Many governments conduct censuses of the white population but not of the indigenous peoples; others attempt to enumerate the whole populace by sex and classify them into three broad age groups, such as 0–18, 19–65, and over 65. In any case it is rare for a previous census to exist which would permit of comparisons.

From the data that have been collected it is clear that in common with the rest of the world the population of Africa is now increasing markedly after a period when it was probably static or increasing but slowly. This is due principally to the effects of the 'medical revolution' now beginning to be experienced in Africa, whereby growing medical knowledge, new drugs and instruction in hygiene are preserving and lengthening lives, especially those of babies and young children. The population pyramids

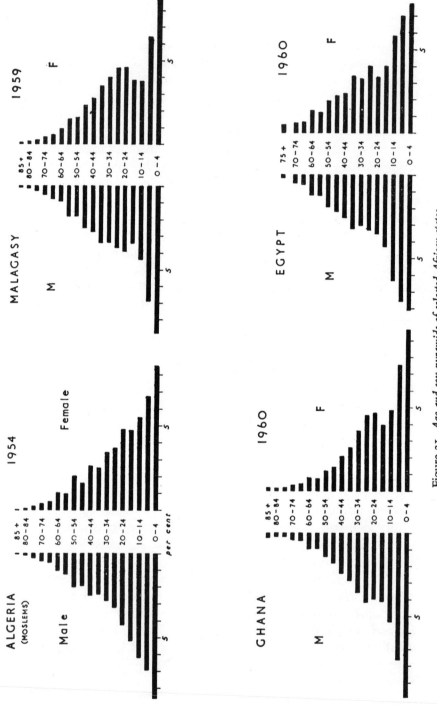

Figure 21 *Age and sex pyramids of selected African states*

(or bar graphs of age and sex distribution) of the few countries where data are available bear this out (Fig. 21) and the very high proportion of young children is a notable factor that will have increasing social and economic impact in future years. Each new member of society adds to demands on education, health and other public services and ultimately requires employment. These needs can only be met by increased capital investment and imply the absorption of a disproportionate amount of capital, so urgently needed in other sectors of the economy. Thus heavy increase of population creating populations of substantial juvenility (where over 40 per cent of populations are under fifteen years of age, as in Mauritius, Tunisia, Egypt and Madagascar) may be expected to retard economic development and even reduce output per head unless vast capital resources are available. Further, the geometric character of population increase must be remembered. The growing numbers of children in African populations with the passing of years will enter the reproductive period and will create populations of unprecedented fecundity. The population 'explosions' of Asia and South America have yet to come in Africa.

THE PEOPLES OF AFRICA (Fig. 22)

The 263 million African people are not homogeneous. They are divided into innumerable tribal groupings, speak about 700 different languages and reveal a variety of physical types. Archaeological and anthropological evidence suggests that Africa has been peopled by a succession of invasions from the east and north-east, particularly by way of the Horn of Africa. Each increment of newcomers has tended to push the established peoples fanwise from East Africa and we now find some of the earliest people still at a most primitive level pushed off the southern savanna grazing and hunting lands to the semi-arid Kalahari. In all cases, over long periods, intermarrying must have occurred: the fusion blurring the physical characteristics of the different stocks so that today ethnic classification relies more on language and culture. The peoples of Africa have been derived from the following stocks or admixture of two of them: Negritos (or Pygmies), Bushmen, Negro, Hamites and Semites. The intermixing of Hamites with the Negroes has produced such sub-types as Nilo-Hamites and Nilotes.

The major classification of African people is according to their Negroid or non-Negroid characteristics. The Sahara, the North African littoral and the Horn of Africa are principally peopled by the Semitic and Hamitic ethnic groups: people akin to Arabs and Jews. There has been much mixing, but Hamitic people of Caucasoid descent occupy the Horn of Africa, the western Sahara and parts of Algeria and Tunisia.

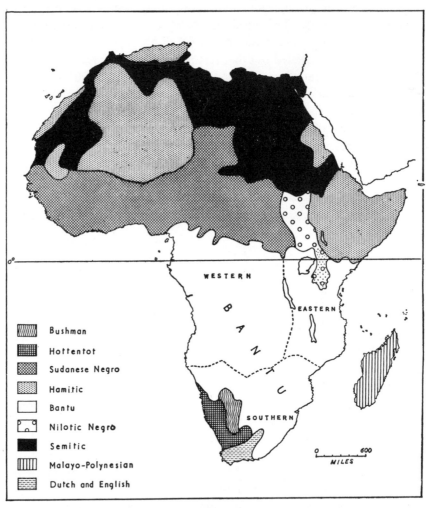

Figure 22 *Distribution of principal ethnic groups in Africa*

They represent the older peoples, many of whom were overcome and absorbed by the Semitic-Mohammedan invasions of the seventh and eleventh and twelfth centuries which led to the immigration of some 400,000 Arabs and the spread of Islam and the Arab language. Intermarriage has frequently made it difficult to distinguish between these peoples. The name Berber is applied to the Hamitic people of North Africa (from the Latin *Barbari*). Anthropologists recognise a number of Berber types, but generally they are fairly tall, light brown or fair-skinned, with brown hair, straight thin noses and non-everted lips. The thinly populated Sahara is the home of the Hamitic Tuareg, Tibu and Fulani. The last show much evidence of dilution with West African Negroid peoples on the southern edge of the desert. In the eastern Sahara the earliest Egyptians were of Hamitic stock and their present descendants, despite much Semitic infusion, still bear many resemblances to their pre-dynastic forerunners. To the south, Hamitic and Semitic peoples extend to the Somali coast. Ethiopian people are mainly Hamitic but Semitic influence in culture and language is strong (the Imperial House claims descent from the Queen of Sheba). In parts of the upper Nile Basin and of the East African plateau, probably as a result of a southward move of Hamites, distinctive hybrid types have developed, partly Hamite and partly Negro. These people are darker than the Hamites but retain the finer non-Negroid facial features with the woolly hair of the Negro. The term Nilotes has been given to these peoples in the Sudanese parts of the Nile valley, particularly the pastoral Shilluk and Dinka. Farther south, on the East African plateau, small groups of Hamito-Negro people exist in a mainly Bantu-Negroid area. Examples are the virile pastoral Nandi and Masai people of Kenya and northern Tanganyika.

South of the Sahara and the Horn of Africa, Africans are members of the Negro race but show considerable variations in stature, pigmentation, hair-form and facial characteristics. Over the centuries, in central and eastern Africa migrations generally south-westward from the lakes and southward down the eastern part have brought about a great mixing of Negroid peoples, usually classed as Bantu-speaking, and have pushed into the equatorial forest the Negroid pygmies and to the Kalahari desert and its fringes the interesting remnants of the Bushmen and Hottentots. The Pygmies average four feet six inches in height and are now confined to the rain forests of the Congo, Gabon and Cameroun. They are hunters, trappers and collectors. They shun outside contacts and have thus preserved their identity. There are probably about 150,000 of them living in small communities in forest clearings. The Bushmen have been reduced to a few surviving bands. Their way of life—among the world's simplest—has continued to be based on hunting and they are hard put to survive in their inhospitable semi-desert environment.

The Hottentots, once herding peoples, have now become servants and labourers of the incoming white peoples and are a major element in the Coloured population of the Cape.

The Bantu-speaking peoples of southern, central and East Africa number perhaps 70 million and occupy nearly one-third of the continent. They speak various dialects of a common language. In the eastern part of Africa, south of the Sahara, on the drier upland plains, except where the tsetse fly is prevalent, pastoral economies are paramount. Cattle are the principal animals reared and in some areas (such as East Africa) a prestige system based upon numbers of cattle possessed irrespective of quality lends a social rather than economic aspect to such a system. The system generally includes agricultural self-sufficiency based on family gardens, but for long there was little exchange of goods except beasts upon ceremonial occasions. Thus the market is a feature fairly new to eastern Africa and there has been little stimulation of native crafts. An exception to this general pattern is seen in the densely peopled area around Lake Victoria, especially in Uganda. Here agriculture prevails, cash crops are increasingly grown and some of the most advanced Bantu are to be found. Farther south the settlement of the white man on the better land and introduction of new ways of living have led to considerable disruption of tribal life. The main Bantu groups are the Suto-Chuana and Zulu-Xhosa. Botswana and Lesotho, formerly High Commission territories with restricted ingress for white men, helped to preserve the way of life and identity of tribes of the first group, but the once great Zulu people, living east and south of the Drakensberg Escarpment, have suffered considerable disintegration by the spread of white settlement which brought with it opportunities for work in farm, mine and factory.

In the lower-lying forested basins and plains of the Congo the heavier rainfall, the prevalence of tsetse fly and other pests and diseases have helped to make agriculture the prime activity rather than pastoralism. Some Bantu peoples, such as the Fang inhabiting parts of equatorial Africa, practise shifting cultivation in forest clearings, rarely staying more than two to three years in one place. Others, such as the Bakuba, occupying a more open part of the Kasai Basin, engage in more settled agriculture. Trade plays a part in the economic and social life and regular markets are maintained.

Some of the purest Negro types are found across the northern savanna lands from the western Sudan into West Africa and comprise the Sudanese Negro type. These Negroes are tall, with black or very dark brown skin, woolly hair, broad nose and thick everted lips; almost all are cultivators. This concentration on agriculture allows the support of a denser population and has facilitated a degree of specialisation and division of labour. Metal-working, textiles, pottery of high quality, exemplify this tradition and have fostered trade, the market and the town of the Guinea coast and western Sudan. Indeed, the passion for trading seems inherent in West African people, from the enterprising Hausa of northern Nigeria to the bustling tribes of the coast where the Yoruba market women—the 'mammies'—with their high, gaily coloured head-dress are a familiar sight. This part of Africa leads in having a well-established middle class: merchants who handle goods rather than produce them and who may well trace back their affluence to ancestors who became 'trade boys', supplying visiting European vessels with much-prized gold and slaves from the hinterland.

The decline of the tribal system

The middle years of the twentieth century are witnessing a rapid decline of the tribal system in Africa. The pace of change varies in different parts of the continent but the process seems inevitable as social and economic values change, as Western technology finds application and as political power becomes a real, desirable and attainable thing. The tribal system has become outmoded. With the principal exception of the more urban West Africa, until recent years there was little division of labour, no notable wealthy class, nor dominant aristocracy among the majority of African people; ideas of class and caste have been alien to the African mind. The common links between members of a group or tribe are duty and obligations to elders and position within the tribe that only advances with age. The self-sufficient organisation of such communities offered little opportunity for innovation or individualism. Problems are decided by communal decision, central authority generally is absent. The system has not fostered inter-tribal links, but rather has tended to emphasise differences and rivalry. It has also tended to keep women in a position of inferior status, and by its system of communal land working and annually changing allotment of land gives the cultivator no incentive to improve the plot he crops. On the whole this system has hindered progress, particularly because it bolsters ignorance, idleness and super-stition.

The undermining and weakening of the tribal system has been the most notable result from the introduction of a money economy, leading to the growth of desire for manufactured novelties and goods not possible to attain under a communal subsistence system. These desires have been fanned by the return of men from the Forces after World War II and since then regularly by others upon their return from mines, industry and town, bringing with them knowledge of new social and economic values.

A major but unexpected result of the white man's occupation of Africa is to be seen in the growing numbers of Africans travelling, often hundreds of miles, in search of employment. Fiscal measures requiring the payment of money taxes, the overcrowding of reserves and tribal lands, and no doubt the desire to be a man and see the world, all contribute to these labour movements where the mines of Zambia, the growing industries of Rhodesia and the mines and industries of the Republic of South Africa are the main magnets (p. 500). The movements are no longer haphazard and quotas are imposed by the receiving countries and the proportion of families accompanying their menfolk slowly increases. All this has had unfortunate effects upon tribal life.

The tribal African entering urban society is confronted by entirely different social and economic values, where individualism is not merely unchecked but often encouraged, where personal responsibility is the rule, where conduct is no longer controlled by tradition and enforced by elders, where he is expected to labour all the time for a set period and often beside men of different tribal origins and habits. He finds himself subjected to all manner of social and moral innovations and temptations. He has entered a new world and returns to his tribal home a changed man, wearing an air of sophistication, sceptical of tribal observances and less impressed by the elders. This continuing process results in growing numbers breaking with the tribe and drifting to permanent employment in the towns—the landless, wage-earning, de-tribalised natives. At times the movement of excessive numbers of able-bodied men to work has caused the collapse of a village economy when the women and older men were unable to maintain adequate cultivation. The imposition of labour quotas and controls has helped to counteract this danger.

Other forces are also at work. The waning of subsistence economies and growth of cash and exchange economies lead to changes in forms of land tenure which strengthen the individual at the expense of the tribe. Improvements in agricultural efficiency require the consolidation of fragmented holdings into a lesser number of larger plots, and the long-term identification of these plots with particular individuals who will then have incentive to improve the husbandry. From this arises the need for the issuing of title deeds and registering of the land, which give security value for the raising of loans and mortgages and thus make it possible for the peasant cultivator to raise the capital for improvements. All this weakens the tribal system which suffers further when nationalism, which to be effective must override tribal boundaries, brings into power those dedicated to a new order. The period of uneasy transition and readjustment will be lengthy, while modern administrative and technical services, government and a new ordering of society gradually evolve as traditional influences slowly wane.

11

Settlement and Health

With the major exception of West Africa the African peoples have not developed towns, but neither is the individual isolated habitation typical. Over most of the continent the pattern, only now becoming disturbed, is for settlement in family groups within the tribe. In Bantu Africa this takes the form of dispersed nucleations of beehive-type, mud-walled, conical thatch-roofed huts, usually with attendant cattle-pens and adjacent gardens or fields. In Negroid Africa the housing form is often clay-walled, thatch-roofed rectangular buildings around a central compound. Thick thorn hedges enclose and protect the human and animal population. This pattern reflects the subsistence character of the economy, is often related to water supply and shaped for defence and mutual protection. Sometimes the grouping may be no more than a hamlet comprising the half-dozen huts of a family group (Plate 12), but in other cases a young 'town' of scores of huts may surround the kraal of the tribal chief.

Among the settled population of North Africa the tribal influence is far less prevalent, but the agglomeration of the agricultural population into villages remains typical. In the Nile valley and delta the mud-walled huts, their flat roofs thatched with millet or maize stalks, cluster in tight nuclei economical of land. In the Algerian Tell dense cactus and prickly-pear hedges surround similar hamlets, while in the less accessible Atlas Mountains houses of mud, stone and date-palm timber cluster, almost precariously, on precipitous crags and ridges. Even the so-called shifting cultivators of the rain forest, who clear and crop a forest patch for two to three years before moving on, act in concert and establish villages, the huts in the clearings being made of stakes and tree-bark with raffia-leaved roofs.

The lure of the towns is now strong throughout Africa. Nevertheless

Africa is still the least urbanised of the continents, for less than 10 per cent of the population lives in communities of more than 5,000 people. The small number of long-established African towns founded by the indigenous peoples is mainly restricted to Arab Africa of the north. Cairo, Algiers, Tunis, Marrakech, Khartoum-Omdurman are examples where administrative and commercial functions burgeoning from favourable locations predated European influence. In parts of West Africa an urban way of life is found chiefly among the Yoruba of western Nigeria (where about 50 per cent of the population lives in settlements of 5,000 or more inhabitants) and the centres of the Moslem emirates of northern Nigeria (where 10 per cent of the population is urban). Examples of these towns are Ibadan, Ife, Kano, Sokoto, Katsina. Elsewhere in Africa, apart from towns of the white man's creation, grouping in villages is predominant.

The modern urban phase in Africa results from contacts with Europeans; the towns and cities of southern Africa in particular are the creations of white man at port, mine or mart. Already in the Republic of South Africa some 25 per cent of Africans are living in towns. The significance of urbanisation to the African in terms of mental, social, economic and political effect must not be underestimated. Urbanised Africans increasingly become Westernised Africans; the town is the door to Western culture and society. The urban setting is attractive to a variety of industries: the agglomeration of people makes possible the provision of pure water, sewerage, gas and electricity supplies, law and order, education, health facilities and so on; all are part of the infrastructure necessary for the establishment of modern manufacturing industry. Thus towns and their rates of growth become something of an index of economic development. Equally, these services and facilities are appreciated by the Africans, the demand for schools and hospitals is overwhelming and it is the towns that generally have first call on these expanding services. Also a far greater range of employment opportunities and a higher standard of living are offered by the town than by the country. New and exciting wage-earning ways of living far different from the ill-rewarded communal toil of agriculture draw the tribesman to the town and in time into the modern world, for the town's European businesses require clerks, shop assistants, domestic servants, drivers, mechanics, factory operatives and labourers.

The pace of urbanisation has speeded since 1939 and a new range of problems has come into being. The influx of new population may bear little relation to the growth in the town's economy and the jobs available.

The unavoidable and often substantial segment of unemployed creates unrest and discontent and often becomes manifest in delinquency, prostitution and political agitation. It is such situations, where numbers swamp the authorities' attempts to house and educate, that have helped to create the suburbs of unsavoury shanty-town slums.

The actual pace of African urbanisation is not easy to assess in view of limited data. In tropical Africa in 1955 out of (est.) 455 towns with a population of more than 5,000 there were only 16 with more than 100,000 and 5 with more than 200,000. These figures exclude North Africa and the Republic of South Africa but suggest that over much of Africa most towns are small, but we find that the rate of growth of the bigger towns (especially of North and South Africa) is particularly high (Table 2).

Table 2   Growth of major African cities, 1940–60

City	1940	1950	1960
Cairo	1,307,000	2,100,000	3,348,000
Alexandria	682,000	925,000	1,516,000
Johannesburg	286,000	880,000	1,111,000
Casablanca	268,000	551,000	965,300
Algiers	252,000	315,000	883,900
Cape Town	187,000	594,000	745,800
Tunis	220,000	365,000	680,000
Durban	115,000	496,000	659,900
Ibadan	387,000	335,000	600,000
Addis Ababa	150,000	300,000	444,000
Pretoria	257,000	245,000	422,000
Leopoldville	—	208,000	402,500
Oran	195,000	260,000	390,000
Accra	73,000	140,000	388,000
Dakar	165,000	230,000	374,000
Khartoum	190,000	240,000	312,500
Port Elizabeth	125,000	148,000	274,000
Salisbury	51,000	120,000	270,000
Nairobi	100,000	112,000	267,000

Figures refer to the nearest census or estimate available

At the time of writing, Africa possesses only five cities of 'million' rank: Cairo (3,600,000), Johannesburg (1,300,000), Casablanca (1,200,000), Alexandria (1,100,000) and Ibadan (1,000,000). They all show a remarkably higher rate of population growth during the last decade than the population as a whole . Of these cities Johannesburg, now having the lowest rate of increase, did in fact grow by 214 per cent between 1940 and 1950. Both European and Asian populations of Africa are highly urbanised but this reflects their major activities of commerce, mining, manufacturing and administration, all essentially urban occupations.

HEALTH AND EDUCATION

Malnutrition, disease, poverty and ignorance are the lot of the majority of black Africans. The full extent of these afflictions has only become appreciated and documented within the last thirty or forty years. Upon improvements in health and nutrition depend most plans for African economic development. Great advances have been made, particularly since the Second World War, but in turn they have brought further problems.

The generally poor health of the African population is related mainly to nutritional diseases such as pellagra, beri-beri and rickets, and to a host of endemic and infectious diseases such as malaria, yellow fever, yaws, tuberculosis and intestinal worm diseases. Not only are diets inadequate in amount (under-nutrition) but they are usually ill-balanced (malnutrition), with serious protein and fat deficiencies and overemphasis on starch. Kwashiorkor, or protein malnutrition of young children, is another result of these conditions where the period of lactation is reduced and weaning is upon starchy diets such as banana and maize. Many of these children die and the prevalence of cancer of the liver in later life has been noticed among those who survive. The nutritional diseases themselves are not heavily fatal but they so debilitate and sap the resistance that endemic and infectious diseases are able to take immense toll.

Malaria is widespread throughout Africa except for the highland areas and the most southerly part of the continent. It is a most debilitating disease and in that sense rather than the fatalities it causes has been a major retarding factor in African development. Since the war vigorous measures with such modern insecticides as DDT have done a great deal to check the disease and also other mosquito-borne diseases such as yellow fever, particularly prevalent in West Africa. The great increases in the incidence of tuberculosis stem from industrialisation and urban life and are associated with poverty and overcrowding. Africans seem poorly resistant to the disease, and measures such as hut taxes which aggravate overcrowding and the lack of timber which prevents traditional burning of the hut of a dead person help to spread this disease.

It is likely that the most widespread diseases of Africa are the helminthic or intestinal worm diseases. There are many kinds of parasitic worms infecting the population, but the most prevalent are hookworm (ankylostomiasis) and bilharzia (schistosomiasis), which produce anaemia, a lowering of vitality and may impair the functions of certain organs. Physical and mental activity is seriously reduced in infected persons. Some 75 per cent of rural Egyptian population suffers from these diseases and an estimate of 80 to 90 per cent for East African population has been given. These diseases are not new (they have been identified in mummies of 1000 B.C.); they are carried and transmitted by water snails. Thus developments in irrigation may spread the disease, for washing and bathing in canals and rivers allow the snail-carried bacteria to enter the human bloodstream through the skin. Eradication of this group of diseases is proving very lengthy. Whereas in our own society it is usual to suffer from a single illness or disease, in Africa it is very common to find several different diseases or illnesses in the same person.

From the waters the people get their food, also their cholera, their dysentery, their typhoid fevers, their malaria; from the earth they get their hookworm; from the crowded villages they get their tuberculosis and their yaws; . . . and from the food which earth, temperature and rain produce, their protein deficiencies, their beri beri.[1]

Great advances are being made in the eradication of these conditions in Africa, thanks especially to the greater use of DDT and anti-biotic drugs such as penicillin, and improvements in hygiene and sanitation. Nutritional improvements depend upon greater productivity (linked with improving health) and especially success in the struggle against trypanosomiasis and the tsetse fly, for the deficiency in animal protein is marked practically all over the continent, where the pot-bellied child (excess cereal consumption) is symptomatic. The task is enormous, but many different agencies make their contributions. Worthington noted:

A visitor . . . cannot help but be impressed by the influence on native health and physique of good regular food and medical attention during a contract for work on the Rand mines . . . the contrast between the incoming and outgoing labour force must be seen to be believed.[2]

Advances in education are of paramount importance to the general social, political and economic advance of African peoples. A UNESCO survey of world illiteracy during the last decade estimated a 95 to 97 per cent illiteracy rate in French Africa; 85 to 95 per cent in Tanganyika and Nigeria; 75 to 85 per cent in Ghana and Kenya. Much investment in education and other social services has been made by ex-colonial powers in Africa since the last war, but it has become apparent that the problem was not merely that of building and equipping schools but of finding teachers for them. The problem is not one that can quickly be solved by capital investment.

The fact that African languages were unwritten raises the problem, in what languages Africans should be taught to read and write. It is uneconomic to print language books for language communities of less than 100,000 and many African languages and dialects have far fewer adherents. Attempts to impose a common African tongue over wide areas (as in Nigeria) have proved unsuccessful. It is clear that both for inter-tribal communication and for administration and commerce the European languages of the colonial or former colonial powers must remain.

12

Farming

The resources of Africa, both natural and human, are underdeveloped. All over the continent annual incomes per head, adjusted to monetary values, are very low—perhaps $40–45 per head in most countries rising to $170 in Rhodesia, Malawi and Ghana, to $250 in Algeria and $335 in the Republic of South Africa (Fig. 117). The character of much of African farming has altered during this century as a result of the impact of the settlement of the white man. Whereas subsistence farming had been practically universal, white settlers opened up new areas (as in the East African highlands), introduced new export crops (such as sisal, coffee, tobacco) or, in response to world demand, organised and expanded native production of existing crops (such as cacao, oil palm) and brought to Africa the two far-reaching alien concepts of private ownership of land and a money economy. These innovations, reinforced by the imposition of taxation to pay for essential services, and the introduction of attractive and desirable manufactured goods (bicycles, sewing machines, coloured cloth, umbrellas and so on), are having notable effects upon African economies.

INDIGENOUS FARMING

One of the most widespread and earliest methods of cultivation in Africa is that of shifting cultivation. It is still the usual method of farming in the forest areas and wetter savannas and represents an adjustment of primitive farming practice to the character of the soils. A virgin plot is cleared of trees and brushwood by cutting and burning and is then cultivated for the two or three years that the soil remains fertile. The whole community then migrates to a fresh area to start the process again. Bush fallowing is a term frequently regarded as synonymous with shifting cultivation, but strictly is much more limited in area—whereby land formerly under cultivation and allowed to lapse to a fallow of secondary bush or forest for a few years is then re-used. This method of farming is in effect a rotation of land rather than a rotation of crops. The humus content of tropical soils is low (p. 81); various pests and diseases preclude the keeping of animals and development of mixed farming and thus no manure can be added. The burning of the cleared vegetation adds phosphate and potash and the first crop of millet or yams sown in the ash is often good but the effect soon wears off. Many regard this system as an admirable adaptation to environment, but the fact remains that it is prodigal in the use of land and in some areas (e.g. in Nigeria) population increase and denser settlement patterns limit the area of land available and necessitate the re-use of land before it has had time to regenerate.

Pastoralism is restricted in many parts of the continent by the prevalence of trypanosomiasis and numerous other pests and diseases such as ticks and rinderpest. Trypanosomiasis is caused by the tsetse fly (which conveys sleeping sickness to humans) widely distributed throughout central Africa (Fig. 23). The fly sucks the blood of man and animal and acts as a carrier of the disease organisms which lurk in the blood of game and cattle. Animals bitten by the fly usually die after a few days and humans after a longer period of increasing lethargy and weakness. Thus over considerable areas of central and West Africa no animals can be kept for meat, milk, manure or transport and this has repercussions upon diet, soil fertility and farming practice. Much research is being done on this disease and inoculation campaigns for men and animals have some limited success. The fact that wild game as well as cattle form the blood bank containing the disease makes its control difficult and has led to emphasis on practical measures to eradicate the fly which is the carrier. The fly needs high temperatures, high humidities and shade, and thus lives and breeds in the thick bush below 5,000 feet. Belts of bush are cleared to isolate blocks of land where the fly is then exterminated. The clearing of vegetation has to be done with care to prevent soil erosion, and the Africans need to be instructed in mixed farming techniques in order to preserve the fertility of the soil. This is no easy matter for it cuts across the traditions of pastoral tribes who generally spurn agriculture as menial, dislike permanent settlement and measure wealth in quantity rather than quality of livestock. It is an uphill fight for the stock breeder and veterinary officer promoting ideas of selective breeding and laying stress on quality rather than quantity, for social custom and habit is against them.

Climate and soils also conspire against the pastoralist over most of Africa. The marked seasonal character of the rainfall over the savannas is inimical to the development of good pastures. The grass grows rapidly during and immediately after the rains and is then nutritious, but as the

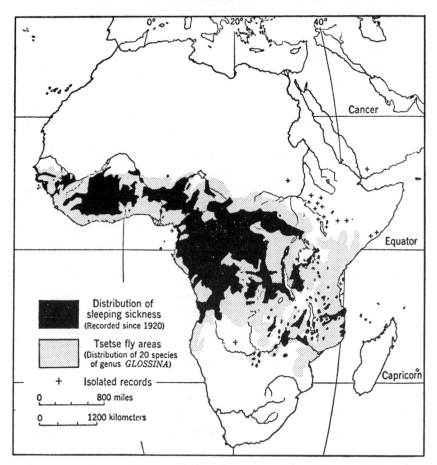

Figure 23 *Sleeping-sickness and tsetse fly areas in Africa* (by permission of L. Dudley Stamp)

dry season progresses the grass coarsens, becomes more fibrous and loses in both protein and water content. If these difficulties are added to the scourges of disease and underscored by the African's lack of interest in quality of animal we may understand why their herds are such a sorry sight.

The pastoral way of life is essentially one of movement, whereby the animals and their owners annually cover considerable areas in search of sustenance. A century ago, for example, the Masai had a quarter of a million sq. miles of East African highland to roam over: today they have only 3,000 sq. miles and can no longer trample on the rights and lands of their agricultural neighbours. The growing restrictions of pastoralism in the face of expanding agriculture in much of east, central and south Africa increase risks of over-grazing with the attendant dangers of soil exhaustion, erosion and lowering of water-tables. Less restriction has occurred on the nomads of the steppe pastures fringing both north and south of the Sahara, where sheep and camels are the dominant stock.

Much subsistence cultivation in the more settled areas is on a bush-fallowing basis where deficiencies of soil fertility, possibilities of soil erosion and actual expenditure of labour are minimised. The tools of agriculture are primitive: a digging stick to make holes for the seeds or cuttings and sometimes to break the clods, a hoe to loosen the surface soil, a knife or axe. The simple form of plough which spread across North Africa early in the Christian era did not penetrate into Negro Africa, perhaps in part owing to the lack of draught animals. These ploughs, often made entirely of wood, do little more than score the surface of the soil. Europeans in Africa have learned to their cost that the deep ploughing of temperate lands is unsuitable under African conditions of leaching and laterisation. All over Africa women take a large share in the cultivation and harvesting of crops. Over most of tropical Africa it is their main duty, the men reserving themselves for the heavier clearing work, for fishing, for arguing matters of high policy, and stock-rearing where possible. The principal crops grown (Fig. 24) are starch foods with little protein value; millet, maize, yams, manioc, bananas in tropical Africa, with wheat and barley assuming importance in the Atlas lands. Yields invariably are poor and malnutrition and under-nutrition all too prevalent. Throughout the tropics crops are grown in untidy-looking gardens rather than in fields in the European sense: the larger tree-stumps remain uncleared and several crops are intersown. In this way native practice retains some roots to hold the soil and supplies a varied vegetative cover, both reducing risks of soil erosion. The expansion of the agrarian population and the gradual adoption of cash crops have both helped to bring about change in certain parts of the continent.

Cash-crop growing by black Africans has developed since the end of

World War II. It has been aided by an expanding world market for certain tropical products and by governmental policies restricting white settlement or plantation development in certain areas. The principal export crops are cocoa (Ghana, Nigeria, Cameroun, Ivory Coast), ground nuts (Nigeria and former French West Africa), palm products (Nigeria, Sierra Leone, former French West Africa), cotton (Egypt, Sudan, Uganda, former French West Africa), coffee (former French West Africa, Angola, Uganda, Congo, Madagascar, Cameroun, Kenya). In the growing urban

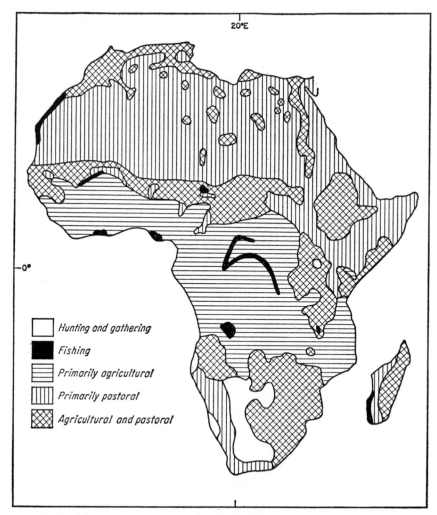

Figure 24 *Modes of living in Africa* (by permission of G. P. Murdock)

areas markets are expanding for more basic foodstuffs such as maize, millet, sugar-cane, fruit and also for tobacco. The growth of cash-crop farming has been in response to the spread of a money economy, for the advantages of monetary buying power have come to be appreciated.

The cash crops are not necessarily new crops and require virtually no extra effort to produce; many fit into the bush fallowing system of agriculture and others are tree crops easily grown among the profusion of crops and trees in the African's 'garden'. The introduction of cash-crop growing has proved a lever by which to force change in land-tenure systems—assured occupation is required if tree crops are to be grown—and to consolidate fragmented holdings; it is leading to one-crop specialism, an idea new to the African agriculturist. Such specialism is generally remunerative to the farmer, but beside having the disadvantage of tying his well-being to distant and often incomprehensible world markets, it leads to monoculture—all too often the preface to soil exhaustion. 'One-crop farming has been rewarding but is self-destroying rather than self-perpetuating and certainly not feasible in a rapidly expanding society. Subsistence crop farming was self-perpetuating, but not rewarding, nor is it any longer feasible.'[3] The adoption of rotation farming, and where possible mixed farming, would seem to be a desirable solution but does not commend itself to the African who from a background of poverty looks for quick riches and suspects the motives of those who recommend often more arduous farming methods bringing in a lower return.

EUROPEAN FARMING

For long, European interest in African agriculture was confined to the tropical parts and the establishment of plantations. The alienation of land and prodigal use of (often forced) labour were the means whereby an economy of exploitation was furthered. Few of the early plantations were successful, but useful lessons were learnt and in this century the more restricted development of plantations has been where land alienation can do least harm and where capital is available to infuse science and technology into this form of tropical agriculture. Cacao has become more and more a peasant-produced crop and coffee plantations in East Africa lose ground to expanding peasant production. Only in the low latitudes, where an equatorial régime allows all-the-year production, and thus fixed-labour requirements, or where, as in East African sisal and tea production, expensive processing machinery is necessary are modern plantations holding their own. Firms such as Lever Bros. in the Congo (palm oil) and Firestone Plantation Co. in Liberia (rubber) lead in enlightened development including fringe benefits of housing, medical services and education for their African employees and their families.

The most developed European agriculture in Africa is to be found in the extreme north and extreme south—in north-west Africa, especially Morocco, and in the Republic of South Africa. Here, several generations of settlers have put a Mediterranean Europe impress upon the landscape with their emphasis on such tree crops as the olive and citrus fruits and on the vine and cereal cultivation. Elsewhere in Africa European settlers are in the uplands: the High Veld, the Kivu highlands of the Congo, the East African highlands. Ranching is possible in the tsetse-free higher lands and progress is slowly being made in cross-breeding European dairy and beef breeds with native cattle, or in some cases acclimatising them. There is a constant struggle with a host of diseases and the sequences of tropical climate make the improvement of pastures difficult. Most of the products of this pastoral industry are designed for the local market. The importance of the European farmer in tropical Africa must not be underestimated. Although there are few European farms it is mainly their produce that sustains the economies of many African states.

13

Minerals, Power and Transport

The output of minerals from Africa is now prodigious in quantity and value and manifold in character (Fig. 25). It seems reasonable to suppose that for a very long time to come the continent's mineral output will expand as new discoveries are made and as increasing investment and development of transport make possible the working of already known but unexploited deposits. The shield character of the continent's structures, comprising a variety of ancient crystalline and metamorphosed rocks, has been particularly favourable to mineralisation. Many parts of the continent still await even reconnaissance mineral surveys; substantial new discoveries are still likely.

Minerals have played a notable rôle in the history of the continent, particularly in influencing exploration and shaping economic development. Long before Europeans came to Africa the gold of Ethiopia was known to seafarers of the Indian Ocean, and old workings and diggings, for example in Rhodesia, have been valuable guides to modern prospectors. Tin and gold have been worked for centuries in West Africa. By the fifteenth century the Guinea lands were providing the gold necessary for the coinage of Portugal, Spain and Italy. The British guinea, dating from the seventeenth century, takes its name from this gold-producing area. The lure of gold as well as of slaves and ivory brought the traders and merchants to Africa's shores.

It was the discovery, in 1886, of the enormously rich goldfield of the Rand, less than twenty years after the opening up of the diamond working at Kimberley, that unlocked European capital and spurred on mineral exploration and exploitation throughout the continent. Interest is always centred first upon the precious metals giving assured returns, but this century has seen increasing investment in exploration and exploitation of base metals for which there is a growing range of industrial uses. The great copper deposits of the Katanga were discovered in 1892 and working began in 1910 when the railway from Beira reached Elisabethville. In 1902 copper was discovered in Northern Rhodesia and lead, zinc and vanadium at Broken Hill; tin became mined in Nigeria (1910) and in

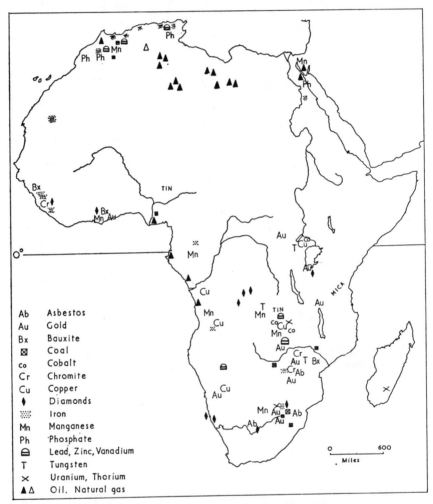

Ab	Asbestos
Au	Gold
Bx	Bauxite
⊠	Coal
co	Cobalt
Cr	Chromite
Cu	Copper
◆	Diamonds
⋯	Iron
Mn	Manganese
Ph	Phosphate
⊟	Lead, Zinc, Vanadium
T	Tungsten
×	Uranium, Thorium
▲△	Oil. Natural gas

Figure 25 *Mining in Africa in the early 1960's*

North Africa phosphates became worked in Algeria in 1895. In 1910 the first oil discoveries were made on the Red Sea coast of Egypt and manganese deposits were discovered in Sinai. The years until World War I saw big advances in mineral exploitation all over the continent and some, such as copper, benefited by increased wartime demand. However, the between-war period was one of capital shortage and economic depression and advances were but moderate.

Major developments in Africa's mineral industry have occurred since 1939 and tremendous capital investment has fructified in the opening up of new workings and expansion of old ones in many parts of the continent. The centre of gravity of the world's oil industry has materially shifted with the opening of the vast Saharan oil- and gas-fields; new iron-ore workings in Mauritania since 1963 have increased the continent's annual output of iron ore by 40 per cent; the great Volta river scheme for aluminium smelting from Ghanaian bauxite will be in operation by 1968. At the same time existing mines such as the copper-mines in Zambia, and the gold and industrial diamond mines of South Africa, have been steadily expanding their output.

Since the war minerals have been the greatest magnet of foreign investment. Of the $8,400 million invested in Africa between 1948 and 1958, over $1,700 million went to the Republic of South Africa, almost $1,680 million to the former Belgian Congo and $840 million to the Rhodesias. Three territories with a combined population of about 34 million thus absorbed half the capital invested in a continent of over 200 million people.

Mineral exploitation is rarely easy in Africa: 'Tropical Africa is no place for the sourdough equipped with a hammer and a hunch.'⁴ African conditions militate against the pioneer prospector; mining in Africa, as a rule, is big business. Two major problems must frequently be overcome by mining concerns in Africa. The first is the provision of adequate labour to operate the mines, the second is in the provision of transport to reduction plants and the coast. Much of Africa is sparsely populated and recruitment of labour for the major mines extends over enormous areas. The Rand gold mines draw upon labour from the High Commission territories and Moçambique (about half a million); Moçambique with Angola and Malawi supplies much labour to the Copperbelt and Rhodesian mines. To attract the many thousands of Africans needed from so far requires inducements such as free housing, medical facilities, free or subsidised food as well as good wages. Actual wages for unskilled labour may be cheaper than in European mines, but in terms of work accomplished and allowing for the extra inducements costs are not markedly different. The days of 'cheap labour' for mine and plantation in Africa are over. The skilled engineers and technicians, almost invariably white men, also require high salaries and high-quality accommodation and living conditions to attract them to the discomforts of tropical mining sites.

Few mines are close to the sea and efficient transport to and from the coast is essential, both for sending out the ore and to import all the supplies, machinery and equipment. Railways, roads and power supplies have to be made available at the outset. It is the lack of these facilities that prevents many known deposits from being worked, the iron-ore deposits of Mount Patti, near Lokoja in Nigeria, for example. The construction of transcontinental lines to serve the Katanga-Zambia copper belt is one of the greatest examples of the power of minerals. The ore travels a single track line almost 1,500 miles either to Beira or Lobito (practically the distance from Paris to Moscow). To stand these freight costs, plus ocean shipment, mining must be highly efficient in order to keep costs down. The expense of long hauls makes it necessary to concentrate or refine ores as near the mines as possible and this introduces problems of fuel and power and has necessitated the development of numerous hydro- and thermal-electric power schemes.

It will be appreciated that mineral exploitation has provided much of the basis of the growing industrial and commercial infrastructure of Africa. Minerals and transport go together and except for a few strategic railways, such as the Mombasa–Lake Victoria line, most of the lengthy rail lines in Africa have grown up in response to mineral exploitation; for minerals can pay for long hauls all round the year and subsidise the less remunerative and more seasonal agricultural freight. Diamonds and gold laid the foundation of South Africa's railway net. Gold, coal and copper drew the railways into the Rhodesias and extended links to Angola and Moçambique (where a new outlet to Lourenço Marques was completed in 1955). Mineral exports have been valuable in spurring on the development of port facilities in many countries: railway sidings, wharfs, deep-water berths and heavy equipment, all of which serve to attract other industries and commercial enterprises. Further, the mines have been foremost in power utilisation and have formulated and speeded numerous power development projects to the benefit of a wider economy.

For a long time to come mining will be controlled and operated by non-African capital and technicians, but already the larger mining concerns are training Africans to take increasingly skilled mining jobs; there is no doubt that a growing participation in mining by African states and peoples is coming. The minerals of Africa that seem likely to remain important in world trade for a long time to come are gold, copper, uranium, diamonds, cobalt, tin, asbestos, chromite, bauxite and iron ore.

POWER

Economic development, whether by agriculture, mining or industry, demands increasing quantities of energy. Most African states today, among the poorest in the world, are vitally concerned with the provision of energy in one form or another to further economic development and raise living standards. Africa is particularly deficient in mineral fuels although during the decade 1950–60 the great Saharan oil and gas discoveries made some redress. The formation of oil requires long periods of marine sedimentary conditions, rarely found over the vast mass of Africa, and although coal seams occur in the Karroo Series the quality is generally poor. This general scarcity of coal and oil deposits renders the few areas that do possess them of particular importance to local economies. The only large coal-field in Africa lies in the Republic and it has been the most important single factor in furthering the development of South Africa's great mining and manufacturing industries. The annual output of bituminous coal is about 44 million tons. The next largest output is from the Wankie colliery in Rhodesia (3 million tons). Other African coal-mines in Nigeria, Morocco, Algeria, Moçambique and the Congo Republic are very small producers each of only a few hundred thousand tons of rather poor-quality coal. Only in Rhodesia and Natal are reasonably good metallurgical coking coals found.

Except for the great resources under the Sahara, and in the Sinai peninsula, Africa is particularly scarce in mineral oil. Angola, Gabon, Nigeria and the Republic of the Congo (Brazzaville) are the only producers in tropical Africa; their total production in 1963 was about 5·8 million tons. However, the great international oil companies continue to carry out considerable exploration in nearly every African state. The consumption of oil in tropical Africa is only 10 gallons a head (cf. Latin America, 80 gallons per head), which itself may be taken as an index of under-development. Oil provides two-fifths of total energy now used in Africa, coal about a half and hydro-electric power the remainder.

The relative scarcity of mineral sources of energy focusses attention upon hydro resources. Here Africa has a tremendous potential, the greatest among all the continents; however, scarcely any of this is yet realised and much of it may never be so. Sites for hydro-electric power stations are generally limited by topography and climate. The greater part of Africa's potential lies in the equatorial zone, particularly in the Congo Basin, remote from centres of industry and population. Electricity becomes more costly the farther it is transmitted; the present economic limit is about 500 miles. Unless some spectacular break-through in electricity transmission costs occurs it does not seem likely that any more than a fraction of equatorial Africa's potential water power will be used.

Some substantial schemes are already in existence, but they are mainly outside the equatorial belt and rely upon great reservoirs to store water to ensure even output throughout the year. The greatest African scheme is that based on the Kariba Dam on the Zambezi, completed 1959. Here an output of 600 MW (to be increased to 1,500 MW by 1970) is shared between Zambia and Rhodesia (p. 405).* A number of lesser plants operate in the Congo, Angola, Uganda, Nigeria and Morocco. Big schemes under construction and likely to be in operation by 1970 are the Volta river scheme of Ghana, the Aswan High Dam in Egypt and the Kouilou Dam in Congo (Brazzaville). The first is specifically related to aluminium production, the Egyptian Dam will make power available for irrigation pumps and a variety of industrial uses, and the power from the Kouilou Dam will supply metallurgical and electro-chemical industries at Pointe-Noire.

It is clear that a marked increase in African hydro-electric output will occur in the coming years, but much of it is likely to be from small plants favourably placed in areas of effective home demand. There may well be considerable scope in the future for employment of nuclear power, and in this connection it should be remembered that the mines of Katanga and the Rand are major uranium producers.

TRANSPORT IN AFRICA

The relatively slow economic development of so much of Africa has been largely the outcome of difficulty of movement and transport. In the north and south the camel and ox-cart have played a major economic rôle but few large areas can pose so many obstacles to travel as tropical Africa where the omnipotent tsetse fly has proscribed draught animals; for centuries it has kept out wheeled carts and given no incentive for the

* MW = one mégawatt or 1,000 kilowatts

development of cart-tracks and roads. Instead a pattern of human porterage on footpaths through bush and forest evolved; it was by such means
that the white man penetrated into and explored tropical Africa. Human
porterage is highly expensive, inefficient and a prodigal use of manpower better employed in a more productive capacity. A man or woman
carrying a 60 lb. head load might travel twenty miles a day but this is
puny compared with the ton-mileage capacity of a modern lorry or
train. Modern developments of transport in tropical Africa have not
replaced the bush and forest paths, for they have become feeders to the
modern transport system and may well be used more now than ever
before. They have proved particularly suitable for bicycle traffic and
provide the lowest tier of the transport system that links farms, hamlets
and villages.

The rivers of Africa have not proved very suitable as large-scale media
of transport (Chapter 3). Falls, generally near the coast, prevent direct
penetration from the sea and others make difficult the passage of boats
on the inland sections. Régimes are highly seasonal, with flood discharges many times the average discharge; channels at times of the year
are shallow and variable. Thus river transport has had far less development
than might have been expected although parts of the Nile, Niger and
Congo are used commercially (Fig. 26). The Congo system is the most
useful of African waterways with 6,000 miles of route for vessels drawing
between 3 and 5 feet. Regular schedules by powered vessels are operated
and short lengths of railway bypass rapids, as at Leopoldville–Matadi and
Ponthierville–Stanleyville.

The penetration, annexation and opening up of Africa by the white
man occurred during the full flush of the railway era. Most of the African
railways were built between 1885 and 1930; the final decade, however,
saw increasing competition from road transport. Railways could offer
relatively speedy bulk transport for commerce and passengers, and could
facilitate administration and the imposition of law and order, but they
were exceedingly costly to build and operate. The range of variation of
relief and climate in Africa is very great: locomotives of the East African
railways have to operate in a temperature range of 35° to 110°F, at
altitudes from sea-level to over 9,000 feet, in tropical rainstorms and
dusty semi-desert conditions. The problem of torrential rains, in some
places lack of ballast, or lack of fuel or water, all have to be overcome,
while distances to be covered are long and population and freight sparse.
Consequently most lines in tropical Africa have been built only where

there was assured freight to make the high cost of construction a worthwhile proposition. The result (Fig. 26) is a pattern of disconnected lines striking inland from the ports to tap mining or cash-crop areas and carry in manufactured goods; traffic that is generally ill-balanced with much

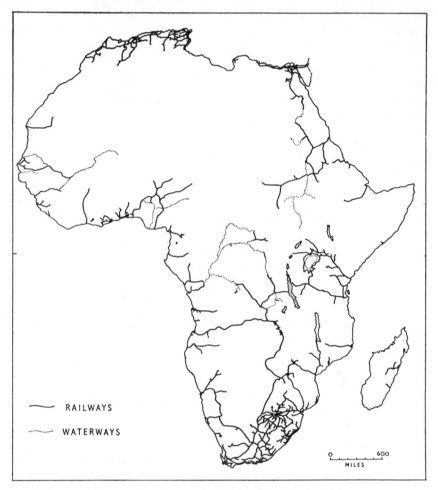

RAILWAYS

WATERWAYS

Figure 26 *Railways and navigable waterways in Africa*

more freight coming out than going in. There is no railway net as we understand it in Western Europe except in the Republic of South Africa, the Atlas lands and the Delta of Egypt. In tropical Africa 14,805 miles of railway serve an area of over 5 million sq. miles, whereas in Britain 51,000 miles of railway serve 88,000 sq. miles.

Roads have come to supplement but not yet supplant railways in Africa, where physical conditions make the cost of road construction and maintenance very high. Most roads are unsurfaced and of little value in the rainy season while in the dry season corrugations on the surface and choking dust render them unpleasant and reduce the lives of vehicles. Lorries require servicing and minor repairs after 400–500 miles and on dirt roads the average lorry is written-off after two years' service. Costs of road-building vary enormously, but in Zambia even dirt roads cost up to £1,000 per mile to construct and in East Africa tarmac all-weather roads cost £8,000–10,000 per mile. In all, Africa has nearly half a million miles of 'motorable' roads, but only a small fraction of this is of all-weather category. Road-building continues apace all over the continent and the numbers of vehicles in use grow appreciably every year, both a symptom and an expression of growing economic development with underlying implications of greater movement and social intercourse among Africa's peoples.

Airways now play a most important rôle in African social and economic life. The world's major airlines operate a multiplicity of routes across the continent linking it with Europe, Asia and North America, while scores of thousands of miles of internal air routes are operated. Little freight can stand the cost of air transport and the amount of cargo carried is still small. The real impact of airways on the continent is in overcoming the obstacles of distance and environment, bringing large parts of Africa within a few hours of the advanced countries whence administrators, advisers and technicians are sought. To such key men and their families medical attention, newspapers and supplies are now readily available and when home 'leave' comes little of it need be used up in travel which earlier in the century often took more than half the period of leave. The isolation and remoteness of the past have been broken down, notably for the white man but also for the African; increasingly internal services are being used by African business men and merchants.

References

1 J. M. May, quoted by A. L. Banks, 'Trends in the geographical pattern of disease', *Geog. Journ.*, 122 (1956), p. 172
2 E. B. Worthington, *Science in the development of Africa* (London, 1958), p. 355
3 G. H. T. Kimble, *Tropical Africa* (New York, 1960), I, p. 139
4 *ibid.*, p. 293

Selected Bibliography

W. Allan, *The African husbandman* (New York, 1965)

K. M. Barbour and R. M. Prothero (eds.), *Essays on African population* (New York, 1962)

P. Gourou, *The tropical world* (London, 1957)

W. A. Hance, *The geography of modern Africa* (New York, 1964)

W. A. Hance, *African economic development* (New York, 1967)

A. M. Kamarck, *The economics of African development* (New York, 1967)

N. de Kun, *The mineral resources of Africa* (Amsterdam, 1965)

J. Phillips, *Agriculture and ecology in Africa* (New York, 1960)

C. G. Seligman, *The races of Africa* (London, 1957)

United Nations, *Demographic yearbook* (New York, annually)

J. C. de Wilde and others, *Agricultural development in tropical Africa* (Baltimore, 1967)

G. F. Deasey, 'The harbours of Africa', *Econ. Geog.*, 18 (1942), 325-42

W. Deshler, 'Cattle in Africa', *Geog. Rev.*, 53 (1963), 52-8

W. Hance, *et al.*, 'Source areas of export production in tropical Africa', *Geog. Rev.*, 51 (1961), 487-99

G. P. Murdock, 'Staple subsistence crops of Africa', *Geog. Rev.*, 50 (1960), 523-40

PART IV

North-West Africa

North Africa has a distinctive and un-African personality, as in many respects also has the Sahara, which effectively separates the North African states from tropical Africa, or *Afrique Noire,* as the French have termed it. For centuries the mass of Africa was regarded as the Dark Continent, but the North African lands have been well known since classical antiquity: their history and development have been bound up with the Mediterranean world, to which their geography also belongs. The ancient Greeks called this region Libya: the Romans later called it Africa. After the Mohammedan conquest, the Arabs, referring more specifically to the ·Atlas lands, called it Gezira-el-Maghreb (Island of the West), and the term Maghreb for north-west Africa remains in use. In the succeeding period of Turkish rule the general name Barbary was used, a reminder of a certain ethnic and cultural unity that transcends haphazard political divisions.

This 2,000-mile sweep of territory is divided politically into Morocco, Algeria and Tunisia (formerly French North Africa). The insular character of North Africa—surrounded by sea and sand—and the great contrast, but unequal opportunities, its diversity of landscapes offers man is epitomised in a reported conversation of King Victor Emmanuel III after the Italian occupation of coastal Libya in 1912: 'We have got the bone of the chop.' Indeed, it is not hard to discern the pattern of a loin chop in the outline of north-west Africa: the bare bone in Libya, a covering of spare flesh in Tunisia and Algeria and the meaty portion in Morocco.

The native population of the Maghreb includes Berbers, Arabs and Jews. The two main Arab invasions of the Maghreb brought in about 150,000 men in the seventh century A.D. and a further 250,000 in the eleventh and twelfth centuries. Ever since the seventh century, Berbers and Arabs have intermarried and it is no longer possible to distinguish clearly between them. Generally the Berber is a village-dwelling mountain man and cultivator, whereas the true Arab at heart is a tent-dwelling herdsman. However, more and more Arabs have taken a semi-settled existence. Another difference is in language; but many Berbers have taken over the language as well as the religion of their conquerors, though a broad distinction between Arabic-speaking and Berber-speaking is possible. The proportion of Berber-speaking increases from east to west, as one might expect from the course of the Arab invasions. In Tunisia barely 1 per cent of the population is Berber-speaking; in Algeria 20 per cent; but in Morocco the proportion is thought to be as high as 40 per cent—much of it spoken in the highland areas and in the south of the kingdom. Most of the half million Jews in North Africa also speak Arabic; nearly half of them are to be found in Morocco.

Throughout the Maghreb there is a repetitive pattern of mountain, plains, steppes and desert, and a related pattern of economic activity is to be discerned throughout the region. The valleys and coastal plains are devoted to peasant farming, here and there with enclaves of European agriculture. Wheat and olives are the predominent crops; sometimes a few sheep and goats are kept. The fellaheen or peasant population live in hamlets or small villages and these days there is a growing attraction to the towns and cities. In the mountain areas livestock-rearing, arboriculture and agriculture are important in that order. The raising of sheep and goats, with seasonal up-and-down migrations in search of pasture, is the prime interest. Fig and olive tree cultivations and, finally, limited cultivation of cereals (often with irrigation) are secondary. The mountains have limited supporting power and many mountain people seek work in farms and towns on the plains. In some cases, as in Kabylia, emigration farther afield—to France—has become an established pattern.

In the steppe country of the plateaux which skirt the Saharan Atlas sheep are reared by semi-nomadic peoples. They move northwards with the summer, usually in small family groups, their movements forming a regular annual pattern. Gradually summer transhumance is diminishing throughout the Maghreb as tribal ties loosen and permanent settlement, cultivation and the towns appear more attractive. The nomadic way of life is still dominant in the Sahara. Agricultural output in the Maghreb states has increased since the war, but production per head has declined in all but Morocco. This is one result of the population explosions which all the Maghreb states are experiencing as a result of the marked reduction of death rates and the maintenance of high birth rates.

The Maghreb is one of the most urban regions of Africa and probably has been so since the founding of Carthage. In Tunisia and Algeria about 20 per cent of the population is urban and a rather lesser proportion in Morocco. Tunisian urban life is of long standing—Morocco in Fez, Rabat and Marrakech has cities dating back to the ninth century. Urban life is more recent in Algeria, much expansion being related to European occupation. Despite early urbanism the Maghreb has never had a single capital. Geography has much to answer for here, for the elongated shape of the area, the east-west trend of physical features, the lack of a natural focus, the clannish character of the mountain people, their antagonism to the plainsmen, all have militated against unity.

14

Geology, Relief and Drainage

GEOLOGY AND STRUCTURE

The Atlas lands present a complicated, corrugated area, stretching nearly 2,000 miles from near the southern boundary of Morocco to the Tunisian Gulf of Gabès. To understand the wide diversity of relief, rock type and landform some knowledge of their mode of formation is required. Essentially the present landscape is an outcome of the folding and uplift during the Tertiary period of sediments deposited over a long period in a geosyncline which lay between the Saharan shield and another land-mass to the north. Of this other land-mass, Tyrrhenia, there now remain only certain fragments, including Corsica, Sardinia, Calabria. A series of Palaeozoic rocks (Cambrian-Silurian, Devonian and Carboniferous) was deposited on the Pre-Cambrian Saharan shield. Some of these rocks have become folded in the Atlas Ranges, but they extend widely over the Sahara to be exposed in the Ahaggar, although generally they are masked by younger rocks. At the end of the Carboniferous period the Hercynian earth-movements elevated and folded these rocks in Morocco and western Algeria. This uplift also made a land surface of the Sahara, parts of which have so remained to this day.

During the following Mesozoic and Tertiary eras various marine transgressions alternated with continental conditions over the present Atlas lands and parts of the Sahara. These younger sediments in the Atlas area became heaved up to form the Atlas Mountains during the Alpine earth-movements. These movements began in North Africa rather earlier than in Europe and persisted sporadically throughout the Tertiary era. The mountains were formed by great pressure between Tyrrhenia and the Saharan shield, the movement and folding being principally towards the Sahara. The earliest movements, the Pyrenean (Cretaceous-Eocene),

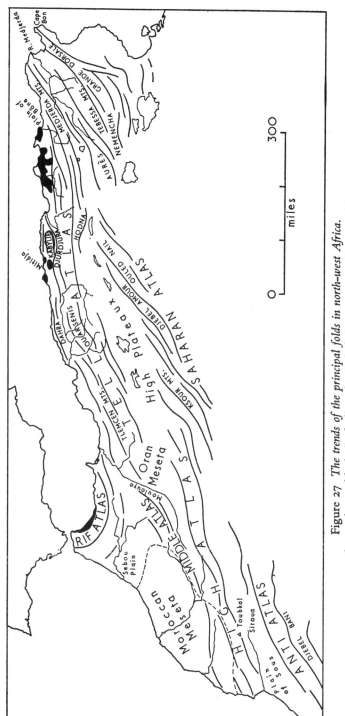

Figure 27 *The trends of the principal folds in north-west Africa.*
Areas shown black (including the Kabylie) represent ancient massifs

were severe. The Rif Atlas were thrust up so forcibly that nappes are present and part of the Hercynian basement was exposed; at the same time the forerunner of the Tell Atlas of northern Algeria was created. Farther south the Saharan platform resisted the fold-waves which were diminished in strength and for the most part only affected the surface veneer of younger rocks. Faulting and fracturing occurred and local vulcanicity followed. In the Miocene period when the main Alpine folding took place in Europe, renewed folding occurred especially of the Tell Atlas of Algeria.

In several ways the pattern of the more recently built mountains has been influenced by the earlier structural movements. The Alpine folds trend east-north-east — west-south-west, but the discontinuity of the ranges, the frequent intermingling of basins and valleys, owe much to the underlying north-south Hercynian trend. The resistance of the Saharan platform permitted only open folding of the overlying sediments in the Middle Atlas and Saharan Atlas ranges, while marginal blocs, such as those known as the Moroccan and Oran Mesetas (Fig. 27), withstood the pressures. Thus the folds lapped round them, creating in Morocco the Rif Atlas, linked with the Spanish Betic Cordillera (the Straits of Gibraltar were formed by fracturing in the Neogene) and the Middle Atlas. The High Atlas, which becomes the more open Saharan Atlas in Algeria, is separated by the down-faulted Plain of Sous from a further limb called the Anti-Atlas.

In Algeria the resistant High Plateaux—a prolongation of the Oran Meseta—did much to confine the later violent Alpine movement to reviving the young Tell Atlas and including in them the shallow-sea limestones and sandstones of early Tertiary age. Thus the Tell Atlas and the Saharan Atlas encompass in the High Plateaux a distinctive area with few positive relief features. The rigid basement resisted the folding and shows only fractures and gentle undulations to mark the struggle; even these are considerably masked by a great mantle of debris.

The two Atlas chains encircling the High Plateaux draw together in the high tumbled mass of the Aurès Mountains, and in eastern Algeria and Tunisia they cease to be distinct entities. Here Pyrenean folds were uplifted and rejuvenated by the later earth-movements and the eastern Tell and northern Tunisia is a tangled upland country with deep gorges penetrating and dissecting the mountain chains. These later Alpine earth-movements caused the foundering of most of the land-mass of Tyrrhenia: an important fragment that remained to be incorporated in Africa was the mountain-mass of Kabylia, between Algiers and Bône.

RELIEF AND DRAINAGE

The series of mountain-building operations has resulted in a sequence of generally parallel relief features trending south-west to north-east and roughly paralleling the coast (Fig. 27). The Atlas system is best developed in Morocco. Here the greatest elevations are attained, the widest geological diversity demonstrated and the greatest scenic grandeur revealed. The great snow-capped buttresses in Morocco have a very different personality from the more lowly broken ridges in Algeria.

The oldest of the fold mountains, the Rif Atlas, lie in the north in former Spanish Morocco and stretch from Tangier to the River Moulouya. Between them and the northern end of the Middle Atlas is a fertile lowland, drained eastward through a narrow pass at Taza to the Moulouya and westward by the Sebou and its tributaries. Before the opening of the Straits of Gibraltar this lowland was a strait giving access between the Atlantic and the Tethys. The lower Sebou Plain for long was a gulf and great thicknesses of marls and clays have been deposited, forming the basis for fertile farming lands and the growth of such venerable cities as Fez and Meknes. South-west of this lowland for some 200 miles down the coast and up to 100 miles inland extends the plateau called the Moroccan Meseta, which rises gently from the coast to meet inland the half-encircling High and Middle Atlas Ranges. Its surface rocks are young horizontal strata, mainly limestones, resting on the old crystalline platform, which is exposed in river gorges and in small areas inland. Nearer the Middle and High Atlas extend great plains of alluvial deposits washed down from the mountains. The resistance of the Archaean Meseta to the Alpine earth-movements served to swing the fold-chains around it on the south and east. It is this positioning of these great fold mountains that has helped to make the Meseta into the home of nearly 50 per cent of the Moroccan people. The mountain slopes facing west or north-west receive the rain-bearing winds from the Atlantic. Thirty to forty inches is experienced over much of the upland and snow is usual from December to March. This precipitation nourishes numerous streams which flow across the Meseta to the sea all through the year.

The highest land in north-west Africa is in the High Atlas (Toubkal, 13,600 feet), which stretch with some majesty east-north-east from the Atlantic coast just south of Mogador, subsequently passing into Algeria as the more subdued Saharan Atlas. In south-western Morocco many peaks exceed 13,000 feet, but very few surpass 5,000 feet in Algeria. Some of the highest country lies inland from Marrakech, where the ancient pre-Hercynian rocks have been elevated to create mountain forms with sharp-crested peaks and displaying much evidence of glacial conditions in the recent geological past. From the centre of the High Atlas the ranges of the Middle Atlas swing northwards. Both ranges act as the Moroccan watershed: their Atlantic sides are well watered, but their east and south-east slopes fall under a Saharan régime. These slopes are scrub-covered and the streams are both fewer and mainly seasonal. The principal rocks in the broad folds of the Middle Atlas are limestones of varying ages. The heavy rain and snowfall has caused severe dissection, creating a wild plateau country interlaced with steep river gorges. This was one of the last parts of Morocco to be pacified after the French occupation. The eastern angle between the Middle and High Atlas constitutes a rather featureless stony plateau, the start of the old resistant Oran Meseta, itself the westernmost portion of the High Plateaux of Algeria. Here the River Moulouya, which receives water from both Atlas ranges, flows north with irregular discharge to the Mediterranean.

In the south of Morocco the Sous Plain, a triangular structural depression opening on the Atlantic, separates the ranges of the High and Anti-Atlas. The Anti-Atlas shows some evidence of folding but broadly represents a disturbed and elevated portion of the Saharan shield, comprising schists, quartzite and dolomitic limestone. With a general summit altitude of about 5,000 feet (but its highest peak rising to 7,795 feet) it presents something of a tabular surface. It is joined to the High Atlas by a mass of recent volcanic rock forming the Siroua and attaining 7,000 feet. These mountains lose height to the east and merge into the Saharan plateau.

In Algeria the mountain system shows three major divisions. In the north the Tell Atlas, sometimes called the Maritime Atlas, parallels the coast and includes coastal hills and the higher uplands inland which mark the northern edge of the second major physical division, the High Plateaux. These mountains differ from the more formidable ranges of Morocco in being lower, generally of younger rocks and far more interrupted. There is no single major range, but rather they comprise discontinuous hills, plateaux and massifs separated from one another by depressions, valleys and plains. The range of rock type is very great: limestones of varying ages predominate but sandstones and marls offer varied upland scenery. The result is a mosaic of individual topographic and economic sub-regions, including the Monts de Tlemçen near the Morocco border, and farther east the coastal Dahra and limestone Ouarsenis (attaining over 6,500 feet) separated by Algeria's principal river, the Chéliff.

Farther east again this river valley is pinched out by the plateau of Médéa and the Atlas de Blida, which form part of the semicircle of hills surrounding the fertile Mitidja, the broad plain opening to the sea at Algiers.

East of Algiers as far as Philippeville, the tangled but dominating mass of the Kabylie highlands marks the geological and structural beginning of eastern Algeria. The Grande Kabylie is one of the most striking regions in the whole of the Atlas and owes much of its personality to the core of Archaean and Pre-Cambrian rocks, once part of Tyrrhenia and now the nucleus of the Djurdjura, itself the heart of the Grande Kabylie. Rising to 7,573 feet in the limestone peak of Lalla Kredidja and with flanking mountains of younger sandstones, limestones and flysch beds, it presents a heavily dissected country of steep gorges and narrow ridges. Difficult to penetrate, it remains a centre of Berber language and culture.

Between the Tell Atlas and the Saharan Atlas and from the basin of the Moulouya river to the foothills of the Aurès extends a vast steppe region known as the High Plateaux. This undulating arid country lies mainly between 2,500–3,500 feet, diminishing in height from west to east. The relief is subdued and amid blunted ridges and escarpments extensive flats are provided by numerous shallow depressions known as chotts. These form a chain of muddy salt basins, occupied by brackish waters during the brief rains. South of Oran lies the great depression of the Chott Chergui, 100 miles in length but partly silted up. Farther to the east the country is drained by an ephemeral headstream of the River Chéliff but for most of the year its course is dry and marked only by springs and wells. Further smaller chotts extend eastwards towards the second largest, the Chott El Hodna at 1,300 feet; this virtually marks the western limit of the High Plateaux.

The Saharan Atlas Mountains which bound the High Plateaux on their southern side extend from eastern Morocco to Tunisia. They are a lower and more open extension of the High Atlas. From the High Plateaux they appear disappointingly low, no more than hills, but from the Saharan side they emerge from an accumulation of debris to heights of

5,000 feet and sometimes over 6,000 feet. The range is somewhat broken and falls into a number of distinct groups such as the Monts des Ksour, Djebel Amour and the Monts des Ouled Naïl. The sandstone tabular mountains contrast with broken limestone ridges and gorges. Between the Monts des Ouled Naïl and the Aurès the Saharan Atlas lose height and merge with the High Plateaux. This provides a Saharan embayment immediately south of the Chott El Hodna, once the route of the Arab invaders and today a focus of roads to the desert from Constantine, Sétif, Bou Saada and Algiers. The higher hills receive annually a moderate 12–15 inches of rainfall, insufficient to nourish permanent streams across thirsty rock and under the great summer heat. The streams flowing northwards across the High Plateaux and those flowing southwards towards the Sahara are all seasonal, their courses being dry for the greater part of the year.

The Aurès Mountains of eastern Algeria consist of folded Jurassic and Lower Tertiary sediments that have weathered into great ridges containing peaks and needles. Several of these peaks are over 7,000 feet and they include the highest mountain in Algeria, Djebel Chelia, 7,638 feet. This has proved another virtually impregnable highland where Berber ways persist. To the north a number of small mountain chains delimit many inland basins, some such as the Plain of Sétif being the beds of former lakes. East and south-east a number of salt-marsh chotts occupy numerous smaller basins (the Constantine Chotts), relics of a great lake that once stretched over this whole region.

In the north a mass of folds, tightly packed ridges and valleys trend south-west to north-east into Tunisia, passing out to sea in headlands and promontories. They help to create good natural harbours, one of which has become the great naval base of Bizerta. The more northerly position and rather higher general elevation of the relief on the Algerian-Tunisian border helps to make it relatively well watered. The principal river, the Medjerda, collects its waters from the upland mass of eastern Algeria and, flowing through the Plain of Tunis, joins the sea through a marshy delta (unique in north-west Africa) between Tunis and Bizerta. South of the Medjerda the Tunisian High Tell, a prolongation of the Nemencha and Tébessa Mountains of Algeria, forms a succession of ridges, domes and basins of limestone or sandstone and trends north-eastwards to end at the Gulf of Tunis, although it is apparently prolonged in the Cap Bon Peninsula. The term Tunisian Dorsale is applied to this line of upland which serves as a climatic divide: to the north more pluvial

1 (A) The Hassi Messaoud-Bougie oil pipeline at M'Zita, Algeria

1 (B) Stock piles of casing tubes at Hassi Messaoud

2 Olive groves in the Tunisian Sahel near Sfax

Mediterranean conditions, to the south semi-desert. South of Cap Bon extend wide semi-arid coastal plains devoted to olive cultivation (Plate 2). To the cultivated coastal plain the term Sahel is given. The platform intermediate between the Sahel and Tell where the plains expand and triumph over the waning hill chains is steppe country.

15

Climate, Soils and Vegetation

CLIMATE

Only a small part of the Maghreb experiences a truly Mediterranean type of climate, for the parallel-trending relief features, themselves parallel with the coast, help to restrict this climate to a limited coastal area. Elsewhere elevation, distance from the sea and proximity to the Sahara are responsible for marked modifications of the Mediterranean characteristics.

Fundamentally the climate of the Barbary lands results from the interplay of air-masses of diverse origins; the summer is dominated by tropical air and the winter season by modified Polar air and associated depressions. In winter the ITC lies just south of the West African coastline and a steadily rising pressure gradient exists between it and the local high-pressure system that forms over the Atlas Mountains (due to elevation and to the northern Sahara being cooler than the Mediterranean). Low pressure over the Mediterranean draws in a series of depressions from the west, some via the Straits of Gibraltar but most from the Bay of Biscay via the Carcassonne Gate. In summer a reversal takes place. High pressure develops over the Mediterranean while the ITC moves northwards across the south-central Sahara, for the desert is now hotter than the Mediterranean and becomes a low-pressure focus for inblowing winds.

In winter westerly winds are dominant over the Atlas lands. These are the winds moving around the series of depressions travelling north-eastwards along the line of the Mediterranean; generally they are rain-bearing winds, most having crossed the Atlantic. They are variable in force and direction since the low-pressure centres moving north-eastwards constantly change in position and intensity. These depressions, and in the summer local depressions over the western Sahara, are also responsible

Table 3

Station	Alt. (feet)	Temp. °F / Rain in.	J	F	M	A	M	J	J	A	S	O	N	D	Year	Temp. range
Mogador (Essaouira)	33	T.	57	59	60	63	65	68	68	68	69	67	63	59	64	12
		R.	2·2	1·5	2·2	0·7	0·6	0·1	—	—	0·2	1·3	2·4	2·0	13·2	
Marrakech	1,542	T.	52	55	59	67	70	77	82	85	76	70	63	54	67	33
		R.	0·8	0·9	1·7	1·3	0·4	0·4	—	0·2	0·4	0·9	1·5	0·7	9·3	
Algiers	72	T.	49	51	53	56	61	68	74	75	70	64	57	52	61	26
		R.	4·0	2·6	3·3	2·0	1·7	0·7	0·1	0·1	1·2	3·4	4·1	4·0	27·4	
Géryville (El Bayadh)	4,280	T.	39	43	46	52	60	70	79	77	68	56	47	40	56	40
		R.	0·9	1·2	2·4	1·7	2·2	0·7	0·2	0·5	1·2	1·5	1·3	1·5	15·3	
Biskra	410	T.	53	61	61	68	77	85	92	91	85	73	61	53	71	39
		R.	0·5	0·7	0·8	1·2	0·6	0·4	0·2	0·1	0·6	0·8	0·4	0·6	6·9	
Tunis	141	T.	49	51	54	58	65	72	78	79	75	67	59	52	63	30
		R.	2·1	2·0	1·9	1·5	0·9	0·5	0·1	0·2	1·0	1·9	2·1	2·4	16·5	

for the fierce off-desert local winds of North Africa, possessing local names but of which the Sirocco is best known. These occur throughout the year but particularly in spring and are drawn to the advancing front of the depressions just as the Mistral and Bora of the northern Mediterranean coastlands are sucked into the rear. Coming from the desert these winds are excessively hot and dry, often dust-laden; they bring considerable bodily and mental discomfort and wither vegetation. Their duration varies greatly; sometimes they blow for less than an hour, sometimes for several days.

The climate of western Morocco differs from that of the rest of Barbary in that it owes much more to Atlantic than to Mediterranean influences. The relief of the kingdom shelters western Morocco from both the Sahara and the Mediterranean, while the cool Canary current flows off-shore and serves both to reduce summer temperatures and rainfall along the coast (see Mogador, Table 3). The Azores summer high-pressure centre (nearer the Canaries in winter) is responsible for north-easterly winds being dominant over Morocco. In winter depressions moving to the Mediterranean account for the frequent intervention of westerly rain-bearing winds, while in summer the intense low pressure over the hot Sahara accentuates the winds from the north-east. The winter winds bring rain to the Atlantic coastal regions and to the High and Middle Atlas ranges athwart their course. Summer is the dry season, for winds blow from the Mediterranean across warmer land and bring no rain except to the higher mountains. In the period May–September, Marrakech receives only 1·5 inches and in the rest of the year 8 inches (see Table 3). No stations exist in the High Atlas behind Marrakech, but rainfall there is probably over 30 inches.

On the Atlantic coast, land and sea breezes are a marked feature; at times in summer the Atlantic breeze is felt some fifty miles inland. The cold off-shore current gives a cold, damp character to these breezes and mist and fog are frequent along the coast. The Meseta experiences 10 to 16 inches annually and the Sebou lowlands to the north and the Taza gap enjoy about 24 inches. Like the Atlas, the Rif Mountains receive over 30 inches, but screen the lowlands to their east, and along the Mediterranean coast into Algeria no more than 10 inches is received. Similarly the lee side of the Atlas is in a rain shadow and Saharan conditions become apparent.

The proximity of the Atlantic and the cool off-shore current modify temperatures and reduce the annual range. Temperatures in July are below 70°F along the coast. Farther from the coast on the Meseta the range of temperature increases and mean July temperatures reach into the eighties as sea influences become weakened. In the High and Middle Atlas winter temperatures below freezing-point persist for several weeks; blizzards are frequent, passes become blocked by snow, which over considerable areas may lie 3 to 4 feet deep and thus provides a substantial reservoir for the west-flowing streams and rivers.

The climate of the rest of the Maghreb ranges between true Mediterranean in the north and Saharan in the south. Three more or less parallel east-west climatic regions are recognised: the Mediterranean coastlands and inner depressions and hills of the Tell, the High Plateaux and Saharan Atlas, and the Sahara. The coastal zone experiences a maritime Mediterranean climate (see Algiers, Table 3), the Inner Tell a Mediterranean climate but with rather more extremes. The whole of the northern part receives winter rains from the winds associated with the succession of cyclones passing along the Mediterranean. In the west on the coastal Plain of Oran this rainfall is as low as 14 inches owing to the screening effect of the Rif Mountains, but the hill ranges of the Tell Atlas (such as the Monts de Tlemçen and the Massif de L'Ouarsenis) receive 20–30 inches. Rainfall increases eastwards (as does the general relief) and east of the Mitidja (Algiers, 30 inches) the Kabylie Mountains and the Monts de Medjerda in Tunisia receive over 40 inches (Fig. 28). The high mass of the Djurdjura receives over 60 inches and this includes a considerable winter snowfall, the distant snow-capped peaks offering a seasonal back-cloth to the groves of golden oranges and tangerines on the Algiers Plain. Always a sharp contrast exists between the exposed and rainy north and west mountain slopes and the sheltered southern slopes.

With cloudless skies, summer temperatures east of Gibraltar become high. The coastal plains are hot and rainless, but moderated increasingly to the east by coastal breezes that raise the humidity of the air and make conditions oppressive. The Mediterranean moderates summer temperatures which along the coast average 75–80°F in August, the hottest month. In winter coastal conditions are cool and rainy and in both seasons the daily range of temperature is small. Winter conditions are cloudier but the proximity of the Mediterranean mitigates temperature and the mean for January, usually the coldest month, is 50–54°F. Frost is rare and the sheltered valleys and plains adjacent to the sea, such as the Mitidja, are suited to orange- and olive-growing. The sirocco winds, some drawn down the pressure gradient from the Sahara and others, more local, descending as föhn-type winds from the High Plateaux, blow about twenty days a year to the Algerian coast and thirty days a year to the Tunisian coast. In winter they are pleasantly warm but in summer their heat, dryness and dustiness have a very enervating effect. The intensity of evaporation is hard to endure, for temperatures exceed 100°F, while relative humidity may fall to under 20 per cent. Vegetation withers and harvests may be lost.

The effect of the Mediterranean is not felt far inland and the sheltered valleys of the Inner Tell and Medjerda valley in Tunisia, cut off from the sea, show more continental conditions. Winters are colder, snow often falling on the ranges of the Tell Atlas, and summers are hotter, with July and August day temperatures of 100°F or more not uncommon in the more sheltered valleys such as that of the Chéliff. Away from the sea a greater range of temperature is apparent: at Bizerta it is 27° (52°F January–79°F August), whereas at Souk el Arba, in the Medjerda valley, it is 35° (48–83°F). In southern Tunisia on the coast at Gabès it is 31° (51–82°F), but inland at Gafsa it is 40° (47–87°F).

The Tell Atlas reduces the precipitation reaching the High Plateaux, and since these plateaux at 2,500–3,500 feet are lower than the surrounding mountains, Mediterranean influences are excluded and continental conditions with marked seasonal contrasts are experienced. The greater distance from the sea and the rain shadow effect result in a precipitation of only 8–12 inches (see Géryville, Table 3). Most of this falls in the spring, filling the temporary lakes or chotts which dry up during the summer. The contrast with the Mediterranean coastlands is heightened by cold winters with mean January temperatures of 40°F and cold, dry north winds which sweep across the open country, often bringing snow and temperatures frequently below freezing-point. Frosts are common in December and January and one must travel as far south as Biskra (150 miles inland) before meeting temperatures as high as those of the coast (50°F). In summer this contrast between the High Plateaux and the Tell is less marked, the plateaux temperatures averaging 80°F (Géryville 79°) in July, and when the sirocco blows (about forty days a year) absolute maxima of over 100° are usual. Skies are cloudless, the air dry and a considerable diurnal range of temperature is experienced.

The ranges of the Saharan Atlas form a marked climatic divide between the steppe climate of the High Plateaux and that of the desert (Fig. 28). With their greater elevation they receive more rainfall than the plateaux proper and this rain is the source of much of the underground water

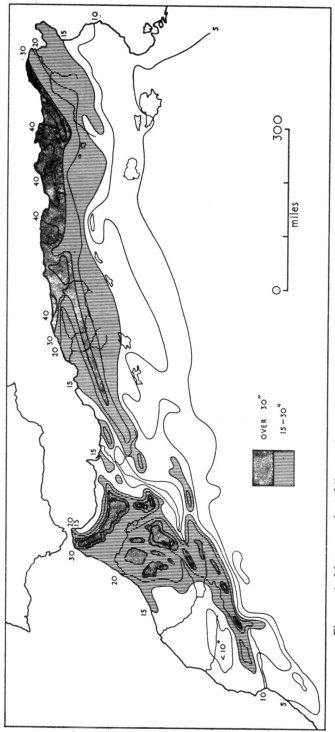

Figure 28 *Mean annual rainfall in north-west Africa.* Isohyets at 5, 10, 15, 20, 30 and 40 inches are shown

supplying the chain of oases along the piedmont zone on the edge of the desert. Biskra stands at the junction of the two climatic types (Table 3). Its rainfall is of the Mediterranean winter type, but the small amount (7 inches) and the great seasonal (and also diurnal) range of temperature is more akin to Saharan conditions which extend across southern Tunisia into Libya.

In Tunisia the seasonal contrasts of climate are as marked as in the rest of North Africa and devolve from similar causes, but modifications of the general pattern are brought about by the extended influence of the sea, for the coastline encompasses two sides of the roughly rectangular state, and by the confinement of a great deal of the highland to the west with broad plains to the east. The influence of the Mediterranean in reducing the range of temperature along the coast is striking. The northern Tunisian lowland has summer temperatures averaging 78°F, but southern and central Tunisia south of the Dorsale and away from the coast lies south of the 82° isotherm. Winters reveal mean January coastal temperatures around 51°F, but much of the interior is distinctly colder (the January mean around 42°F) and although temperatures are not as low as on the Algerian High Plateaux frosts are common. The highest rainfall of over 35 inches is experienced in the mountainous north-west. The annual rainfall diminishes to as little as 4 inches in the extreme south. The isohyets trend south-west – north-east following the predominant grain of the relief. North of the Dorsale over 60 inches is experienced, but to the south the Sahel and low steppes behind Sous and Sfax average 10–12 inches.

SOILS AND VEGETATION

The distribution of plant life depends upon the complex interaction of three factors: climatic, edaphic (soils) and biotic (plants and animals, especially man). Of these climate usually exerts the most powerful influence and in North Africa the amount and incidence of rainfall are of paramount importance. These in turn influence soil-formation. The moderate to low rainfall of the Atlas lands retards rock-weathering, causing much of the soil to be immature and restricts vegetative growth, affording little humus. With the wide variations of relief and geology the soils are very mixed and show close relationship with parent rock. Brown soils predominate, but the soils derived from limestones (rendzinas) are red. The amount of lime in the soil exerts some influence on the character of the vegetation. On the High Plateaux and steppe land of Tunisia soils formed by aeolian (wind-borne) materials are important.

Most of this region of Africa is subject to two main types of climate, the Mediterranean in the north and the Saharan in the south, separated by a transitional steppe region. The mild wet winters of the Mediterranean favour plant growth, whereas the summer droughts with their high rates of evaporation hinder growth. The greatest vegetative growth occurs in the spring when temperatures rise before the onset of the summer drought, and in the autumn when rainfall occurs before temperatures reach their minimum. This marked seasonal variation of rain and drought produces a rhythm of plant growth and structural adaptation to withstand the rainless period. The vegetation is characteristically xerophytic and demonstrates a range of adaptations for reducing transpiration; the bearing of spiny leaves and thorns, waxy coverings and thickened cuticles. Much of the region once bore woodland. Biotic influences in particular have reduced a good deal of this to evergreen thickets or maquis. The maquis consists of evergreen hard-leaved shrubs and low trees from 4 to 20 feet high. These include laurel, arbutus, myrtle, lentisk, rosemary, broom, buckthorns and aromatic shrubs such as lavender and thyme. They form dense tangles and thickets: well-developed maquis is impenetrable without mechanical aid. On the permeable limestone the maquis itself degenerates into heath and poor scrub known as 'garigue', where the vegetation is of patches of low-growing shrubs interspersed among bare rocks and soil. These include gorse, lavender and sage. It will be noted that destruction of woodland either by man or the ubiquitous and omnivorous goat does not extend grassland, which is rare in the Barbary lands: brush and scrub of plants adapted to the seasonal climatic rhythm succeeds the woodland.

One of the largest areas modified by man is Atlantic Morocco or the low platform of the Meseta and the lowlands of the Sebou to the north. The original vegetation was probably cork oak forest but now much land is under cultivation or, especially in the south, forms rough grazing of low open maquis-type brushwood. Groups of degenerate cork oaks remain here and there, and are useful both for their bark and charcoal.

In the well-watered regions where there has been least interference evergreen woodland predominates. This clothes the seaward-facing slopes of the Atlas and Rif of Morocco and the coastal hills and Tell Atlas of Algeria and Tunisia. Oaks and conifers are the dominant species. At the lower levels where destruction by man and animal has been greatest, brushwood and maquis prevail; from 3,000 feet evergreen oaks and junipers predominate with cork oak on the more siliceous soils in eastern Algeria and Tunisia. On the well-watered southern ranges of the Tell Atlas such as the Ouarsenis the Aleppo pine with dense undergrowth is common. From 5,000 feet cedars and thurifers form open forests and a valuable source of good timber. On the coastal mountains of eastern Algeria and north-western Tunisia deciduous trees such as Portuguese oak, elm and ash grow in the deeper soils. The timber line is surpassed only in the High Atlas where it is at about 12,000 feet. Above this height stony scrubland with spiny plants is the nearest approach to the Alpine vegetation of the north side of the Mediterranean.

Generally the vegetation of North Africa becomes progressively poorer from north to south with diminishing rainfall. The central zone of upland from eastern Morocco through Algeria into Tunisia (the High Plateaux) averaging 3,000 feet in height has a long dry season of six to seven months and a lower rainfall of between 8 and 12 inches. Summers are hot and winters cold. Forests here give way to steppe vegetation which is characterised by the absence of trees and shrubs and composed of tufts of herbs and dwarf plants interspersed with patches of bare soil. The steppes are drier in the west, being in the rain shadow of the mountains of Morocco. Here large areas are covered with alfa (*Stipa tenacissima*), white wormwood, sparte and long-rooted drinn grass. Farther east the plateaux are a little wetter and south of Constantine much is under cultivation; elsewhere alfa gives its prominent position to the jujube. The clay basins around the chotts, rich in mineral salts, provide a habitat for salt-steppe plants (halophytic) including sea lavenders, sea rushes and rice grass. They remain green throughout the dry season and provide food for flocks and herds in all seasons. This steppe country, pinched out by the Tébessa Mountains and the Dorsale, descends to the coast in central Tunisia in the Low Steppes and Sahels of Sous and Sfax. Inland, alfa and drinn grass steppes with red juniper on the higher ridges give way to jujube scrub and coarse grasses on the uncultivated parts of the Sahels. Around the chotts and coastal salt-marshes halophytes and members of the chenopod family flourish.

The Anti-Atlas of Morocco and the Saharan Atlas mark a clear limit between Mediterranean and Saharan conditions. These ranges receive more rainfall than the High Plateaux and they support forest growth, in the west mainly Aleppo pine and holm oak and in the east cedar and thurifer on the higher parts (e.g. of the Aurès) with Aleppo pine and red juniper at lower levels.

16

Morocco

The Kingdom of Morocco, a land of great beauty and variety, is only separated from Europe by the eleven-mile-wide Straits of Gibraltar. It has strong religious and cultural ties with the Arab world, but also forms a link with Europe whose capital and technical help it welcomes in its struggle for economic betterment. The kingdom has an area of 171,300 sq. miles, about the size of Sweden, but with a population 60 per cent greater than that of Sweden. The population, mainly of Berbers and Arabs, but also including some Europeans, Jews and Negroes, now totals 13 million (1965). Europeans, mainly French, number about 300,000. The common language is Arabic, and Islam is the common religion, both adopted in the eighth century. There is a deep national consciousness and pride in the country's long history and cultural inheritance.

Since 1956 the country has been a sovereign independent monarchy. Previously, from 1912 it had been divided into two Protectorates by France and Spain. The Spanish Protectorate was the smaller and consisted of the strip of territory flanking the Straits of Gibraltar, mainly comprising the Rif Atlas. While ceding the bulk of the territory in 1956, Spain retained sovereignty over the coastal towns of Alhucemas, Ceuta, Chafarinas, Melilla and Penon de Velez. She also retained possession of Ifni, a small coastal enclave of semi-desert near the southern boundary of Morocco which was ceded to her by Morocco in 1860. In 1923 the port of Tangier and its immediate surroundings was declared an International Zone, but this also reverted to the Kingdom of Morocco in 1956. The eastern and southern boundaries of the kingdom have never been fixed precisely and this has led to a number of frontier incidents with Algeria.

On the basis of relief, climate and way of life Morocco may be divided into three distinctive parts (Fig. 29): Atlantic Morocco, comprising the three lowland regions of Sebou–Taza, the Meseta and the Sous Plain; the Atlas Mountains with their series of distinctive ranges; and the plateau land to the east which may be regarded as an extension of the High Plateaux of Algeria (p. 202), and will not be dealt with here.

The Atlantic lowlands

The bulk of the Moroccan population lives and works on the plains and plateaux facing the Atlantic. Here are the major cities, ports, industries and agriculture. In the north is the rich alluvial lowland of the *Sebou Basin and Rharb*, prolonged eastward in the Taza corridor. Atlantic influences penetrate far inland tending to reduce temperature ranges; water is adequate and agriculture flourishes. The plains around Fez and Meknès through which a number of tributaries of the River Sebou now pass are particularly fertile, being derived from the floor of an old fresh-water lake. Rainfall is only 20 inches, adequate for the predominant cereal cultivation, but the whole Sebou Basin is well watered by the springs and streams from the Rif and Middle Atlas, facilitating the widespread development of orchards, orange groves and vineyards, mainly as a result of French colonisation. Between Rabat and Meknès population is sparser in the former cork oak forest of Mamora. Over-felling and land clearance has reduced much of it to the appearance of neglected park rather than forest. The Sebou is subjected to considerable spring flooding with the snow melt off the Atlas. For the last 50 miles to the sea, in the Rharb, its meandering course is raised above the general level of the plain and its flooding causes serious inundation. Sand-dunes hamper its outflow to the sea and extensive marshes (*merjas*) result. In winter they are water-covered and harbour fish, water fowl and game; in summer they offer rough pasture to sheep and cattle.

South of Rabat between the Atlas and the Atlantic is the gently sloping platform of the *Moroccan Meseta*, rising from sea-level to more than 3,000 feet. The higher inland portion is a dissected peneplain with the ancient rocks levelled down and thinly covered with Upper Cretaceous and Lower Eocene deposits. Several snow-fed rivers cross this plain to the coast and although their volume is reduced in summer they make a valuable contribution to the agricultural economy. Chief among the rivers are the Tensift and the Oum er Rbia. In places these rivers have cut gorges through the Quaternary limestones and occasionally the old Palaeozoic rocks are exposed. Land use varies considerably, with the best agricultural land stretching along the coast south from Casablanca, the country of the Chaouia and Doukkala groups of tribes. Here the coastal

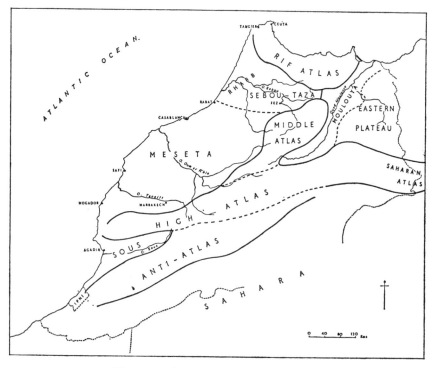

Figure 29 *Geographical regions of Morocco*

plain is up to 50 miles wide and of fertile black soils ('tirs'). Traditional cultivation of wheat, barley and maize vies with expanding acreage devoted to sugar-beet, early vegetables and market gardening. The coast is inhospitable. There are few natural inlets to protect shipping from the strong Atlantic swell and most river mouths are obstructed by sand-bars. Farther from the sea, steppe vegetation offers sheep-grazing until cultivation recurs on a series of plains nearer the foot of the mountains.

A large number of small oueds* descend from the mountains and water this immediate piedmont zone, supplying oases and garden-type settlements and gradually losing their water in canals and small irrigation channels. Marrakech is in this zone. The drier climate renders irrigation necessary and this city, white and red brown from Saharan dust, stands at the foot of the mountains amid the fertile irrigated Haouz plain where palms, the vine, citrus fruit and market gardening flourish.

The remaining lowland, south of the Meseta and separated from it by the High Atlas, is the triangular downfolded *Sous Plain* extending some 80 miles inland from Agadir. The southerly position and enclosed character of the plain are responsible for a near Saharan climate (Taroud-dant, January 81°F, August 113°F, rainfall 8 inches). Agriculture and settlement are related to the irrigation from the River Sous and its tributaries although these are irregular in flow and almost dry up in summer. Palms, citrus fruits and cereals are produced in these irrigated gardens; elsewhere the landscape is bare but for clumps of coarse grasses, fleshy spurge and argan trees which provide some grazing for sheep and the black Moroccan goats. The only other lowland of significance in Morocco is the valley of the River Moulouya which gathers its waters from both the High and Middle Atlas. The upper and middle valley is remote and inhospitable lying in the rain shadow of the Middle Atlas, with only 6–7 inches a year, but nearer the coast cereals and vines are grown.

The Atlas Mountains

The great mountain chains of Morocco cover almost one-third of the country and support nearly two-fifths of the population. The *High Atlas*, at their widest here and attaining over 13,500 feet south of Marrakech, form a great physical and climatic barrier. The contrast between the Saharan and Atlantic side is remarkable. The north- and west-facing slopes are well watered and forested and the Berber peoples from their defensively sited and nucleated villages cultivate olives (up to 5,000 feet), other tree fruits and cereals on terraced slopes. These days the mountain villages provide a reservoir of seasonal manpower for the farms and towns of the plains. The Saharan-facing slopes are dry, sunbaked and support only poor scrub. Here the tribes are more pastoral than agricul-

* Oued = river, stream or dry water-course. In the eastern Sahara the term *wadi* is used

tural. Settled life and cultivation is in oases dependent on irrigation from the small streams, many seasonal, that flow southwards to lose themselves in the desert. The most extensive of the foothill oases is that of Tafilelt by the Oued Ziz. Otherwise this is the domain of nomads with their flocks and herds. The massive northerly spur of the *Middle Atlas* comprises Jurassic limestone (giving a karstic landscape in the east) and has been likened to 'a giant Jura with, to the west, some aspects of the Auvergne'; this with the well-forested western slopes and the relatively heavy rain and snowfall has made this area the main reservoir of the country ('*le château d'eau du Maroc*'). Much of the precipitation sinks into the fissured limestone and issues out as springs around the base of the mountains. The largest rivers of Morocco rise in the Middle Atlas and include the Oum er Rbia, the Sebou and the Moulouya. Here mountain pastures are the main resource and stock rearing is of greater importance than in the High Atlas. There is a double migration of the semi-nomadic Berber population—upwards in summer to the pastures exposed by the snow melt and downwards in winter.[1] The village 'base', midway between the upper and lower limits of migration, is sited where cultivation is possible and crops can be stored securely while the men are away with the animals.

THE ECONOMY AND WAY OF LIFE

It is not easy to discuss the Moroccan economy without becoming aware that it is comprised of two distinct and unequal parts; these might be termed the traditional and the modern. The basis of the traditional economy is the agriculture that has evolved to satisfy the subsistence wants of more or less self-contained rural communities. Commerce is unorganised and local, depending upon incidental marketable surpluses. These activities are complemented by the traditional handicraft industries. The modern economy results from the French occupation, investment and settlement. Much is due to their first and outstanding Resident-General, Marshal Lyautey (1912–25), who after his successful subjugation devoted himself to Moroccan development. His are the motor roads that have opened up the country. The desire that the impact of modern civilisation should not cause the speedy disintegration of the traditional urban and tribal society led to the housing of European and Moorish communities in separate towns and suburbs. Today's monument to this policy is the phenomenal growth of the port-city of Casablanca (Plate

1A). In fifty years it has grown from a small town of 20,000 to 1 million inhabitants. It is now a city of huge modern offices and flats, the geographical centre and mainspring of the modern economy which encompasses European agriculture, forestry, fishing, mining, manufacturing, trade and transport. These developments derive from European investment, enterprise, technology and skill. Moroccan participation in them is mainly as semi-skilled and unskilled labour. This dual element in the economy applies also to the other Barbary states and, in fact, to most of the colonial or former colonial states in Africa. The full significance may be realised from the fact that the modern economy accounts for over two-thirds of the country's total production although it employs only about 30 per cent of the total occupied population. If the subsistence element in the traditional economy is discounted, its share in the money economy is less than 15 per cent of total production. In other words, only a small proportion of Moroccans are involved in the money economy; the mass of the population, existing mainly on a subsistence basis, has virtually no purchasing power nor resources for investment. The traditional economy is generally one of stagnation. This underlines the difference between the two economies, for the modern economy in the long term demonstrates cumulative growth and is expanding. Since 1949 much of this expansion has been made possible by a substantial increase in basic facilities and utilities, especially roads, railways and ports installed with borrowed foreign capital. A 5-year plan for modernising agriculture and intensifying technical development was introduced in 1960. This was followed in 1965 by a 3-year plan giving priority to agriculture, tourism and hotels and requiring an investment of $430 million.

Agriculture

The principal occupation of Morocco, agriculture engages some 80 per cent of the working population. Moroccans own about 90 per cent of the farmland and 95 per cent of the livestock. Their methods of agriculture are usually primitive, traditional and extensive. Animal power is applied to primitive implements such as wooden ploughs, and much hand labour is employed. Fertilisers are scarcely ever used, rotations are rare, yields poor. Climate, particularly rainfall, influences the pattern of agriculture. The relatively well-watered Atlantic seaboard and mountain valleys are the scenes of cultivation and settled ways of life, but as the rainfall diminishes from north to south and from east to west the emphasis on livestock rearing increases under semi-nomadic or nomadic régimes. Moroccan farm holdings number about 900,000. The farming population may be divided into three groups: first are the large landowners who rely on hired labour: they own over 50 per cent of the farmland and represent 10 per cent of the rural population. Second are the small farmers who work their own land, occasionally with hired labour. They own less than half the land and form 30 per cent of the rural population. Finally, there are the landless share-croppers and wage-labourers. From these percentages the maldistribution of the agricultural income may be deduced.

Whereas most Moroccan farms and holdings are small, the European farms offer great contrast. European land settlement has been sharply restricted and there are only about 6,000 holdings, but the average size is 400 acres and many are of more than 2,000 acres. The fields of regular outline are scrupulously tended, the buildings are spacious and well kept. Seventy per cent of French agricultural settlement is in the relatively well-watered region of Rabat, Casablanca and the Rharb. Large-scale commercial farming is the rule, with a high degree of mechanisation and therefore relatively small use of manpower. Crop rotation is practised; fertilisers and selected seed are used and irrigation methods applied to relieve dependence on rainfall. Moroccan cereal yields fluctuate from year to year with the dependence on the winter rainfall but average 10 bushels per acre, whereas European farms average 14 bushels per acre. The higher returns from European agriculture also reflect the emphasis on more remunerative crops such as tree crops and garden vegetables, particularly by the smaller farms. Fruit trees are very important in Morocco; the olive (12 million trees) is dominant, followed by almonds, figs, dates (there are about 4 million palms in the south) and citrus fruits.

The traditional agriculture is concerned with producing basic foods and in fact 85 per cent of the cultivated area is under cereals, mainly barley and wheat. Moroccan agriculture provides most of the cereal exports (mainly barley) while the vegetables, wine and citrus fruits for export are produced chiefly on European farms and find a market in France. The static character of traditional agriculture may be deduced from cereal yields. Output of the capitalised European agriculture has nearly doubled since the war, but Moroccan output remains static if allowance is made for favourable and unfavourable seasons. Nevertheless, the outlook need not be gloomy, for there is great scope for improvement in traditional agriculture and with proper attention production of food could for many years be increased even more rapidly than the rate of population. This will require, however, capital, agrarian education and measures of land reform.

Arable agriculture with permanent settlement lies mainly in the better-watered northern half of the Atlantic Plain, southwards along the coast and inland, with irrigation, at the foot of the mountains. In the semi-arid steppe areas the ground is scratched rather than ploughed and cereals planted: the bulk of the population seeks summer pasture for the sheep and goats. There are also similar movements within the mountains, especially in the Middle Atlas. Here in November sheep and goats move down to the steppe of the Moulouya and the plains around Fez and Meknès and the Tadla Plain of the upper Oum er Rbia. Most of the family accompanies the animals. In spring beasts and men return to the Atlas valley villages and the cultivation of maize, barley and wheat is put in hand. In June a proportion of the animals is taken higher up to the mountain pastures, but the bulk of the people remains in the valleys with their arable crops and fruit trees. All these movements, whether of the semi-nomads or true nomads of the desert, follow traditional tribal routes and use tribal grazing lands. This element in the lives of a high proportion of Moroccans is further shown in a seasonal movement of labour, principally from the poorer south mainly to the farms of the coast and around Marrakech. As the year advances there is a movement northwards to the Chaouia and the Rharb. In the north-east many seasonal labourers move into Algeria.

Stock-raising

One of Morocco's oldest occupations, stock-raising is a natural response to a climate frequently unfavourable to arable agriculture. Stock can withstand the seasonal character and the variability of the rainfall better than crops and can take advantage of the pastures that range of altitude offers. The beasts, mainly sheep and goats, furnish all the essentials for nourishment and clothing and are also mobile and hardy. Some 95 per cent of the stock are owned by Moroccans: they do not lavish much care upon their beasts, whose quality is poor. Sheep probably number about 16 million and there is a small export of wool; goats (10 million) and cattle (3 million) are next in order of importance.

Fishing

The fishing industry of Morocco is assuming some importance. Many kinds of fish thrive in the cold waters of the Canary current off the coast; the principal varieties caught are the sardine, the bonito and tunny. The annual catch is about 100,000 metric tons and the chief fishing ports where fish-canning and -curing for export take place are Casablanca, Agadir, Safi and Rabat. Approximately one-third of the catch is exported.

Irrigation

Just under one-quarter of Morocco receives annually more than 24 inches of rain; another quarter, with 12 to 24 inches, is semi-arid, and the remaining half is occupied by desert and steppe (Fig. 28). In such a country the strengthening and development of the agricultural economy must give high place to irrigation. About 600,000 acres are watered perennially, the rest being under primitive indigenous methods. In general, surface flow is utilised in the north, but underground supplies in the south and east. Some progress has been made in improving the indigenous wells and foggaras and small reservoirs have been built in the mountains to the south to store water for the summer. Major irrigation schemes involving large dam and canal construction have been and are being carried out on the Sebou tributaries, Oum er Rbia and its tributaries and the N'fis tributary of the Oued Tensift (Fig. 30).

The problems to be overcome include the violent seasonal variability of the rivers, the permeable character of the limestones and the silting up of reservoirs. The schemes tend to be costly and so far have benefited European farmers more than Moroccan. This is mainly due to the conservatism of the native farmers and to the need to educate them in irrigation farming. In some newly irrigated areas as at Beni Amir, on the Tadla Plain of the upper Oum er Rbia (Fig. 30), Europeans are debarred from holding land; since 1941 the Office de Beni Amir-Beni Moussa has operated to control the scheme, to operate public works and a health service, to consolidate fragmented holdings and train the peasantry in a new mode of life. Previously in this 14-inch-rainfall zone the population was semi-nomadic, taking poor crops from plots beside the river and then ranging over the steppe to the mountain grazing. The scheme has met with success: already 10,000 acres of steppe have been

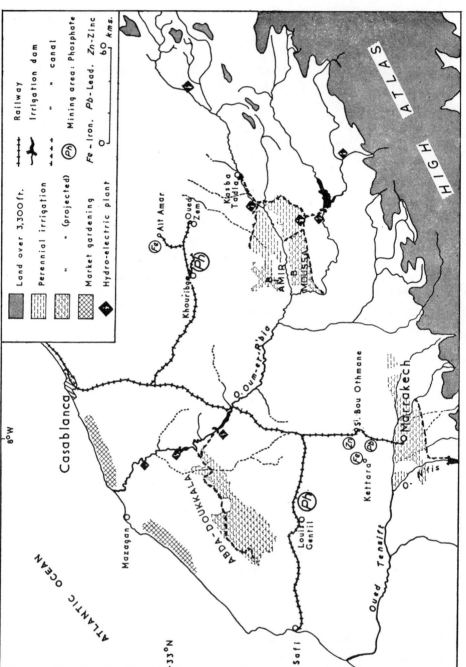

Figure 30 *Economic development in the Moroccan Meseta*

reclaimed at Beni Amir and Beni Moussa out of a planned total (first stage) of 160,000 acres. Later, further irrigation will be introduced down-stream at Abda Doukkala (Fig. 30). The Office is settling annually be-tween 500 and 1,000 families in the newly irrigated areas.

Mining

Mining is an important activity in Morocco. The industry is efficiently organised for an export market and minerals account for rather more than one-third of total exports by value. The principal mineral produced (under a government monopoly) is phosphate of lime, and Morocco is the world's leading exporter and second producer to the USA, producing one-fifth of world output. The deposits occur in a band of limestone roughly paralleling the coast a few miles behind Casablanca, Mazagan and Safi (Fig. 31). The limestone is soft, easily mined and very rich in phosphate. The two main centres of production, favourably located for exporting, are at Khouribga on the Ouled Abdoun plateau and Louis Gentil in the Gantour Basin. Exports are via Casablanca and Safi respec-tively. A factory at Casablanca processes small quantities of the phosphate to produce superphosphate for domestic agriculture.

Table 4   Morocco mineral production

Production (000's of tons)

	1952	1957	1962
Phosphate	3,953	5,520	8,160
Iron ore	650*	1,800	1,149
Coal	460	482	410
Manganese ore	426	484	567
Lead ore	115	91	99
Zinc ore	51	48	38
Crude oil	101	97	80

* Not including Spanish Morocco production

Other minerals produced and exported are indicated in Table 4. Manganese is mined in eastern Morocco at Bou Arfa and El Aioun and iron ore (56 per cent Fe) is mined principally at Uixan, near Melilla in the Rif and Ait Amar inland of Casablanca. Coal production amounts annually to about half a million tons of anthracite. Mining takes place at

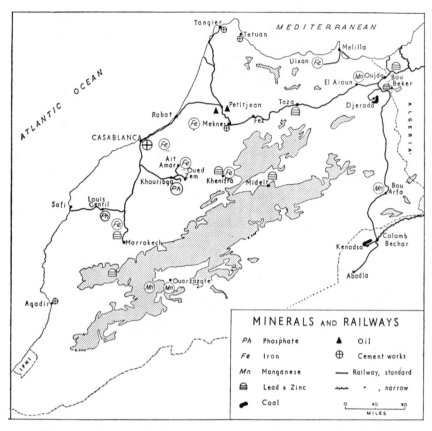

Figure 31 *Mining and railways in Morocco*. Land over 5,000 feet, shaded

Djerada in eastern Morocco and about half the production is exported. Prospecting during World War II revealed the existence of large reserves of lead and zinc ore in eastern Morocco at Bou Beker near Oujda and in the upper Moulouya valley. Other deposits are mined in both the High and Middle Atlas. Morocco's mineral exports are widely disseminated. Phosphates are shipped to most countries of Western Europe. Manganese, lead and zinc are exported mainly to France and much of the iron ore to the United Kingdom.

Manufacturing Industry

Morocco is mainly an agricultural country but there has been substantial development of manufacturing industry since World War II. Again a division between traditional manufacturing—mainly by native craftsmen in small establishments—and the larger European-directed factory establishments is notable. Numbers employed in secondary industry are estimated at nearly 300,000. Over half of these are Moroccan artisans engaged in traditional handicrafts. Modern plants permanently employ up to 80,000 Europeans and Moroccans and about half that number on a seasonal basis. Generally the output of the modern industrial sector is reckoned to be more than four times that of the traditional handicrafts, although the labour force used is much smaller. Traditional handicrafts, especially in textiles, ceramics and leatherwork, are carried on throughout Morocco, but are particularly important in the large towns where the artisans and their families form a large part of the Moroccan population.

The principal modern industrial region is the Chaouia and centres on Casablanca. Seventy per cent of industrial establishments are in and around this city. The leading industries are associated with the country's primary production and for the most part serve a home market. They include milling, brewing, sugar refining, tobacco manufacturing, vegetable oilseed refining, soap and candle manufactures; curing, canning and preserving fish, fruit and vegetables. Cement manufacture (from local raw materials) has expanded since the war; the original factory at Casablanca was supplemented by one at Agadir in 1952 and by another at Meknès in 1953. The country is now almost self-sufficient in cement. Another notable post-war development has been in the oil-refining and chemical industry, carried on almost entirely in Casablanca until 1965 when, at Safi, a large fertiliser factory producing superphosphate from local phosphate sulphur and pyrites was opened.

The one major export from manufacturing industry is tinned fish, particularly sardines. The industry has been developed for export markets. There are 200 plants, nearly 90 per cent of them established by Europeans. Less than a fifth of these plants are at Casablanca, the remainder being distributed along the coast particularly at Safi, Essaouira (Mogador) and Agadir. Vegetable canning is centred on the market-gardening district around Casablanca. Most of the exports of fish and vegetables are to France.

Traditional Moroccan industries have declined during this century, mainly as a result of imported manufactured goods. One native industry that has held its own is carpet manufacture centred upon Fez, Rabat and Casablanca; another now facing difficulty from imports is the leather industry centred upon Marrakech, Safi and Fez. The traditional artisan industries are strongest in the old towns such as Fez, Meknès and Marrakech, noted for embroidery, textiles, leather ware, pottery and jewellery.

Industrial development in Morocco has been hampered by problems of the provision of power. With little coal or oil available emphasis in recent years has been upon the development of water power. A large number of small- and medium-sized hydro-electrical plants is now established at the irrigation dams in the High and Middle Atlas. These are supplemented in low-water periods by thermal-electric plants in the larger towns. Hydro-power accounts for 80 per cent of all electricity produced. Small quantities of bituminous coal and coke are imported but the major energy import is of petroleum products, for, except for some very small oil-wells near Petitjean in the Sebou Basin, Morocco lacks oil. Since 1938 the total supply of energy from all sources has increased nearly fivefold, but within these figures hydro-electric power has multiplied nearly eightfold and is responsible for nearly 1,000 million kwh annually.

The growth of Morocco's economy and prosperity has been uneven since the end of World War II. Local savings accumulated during the war and a spate of foreign capital (mainly French) in the early post-war years led to a marked expansion of the modern economy and the considerable enlargement of public utilities and basic services such as roads, railways, ports and power supplies. By 1955, however, industrial expansion began to level off. Political uncertainty attendant upon the granting of independence by the French was a contributory cause, but the major problem since that period has been the search for markets. The future expansion and attraction of capital would seem to hinge principally upon an expansion of the domestic market, at the moment remarkably small because of the low level of money income of most of the population. Such expansion can only come about by marked changes in the traditional economy (accounting for two-thirds of the active population) which will involve far-reaching changes in outlooks, customs and attitudes of the people.

POPULATION AND SETTLEMENT

Seventy per cent of Morocco's 12 million population is rural. The urban proportion is increasing rapidly and there are now eight towns each with more than 100,000 population, headed by Casablanca which has achieved the distinction of becoming Africa's fourth 'million' city. The map (Fig. 32) demonstrates that the major part of Morocco's population is found north and west of the Atlas ranges and that the most favoured areas are the Sebou Plain, the south-facing Rif foothills, the

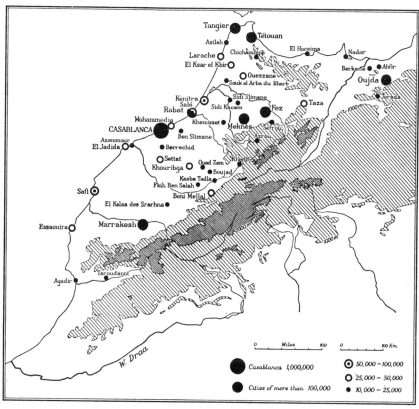

Figure 32 *Cities of Morocco* (by permission of H. Awad)

Atlantic face of the Meseta and the irrigated western foothill zone of the Atlas ranges. In all these areas which favour agriculture densities exceed 100 per sq. mile. The densities contrast severely with the few inhabitants living south of the High Atlas, who are to be found in oases near oueds and water points. Moroccans are not town-dwellers and the rise of the few large towns is closely related to the influx of Europeans

and the growth of the modern sector of the economy. Townsmen and
their way of life are regarded coolly by the country and mountain folk.
They are a mixture of Arab, Berber and Jew, but Arabic is the town
language and townsmen are far more Arabised than the country people.
Urban life was revitalised by the Moslems expelled from Spain during
the sixteenth and seventeenth centuries; their descendants are still known
as *Moriscos* and *Andalous* (Moors and Andalusians). In recent years the
disdain for the town life among country and mountain folk is diminishing
with the recognition, and the growing acceptance, of the greater opportunities of employment and progress that towns offer. There has been a
marked increase in urbanisation since 1945 (Fig. 33).

The dispersed character of the population has brought into prominence
the *souk* or weekly market, an individual feature of rural Moroccan life.
There are very few equivalents of European country market towns;
instead, the market is held in the open at predetermined sites which are
deserted for the rest of the week. These *souks* are so located within tribal
areas that tribesmen may visit them and return home within a single
day; thus they may be 20 to 30 miles apart. They are generally named
according to the regular day of the week on which they are held.
Moroccans are great walkers but travel to market by bus is increasing
and merchants also arrive by bus or car with their bales of cloth, imported
groceries (tea, coffee, etc.); artisans such as blacksmiths, barbers, cobblers,
makers of pots and pans and the travelling medicine man are all part
of the pattern. These gatherings are social and political as well as commercial: news and gossip are exchanged, problems resolved and legal
transactions discussed. The markets facilitate the exchange of rural
surplus commodities for urban goods and further the exchange of local
products, playing a large part in the life of the countryside. In the towns
there may be a number of *souks* housed in narrow streets each specialising
in particular classes of merchandise.

The usual dwelling of the sedentary Berber or Arab is a one-roomed
abode made of sun-dried clay with clay-tiled roof. In mountainous areas
these houses are often so huddled on the slopes that they rise in tiers, one
man's roof being another man's roadway. In the Atlas of southern
Morocco, in addition, gigantic 'kasbas' or strongholds of the Berber
chieftains provide relics of a departed military power. The towns are
little more than such groupings on a larger scale with ramparts and a
mosque. The four elements discernible in the larger towns today are the
huddle of Moroccan houses making up the 'medina', the Ghetto quarter

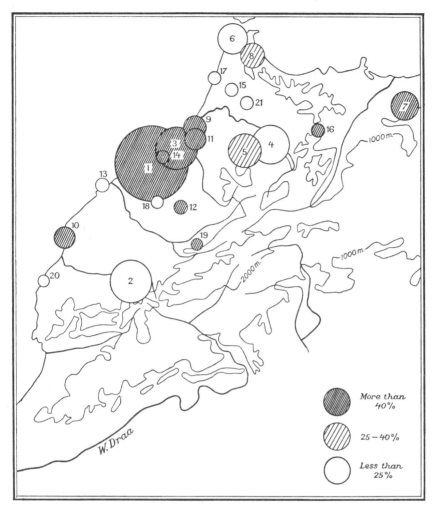

Figure 33 *Urban population growth in Morocco 1952–60* (by permission of
H. Awad)

1. Casablanca. 2. Marrakech. 3. Rabat. 4. Fez. 5. Meknès. 6. Tangier. 7. Oujda.
8. Tétouan. 9. Kenitra. 10. Safi. 11. Salé. 12. Khouribga. 13. El Jadida.
14. Mohammedia. 15. El Ksar el Kbir. 16. Taza. 17. Larache. 18. Settat.
19. Beni Mellal. 20. Essaouira. 21. Ouezzane

('mellah') of the Jews who have played an important part in commercial
life, the kasba of the governor and the European quarter, usually somewhat detached from the congested older agglomeration and much more
spaciously planned (Fig. 34).

CASABLANCA (pop. 1,200,000), the largest city, major port and economic capital of the kingdom, is essentially a modern creation, although the small native settlement was known to exist in the twelfth century. By the end of the nineteenth century it had a population of 20,000 and its trade with Europe was growing markedly.

In 1907, after some assassinations of Europeans, the French occupied the port and made it the base for their subsequent subjugation of the kingdom. Today the well-planned European-type city, with spacious boulevards, banks, department stores and gleaming slabs of modern air-conditioned office blocks, reminds one of Los Angeles rather than an African town. The original small roadstead has been transformed into a deep-water port with two great concrete moles giving shelter from the Atlantic swell. This port (Plate 1A) handles about 70 per cent of Morocco's foreign trade. The industries of the port include fish canning and curing, flour milling, cereal processing, ship repairing, sugar refining, oil-refining, cement and fertiliser manufactures. Excellent road and rail communications link Casablanca with its important hinterland of northern Morocco, with the coastal plain to the south and Marrakech.

FEZ (pop. 250,000) has grown up at the crossing of two ancient and important routes. These are the great east-west trade route linking Algeria and the eastern Maghreb with the Atlantic cities via the Taza corridor, and the north-south caravan route from the Mediterranean coast at Tangier to the Sahara via the passes in the Atlas. It sprawls its jungle of narrow lanes and alleys on both sides of the Oued Fez, near its confluence with the Sebou. The town dates from A.D. 801 and for much of its history has been a capital city. In the thirteenth century it is thought its population was twice that of today. It remains a great centre of Arab life, religious and cultural, is the foremost native industrial and commercial centre and enjoys a great reputation for its carpets and leather work.

MEKNÈS (pop. 205,000) took on a new lease of life with the French occupation and the agricultural development of the surrounding fertile land for which it is an important market. Its crafts include ornamental brasswork, jewellery, carpet-weaving and leatherwork. As at Fez a well-laid-out European town has grown up a short distance from the native city.

MARRAKECH (pop. 264,000) is the largest native city in Morocco (Fig.34)
It was established in A.D. 1062 and has grown up on the Haouz plain in the
valley of the Oued Tensift about 40 miles from the foothills of the snow-
capped High Atlas. It is at the meeting of two natural routes through the
mountains from the south-west and the south-east. The old city is walled

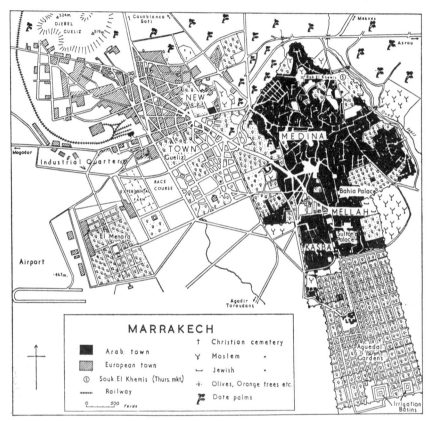

Figure 34 *Marrakech*. This town plan demonstrates the customary components
of the larger Arab towns in the Maghreb: the Kasba, Medina, Mellah and
European sector

and bastioned and throughout its history has vied with Fez as capital. It is the
great mart for the tribesmen of the High Atlas and much of the north-west
Sahara. It has spread over a well-irrigated plain and represents a vast oasis
settlement in a semi-arid region (av. rainfall 9 inches), being surrounded
by date-palms, vineyards and groves of oranges and olives and other fruit
trees. Native industries include carpet, pottery and jewellery manufacture.

RABAT (pop. 261,000) is the administrative capital of Morocco and with its twin town of Salé, on the north side, straddles the estuary of the small river, Bou Regreg. A large European town surrounds the medina and includes the Sultan's palace and government offices. The port (max. harbour depth 16 feet) has diminished in importance with the rise of the deep-water port of Casablanca.

TANGIER (pop. 166,000) is one of Morocco's oldest towns and was probably a Phoenician trading station in the sixth century B.C. Until World War II Tangier was Morocco's chief port, but it has declined with the rise of Casablanca. The walled old town and citadel is highly congested, whereas the contiguous European quarters are open and spacious. From 1925 to 1959 Tangier was administered as a demilitarised International Zone, but this status was abolished in 1956 and in 1962 Tangier was declared a free port. Much of the life and trade of the town arises from its position at the western entrance to the Mediterranean, as port of call for tourist liners and attraction for tourists from Spain and Gibraltar—a mere 14 miles across the Straits.

COMMUNICATIONS AND TRADE

Part of the French legacy to Morocco has been a relatively good network of communications. There are 1,100 miles of railway, mostly of standard gauge, linking the Atlantic coast with Algeria, Tangier and Marrakech (Fig. 31). The first railways were of narrow gauge and constructed for military purposes, later to be converted to standard gauge for commercial development. The railways do not form a net, but reflect economic development in linking the rich Fez-Meknès area with the coast, and the phosphate workings and Marrakech area with the ports of Safi and Casablanca. Another line through the Taza corridor links Morocco with Algeria and a spur from it serves the Bou Arfa mining district.

There are 6,800 miles of surfaced roads, many of them of first quality and constructed during the great period of development early in the 1950's. The road network mainly serves the modern economy and is thickest in the Sebou Plain and in Atlantic Morocco. All-weather surfaced roads have been made over the passes of the Middle and High Atlas.

The bulk of Morocco's trade is with Europe, mainly France. The chief exports are the minerals: phosphates, manganese, iron ore and lead, but others of importance are barley, fruits and early vegetables. The principal imports are petroleum products, vehicles, tractors and certain foodstuffs.

17

Algeria

Algeria, under French dominion from 1830, became an independent republic in 1962.* It includes a very large part of the Sahara (about 765,000 sq. miles), but the habitable portion, northern Algeria, is quite small, being about 80,000 sq. miles. Thanks to over a century of vigorous French colonisation, Algeria is the most developed of the three Barbary states. This progress has been aided by a physique less extreme than in Morocco. Sheltered plains and valleys benefit from their proximity to the Mediterranean and high mountains are much restricted. However, the area of steppe, encouraging transhumance from the desert border, is much greater.

The marked east-west trend of the relief and the related climatic zonation gives an impress of homogeneity that detailed study belies. Indeed, within that broad framework Algeria is a country displaying the great diversity that a varying distance from sea, variation of altitude, of geology and aspect would lead one to expect. One consequence has been the lack of a natural centre and a history of numerous and varied capital cities looking either eastwards to Tunisia or westwards to Morocco. The French tended to continue an earlier Turkish tripartite division, for long administering through three *départements* based upon Constantine, Algiers and Oran.

GEOGRAPHICAL REGIONS (Fig. 35)

The Tell

This region stretches from the boundary with Morocco to the district around the port of Bougie (Bejaïa) and comprises the coastal plains and hills, the series of elongated massifs and inland plateaux forming the Tell

*In 1964, a number of French names of towns was changed. The new names are given following the more familiar ones.

Atlas, and the intermediate river valleys and basins. There is a considerable diversity of relief, geology and soils, and numerous sub-regions may be recognised, but exigencies of space will allow only samples of these to be studied here; the more important that we shall consider being the Chéliff valley, the Mitidja Plain and the Grande Kabylie or Djurdjura Mountains. The climate is characteristically Mediterranean and the climatic and geological affinities with southern France, the proximity of the coast and ports, the relative ease of movement along the valleys coupled with harsher environment and poorer facilities elsewhere made this region the principal area of French settlement and the most productive part of Algeria.

Except for the great mass of the Djurdjura, the coastal hills and Tell Atlas are of folded rocks but display great variety of character and age. They present a diversity difficult to generalise upon and only understandable in the light of the tectonic history. It is also this history that helps to explain the broken character of these folded hills and mountains giving discontinuous hill-masses and plateau formations. Aridity increases as one goes westward and this allied to the character of the soil shows a marked effect on localising settlement and cultivation, for from the Chéliff valley westwards increasing preference is shown for the alluvial fans and terraces of the valley sides, whereas the compacted alkaline alluvium of the centre of the valleys and plains bears thin crops and provides sparse pasture for sheep. Numerous small streams, many seasonal, water the lowland, but the more important parts of the Tell comprise the valleys of the Mékerra-Sig, Chéliff, Isser and Soummam. The Chéliff can trace some of its seasonal headstreams to the Saharan Atlas, but the others rise in the Tell Atlas and have shorter courses to the coast.

THE CHÉLIFF VALLEY The Chéliff, over 400 miles in length, is Algeria's longest river. Its middle and lower course forms the central part of the Tell lowland. The farthermost headstream rises in the Djebel Amour of the Saharan Atlas, but for most of the year in crossing the steppe country of the High Plateaux it is no more than a chain of marshes and muddy pools. Reinforced by other tributaries, in a series of entrenched meanders the river divides the Ouarsenis from the Plateau of Médéa. Below Dollfusville it swings to the west, flowing for some 145 miles parallel with the Mediterranean in a depression, formerly an arm of the sea, between the coastal hills and the Tell Atlas. This provides a natural

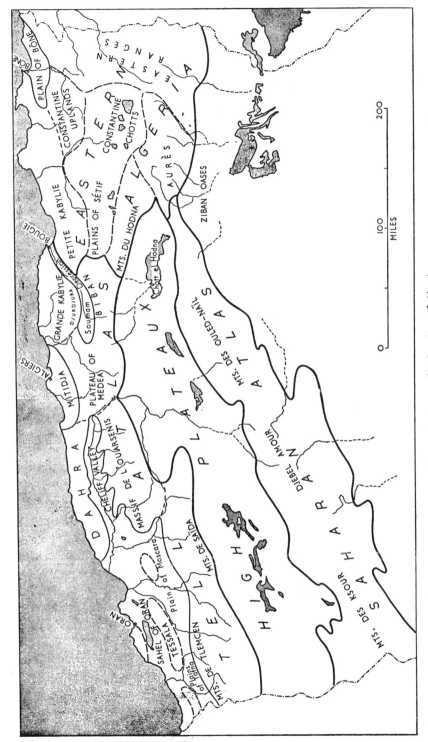

Figure 35 *Geographical regions of Algeria*

route westwards; the principal east-west roads and railways follow the valley and pass through the busy local market towns of Relizane (Ighil Izane), Orléansville (El Asnam) and Affreville-Miliana (Khemis Miliana), with their brick and tile works, flour mills and cooperies.

The valley, being on the lee side of the coastal ranges, experiences a low rainfall together with intensive evaporation, for the enclosed valley becomes uncomfortably hot in summer (Orléansville 16·3 inches per annum, mean daily max. July and August 99°F). In addition to tree crops such as olives, figs and apricots, vines and cereals are the main crops grown. The vineyards were almost entirely developed by the French settlers, who found that the vine, not needing irrigation, was well suited to the sandy soils. There is a marked difference in the character of the farms and husbandry of the two peoples. The farms of French origin, larger and on the better land, consist of modern buildings and well-tended stone-walled fields, each of several acres; whereas the native peoples cling to traditional and primitive ways of farming, living in tightly clustered low stone hovels, their surrounding stony fields, often no more than 50 yards square, being contained within impenetrable hedges of cactus and prickly pear. Nondescript herds of goats and often sheep also browse the maquis-covered hill-slopes in the charge of numerous barefooted ragged children. Many of the French farms taken over by the Algerian government in 1963 are being worked as co-operatives, while some of the smaller ones have been divided among the Algerian peasantry.

The valley varies between 10 and 20 miles in width and cultivation extends to, but not up, the hillsides which are usually maquis-covered or wooded, with occasional gashes of bare red-brown rock. A number of small irrigation and hydro-electric projects has been completed in recent years, including the tapping of underground water supplies and dam construction near Orléansville and near Dollfusville.

THE SAHEL OF ALGIERS AND MITIDJA The most populous and developed part of the Tell is the Mitidja and Sahel of Algiers. This was the scene of early French colonisation and over a century immense changes have been wrought. The Sahel is a region of low hills lying between the sea and the Mitidja Plain, mainly on the west of Algiers. The hills are of soft Pliocene limestones and rest on marly clays, so giving rise to springs and helping to form an attractive undulating green countryside. The Mitidja Plain, some 60 miles long by about 12 miles broad, slopes gently from the Blida Mountains of the Tell Atlas down to the Sahel and the sea. The plain is fairly level, although in fact it comprises an integration of many alluvial cones created by the swift seasonal Atlas streams infilling a local syncline. Originally much of the Mitidja was marshy and malarial, but nearly all has now been reclaimed and converted into fertile vineyards, orange groves, orchards and fields of tobacco, early vegetables and flowers for scent making. The whole area became the show-piece of French colonisation. Much of the land became consolidated into large holdings. Well-appointed houses and farm buildings are centrally situated and stand amid orderly fields, groves or vineyards each averaging 4 to 5 acres, surrounded and protected by hedges of young conifers. Native farms and holdings, mainly more peripheral, appear more haphazard with cereals and vegetables growing beneath the fruit and olive trees. The whole Algiers Plain is densely peopled; in addition to the capital and chief port it includes a number of local market and manufacturing towns such as Blida, Boufarik and Maison Carrée, where the French imprint of rectangular street plan, solid buff-coloured houses with painted wooden shutters and iron balconies creates a European quarter distinct from the poorer and more closely knit native sector. Before the granting of independence a third of these towns' populations was French, but most of the French returned to France at considerable loss when Algeria became independent. These towns contain brick and tile works, elevators and flour mills, cooperies, tanneries, scent distilleries and, at Maison Carrée, chemical works and an oil refinery.

GRANDE KABYLIE East of the Algiers Plain lies another most distinctive sub-region of the Tell. This is the highland region known as the Grande Kabylie and from some points of view might equally be included in eastern Algeria. On the north it is bounded by the Mediterranean and on the south and east by the easternmost part of the Oran-Bougie depression. The core of the upland is of Archaean and Pre-Cambrian rocks (mainly schists and gneisses) flanked on the northeast and south by Jurassic, Cretaceous and younger limestone, sandstone and clays. The young limestones and sandstones to the south form the Djebel Djurdjura, the most imposing and impressive range in Algeria. It extends some 40 miles east-west in a double chain of serrated crests, mostly over 6,000 feet high. The landscape is harsh with scree-girt ridges scored by the deep gorges of swirling streams. The higher areas receive over 60 inches of rainfall and snow lies on these parts from November to the end of May. Much of this heavy precipitation drains northward into the Oued Sebaou, creating a series of deep gorge-like valleys separated by narrow ridges which carry roads, tracks and villages.

Central Kabylie consisting of the older rocks carries a high population. In contrast to the many bare slopes of the younger limestones, here slopes are clothed with oaks, ash, olives and figs (up to about 2,600 feet), the ground beneath being worked in small plots by hand tools and primitive ploughs. Numerous villages cluster tightly on the ridge-tops between 2,000 and 4,000 feet. The Grande Kabylie is one of the most densely peopled areas in Algeria, much of it carrying over 600 people per sq. mile, generally living in great poverty. Such a population cannot be supported solely by the primitive farming and most families have one or two members away in city or town employment, or in France, who send remittances home. Here in this mountain fastness, sheltered from external influences, Berber race, language and customs survive in their purest forms. The mountain strongholds have proved difficult to subdue; they have withstood Romans, Arabs and Turks. The French only pacified Kabylie after a full campaign and the establishment of Fort National to control it in 1857. In the 1954–62 rebellion, in order to control the area which harboured nationalist rebels, there were wholesale removals of population by the French to newly sited villages in the foothills.

The High Plateaux

South of the Tell Atlas and extending from the Moulouya river in the west to the saline Chott el Hodna in the east is the distinctive region of upland steppes usually designated the High Plateaux. Their southern boundary is formed by the Saharan Atlas which separate them from the Sahara. The High Plateaux offer abrupt contrasts with the fertile and populous Tell. Averaging rather more than 3,000 feet in height, the undulating landscape is open and for most of the year drab. The low rainfall (8–12 inches) and its highly seasonal incidence, insufficient for trees and shrubs, supports *sparte* and alfa grasses, tufted herbs and dwarf plants which develop with the scanty winter rainfall and remain green for no more than the first month of the seven-month dry season. Sheep roam widely over the steppe, grazing on the dried-up grasses and woody, salty plants. As summer advances they move northward accompanied by their nomadic masters along recognised sheep walks to the greener pastures of the Tell Atlas.

An important activity of many members of the tribes engaged in this seasonal migration across the steppes with their flocks and camel herds is the collection of alfa leaves—esparto grass—which forms an important export of Algeria and is used for making high-quality paper. Locally it is of importance for the manufacture of rope, mats and baskets. The grass is extremely resistant to drought and grows in large tufts up to 3 feet high. It is harvested by pulling after being wound round short sticks, and provides a lucrative seasonal occupation for the whole family. Since the alfa grass is a defence against soil erosion, the amount to be harvested each year is determined by the authorities and the grass rights are sold to companies who establish posts where camel loads can be weighed, stacked and dried before large lorries and trailers start the journey to the coast. Ruins of old irrigation works and buildings around the Chott el Hodna are a reminder that in the more pluvial past, and perhaps up to the Middle Ages, much of this land was more productive; grain crops and olives certainly were grown in Roman times. Today wells and small irrigation works here and at the Chott Chergui provide water for stock.

The Saharan Atlas

These ranges, attaining over 6,000 feet, are slightly better watered than the High Plateaux and offer woodland, thickets and pasture on their slopes. Probably of greater significance are the water-courses on the southern side which lose themselves in the desert fringe, but supply the wells of numerous oases stretching along the desert edge (Fig. 35). Notable in this piedmont zone are the fifty-nine Ziban oases of which Biskra, with its 25,000 population and 150,000 palms, is the chief. This group of oases extending 30 miles west and 60 miles east of Biskra contains more than a million palm trees and over half a million other fruit trees. Farther west are the oasis towns of Laghouat, Figuig and Colomb-Béchar (Béchar), each with several thousand palms. Other fruit trees, vines, vegetables and cereals are grown beneath the palms.

Eastern Algeria

Eastern Algeria differs from the western two-thirds of the country in being a complex upland displaying deeply dissected mountain knots and chains interspersed with limited plateaux and basins, some the beds of former lakes. Greater precipitation on the mountains, especially near the coast, allows considerable forest cover, mainly cork oak and cedar. Farther inland in the enclosed plains, such as the Constantine Chotts, it is enough to permit some cereal cultivation and the sustenance of thousands of sheep. The rainfall is marginal for cereals and in poor years wheat may be only 8 inches high; nevertheless, by sickle and by hand every ear is harvested by the Arabs.

French colonisation has transformed favoured parts of the coast, such as the Plain of Bône (about the size of the Mitidja), where former malarial marshes and lakes have been contained and reduced and in the fertile soils the vine, tobacco, vegetables and citrus fruits are grown. Inland the population is more sparse and the way of life harder. Cereals are the principal arable crops, mainly native grown with emphasis on olive, figs and other tree fruits on the higher land. The salt marshes around the Constantine Chotts offer good rough grazing over which there are seasonal migrations from spring to autumn of the flocks and herds of Arab tribes from the desert, mainly the Arab Cheraga and Arab Gheraba from the Touggourt district (Fig. 36). From the chotts many of the younger Arabs temporarily leave their families for harvest work (formerly on European farms) and use their camels to convey grain to market.

These migrations skirt the Aurès Massif, mainly the home of the Chaouia people. This deeply ravined mountain mass with peaks over 7,000 feet is a formidable and virtually impregnable region where, like the Djurdjura, Berber ways and language have been preserved. The mountains have proved a refuge and bulwark against both Arab and French invaders. Even today communication within the mountain mass is very difficult and only one indifferent road passes through it (mules have a longer expectation of life than cars in the Aurès). But despite their elevation, and because of the southerly position of the mountains, rainfall is nowhere abundant. Probably it is over 20 inches in the north but only half that on the Saharan fringe. Climate and physique prevent a purely sedentary way of life. In the deep valleys vines, fruit trees, water melons and cereals are grown, sometimes on small irrigated terraces, and on the hillside small irregularly shaped fields are sown to oats, barley and beans, while olives, apricots and figs are valuable tree crops. By the end of July figs and apricots have been gathered and dried in the sun and cereals harvested, local pasture has become exhausted and a wholesale northerly movement of communities to high mountain pastures or across the Chott plateaux begins. By October the return south commences, followed in November by a lesser southerly movement to the oases belt around Biskra to gather dates from the few palms that each family likes to possess.

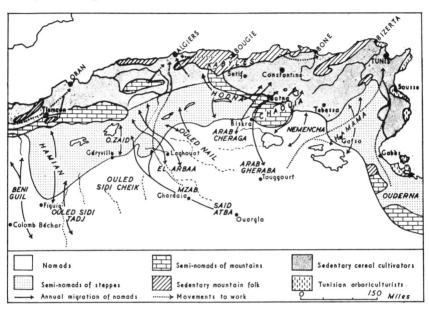

Figure 36 *Ways of life in Algeria and the northern Sahara* (after Despois)

While the Chaouia are away most houses are closed and their contents stored in the village strong house or *guelaa*.

This is the architectural *pièce de résistance* of Barbary. Built of mud, stone and date palm timbers, it is often three or four storeys high and occupies the most easily defended position in or near the village. Many a *guelaa* is only accessible by scrambling up the face of a cliff or by a really hazardous ascent of a rope ladder; for the store house it should be noted becomes the village castle in time of trouble. In this semi-arid country there are many hungry people who find it hard to resist the temptation of plundering the *guelaa* of an almost deserted village, and usually they are very well worth plundering. For instance the one at Baniane in the Oued el Abiod has 55 separate chambers, approximately one for each family in the village; in these chambers are stored the year's crop of fruit and grain, and in addition such household goods e.g. carpets, that cannot conveniently be taken to the summer pastures.[2]

Defence plays a large part in the character and siting of the Berber mountain villages. Tightly knit, they perch on scarcely accessible slopes or ridges, the houses built of mud, stone or palm timber rising in tiers as in the High Atlas. Deep conservatism met French attempts to improve conditions and progress has been slow. On the lower land surrounding the mountains numerous Roman ruins including those of the spacious colonnades and elegant baths of Timgad, once headquarters of the Third Legion, remind one of the more bountiful days gone by.

THE ECONOMY

Most of Algeria is of limited value for agriculture, and moderately endowed with mineral wealth. Most of the agricultural wealth of the republic is derived from the limited area of fertile valleys and basins near the coast that have been developed by Europeans throughout the past century. Elsewhere, the mountains and steppes offer forests and grazing rather than agricultural opportunity, and with subsistence cultivation and herding the majority of the Arab and Berber population is poor. The dual division of the economy into modern and traditional sectors, discussed under Morocco, is thus also apparent in Algeria. At the time of writing Algeria's economy is weak and uncertain. From 1954 to 1962 armed rebellion of Moslems against the French gradually brought the economy to a standstill. With the granting of independence tremendous problems faced the new administration. Not only had physical damage to be made good but the emigration, at great loss to themselves, of three-quarters of the Europeans dealt a crippling blow to the newly created republic. The thousands who departed, mostly back to France, were farmers, engineers, industrialists, managers, accountants, teachers: the sort of people that no young developing country could afford to lose. Land abandoned by Europeans totalled almost 2,500,000 acres or nearly 40 per cent of European holdings; subsequently the remainder of these holdings was expropriated by the state. Also abandoned were several hundred industrial undertakings. Instead of a million Europeans, less than 100,000 remain. Attempts to continue large-scale capitalised commercial production were made by taking over abandoned and expropriated farms as state farms and not dividing them into peasant plots. They were run by workers' committees; similarly workers' committees took over abandoned factories. Committees composed of illiterate peasants without technical or managerial training found it very difficult to keep farms running smoothly and levels of husbandry and agricultural production have fallen.

Farming

Much that has been said about the character of European and Moroccan agriculture also applies to Algeria except that restrictions on European land-holding were lighter than in Morocco and a third of land under cultivation was formerly owned by Europeans. Prior to the rebellion (1954) 22,000 European farmers owned 5·9 million acres, whereas 6·3 million Moslem farmers shared 11·9 million acres, many of their holdings being fragmented and too small to be viable. Some 600,000 peasants were landless and over 40% of the rural population was either un- or under-employed. By 1963 it was estimated that 800,000 were totally unemployed. Most agricultural exports were derived from the European holdings. Cereals are the chief crop of Algeria (wheat, barley and oats), the best coming from the Tell and the high plains of Constantine around Sétif, Constantine and Guelma. The vine is the principal commercial fruit grown and is generally confined to within 60 miles of the coast. Viticulture is related to European settlement and is most important in the Oran area. France is the chief market for the wine which is often blended with the French *vin ordinaire*. However, the future of viticulture in Algeria is uncertain, with the departure of the French and the imposition by France of tariffs on imported wines. The olive is widespread and among the principal fruits grown are oranges, figs, apricots and dates. The mildness of the winter along the coast has led to the growing of early vegetables and their export to Europe. Tobacco is another important crop especially in the east of Algeria and is mainly in the hands of native Algerian farmers. The area under irrigated crops is just under 400,000 acres and is unlikely to expand by any marked amount owing to the paucity of the water resources.

Stock rearing is an important occupation suited to the considerable areas of steppe and seasonal pasture. There are over 5 million sheep spread widely between the sea and the semi-arid desert edge. There is a movement northwards with the pasture from the desert edge in early summer and many of these sheep are sold in the autumn to farmers (formerly European) in the Tell for fattening before export. Algerian wool is coarse and uneven in length; the clip is small and is mainly used within Algeria. Both meat and wool could be improved with the betterment of breeds and greater care of the stock.

The bulk of Algerian cattle is found in the Tell, where water and grass are available. Pastures, however, are generally poor during the summer and few fodder crops are available. Most of the cattle are owned by native Algerians who are less attentive to their animals than Europeans and the animals are considered inferior, both in size and meat quality, to European breeds. Eastern Algeria, where the rainfall is better, carries most stock and the chief cattle-breeding areas are the plains of Constantine and Guelma. Algerian cattle are hardy and strong and are much used for draught purposes as well as for meat and milk. Another most useful animal in Algeria and one needing little attention is the goat; there are 2 million in the country, practically all native-owned and for the most part running wild, grazing on whatever they can find. The hair, milk, meat and skin are all used, the skins being exported to France, many for glove making.

Mining (Fig. 37)

Algeria possesses valuable mineral resources, the most important being phosphate, iron ore and mineral oil. The phosphate workings at Kouif, near Tébessa, produce annually half a million tons, most of which is exported. The iron ore is phosphor-free with a high iron content and suitable for high-grade steel making. It is mined beside the Tébessa— Souk Ahras railway near the Tunisian border and in the Tell, especially in the Chéliff valley, from a long band of Mesozoic limestone paralleling the coast. Beni Saf just west of Oran is a specialist iron-ore port, but most Algerian ports export some ore, and the great red piles of ore at the docks awaiting shipment are a most striking sight. Until Algeria's own iron and steel plant is completed all the ore is exported (av. 3 million tons per annum), mainly to Great Britain and Germany. Zinc and lead ores are present and are worked from a number of small mines mainly in moun-tainous eastern Algeria.

There is a small coal field at Kenadsa about 20 miles west of Colomb Béchar. Production at 120,000 tons is insufficient for Algeria's needs and nearly three times as much is imported. The discovery of oil and natural gas in the Algerian Sahara (p. 243) is of great significance, not only in providing considerable royalty income but also new sources of cheap power for future industrial development, and pipelines carrying natural gas have been completed from the main fields around Hassi R'Mel to Oran, Algiers and Arzew, whence exports to Britain are made.

Manufacturing Industry

Up to World War II little industrial development was encouraged in Algeria, for France monopolised 90 per cent of the trade in manufactured goods and regarded Algeria as a market and outlet for French products. In return, Algerian agricultural products and minerals were sent to France. This policy channelled most capital and skill into agriculture and mining. In the last war the isolation of North Africa from France gave an impetus to the rise of varied industries, many of which have since continued. The limited character of supplies of fuel and energy has also been a further hindrance to industrial development but this situation may change with the availability of oil and natural gas. The republic is essentially agricultural and the principal industries, expropriated from the French, are related to the agricultural economy. They are concerned with food processing, flour milling, fish canning, wine and olive-oil manufacture, the preserving of fruit and vegetables, tobacco, leather and textile manufacture. Other industries produce fertilisers, soaps, matches, glass, cement.

Not unexpectedly most of these industries are located within the Tell, and particularly in the three major port areas: Algiers, Oran and Bône. All the major towns and ports have modern flour mills and the major ports and some smaller ones such as Beni Saf and Nemours have fish-curing and -canning factories dealing mainly with sardines, anchovies and mackerel. Fruit and vegetable canning takes place at Orléansville, Relizane and near Philippeville (Skikda). Fertiliser factories at Oran, Maison Carrée (near Algiers) and Bône (Annaba) make mainly super-phosphates from local phosphates, and a wide development of the chemical industry may follow the establishment of the oil refinery at Maison Carrée. Native craftsmen industries have become much reduced with the import of cheap manufactured goods and although still carried on throughout Algeria, only the manufacture of carpets and leather goods is important.

The raising of the standard of living in Algeria clearly calls for more industrial development as well as an improvement in agriculture. Obstacles to be overcome were well demonstrated in the early period after independence when French firms were taken over by workers' committees and in the chaos that followed industrial production fell by as much as 50 per cent. They include lack of skilled and semi-skilled labour (most of the Moslem population is illiterate), lack of capital, lack of a market (the purchasing power of the population is very small) and (formerly) lack of fuel and power resources. With growing oil and natural gas supplies, oil royalties, stabilisation of the new régime and help from France, these difficulties will slowly be surmounted. Plans for industrial development formulated in the Constantine Plan of 1958 were being implemented only slowly after independence, for foreign investment (apart from French aid) became insignificant until Russian credits were made available from 1963. These plans include the building of an iron and steel works at Bône (not far from Ouenza iron-ore mine): this is expected to stimulate in the area the establishment of other industries dependent on its products. Around Oran is developing a chemical centre based upon the oil and natural gas piped from the Sahara, while a range of consumer goods industries is planned for Algiers where a beginning has been made by more than doubling the electrical power-plant capacity. These major measures will reinforce the existing centres of industry and will attract more population to them. Many Algerians point out that the greatest poverty lies in the rural areas and further benefits might accrue if new industry could be more widely disseminated. Substantial though these measures will be, it is hard to see how living standards can be raised so long as the present high population increase goes unchecked.

POPULATION

Indigenous peoples increased rapidly under French rule, from about 2 million in 1830 to 9·2 million in 1958. European settlers (mainly French) totalled about 1 million in 1954, but after that the number diminished as armed rebellion flared up. In 1964 it was estimated that Europeans numbered less than 100,000. The bulk of the population (at least 80 per cent) lives in the Tell but exact distribution can no longer be shown owing to large-scale movements and resettlement of Moslem population by the French authorities during the rebellion. Two million Moslems (24 per cent of Moslem population) were moved, many of them from less accessible mountainous areas which harboured the rebels. Often their houses were bulldozed and demolished and with their beasts and movable possessions some were installed in foothill villages and others farther away, sometimes in a newly created village. Generally they were moved to existing settlements, many of which doubled or trebled their numbers before the end of the rebellion.

The most densely peopled parts of the Tell coincide with areas of heavy rainfall, mainly mountainous and in the east: Grande Kabylie and Petite Kabylie; and those parts most easy of access from the coast: the Mitidja, the Plains of Bône and Philippeville. Native Algerians whether of Arab or Berber stock have been slow to become town dwellers, although urbanisation of the population is now speeding up. The population as a whole is about 25 per cent urban, but some 70 per cent of the European population in 1960 was urban.

With improving medical care of the Moslem population the death rate has been reduced considerably in the last 20 years, but birth rates remain among the highest in the world: 1959 Moslem crude birthrate 47, European crude birth rate 21, per 1,000 of the population; Moslem crude death rate 11, European crude death rate 9, per 1,000 of the population. As a consequence, if this rate of increase (of over 3 per cent per annum) continues, the Moslem population may double itself within the next 20 years. The 11 million Algerians of today are expected to increase to 15·5 million by 1975, thus presenting appalling social and economic problems to the government. Already the rapid population increase has contributed to unemployment problems in town and country, to movement from country to town in search of work and to political unrest.

SETTLEMENT

The way of life influences the styles of housing. In the Sahara and High Plateaux, the scantily populated districts used by pastoral nomads, the tent made of material woven from wool, goats' hair and esparto grass is used. In the Tell the semi-nomad owns fields as well as herds, and the stone or clay hut (or *gourbi*) is common. It stands alone near the fields and is used only while crops are sown or reaped. More permanent native dwellings are of mud-and-clay-plastered sticks, flat-topped, huddled together with ragged vegetable gardens alongside, the whole often enclosed by a thick hedge of prickly pear. In the hills the clay- and stone-walled houses occupy defensive sites, often terraced. Houses of European style have increased greatly in number but generally are still confined to the principal towns.

Towns

ALGIERS (pop. 884,000) is the capital, seat of government and principal port of the republic. The original Turkish town with its kasba grew up on an easily defended rocky area at the northern end of an east-facing bay; for long it harboured the Barbary corsairs. Today the kasba is a maze of dark alleys, huddled houses with barred windows, noisy crowds and malodorous smells. More modern buildings spill down in pink and white cubes into the modern town and port. French building has extended the town for six miles around the bay. Long concrete jetties and moles protect the harbour in which large wharfs, quays and basins have been developed as the port has expanded. The trade of the port, mainly with Marseilles, amounts to over 3 million tons a year. Principal exports are wine, cereals, olive oil, esparto grass, iron ore and phosphates; the main imports are manufactured goods, chemicals, coal and coke. The city is also the leading industrial centre, with factories making chemicals, soaps, cigarettes, barrels and tin cans for the preserving industry. There are flour mills, breweries, cement works and a fertiliser factory.

ORAN (pop. 390,000) The long, narrow and discontinuous character of the Tell helps to account for the growth of a number of ports each with a fairly restricted hinterland; among them is Oran, the second port and second city of Algeria. Its harbour is entirely artificial, being sheltered by concrete jetties, and just to the west is the naval base of Mers el Kebir, a former pirate stronghold. Oran is second only to Algiers as an industrial centre, having large fish canneries, flour mills, brick works, cement and lime works, chemical and tobacco factories.

CONSTANTINE (pop. 220,000), the third largest city, is 40 miles from the coast at Philippeville. The town has grown up on a rocky calcareous plateau, with gorges on three sides carved by the great loop of the River Rummel. It is a natural fortress. The newer suburbs of the town with regular street patterns lie to the south-west. In the old town the native quarter has been little disturbed; its tortuous narrow streets are frequently devoted to a particular trade such as tanning or shoe making, with oriental architecture and houses almost meeting overhead. Native industries, mainly the manufacture of leather and woollen goods, have remained important in the city, where there are also factories producing flour, tobacco, corks, bricks and cement.

BÔNE (Annaba, pop. 164,000) is eastern Algeria's largest port and a main industrial centre. The original foundation was probably Roman; it fell to the Moslem invaders in A.D. 697 and changed hands several times before coming under the beys of Tunis, who lost it to the French in 1832. The

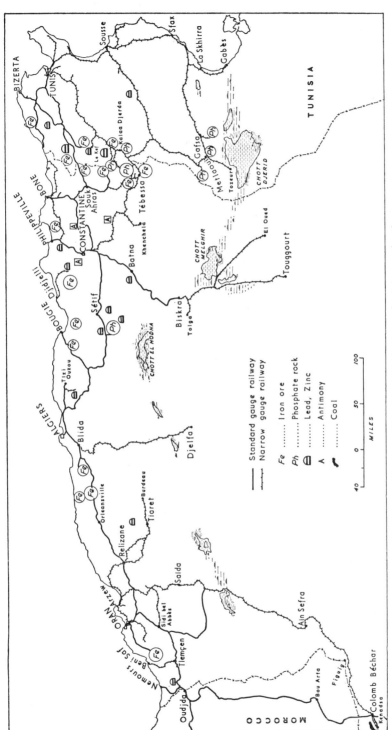

Figure 37 *Algeria and Tunisia*: distribution of mining and railways

development of the port owes much to the phosphate and later the iron-ore workings inland, near Tébessa. Bône is a growing industrial centre with cork, tobacco and chemical factories, flour mills, fish canneries, railway workshops and general engineering. The planned oil refinery and iron-and-steel plant will add considerably to this industrial stature.

COMMUNICATIONS

The east-west trend of the relief and the favourable character of the coastal lowlands for settlement and agriculture are clearly revealed in the pattern of communications. There are 2,700 miles of railway, almost equally divided between standard and narrow gauge, and a rudimentary network is discernible (Fig. 37). The main line (of standard gauge) traverses the Tell from the Moroccan boundary via Algiers into Tunisia. All the other main ports are on branches from this main line. A number of lines (mainly narrow gauge) cross the High Plateaux to the edge of the Sahara. In this way Colomb-Béchar and the coal mine at Kenadsa are linked with Oran and the Saharan oasis towns of Touggourt and Biskra are linked with Philippeville, Constantine and the main line. A good road network also exists in the Tell and metalled roads now extend to the principal north Saharan oases. In its railways, roads and ports the republic has inherited a better infrastructure for economic development than most new African states, but for some time may not be in a position to take advantage of it.

18

Tunisia

Tunisia, the smallest of the three political divisions of the Maghreb, has the longest history. Her position on the threshold of the western basin of the Mediterranean and but 90 miles from Sicily led to early colonisation first by the Phoenicians, who founded Carthage near the site of modern Tunis, and then by the Romans who gave it the name of Africa, and held it with some interruptions until the Arab invasions of the seventh century. Arab and Berber dynasties held the country until the conquest by the Turks in the sixteenth century. From this evolved an element of independence, and hereditary sovereignty and an economy largely based upon piracy, which exploited to the full the position commanding the narrows of the Mediterranean. During the nineteenth century the French tended to regard Tunisia as a natural extension of Algeria. They viewed unfavourably the growing predominance and influence of Italians in commerce and industry and in 1881 entered Tunisia and forced the bey to accept the French Protectorate. Independence was granted Tunisia in 1956, and the young republic faces severe social and economic problems for many years.

GEOGRAPHICAL REGIONS

Broadly speaking, western Tunisia is high (with the highest land in the north-west) and eastern (or maritime) Tunisia is low. The annual rainfall, here the most significant element in the climate, is highest in the north (over 40 inches) but diminishes to as little as 5 inches in the south. The interplay of these factors permits a division of Tunisia into three major parts: northern, central and southern (or Saharan), each including a number of subdivisions (Fig. 38).

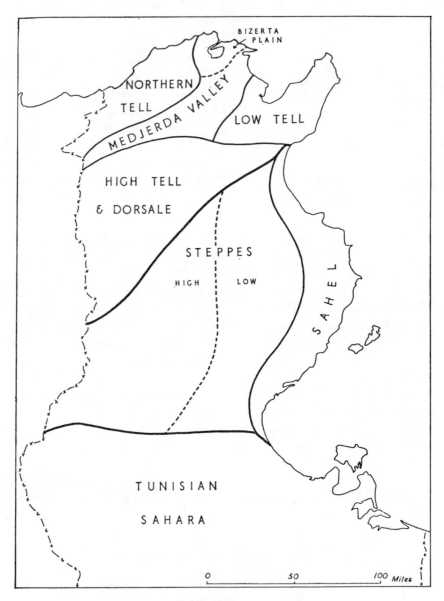

Figure 38 *Geographical regions of Tunisia*

Northern Tunisia

This comprises a sequence of ridges and valleys generally trending to the north-north-east. The valley of the River Medjerda provides a series of closed basins separating the steep sandstone ranges of the north coast from the domes and basins of the sandstone and limestone High Tell and Dorsale. The northern coastal hills, the Monts de la Medjerda, with their sandstone-derived soils and heavy winter rain, support dense forests of cork and Portuguese oaks. In the Kroumirie ranges these mountains reach the sea in rugged cliffs. Debarked cork oak trees and stacks of cork awaiting collection are often the only evidence of man for many miles. Outside the forests in clearings and depressions the reliable rainfall favours cultivation and a sedentary way of life. Cereals, particularly barley, are the main crops; some cattle and goats are kept. The population is sparse: hamlets and villages, many on cleared slopes encircled by brushwood and prickly pear hedges, are few and far between.

THE VALLEY OF THE RIVER MEDJERDA which drains much of the High Plains of Constantine in Algeria is divided by rocky narrows into a succession of enclosed plains, formerly old lake basins now infilled and offering rich alluvial soil to the agriculturalist. These well-watered dark soils yield heavy cereal crops and formerly much of the middle Medjerda valley was farmed by European colonists. These farms have been relinquished or expropriated and are now run as co-operatives. The strongly seasonal character of the rainfall renders the Medjerda liable to dangerous flooding, occasionally submerging the whole flood plain between Tebourba and the coast and limiting settlement sites to higher ground. The malarial character of the delta (now improved) was an additional limitation to settlement. Stock rearing supplements grain growing and a number of small towns such as Souk el Arba ('market four', i.e. Wednesday), Beja and Medjez-el-Bab have become local market and administrative centres. North-west of the delta is the low-lying Plain of Bizerta. Well farmed by the French, this forms good agricultural land surrounding the lakes of Bizerta and Garait Achkel. These constituted a basin of internal drainage but have since been flooded by the sea. This has helped to make Bizerta a sheltered and powerful naval base on a North African shore which generally lacks good harbours.

THE HIGH TELL AND DORSALE represent the easternmost extension of the Saharan Atlas, of which the prevailing structure of domes and basins is reminiscent. Most of the area is above 2,000 feet and among the chain of heights forming the Zeugitane Mountains or Dorsale is Djebel Chambi (5,065 feet), the highest peak in Tunisia. The south-west to north-east trend is dominant and the Eocene and Cretaceous limestones and sandstones are in complex structures of faulted and truncated synclines and anticlines giving broken relief of mountain-masses separated by valleys and basins, many the sites of former lakes. The better-watered northern parts support a sedentary farming population: nowadays in the drier south the tent is slowly giving way to the hut. The old settlements perch on defensive hill sites but the newer villages, as a result of security under French rule, have more varied locations. Cereals and olives are the major cultivations, sheep and goats the principal stock.

THE LOW TELL AND PLAIN OF TUNIS girt by hills are climatically somewhat distinctive. The rainfall (Tunis 17 inches) is akin to that of the Sahel to the south and is considerably less than on the north coast (Bizerta 25 inches). Evaporation is high and the region is open to southerly winds and subjected to the sirocco. The enclosed lowland and Cap Bon Peninsula is little affected by the proximity of the sea. Here cereals play a lesser part in the farming but the vine is characteristic; olives also are of some importance and other crops are vegetables, citrus fruits and tobacco.

Central Tunisia

South of the Dorsale in the TUNISIAN STEPPES the relief is more subdued. The pattern of north-east trending discontinuous upland plains persists but the lowland is more extensive. The steppe character of the natural vegetation results from the dry climate: rainfall decreases rapidly from north to south ranging from about 15 to 8 inches and alfa grass and scrub of jujube trees become dominant, but to the south the terrain becomes increasingly barren. In the west altitude varies from 2,300 to 1,000 feet and this area constitutes the High Steppe, contrasting with the Low Steppes to the east, hummocky distributary plains that descend to the coast plain. Camel- and sheep-owning nomads traditionally occupy these steppes but here and there meagre harvests of cereals are produced in the depressions, while nearer the coast olives are grown. Generally, however, cereal growing here requires irrigation. Abundant remains of

Roman irrigation works and buildings suggest at one time a denser population, but one probably based on olive cultivation rather than cereals. The phosphate deposits in the hills around Gafsa provide the only real wealth of the region.

THE SAHEL is no more than the coastal termination of the steppes where the solid rock is masked by young and recent deposits, generally of a sandy character. The sandy soil retains moisture and subsoil water is available. The low rainfall is also supplemented by copious dew and it is possible for cereals to be grown without irrigation. In the main, however, it is the olive that has transformed this region. The Sahel extends from Hammamet to just south of Sfax and inland some 25 miles to the zone of sebkhas or saltmarshes into which the intermittent drainage of the Steppes occasionally finds its way. The Sahel contrasts with the Steppes in that it contains a large population, including a number of ancient towns such as Sousse, Sfax, Monastir and Moknine, where gardens and cornfields have been tilled since the days of Carthage. The real development of this coastal plain came with the granting of large areas to French Land Companies near the end of the last century. Viticulture was less successful than in the north but the olive, able to resist moderate drought, proved eminently suitable without irrigation and thousands of acres were planted. Today there are over 8 million trees in the Sahel of Sousse and over 6 million in the Sahel of Sfax: thousands of acres of semi-arid land under widely spaced, evenly planted olive trees (Plate 1B). This coast bulges between the broad sweeps of the Gulfs of Hammamet and Gabès where long lines of dunes enclose lagoons and sebkhas. Here and there. as at Monastir, accumulations of sand have joined islands to the mainland, The sea off this east coast is very shallow and fishing is a major activity.

Southern Tunisia

The southern termination of the Tunisian Steppes is in the east-west trending Djebel Cherb. At their foot on the southern side is a number of extensive muddy, saline depressions, part of the group of chotts extending from near Biskra in Algeria to Gabès. They comprise the Chott el Rharsa in the west (69 feet below sea-level), the Chott Djerib (52 feet below sea-level) and the Chott el Fedjadj. They probably represent a foundered dome of which Djebel Cherb and Djebel Tebaga in the south are the remaining limbs. On the higher land between them and around their shores are valuable groves of date-palms, the irrigation wells depending upon the water received by the limestone hills to the north. In the Kriz-Tozeur district between the Chotts Rharsa and Djerid are a number of oasis settlements and nearly a million date-palms. Both here and in the Kebili district south-east of the Chott el Djerid, where there are 500,000 palms, screens are erected to halt encroaching sand dunes of the Grand Erg Oriental to the west.

South of the chotts desert conditions increase and the relief and structure are Saharan: no longer are there folded strata, but plateaux and tablelands here and there eroded and fretted into isolated hills. Rainfall over most of the area is scanty and unreliable, averaging 6 to 8 inches along the coastal margin and rising to 10 inches on the Monts des Ksour (2,000 feet) some 30 miles inland, but elsewhere being below 5 inches. The coast is fringed with lagoons and sebkhas and the gravelly coastal plain, the Jeffara—throughout the centuries a major highway into the Maghreb—is sparsely settled, mainly along the coast itself. There are also a few oases along a spring line at the foot of the Monts des Ksour escarpment. These hills, being slightly better watered, permit pockets of sedentary cultivation but, like the western oued-seamed dip slope descending to the Grand Erg Oriental, much of the land provides scrubby pasture for the camels and goats of nomads.

ECONOMY

Tunisia is not a potentially rich country. Her physical resources are modest and the per capita income is very low. The pattern already noticed in the other parts of the Maghreb of traditional and capitalist sectors of the economy is also evident in Tunisia. Three-quarters of the population find a precarious living in time-honoured fashion, consuming most of what they produce, bartering a small proportion but rarely engaging in money transactions. Agriculture and handicrafts are the mainstays of the economy. Not all Tunisians are subsistence farmers but the majority of large modern farms until 1964 were in the hands of, or were created by, Europeans. As Europeans have left Tunisia some of these large farms have been broken up but others have become state owned and worked on co-operative lines. Of the 1,250,000 acres owned by Europeans in 1955 about 500,000 acres had been taken over by 1964 and were worked by Tunisian smallholders. The remaining land owned by foreigners (mainly French, but some Italians and Maltese) was expropriated in 1964. These large farms using modern methods (and admittedly holding some of the best agricultural land) produce almost as much grain as the vast mass of peasantry. Viticulture (about 65,000 acres) localised in the Plain of Tunis and Grombalia was almost entirely in the hands of French and Italian settlers but most of the republic's 25 million olive trees belonged to native Tunisians. The more orderly attainment of independence from France in 1956 and more moderate socialist and nationalist policies prevented a mass exodus of Europeans with the attendant economic and social repercussions experienced in Algeria. Nevertheless over the years nearly half the European population has departed. Today the republic needs capital, technicians and education to further the economic development so urgently required to provide work and support for a rapidly expanding population.

Agriculture and fishing

Agriculture occupies 80 per cent of the population and is responsible for about half the national income. Much of the country, however, is agriculturally unproductive, especially in the more arid south where dry farming methods have been introduced. Unlike Morocco and Algeria there are practically no irrigation schemes in operation, merely a few local schemes supplying the Plains of Tebourba, Kasserine and others. About half the productive acreage is under cereals; wheat and barley are the principal grains, their cultivation being widespread throughout the country. Relief and rainfall help to restrict the distribution of the other principal crops into fairly distinctive zones. The vine and citrus fruit predominate around Tunis and Cape Bon, the olive in the Sahel and Low Steppe and the date in the Saharan south. Tunisia is the second largest exporter of olive oil in the world. Tunisian fisheries are also highly productive; the varying character of the coast, depth of water and presence of salt lagoons being responsible for the great variety of fish found. Over 4,000 boats are used and 14,000 men employed. Tunny, sardine, mackerel and crayfish feature largely in the catches and sponge fishing is an important specialism of the port of Sfax.

Mining and industry

Tunisia is fortunate in possessing rich and practically inexhaustible phosphate deposits as well as lesser quantities of iron, lead and zinc ores

(Fig. 37). The principal area of phosphate mining is around Gafsa (Met-laoui, Ain-Moularès and Redeyef) and exports are via Sfax. Other phosphates are mined at Kalaa-Djerda and Kalaat es Senan, a Tunisian extension of the Tébessa deposits. These are exported through Tunis. Production averages 2 million metric tons a year, most of it being ex-ported to Europe. The mining is in the hands of powerful companies deploying European, mainly French, capital.

Iron-ore is widespread in the Cretaceous and Eocene limestones and sand-stones of north and central Tunisia but the exploitation depended upon rail-way construction early this century. Nearly a million tons of haematite (50–55 per cent Fe) is produced annually, the two principal mining areas being in the Tunisian part of the Monts de Tébessa and in the Monts de Medjerda.

Lead and zinc, usually found together, are widely dispersed over north and central Tunisia. The mineral veins are usually found penetrating limestones of varying geological age. None of the occurrences is large, all the mines are small and many are disused. Some date from Carthaginian and Roman times. About 30,000 tons of lead and 6,000 tons of zinc are produced annually, nearly all for export. Other minerals found and worked in small quantities are silver, mercury, manganese, copper and iron pyrites. Oil prospecting so far has lacked success but optimism has been renewed by recent discoveries in Saharan Algeria and Libya. Pipe-lines from the Algerian field at Edjelé carry oil to the coast at La Skhirra and a small refinery operates at Bizerta.

Lack of fuel resources is a principal reason for the export of untreated minerals and a contributive reason for the very limited range of manu-facturing industry in the republic. Small plants manufacture super-phosphate at Sfax and Tunis for use by Tunisian farmers. Other industries are concerned with the processing of agricultural produce: milling, the manufacture of macaroni and spaghetti, brewing and distilling, canning and preserving (mainly tomatoes and fish), and cement manufacture. Native industries and crafts continue in their traditional form, supplying to village requirements and in some cases, for example carpets from Kairouan, being exported. These industries include the manufacture of wool, cotton and silk textiles, pottery, leather, brass and copper ware.

WAY OF LIFE (Fig. 39)

The pattern of rural life noted in the rest of the Maghreb is also exemplified in Tunisia and demonstrates a close relationship to natural conditions. A sedentary way of life in permanent houses based upon cereal and tree crops is found in the better-watered north and in the Sahel as far south as Sfax and also in the scattered oases in the south. It is the cultivation of fruit trees that imposes the more settled way of life, for they need

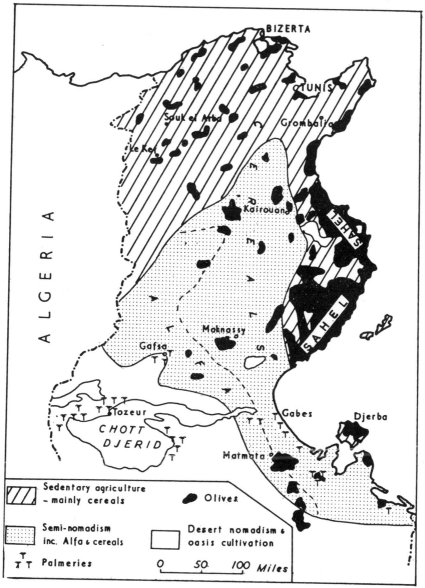

Figure 39 *Tunisia:* ways of life and land use (after K. Thompson)

constant care and attention and take several years before becoming productive. The vine, citrus fruits, the olive and date are the principal fruit crops. Cereals need little attention once they are sown and cereal farmers except at sowing and harvest time are free to wander with their flocks and adopt a semi-nomadic way of life. Generally the flocks move to the nearest uplands for the heat of the summer and return to tribal territory for the winter.

In the south this transhumance affects most of the tribe and becomes a seasonal migration. In the east of the Monts des Ksour, their lands stretching down to the dry Jeffara, live the Ouderna who number 40,000. Their lands fall into three divisions. First there is the privately owned upland where trees are grown around 'the Ksours' or fortified granaries. Then at the foot of the hills a strip a few miles wide worked on a family basis (although actually communal ground) where, fig, olive and date-palm plantations are increasing. The remaining division is on the dry Jeffara which provides scattered scrub grazing, but here and there small cultivation patches in wadis and the moister hollows.

Towards the end of October, when temperatures are lower and the figs and many of the dates have been gathered, tents are loaded on camels and then many families slowly move their flocks of sheep and herds of goats towards the communal grazing lands. This is not a general exodus for some may not depart until the end of the date harvest or even the olive harvest which occurs at the end of the year, while others may leave at the end of October and return specially for the olive harvest in December. Immediately rain falls on the Jeffara there is a rush to the moister basins which form the best cultivation patches. The first-comer chooses the best land. . . . Plowing and sowing over, the families hurry to the pastures which are now green again so that flocks can fatten and fortify themselves for the approaching dry season. In spring everyone is down on the Jeffara and the villages of the Jebel are deserted. It is the blessed season; it is mild, there is plenty of milk, and work is rare, for the men at least, because women perform all the menial tasks. By the end of April milk becomes more scarce, so the flocks are left in the hands of herdsmen while the wheat and barley is harvested—if there is any to harvest, for the yield is as uncertain as anywhere else in the south. It is trodden and winnowed on the spot, and camels take the grain and straw to the 'ksours' or to underground silos. There the families settle down temporarily, living usually in quickly constructed huts of palm fronds, cooler than black tents. The fig gathering commences in July and all hands are needed for this pleasant task.[3]

Thus the Ouderna spend only two to four months in cave dwellings or 'ksours' and the rest of the year under the tent, although their migrations are not extensive. West of the Monts des Ksour the Gherib wander with their camels and goats over the arid wastes south of the Chott el Djerid, spending no more than a few weeks in October or November at the Sabria oasis. Improved artesian supplies from new wells are gradually reducing nomadism here in the south. There is an extension of oases and the planting of more date-palms, but cultivation is still repugnant to many nomads.

POPULATION, SETTLEMENT AND COMMUNICATIONS

Population

The estimated population of Tunisia in 1963 was 4.2 million, including 60,000 French and 40,000 Italians. At the census of 1956 there were 255,000 Europeans including 180,000 French and 67,000 Italians. The loss of nearly 100,000 Europeans in five years is a serious matter for the young republic, for many who departed were officials, administrators, teachers and business men. The standard of living of the mass of the population is very low and greater development of Tunisia's resources is urgently needed both to improve those living conditions and to provide work and sustenance for the considerable natural increase to the population. The loss of key officials, technicians and entrepreneurs is therefore particularly serious.

Berber and Arab are inextricably mixed in Tunisia, indeed it is now said to be virtually impossible to distinguish between Arabised-Berber and Berberised-Arab. All profess Islam, which is recognised as the state religion. The much reduced European population is mainly French and Italian. The French included officials, professional men, merchants, employers of labour in agriculture and industry. The Italian elements on the other hand were mainly peasant stock from overcrowded Sicily and southern Italy, and had become hard-working small farmers, petty tradesmen and urban workmen, disliked by the Moslems, for they lacked the standing of the French and competed with native farmers and workmen.

The Moslem birth rate has increased during the last decade and is now about 40 per 1,000 of the population, or nearly twice the European birth rate. With improving medical facilities the death rate has fallen, now probably to less than 20 per 1,000 of the population. Such a rate of increase (around 2 per cent per annum) if maintained is sufficient to double the present population within the next thirty-five years. More than half of the Tunisians are under the age of twenty, and 42 per cent are under the age of fifteen.

Settlement

A general relationship between density of settlement and annual rainfall can be discerned, with rural densities of more than 100 per sq. mile where the annual rainfall exceeds 25 inches and below 50 per sq. mile where the annual rainfall is below 10 inches. South of the chotts the population density is probably less than 5 per sq. mile. Thus four-fifths of Tunisia's population live in the northern half of the country, or generally north of a line from the mining town of Kalaa-Djerda to Sfax. The most densely peopled areas are in the plains around Tunis and Bizerta, in the coastal bulge Sousse-Monastir-Moknine, around Sfax and the Isle of Djerba.

TUNIS, the capital, is the only real city in the republic. In 1960 it had a population of 680,000, a more than threefold increase over the last thirty years. The next largest towns are *Sfax* (65,000), *Sousse* (48,000) and *Bizerta* (47,000). Tunis is the natural market and outlet for much of the Tell, the Medjerda valley and the northern Sahel. It is built on a hilly isthmus separating the marshy Sebkret es Sedjoumi and the shallow Lac de Tunis, a lagoon which by separating the town from the sea preserved it from such a fate as that of Carthage and from the later attacks of Christian fleets. There are distinct native and European towns, the old native town being on the higher land; the modern European town, regularly laid out, has developed on the flat ground between Tunis and its lake. It was not until 1893 that the city became a port by the digging of a sea channel 6 miles long across the lake to the outport of La Goulette. Together the two constitute the republic's major port, handling annually over 2 million tons of cargo, more than half being exports—mainly wine, fruit and vegetables, iron ore and phosphates. The major imports are textiles, raw materials and fuel.

The effective development of roads and railways in Tunisia occurred after the French established the Protectorate. Tunis became the focal point for communications, but subsequently a railway line was constructed from Sfax to the phosphate deposits at Gafsa and later extended to the oasis town of Tozeur (Fig. 37). Other lines were built for the export of phosphate and ores from the Mont de Tébessa region. The railways in the north are of standard gauge and link with those of Algeria (and thence Morocco), but all the other lines are of metre gauge. There are now 1,250 miles of railway and an excellent road system.

References

1   J. Despois, *L'Afrique du Nord* (Paris, 1949), p. 258
2   G. H. T. Kimble, 'The Berbers of Eastern Algeria', *Geog. Journ.*, 97 (1941), p. 342
3   J. I. Clarke, 'Semi-nomadism in North Africa', *Econ. Geog.*, 35 (1959), p. 104

Selected Bibliography

Oxford regional economic atlas: *The Middle East and North Africa* (Oxford, 1960)
Atlas du Maroc (Rabat, 1954 *et seq.*)
Atlas d'Algérie et de Tunisie (Paris, 1933)
N. Barbour, *A survey of north-west Africa (The Maghreb)* (London, 1962)
P. Birot and J. Dresch, *La méditerranée et le moyen-orient* (Vol. I) (Paris, 1953)
J. Dresch *et al.*, *Aspects de la géomorpholgie du Maroc* (Casablanca, 1952)
J. Despois, *La Tunisie orientale: Sahel et basse steppe* (Paris, 1955)
F.A.O., *Mediterranean Development Project* (Rome, 1959)
E. Gautier, *Structure de l'Algérie* (Paris, 1922)
United Nations, *Structure and growth of selected African economies* (New York, 1958)

J. Bouquerel, 'Safi, deuxième port du Maroc', *Cahiers d'Outre Mer,* 18 (1963), 217–57
J. Houston, 'Significance of irrigation in Morocco's economic development', *Geog. Journ.*, 120 (1954), 314–28
J. Loup, 'L'Oum er R'bia', *Rev. Géog. Alpine*, 50 (1962), 519–55
M. Mikesell, 'The rôle of tribal markets in Morocco', *Geog. Rev.*, 48 (1958), 494–511
R. Murphy, 'Decline of North Africa', *Ann. Assoc. Am. Geogr.*, 41 (1951), 116–32

D. Noin, 'Aspects du sous développement au Maroc', *Ann. de Géog.*, 75 (1966), 410–31

H. Isnard, 'La vigne et colonisation en Algérie', *Ann. de Géog.*, 58 (1949), 212–19

H. Isnard, 'La répartition saisonnière . . . des pluies en Algérie', *Ann. de Géog.*, 59 (1950), 354–61

G. Taylor, 'Sea to Sahara: Settlement zones in Eastern Algeria', *Geog. Rev.*, 29 (1939), 177–95

J. I. Clarke, 'Summer nomadism in Tunisia', *Econ. Geog.*, 31 (1955), 157–67

J. Despois, 'Régions naturelles et régions humaines en Tunisie', *Ann. de Géog.*, 51 (1942), 112–28

J. Poncet, 'Quelque problèmes . . . des campagnes Tunisiennes', *Ann. de Géog.*, 60 (1951), 255–69

K. Thompson, 'Tunisia', *Focus*, 8 (1957)

PART V

The Sahara

The Sahara is the world's largest desert and gets its name from the Arab word *Sahra* (wilderness). It extends in unbroken aridity from the Atlantic to the Red Sea, at its maximum exceeding 3,000 miles; from north to south it varies between 800 and 1,000 miles. Its total area, approximately 3 million sq. miles, is nearly one quarter of the continent. This great width of desert is only breached in the east by the Nile passing waters from the equatorial highland northward to the Mediterranean. Politically the Sahara is much divided, originally by the major powers who occupied and pacified it from their colonial territories to north and south, now except for Spanish Sahara, by their independent successors: Morocco, Algeria, Libya, Chad, Niger, Mali, Mauritania and, in the east, Egypt and the Sudan.

19

The Physical Environment

The Sahara is underlain by the crystalline Basement Complex which in places outcrops at the surface. It comprises a broad platform of Archaean granites and gneisses, once folded and then denuded to peneplain form. Unevenly distributed upon this platform is a series of younger deposits many accumulated under long periods of continental conditions, such as those of Nubian Sandstone spanning the long period from the end of the Carboniferous into the Cretaceous and 1,600 feet thick in Egypt. During the Cretaceous much of the Sahara was submerged, the sea depositing wide expanses of limestone. This was followed in Tertiary times by continental conditions alternating with a number of lesser marine transgressions, particularly in the north. The vast quantities of sand in the Sahara are not of marine origin, for there has been no major marine transgression since the Eocene. The sands are more recent and represent the weathered material and river deposits of the later Tertiary and Quaternary; recent wind action has been responsible for a limited amount of re-sorting and the creation of dunes. Volcanic rocks, the remains of volcanoes associated with the ancient Saharan platform, appear in the Anti-Atlas Mountains of Morocco, in the Ahaggar of the west-central Sahara and are widespread in the Red Sea Hills of Egypt. More extensive and younger volcanic rocks, many dating from the dislocations associated with the period of Alpine mountain building to the north, help to form the high mountains across the central Sahara, notably the Ahaggar, Tibesti and the Marra Mountains of Darfur in the Sudan.

RELIEF AND LANDSCAPE (Fig. 40)

The upstanding and mountainous character of the volcanic rocks is in striking contrast with the wide plains and plateaux of strata such as the

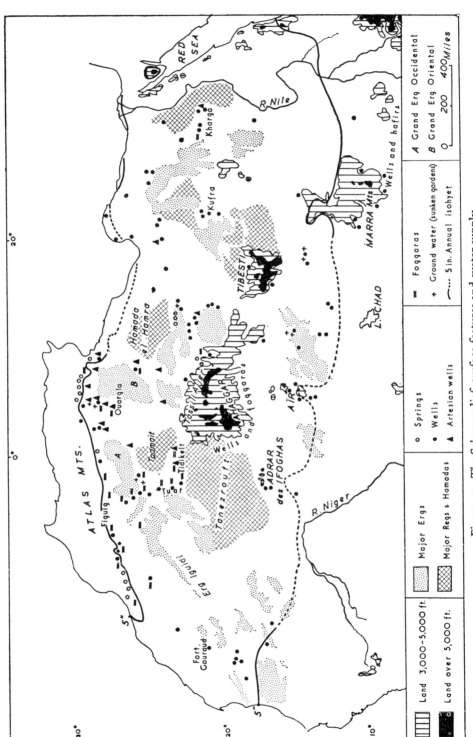

Figure 40 *The Sahara:* relief, surface features and water supply

Legend:

A	Grand Erg Occidental
B	Grand Erg Oriental

0 200 400 *Miles*

Foggaras

+ Ground water (sunken gardens)

⋯⋯ 5 in. Annual isohyet

o Springs

• Wells

▲ Artesian wells

Land 3,000–5,000 ft.

Major Ergs

Major Regs & Hamadas

Land over 5,000 ft.

practically horizontally bedded Cretaceous limestone, here and there fretted into vales and escarpments by former river channels or containing broad basins etched out by the wind. These forms related to the structure give but the bony frame of the landscape: the character of the covering is the result of the interaction of three weathering agents: insolation, wind action and the effect of water (much of it in the past rather than now). The surface rock, unprotected by soil and vegetation, is exposed to immense variation of temperature between the burning sun by day and great heat loss through radiation by night, a range of temperature at times amounting to 170°F. The expansion and contraction of the surface layers may lead to their disintegration if the rocks are sufficiently weak, but most cases of crumbling and 'exfoliation' are now thought to represent chemical weathering in the presence of minute quantities of moisture. The processes of rock weathering give rise to three types of scenery and surface (Fig. 40). The first is the *erg* or sandy desert of shifting dunes, difficult to traverse and avoided by travellers. Contrary to popular belief these soft-sand deserts form a relatively small proportion of the Saharan surface and their positions, if not their precise bounds, are mapped. Two of the largest sand deserts are the Grands Ergs Occidental and Oriental in the Algerian Sahara, separated by a stony and rocky desert that permits relatively easy travel south to the Ahaggar Mountains. Other notable *erg* deserts lie in south-western Algeria, in Mauritania and in Libya, with barchans and various forms of sand ridges. Very different is the second type of desert, the windswept *hammada* or rock waste of boulders and bare rocky platforms such as that practically surrounding the Ahaggar and Tibesti Mountains and comprising a considerable part of Rio de Oro. In some areas the mountains are flanked by gently sloping pediments cut in rock; in other cases they rise sharply, sometimes at angles of 80°, from rock surfaces that are quite level or even show slight depressions immediately at the bases of the mountains. The origin of these features is by no means clearly understood, though the pediments are certainly the result of water action. The third type, the *reg* desert, is intermediate between the other two and consists of gravel and pebble spreads, sometimes of even surface for scores of miles as in the Tanezrouft, where camel and car can travel without difficulty. In the mountains of the central Sahara evidence of desert sculpturing processes is abundantly manifest in the mountain flanks seamed with gorges and wadis of intermittent and irregular torrents, the heavy screes of shattered rock and the bizarre forms of wind-eroded and undercut rock pillars and blocks.

From north-west to south-east across the central Sahara sandstone and crystalline plateaux—part of the Saharan shield—form the plinths for the volcanic mountains of Ahaggar, Tassili, Aïr, Tibesti and Darfur. Here lava outpourings from the Pliocene onwards are mainly responsible for abruptly rising mountain masses up to and sometimes above 10,000 feet in height. The Ahaggar Mountains are the size of England and attain 9,840 feet; 700 miles to the south-east the Tibesti Mountains of similar character attain in the extinct volcano of Emi-Koussi, 11,204 feet. These mountains are stark and inhospitable. The uplift of the old planation surface, and the outpourings of lava, related to the folding of the Atlas, gave new vigour to erosion which bears the stamp of fluvial processes. Networks of valleys dissect and splay out from the main mountain-masses, but there is no longer running water; they are the fossil river systems of the Pleistocene. Then, when Europe was ice covered, the Sahara was an inhabited steppe traversed by great rivers. The form of the valleys suggests a cycle of erosion arrested at the youthful stage, for they radiate in a simple pattern as consequents, with steep ungraded profiles. Here and there the deep and narrow canyons, formerly containing rapids, open upon level expanses that might have been lakes and marshes (often a dampness here now supports pasture), giving the typical ungraded profile of the youthful stream. The great height of these central Saharan Mountains favours some precipitation, usually in the form of short storms. Of more lasting value is a persistent cloud cover sufficient to nourish pasture and, incidentally, to saturate the paper of one's field notebook. The highest parts of the Ahaggar are snow covered for a few days each year, but farther inland in the Tibesti Mountains the humidity is very low. While freezing temperatures are common during winter nights, the absence of water reduces the effectiveness of frost as an agent of weathering at the present day, though it was undoubtedly more active in the Quaternary.

CLIMATE

The climate of the desert is characterised by aridity, a considerable temperature range (both seasonal and diurnal), a dry atmosphere, clear skies and a maximum amount of sunshine throughout the year. The weather is remarkably stable. During winter, pressure falls towards a tongue of low pressure just south of the Guinea coast from a fairly constant high-pressure system over the Moroccan Atlas and High Plateaux of

Algeria. Thus the greater part of the Sahara receives northerly cT winds which for a time carry Saharan conditions to West Africa and are slowly filling up the Chad Basin with desert dust from the north-east. In West Africa this dry dusty wind is known as the Harmattan. In summer with the land-mass warmer than the surrounding oceans, the Inter-Tropical Convergence Zone of low pressure moves north over the southern Sahara. Thus winds blow towards the southern part of the desert from all directions. Over the northern part of the desert northerly winds continue to blow strongly almost every day. In the southern Sahara mE winds from the south-west are common: monsoonal indraughts bringing rain from the Gulf of Guinea are experienced as far north as Ardrar Des Iforas, the Aïr, and in some years may even reach the Ahaggar, but by then these airstreams are almost dry. There is across the central Sahara a gap between the southern limit of the Mediterranean front rains and the northern limit of the tropical monsoon rains. The cold current off the Atlantic coast is responsible for the aridity there, for the mT air is cooled and stabilised, giving no rain. Villa Cisneros in Spanish Sahara has 1·75 inches and Port Etienne in Mauritania 1·0 inches.

Rainfall

Rainfall is irregular and usually in the form of short and often violent storms. In some parts of the desert (e.g. the Libyan desert) years may pass between such storms. The term 'mean annual rainfall' has little significance under such conditions. It is probable that except for the mountain-masses the greater part of the central Sahara annually receives under 1 inch, while it is estimated that of the mountainous areas the Ahaggar and Aïr may receive up to 10 inches and Tibesti 5 inches. The aridity of the air is due to the character of the prevailing northerly and north-easterly winds, mainly descending from the upper atmosphere in the sub-tropical high-pressure zone and becoming warmed by compression. The farther south they blow, the greater the diminution in their relative humidity. The soil also receives some water in the form of dew. This is difficult to measure but is appreciable along the Atlantic littoral, in the beds of wadis and in dune areas. It is doubtful if this penetrates far enough into the soil to affect the water table.

Table 5

Station	Alt. (feet)		J	F	M	A	M	J	J	A	S	O	N	D	Year	Temp. range
Tripoli	56	Temp. °F	54	56	60	65	69	74	79	80	78	74	65	58	66	26
		Rain in.	3·3	1·8	0·9	0·5	0·3	0·1	—	—	0·5	1·8	2·4	4·7	16·3	
In Salah	919	T.	55	60	68	76	86	94	99	97	92	80	68	58	78	44
		R.	—	—	—	—	—	—	—	—	—	—	—	—	—	
Aswan	400	T.	59	63	70	78	85	90	91	90	88	82	72	62	73	32
		R.	—	—	—	—	—	—	—	—	—	—	—	—	—	
Agadès	1,706	T.	66	72	81	88	94	95	90	87	89	86	77	72	83	29
		R.	—	—	0·2	—	0·3	1·9	3·7	3·7	0·7	—	—	—	6·8	

The Sahara is one of the hottest parts of the earth's surface. The clear skies favour unbroken sunshine and the world's highest summer temperatures have been recorded here (136°F at Azizia in Tripolitania, 13th September 1922). Large areas experience mean July temperatures of over 100°F and in many years mean temperatures of over 120°F have been recorded. The annual range of temperature (about 30°F) is of less significance than the great diurnal range. By midday the desert surface is oven hot, but immediately the sun falls there is a rapid loss of heat from the bare ground, for the air is clean and dry and the sky generally cloudless. The nocturnal fall of temperature is remarkable, in summer dropping to around 60°F and in winter nearly to, and occasionally below, freezing-point, creating in general a diurnal range of 30° to 40°F throughout the year. Saharan travellers have recorded diurnal ranges of more than 50°F.

The following morning [March 10th], just before dawn the minimum thermometer which had been lying in its open case on the ground registered 33°F., and there was ice in the water skins. During the course of the day we worked to the west of the plateaux [of the Ahaggar], where we were sheltered from the cool winds. There was now a marked difference in temperature, and in the shade at mid-day it was always in the neighbourhood of 100°F. This variation of nearly 70° in temperature in some seven hours we experienced on most of the days we were travelling through this country.[1]

Frost occurs regularly each year in a number of the oases: Biskra, Touggourt and Ouargla have more days with frost than Algiers. These great extremes are counteracted by the wearing of heavy clothing, both to give protection against chilly nights and from the heat, glare and dust of the day. It is the dryness of the air the traveller from more humid parts notices most. Nails soon become brittle, lips crack and the skin becomes roughened; the fierce heat, often burning the sand surface to 160°F or more, militates against plant life and evaporates body moisture from the pores at an astounding rate. There is a constant feeling of thirst but no visible perspiration. In the summer manual workers at Hassi Messaoud oil wells lose (and drink) over three gallons of water a day.

Strong convection currents often associated with shallow depressions give rise to powerful winds that whip up dust and sand and blow locally as the sirocco of Algeria, the simoon of Libya and the khamsin of Egypt. There are numerous types of these winds, some are purely local 'dust devils', but others are on a larger scale and may last two to three days. These winds appear with startling suddenness, the clear sky and intensely still air being replaced by a yellowish-grey pall of scorching, rushing air laden with blistering sand, penetrating houses despite closed doors and windows, sand blasting uncovered windscreens and, being hot and excessively dry, often causing fatal cases of heat stroke.

VEGETATION

Saharan vegetation is related to the character of the surface rock and the presence of surface or subsoil water. Large areas are devoid of all vegetation, but the sudden irregular rainstorm often has surprising results, particularly on the *hammada*, being followed for a short period by rapidly growing grass and shrubs that have the power of remaining dormant over months or even years. The gravel and pebble *reg* and the sandy *erg* sustain least vegetation. The southern and northern desert edges support more regular vegetation. Streams from the Atlas that lose themselves in the desert still support tufted bushes and grass, predominantly tamarisk and the purple and white flowered broom (*Retama Raetam*), along the line of their beds after their waters have seeped below the surface, while at intervals depressions facilitating well digging support date-palms, gardens and population. The Tuat oases of southern Algeria are a good example. They extend along the seasonally watered channel of the Saoura-Messaoued from the Saharan Atlas at Figuig for nearly 400 miles into the desert at Tidikelt (Fig. 40).

The highlands within the Sahara have proved disappointing to botanists in that their bare sheets and faces of rock permit little vegetation. In the fissures and ravines and on the beds of the wadis debouching on to the surrounding plateaux stunted acacia species, dry tufted herbs with woody root stocks and pasture such as the *Panicum* grass and tufted grasses survive and support sheep, goats and camels. Thus contrary to popular ideas a large part of the Sahara has a permanent vegetation of trees, shrubs and bushes. Distribution is confined to the general drainage lines but is to be found right across the continent.

The vegetation of the oases, including date-palms, Mediterranean fruit trees and cereals, is man-introduced and continues only so long as man remains in control. Where oases have been deserted the vegetation introduced (much, of course, entering as seed with the crops or with merchandise) rapidly dies out and even date-palms become tufted, ragged and soon degenerate. Wind and detritus choke the water supply and soon, once man has withdrawn, the character of an 'oasis' no longer applies. It follows that any depression or dry river-course where the water table is not far below the surface is a potential oasis awaiting only man's efforts and the introduction of new plants.

20

Human and Economic Geography

Agriculture in the Sahara is necessarily confined to the oases and in scale is akin to gardening. The plots are usually small and rectangular, being no more than 10 feet long and bounded by small earth ramparts permitting a flooding every few days. Two crops a year are possible; the principal ones are barley, millet, beans, wheat, vegetables and, in addition to the date-palm, citrus fruit, peaches and apricots are usual. There are, in fact, several levels of vegetation: vegetables at ground level, fruit trees above them and date-palms towering above all. Cereals are usually sown separately out of the shade of the trees. Generally the oasis cultivators are of semi-slave status, of Negroid origin, either toiling directly for Arab or Berber masters (sometimes nomads) who regard agriculture as menial or as *khammes* on a harsh share-cropping tenancy basis. *Khammes* means 'fifth' and the standard share is one-fifth of the harvest, but in certain oases more is allowed.

Permanent settlement in the central Sahara consists of hamlets of stone or hardened-clay huts situated at the debouchments of the principal oueds around the upland periphery. Wells in the beds of the dry oueds provide irrigation water for the gardens maintained for the ruling Berber people by the servile or slave class, particularly the bronze-complexioned half-castes known as Haratin. The Tuareg of the Ahaggar and Aïr and the Tibu of Tibesti do not engage in cultivation but herd camels, sheep and goats. The harshness of the environment obliges them to live in a state of continual movement between oueds and wells and over sparse mountain pasture. They move in small groups with quickly erected grass and matting huts for shelter, although stone shelters and huts are used in the rocky Tibesti. The Tuareg formerly levied tribute from trans-Saharan caravans. They are the 'people of the veil', so called because the males constantly wear a long strip of cloth wound round the head to form a hood and covering the mouth and nose, only the eyes being visible.

The Tibu not only harried travellers, but in the past also swept out of the desert to raid oases in Egypt, Cyrenaica and the Chad area. These operations must have carried them over enormous stretches of desert with gaps of hundreds of miles between waterholes.

> They . . . are perfectly at home in the desert, and travel very quickly, guiding themselves by the sun by day, by moon and stars at night. They also recognise minute details to guide them to their objective, and are expert trackers. On the march they are indefatigable, and in urgent cases can travel 100 kilometres a day for several days. Their fortitude, strength, and stamina are tremendous. They can go twenty-four hours without water easily, and their physical resistance enables them to cover great distances on foot.[2]

The true nomads of the Sahara are a dwindling force: tent dwellers moving with their camels from well to well, the animals subsisting on sparse acacia and salt bush grazing; a hard but mainly self-sufficient way of life out of tune with modern living. Many tribes of the northern Sahara move north with the season from the Sahara into the steppes of the Atlas lands, where they spend the summer, returning by October to pick dates in the oases and winter in the desert (Fig. 41). Some of these, such as the Arbaa and Ouled Zekri of south Algeria, breed sheep. Sheep can thrive on salty vegetation and can stand the winter cold of the desert but need watering regularly during the summer. This routine of migration is known in Algeria as *achaba*. The Arbaa, for example, winter south of Laghouat but spend the summer with their flocks on the steppes of the High Plateaux south of the Ouarsenis (fig. 36). Attempts are increasing in Algeria and Libya to settle the nomads in order to facilitate administration, education and the raising of their standard of living. New possibilities of lucrative employment in the new mining and oil-well settlements (once the rudiments of Western living have been absorbed) are a further lure that may help to break down their proud tradition.

WATER AND MINERALS

The successful exploitation of underground wealth in the Algerian and Libyan Sahara since World War II is having far-reaching effects on

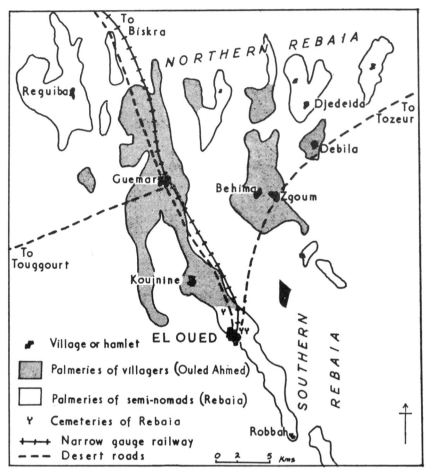

Figure 41 *Palmeries of the Souf oasis (El Oued)*. In most of the north Saharan oases some of the date palms are owned by semi-nomadic peoples, here the Rebaia. The settled tribe is the Ouled Ahmed

traditional nomadic and oasis economies. Success has attended searches for water, oil, natural gas and minerals. Great deep-seated basins in the north Sahara, Tanezrouft and Fezzan contain bountiful artesian aquifers, the most celebrated being the great nodular sandstone bed of Cretaceous-Jurassic age known as the *nappe albienne* or Continental Intercalaire extending under the northern Sahara and, in the Egyptian Sahara, the Nubian Sandstone. Much of the water must have been accumulating over several thousand years in fact, but there is some annual replenishment from

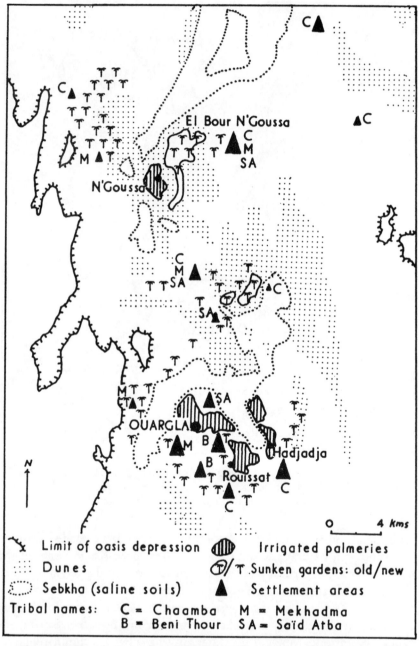

Figure 42 *Ouargla Oasis:* the palmeries and the growing settlement of nomads
(after Rovillois–Brigol)

the rainfall in the upland marginal areas where these beds are exposed. It is the tapping of these subterranean waters 3,000–4,000 feet deep in the northern Sahara that is reviving dying oases and permitting the establishment of permanent settlements for mining and oil exploration.

In many oases the water supply is obtained from wells or waterholes penetrating into seepage layers below the dry oueds, the water being hauled up in a skin by a camel, donkey or bullock. In other cases *foggaras* are constructed. These are subterranean channels dug to tap seepage areas and to lead the water by gravity to the cultivated plots (Fig. 43). In a few cases, as at Ouargla in Algeria (Fig. 42), artesian waters are used; over

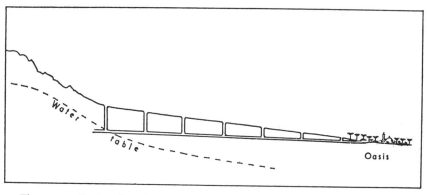

Figure 43 *Section through a Foggara.* The channel of the foggara taps the underground water table and conveys the water by gravity to the surface, often a considerable distance away. The line of shafts which identify a foggara from the air is dug for ventilation and the removal of the excavated material both initially and for subsequent maintenance work

1,000 wells irrigating nearly 2 million date-palms. Over the years the level of the water table fell, but since World War II deep boring has reached water under great pressure in the Continental Intercalaire at 3,500 feet and this has led to a resuscitation of these oases, where the population is now 40,000.

Oil exploration since World War II was successful in 1956 at Hassi Messaoud ('Blessed well'), 100 miles south of Touggourt (Plate 1A-B). Oil was struck at 11,000 feet, artesian water being reached at 4,000 feet, so making the opening up of an oilfield possible. The crude oil is greenish in colour and very light. It is free of sulphur and can be used unrefined to drive diesel engines such as are employed in drilling operations. In 1964, 26 million tons were produced. Pipelines carry the oil to the Algerian ports of Bougie and Arzew and a refinery was completed at Maison Carrée, near Algiers, in 1963. Now, at Hassi Messaoud, a town for 30,000 is being created; 50,000 trees have been planted and swimming pools, lawns, flowering shrubs accompany air-conditioned housing. Other oilfields have since been opened up at El Gassi, 75 miles to the south, and at Edjelé (actually the first Saharan discovery, where oil is reached at only 1,300–1,650 feet) 300 miles to the east across the Grand Erg Oriental and beside the Libyan border. These wells are linked by pipeline to the new oil port of La Skhirra near Gabès in Tunisia. Even more recently fields have been discovered and have begun producing at Zelten and Dahra in Libya (p. 251). A natural gas field is now being exploited at Hassi R'Mel, near Ghardaia, with pipelines to the coast at Arzew and to Algiers and Oran. Hopes for substantial exports to Europe have been lessened by the big natural gas discoveries in Groningen, Netherlands, but regular exports to Britain commenced in 1964.

A variety of mineral ores has also been discovered (Fig. 25) but progress in exploitation is slow owing to economic difficulties arising from remoteness, the cost of establishing transport facilities and uncertainty over the size of ore bodies. Large, good-quality iron-ore deposits exist 80 miles south-east of Tindouf in Algeria. Unfortunately they are 800 miles from the coast and would be uneconomic to work at present. In eastern Egypt oil, phosphate and iron-ore are successfully exploited; coal is mined at Kenadsa near Colomb-Béchar (p. 208) and nearby deposits of manganese, copper and lead are known. The only other Saharan mineral now being worked on a massive scale is the large deposit of high-quality (63–68 per cent Fe) iron ore in the Kédia d'Idjil Hills near Fort Gouraud in Mauritania. It is now being exploited for export after the construction of a 400-mile rail link to the coast at Port Etienne (p. 261).

COMMUNICATIONS

Transport across the great desert has always been difficult but neverthe-less possible, thanks to the camel. For centuries considerable trade between the summer-rain Sudan and the cool-season-rain Maghreb has been carried across the desert by caravan. The trade moving south included silk and woollen textiles from Morocco, olive oils and sponges from Tunisia, brass, pottery and Venetian glass through Algeria. The trade moving north included slaves, gold, spices, ivory, ebony, skins and leather. Caravans from Kano in northern Nigeria to Morocco took from 90 to

150 days on the journey. Camel traffic is still important for the nomad calling at the oases to trade animals, wool, leather and salt for grain and fruits. Oases such as Ghardaia, Biskra, Kufra, Agadès and Atar still are busy centres for local camel caravans.

Modern means of communication, notably the car and the aeroplane, are doing much to open up the desert and to lessen its hazards. The first motor-car crossed the desert in 1924. Regular bus services (taking about six days) now cross the Sahara except during the hottest months. There is a number of roads available to cars and lorries but the two main trans-Saharan roads used by buses are from Algiers, El Goléa, In Salah, Tamanrasset to Agadés and Kano, and another from Colomb Béchar to Gao on the Niger. For the most part the roads are the natural desert floor, but from northern Algeria bitumen-surfaced roads are gradually being extended to the oases and oilfields in the north of the desert. Already 1,100 miles of surfaced roads reach southwards to Colomb Béchar, El Goléa and Hassi Messaoud.

First mooted in 1876, several projects to construct north-south trans-Saharan railways have been examined and surveys carried out. The project is technically feasible, but only at very great expense, and it is doubtful whether the quantity of freight available would merit such expenditure. Construction of such a line from Colomb-Béchar to Gao actually began in 1942, but stopped after 82 miles had been built from Colomb-Béchar. The line was standard gauge and the terminal would have been Oran. The most recent railway construction in the Sahara has been the 400-mile line from Fort Gouraud to Port Etienne, built specifically for the movement of iron ore.

All these developments are indicative of the great changes now occurring in the human geography of the Sahara. The feudal system of the oases is becoming disrupted. Slavery, abolished in name, has persisted in fact, for the Negro slaves and their descendants have remained bound to their masters in the isolation of the oases through lack of alternative employment. Now paid employment is becoming available, a road network extended and the Negroes discover a new mobility which permits them to move to new work and become financially better off than their camel-owning former masters. These changes are timely, for previously, with a lowering water level in the oasis wells and a growing rate of population increase as new medical knowledge was applied, the plight of the oasis cultivators and Khammés was becoming acute. Much still needs to be done, but the impact of new people, new ideas and ways of life, new spending power and new accessibility is beginning to change the outlook of the Saharan peoples. In the Algerian Sahara, however, the prospects are less bright for the time being. Here, the gradual withdrawal of French military personnel has affected the economy of a number of remote oases and has led to lesser desert tracks no longer being maintained.

21

The Saharan States

The Sahara is divided among numerous countries. Originally (excepting Libya, which was Italian) most of it was in the hands of France, but during the middle decade of this century her former colonies obtained their independence and the map of the desert is now much intersected by political boundaries. Algeria still holds the major share of the desert on the north, and to the south it is shared between a chain of states formerly comprising French West Africa and part of French Equatorial Africa. These are now Chad, Niger, Mali and Mauritania and stretch across the intermediate zone between the savanna and the true desert. Thus within their borders they include vegetation belts responding from south to north to the diminishing rainfall. Much of the Atlantic coast remains in the hands of Spain, as do the offshore Canary Islands. In the east (and examined under 'The Nile Basin') are the two independent states of Egypt (United Arab Republic) and the Sudan.

LIBYA (Fig. 44)

The Kingdom of Libya (679,400 sq. miles) came into being in December 1951, when the three distinct territories of Tripolitania, Cyrenaica and the Fezzan under United Nations auspices were united under one king. In many ways the union was an act of faith for it brought together diverse territories and peoples of very different viewpoints and histories. It is doubtful if in this part of North Africa such a union has ever been achieved before. This state, midway along the Mediterranean where the sea laps the Sahara, has never had individuality or entity. Between Cyrenaica and Tripolitania is a waste of bleached desert and scrub. Cyrenaica looks eastward towards Egypt and the Middle East; Tripolitania looks westward to the Maghreb, a situation the Romans recognised by incorporating Tripolitania in the province of Africa, under Carthage, and Cyrenaica within the province of Crete. In this century the Italians ruled them as two separate colonies. Like the rest of North Africa the territory came under Turkish suzerainty until Italy, seeking African colonies, occupied Tripoli in 1911 and became recognised as the sovereign power by Turkey in the following year. These territories were wrested from Italy in World War II. By the time of the outbreak of war many millions of lire had been poured into these colonies and over 100,000 Italians were settled in them. Less than half that number of Italians now remains. Italian holdings were of two kinds: (1) private concessions usually of up to 30 hectares developed with private capital and hired unskilled Arab labour; (2) so-called demographic settlements, generally on poorer land requiring greater capital investment and provided for by government agencies, the tenants repaying capital back over a lengthy period. It is notable that the first group of farmers, now much reduced in numbers, produces a disproportionately large share of Libyan agricultural produce and their farming is much in advance of that of the Arabs.

At first the division of outlook and interest between the mainly agricultural Tripolitania and the mainly pastoralist Cyrenaica was acknowledged by a complicated federal constitution providing one federal and three territorial governments under the king. Tripoli and Benghazi were both federal capitals, and the government shuttled the 700 miles from one to the other: Tripoli in winter, Benghazi in summer. The cost of duplicating capitals, administrative offices and residences was prodigious and the inconvenience great. Such a system has little justification except in creating a united state out of three widely separated regions, two fearing they would be swamped by the more advanced and populous Tripolitania. After a decade a sense of Libyan patriotism had developed and provincial loyalties diminished enough for a marked reduction of territorial powers and a strengthening of federal power preparatory to the creation of a central government. Thus, in 1962, the provincial system of government was abolished and ten administrative districts were created. In 1963 the new town of Beida, in Cyrenaica, became the seat of government.

Libya is a desert country; maritime influences touch only a small northern fringe of the kingdom, giving some mitigation from the fierce heat. Tripoli has an annual range of 26°F compared with 44°F at In Salah (Table 5). Nevertheless temperatures of over 100°F are recorded regularly at Tripoli during the summer. The rainfall reaches only a narrow coastal strip and diminishes in amount from west to east. Tripoli averages 16 inches a year, but Benghazi farther east only 11 inches. Except for a short distance from the coast desert conditions pertain. It is in discontinuous stretches along the coast that the bulk of Libya's population is to be found. Two-thirds of the population live in Tripolitania, mainly between Zuara and Misurata, in a series of coastal oases where about 10 inches of rain fall in the average year. The triangle Garian–Tripoli–Homs is the best watered, with 13 inches, and was a major scene of Italian colonisation. This area marks the eastern end of the Jeffara, the steppe land extending eastward from Tunisia and rising gently from the coast to the Tripolitania Jebel, a series of fault scarps attaining over 2,500 feet which begin the African plateau and mark off

Figure 44 *Libya:* surface features and economic development

the coastal zone from the interior. Inland are stony plateaux of limestone and sandstone such as the Hamada el Homra (or red, stony desert) with sparse scrub scattered here and there. To the south-east are gaunt lava areas, and the purplish-black hills of the Jebel el Sauda. In the south-west, comprising much of the Fezzan, are great sand seas. There are wide depressions between the sandy areas in which occurs a surprising number of oases, some very large such as Ghat, Sebha and Brac. The Fezzan is virtually rainless and settlement is sharply confined to these favoured patches. Yet in total the Fezzan has nearly 7,000 acres of irrigated gardens and nearly 300,000 acres are planted with date-palms.

Cyrenaica bulges northward into the Mediterranean and its hills, the Jebel el Akhdar (2,500 feet), in places drop steeply to the sea. Coastal plains are confined to the neighbourhood of Benghazi and Agedabia; round to the Egyptian frontier the coast is rugged. The greater rainfall (22–23 inches) on this hilly limestone area allows woods of cypress and junipers and some slopes clothed with open maquis, but little settlement. Much of the settlement is near the foot of the hills along the coast where springs create oasis conditions and the terraced slopes with glimpses of the sea are more akin to Greece than the Sahara.

THE ECONOMY

AGRICULTURE High summer temperatures, desiccating desert winds, lack of rainfall and poor soils all contribute to the scantiness and poverty of Libyan agriculture. Less than 1 per cent of Libyan land is productive and three-quarters of this is suitable only for grazing. Much of the agriculture is carried on extensively after the rains on semi-arid or marginal land and yields are low. Cereals (barley and wheat in the north, wheat and millet in the south) are the principal crops, much being grown in oases. Over 3 million olive trees (most planted by the Italians) are now in production, particularly in the Tripolitania Jebel (where almond trees also grow) and the coastal oases, while date-palms provide a staple food in the south. Figs and citrus fruits are also grown near the coastal towns and some are exported.

The marginal climatic régime gives prominence to animal husbandry within the economy. Goats, sheep and cattle are kept in the north and camels take the place of cattle in the desert regions. Pastoralism is particularly paramount in Cyrenaica. After the winter rains begin, flocks and herds move over the steppe but concentrate round wells and water points during the dry season. The tribes have their own age-old grazing grounds, often with communal wells. In some cases cereal cultivation also takes a place in the annual cycle and this may involve more complex evolutions: sowing in the north with the winter rains, a movement south, a return for harvesting and a further but lesser movement south in the late summer. Sheep are more numerous than all other animals and have a high place in the Arabs' esteem, giving as they do the triple yield of meat, milk and wool.

Esparto grass is collected and is a regular export, but there are few other agricultural resources, and the fishing (sponges, sardines, tunny), while offering potentialities, is as yet little developed. Libya has little manufacturing industry. Craftsmen still make carpets and leather goods, and dye and weave local wool but there are no modern factory industries.

OIL The fortunes of this new impoverished state took a favourable turn in 1959 when oil in commercial quantities was discovered at Zelten, about 200 miles south of Benghazi. The success attending oil prospecting in the Algerian Sahara encouraged the major companies to seek concessions in Libya and to spend vast sums in exploration over several years. The Zelten discoveries were the first of a series that ringed the Gulf of Sirte, other major discoveries being at Dahra and Beda. Pipelines connect Dahra and Zelten with newly created coastal terminals at Ras el Sidra and Port Brega, both on the Gulf of Sirte, and Tobruk became the third oil port in 1967. A small refinery has been constructed at Port Brega. Other oil discoveries have been made in western Tripolitania and the Fezzan but these are not yet actively developed; nevertheless Libya is now the largest producer and exporter of mineral oil in Africa. Export of oil began in 1961 and by 1965 58 million metric tons were exported, much of it to Britain. From Britain the distance to Port Brega is 2,450 miles compared with 6,330 miles from Kuwait; thus a tanker from the Libyan port can carry twice as much to Britain in a given period than can one from the Persian Gulf. However, simple substitution is not possible, for Saharan crude is lighter than Middle East crude and the technical problem of keeping the balance of refinery yields has to be overcome.

WATER PROBLEMS The character and degree of future development of Libya are bound up with the problems of water supply. The country possesses no perennial rivers, the supply of surface water is scanty and erratic, run-off is rapid and evaporation intense. In a good year the cereal crop may total 150,000 tons, but in a drought year barely 15,000 tons; and this happens every fourth or fifth year. Underground water sources must be tapped and surface storage made from springs and seepages—a situation familiar to the Romans who made effective use of dams and cisterns, many of which remain to this day. Much foreign aid to Libya has gone into hydrological surveys, into the reconditioning of old cisterns and irrigation works and the boring of new wells. The development of artesian supplies was begun by the Italians but great progress has been made since the war, leading to a marked change from dry to irrigation farming in Tripolitania. Irrigation agriculture depends almost entirely upon semi-artesian and artesian water from Quaternary and Miocene formations and has helped to intensify cultivation in the Tripolitania coastal belt although some of the water has a high saline content. In Cyrenaica water reserves are known to exist deep down, but considerable pumping would be necessary for the extension of agriculture in the Jebel Akhdar where climate and soils are suitable. Under these conditions tree crops—olives, almonds, citrus fruits—are likely to become increasingly important in the economy and this in turn lays stress upon an increase in permanent settlement and a reduction in nomadism.

POPULATION AND SETTLEMENT

The population of Libya is estimated at nearly 1,600,000, of whom 1,000,000 live in Tripolitania, 450,000 in Cyrenaica and only 80,000 in the Fezzan. Nearly one-third of the total population now lives in the two regional capitals of Tripoli and Benghazi. The population is mostly of Moslem Arabs and Berbers and only 35,000 Italians remain, almost all in Tripolitania and nearly all urban dwellers. In Cyrenaica nomads and semi-nomads form more than half the population, in Tripolitania the settled agriculturalists are twice as numerous as the nomads. In the Fezzan Sebha the capital is but a large village, but like the other oasis settlements has a settled population. Perhaps a quarter to a fifth of Fezzan population are nomads. All the provinces are poor, but Tripolitania is more developed and apparently richer than Cyrenaica, which in turn easily surpasses the Fezzan.

The inevitable but slow reduction of the nomadic population is becoming evident in Libya as in the Maghreb. The desertion of their farms by Italians during and after the war—thus allowing favourable settlement schemes—and subsequently the paid employment available in oil camps have contributed to this trend. Thriving Greek and Roman agricultural communities existed in Libya 2,000 years ago, but after the collapse of the Roman Empire, Arabs roamed over the countryside with flocks and herds and the carefully constructed irrigation works, the backbone of the settled way of life, fell into decay. The Italians realised the inefficiency of this form of land use and alienated the best lands from the Bedouin and established communities of Italian peasant farmers; for example from Barce to Gubba in Cyrenaica they laid out a 'demographic settlement' of 1,820 small farms spaced equidistantly along a geometrical grid of roads. These farms still survive, now tenanted by those born to a pastoral tradition who tend with care the recently planted olives, figs and peaches and gradually reduce their herds of destructive goats.

The growth and spread of the oil industry provides hosts of new well-paid jobs and the circulation of much money. Drivers, contractors, builders, farmers, hoteliers all benefit, and so does the nomad, drawn in by the increasing demand for labour. High wages in the oil and related industries draw cultivators off the land and there is a danger that marginal lands may go permanently out of cultivation, leading to greater reliance upon imported foodstuffs.

Libya is a country of great distances but hopelessly inadequate communications. It is particularly deficient in good roads and possesses (in Cyrenaica) only 100 miles of railway. The only respectable motor road is the coastal one, followed by the Eighth Army from Egypt to Tunis. A new road connecting Sebha with the coast road has now been built.

The future

The successful exploitation of Libya's oil deposits has relieved her of former total dependence upon foreign aid, particularly British and American funds given in return for military concessions. Royalties from oil 1965-6 were $280 million—more than twice the country's whole budget for 1959-60 (royalties for 1966-67 were expected to total $392 million). The oil revenues are of prime importance to the new state, but initially of even greater impact were the investment and spending of vast sums by the prospecting companies. In 1960 the oil companies imported $60 million of equipment and spent $225 million on exploration, a third of this going for local goods and services. The responsibilities attendant upon the use of this money are great. The experiences of other oil-rich Arab states have not all been happy. Foreign aid has been used well in maintaining the roads inherited from the Italians, in improving agriculture and furthering progress of education. A five-year development plan was launched in 1963 and envisaged the investment of $550 million. Much of this was allotted to transport and urban development and perhaps not enough to agricultural and conservation projects. In recent years thousands of rural workers have been attracted to the novel life and wage-employment in the towns. Agricultural production has not expanded with the growing demand for food and much now has to be imported. In the long term the main wealth of Libya is agricultural and there is much to be done in furthering irrigation, bringing more land under cultivation (particularly for tree crops), eliminating pests, introducing better seeds and breeds of cattle and increasing the proportion of settled population. At present the income per head is one of the lowest in the world but prospects of betterment are now very great. A more difficult task lies in the human field, in the creation of a settled peasantry from nomadic stock and the training of artisans and professional men to take over from the foreign engineers, doctors and administrators.

CHAD

Chad is an entirely inland state which became independent in 1960, previously having been the northward component of French Equatorial Africa. The inclusion of a desert and semi-desert area within French Equatorial Africa is a result of the history of discovery and occupation, which originated from the French Congo and not from the adjoining Saharan lands of French West Africa (see Chapter 9).

The most significant physical feature within Chad is the great depression or downwarp in which lies Lake Chad. The basin is surrounded by exposures of the Archaean Basement Complex, particularly pronounced in the north where they form a significant part of Tibesti and in the east where they create, in the Ennedi-Darfur highlands a watershed between the Chad inland drainage basin and the Nile. Upon these ancient crystalline rocks sandstones of varying ages were deposited, particularly the Nubian Sandstone during the late Carboniferous to Cretaceous period. The rain that falls on the highlands runs off into these surrounding sandstone plateaux to become available in them as artesian supplies in distant arid areas. The widespread tectonic disturbances towards the close of the Tertiary and in the early Quaternary led to volcanic activity, particularly in the north and east, building up the present highlands, and it is probable that the downwarping of the Chad Basin dates from the early Quaternary period.

Much of Chad averages about 1,000 feet above sea-level, but the lake itself is at a height of 750 feet. North of the lake is dune and sparse scrub country, Kanem, containing a number of even lower depressions. North of this again the ground rises to the Tibesti and the Libyan border and east to the plateaux of Erdi and Ennedi, there attaining nearly 4,000 feet. The permanent drainage of this inland drainage basin comes from the better-watered Ubangi-Shari plateau to the south via the Shari and Logone river systems. These flow from the Ubangi-Shari plateau over undulating grassy plains broken here and there by granite tors before the country becomes drier. North-west from Fort Archambault the rivers wind their way across the great grass and thorn-bush-covered plains of Baguirmi. These plains flood after the rains and near the lake the rivers become a maze of channels and swamps.

The soil near the river is of black fertile alluvium—cracking open in the heat, sticky and impervious in the wet. Villages here are sited on knolls or rising ground to avoid the annual floods. Lake Chad varies in size from season to season and from year to year according to the rain received in the south. The lake is shallow and the northern part distinctly seasonal. In the south are thick reed beds and water permanently deep enough for boats (Plate 3). Desert conditions prevail north from Lake Chad but in the depressions there is abundant water below the surface and wells and occasional springs create oasis settlements. The northern and eastern sandstone and volcanic highlands are rugged and inhospitable although water and pasture are available around their base. This area north of Lake Chad receives slight and irregular rains of perhaps 5 inches in July and August. Fort Lamy (91,000), the capital, lying south of the lake, receives about 25 inches while on the higher southern border with the Central African Republic 40 inches is experienced during a more prolonged summer wet season.

These physical circumstances divide the country into two: the dry pastoral steppe and desert zone in the north and the better-watered south where agriculture is possible and a denser population is sustained. In the pastoral north the sparse population is of a mixture of Hamitic-Negroid stock acknowledging Islam; in the agricultural south the Negroid element is predominant. Here mixed farming prevails: millets

and pulses are the main subsistence crops and cotton the major cash
crop. Cattle and goats are the main stock kept. The pastoralists are of
necessity nomadic or semi-nomadic. Generally a northerly movement
precedes the rains, to avoid the tsetse fly, and a southerly movement
follows them. Cattle and sheep are the principal animals. At the oases
cereals, figs and vegetables are grown. Exports are limited in kind and
in amount and mainly comprise cotton, groundnuts, cattle and meat
products.

Chad covers an enormous area, just over 496,000 sq. miles or the
equivalent of Spain, France and Western Germany together. Within this
great area the population only totals 3,300,000 and includes about 51,000
Europeans. Economic development is retarded by the lack of population.
which is mainly concerned with subsistence production and depends
almost entirely upon outside aid. Considerable investment has been
made in recent years in developing the lower Logone and Shari rivers
for rice and cotton production, in improving the trunk roads to the south
and furthering programmes of schools, agrarian education and water
supply in the semi-arid areas.

THE NIGER REPUBLIC

West of Chad lies the Republic of the Niger. Covering an area of 494,000
sq. miles it is almost as large as Chad. With a population of 3,400,000 its
density is only 7 per sq. mile. The northern two-thirds of the country is
desert or semi-desert and most people live in the Jerma Ganda region
bordering the Niger or in the southern border districts of Gobir, Damagaram and Mounio. A few live in the Aïr Plateau or on the pastures of
Tessellaman and northern Azawak. From Jerma Ganda to the port of
Cotonou it is over 500 miles by road and rail. The Niger tends to be
isolated and much of its produce finds its way to the coast across Nigeria
despite close relations with Dahomey.

REGIONAL DIVISIONS In the south-west Jerma Ganda consists of the
floodplain of the Middle Niger valley which with 20–25 inches of rainfall
annually has the highest totals in the country. As elsewhere in the Sudanic
zone, the economy depends on sorghum, millet, maize, groundnuts and
cotton, with cattle, sheep and goats on fringing grazing grounds. To the
north-east are the 'dallols' (broad shallow streams), the largest of which

is the Dallol Bosso draining the Tessellaman Depression. In the south are the high sandy plains of Gobir, Damagaram and Mounio producing groundnuts, goatskins and hides, with some floodland and irrigated cultivation of wheat and maize. In the south-east is the wasteland of Manga in the Chad Basin, with pastures near the lake. To the north of these regions are the low tablelands of Tegama and, where the Pre-Cambrian rocks outcrop, the high plateau of Aïr (summits up to 5,000 feet) with its local capital of Agadès (2,000 feet). The Tenere desert, east of the Aïr, is a waste of sand-dunes containing the small oasis of Bilma from which salt is still exported by caravan trains.

ECONOMY The productive zone extends from Lake Chad to Niamey and the Niger river. Much of this is steppe and harvests fluctuate from year to year, dependent on the rainfall. To the north, cultivation patches disappear, trees become fewer and stunted and the scrub thinner. Here nomads and their flocks eke out a precarious existence. The Niger is divided between the former Songhay Empire in the west and the former Hausa states in the east. The Songhay area contains the present capital of Niamey (pop. 45,000), built on the banks of the Niger; the area depends on the export of groundnuts and dried fish, a trade via Dahomey, and the regular migration of its fishermen down the Niger as far as Onitsha in southern Nigeria. The Hausa area has a local capital in Zinder (pop. 11,000), capital of the Niger from 1900 to 1926 and commercial capital still, since it is the largest market for groundnuts, hides, skins and gum arabic exported via Nigeria. Political unity is difficult to achieve, productivity is low and exports are worth annually only about $10 per head.

MALI

The former French Soudan became the independent Republic of Mali in 1960. It is entirely land-locked and its quarrel and withdrawal from the union with Senegal deprived it from 1960-3 of its best outlet for overseas trade. The steamer and rail route via Kouroussa or Kankan to Conakry offered an alternative, but the railway is in a bad state of repair. Road routes to Abidjan in the Ivory Coast are preferred despite high cost. With an area of 465,000 sq. miles and a population of 4,650,000 the density is only 10 per sq. mile. Much of the huge territory is dry

and most arable agriculture, confined to the south, depends upon irrigation from the Niger and its tributaries. Over half the republic receives
annually less than 10 inches of rain; the northern portions of Mali are
desert and most of the population is confined to the south-western third
of the country.

PHYSICAL REGIONS　Mali consists of the broad upper Niger Basin, the
Inland Niger Delta and the narrow middle Niger valley, with sandstone
plateaux on each side, and, to the north, the desert and the plateau of
Adrar des Iforas. The upper Niger Basin contains the valleys of the Niger
and Bani and their tributaries, a region of sorghum and millet cultivation
above flood-levels and irrigated rice cultivation below. Numerous small
irrigation schemes have been developed by the French and ox-drawn
ploughs introduced. The Inland Niger Delta occupies the structural basin
of Ségou. It consists of the abandoned 'dead' delta of the left bank between
Sansanding and Diafarabé and the 'live' delta from Diafarabé to Kabara,
the port of Timbuktu. At Sansanding a barrage has been constructed
that raises the level of the Niger by 14 feet and supplies water via the
abandoned channels of the dead delta to the rice- and cotton-growing
colonies of the Niger Irrigation Scheme at Niono and Molodo in the
north and Boky-Were and Kokry in the south. This is the largest irrigation scheme in West Africa. Land is mechanically cleared, levelled and
ploughed. Villages are built to receive selected colonists from overcrowded parts. Originally it was hoped to produce Egyptian-type
cotton, but rice is now the prime crop and local food. There are now
about 30,000 colonists in the inland delta area and another 4,000 in a
smaller scheme near Bamako. Some attempts have been made to control
water in the live delta especially near the lakes, but here cultivators are
already established and pastoralists seek dry-season grazing (see p. 625).
The Timbuktu area has swamps and sand-dunes, but at Tosaye the river
reaches the point where the former Lake Araouane overflowed eastward
(see Chapter 3), and enters a gorge eventually opening out to the valley
containing the old Songhay capital of Gao (pop. 6,500). Here 'dallols'
enter on the left bank for brief periods. The plateaux consist of the
Mandingo plateau in the west crossed by the Bakhoy, and the Sikasso
plateau east of the Niger and Bani. Summit levels are at about 2,500
feet. Steep escarpments are frequent features and the eastern edge of
the Sikasso plateau is marked by the escarpments of Banfora (upper
Volta) and Bandiagara. In the extreme west are the valleys of the Senegal

and Faleme. Kayes (pop. 20,000), on the Senegal, is an important link in the rail and river routes between Senegal and Mali.

ECONOMY Mali has very little overseas trade. River transport can be cheap, but the rail-head at Koulikoro is 800 miles inland. The main export is groundnuts and rice is supplied to other West African countries. Cotton has proved difficult to grow despite the vast expenditure on the Niger Irrigation Scheme which is now mainly producing food crops at immense cost. Other products include shea butter, kapok, gum arabic, and fish which, dried and salted, find markets as far away as Ghana. The greatest resources lie in the 3 million cattle and 7 million sheep and goats, of which large numbers are driven annually on the hoof to Dakar, Abidjan, Kumasi and Accra. Bamako (pop. 150,000) is the capital, grown from a mere village in 1883. Timbuktu (pop. 7,000) has lost its importance with the decline of the desert caravans.

So much of Mali is arid and semi-arid that economic development is inevitably bound up with the provision of water. The future may see the tapping of underground supplies in the aquifers of the Continental Intercalaire and the younger Terminal Continental that are proving so productive in the north Sahara. Here the beds are less extensive; they lie north of the Niger bend beneath ergs between the Adrar and the western edge of the Tannezrouft.

MAURITANIA

The Islamic Republic attained independence in 1960, the last French West African dependency to do so. It has an area of 419,000 sq. miles and is almost entirely a desert state still dependent on considerable overseas financial support. This situation is likely to change with the exploitation of substantial resources of iron and copper.

PHYSICAL REGIONS Mauritania has a smooth coastline with sand-dunes and temporary marshes or lakes termed 'sebkhas' often associated with salt deposits. The River Senegal forms the southern boundary and its northern valley side provides the home of most of the republic's 920,000 population. The alluvial soil is flooded annually by the river and autumn rains give between 12 and 20 inches. This region is known as the Chemama and is the only large area of settled agriculture. Millet,

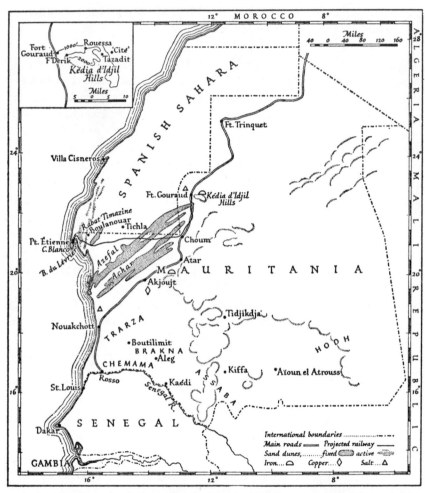

Figure 45 *Mauritania* (by permission of R. J. Harrison Church). The mineral
railway between Port Etienne and Fort Gouraud was completed in 1963

maize and rice are grown. To the north lie the low clayey and dune-
covered Plains of Trarza and Brakna, where rainfall is under 10 inches.
Here sparse grasses offer temporary grazing to cattle and sheep and acacia
gum is collected. Farther north the climate becomes even drier and the
dunes more mobile. On the boundary with Rio de Oro higher impervious
granite outcrops receive a little more moisture and support acacias,
shrubs and grasses providing a camel-rearing area.

The whole of eastern Mauritania comprises escarpment-fronted, barren and infertile sandstone plateaux, notably of Adrar, Tagant and Assaba. The imposing scarp edges, fretted by ravines, tower over occasional springs where oases have arisen, notably at Atar and Tidjikdja. Beyond lies the Sahara and, to the south, the barren basin of the Hodh.

ECONOMY In the past the chief exports have been gum arabic and dates and the population has depended mainly on sorghum, millet, rice and maize grown in the Chemama, and on the herds of cattle, sheep and goats raised on the Sahelian pastures. There is good fishing off-shore as a result of a 40-mile-wide coastal shelf over which flows the cool Canary Current, rich in plankton. Port Etienne, on the sheltered side of a 25-mile spit, provides a good base for fishing vessels and for canning factories, but hitherto it has had no hinterland and depends on distilled sea-water for its water supply. These conditions have changed, for a 400-mile-long railway (Fig. 45) has been built from the port entirely on Mauritanian territory to Fort Gouraud where opencast iron-ore mining takes place (p. 244) and rock salt is quarried. A branch line to Akjoujt is projected to enable mining of the copper ores there. A new township of 4,000 people is developing at Port Etienne, for this deep-water harbour can accommodate the big 40-foot-draught ore-carriers. Some 6 million tons of ore are being sent annually to Europe. Water is now brought to the growing port by pipeline from Boulanouar, 56 miles to the north-east.

NOUAKCHOTT (pop. 10,000) is the new capital, replacing St. Louis in Senegal. It is 200 miles north of St. Louis and the site, 4 miles from the coast, is of loose sand. Water has to be piped from 40 miles away. It represents an act of faith in the re-orientation of the economy giving greater importance to the north with the hope that minerals will provide the capital to pay for agricultural improvements. With this in view a modest four-year development plan was started in 1963. Some $56 million was to be invested, with emphasis on mining, agriculture and education.

SPANISH SAHARA

The Spanish territories of the Sahara comprise the adjoining territories of *Rio do Oro* and *Sekia el Hamra*, while to the north is *Ifni*, an enclave in Morocco to the south of the Plain of Sous. The first two territories, comprising Spanish Sahara, extend along the Atlantic coast for 600 miles between Mauritania and Morocco. Here the desert comes down to the dune-fringed coast where strong on-shore winds (mTs) from the Atlantic mitigate the heat, although they rarely bring rain (Villa Cisneros, 1·75 inches). Inland stretch great hammadas and tablelands, much dissected by former water-courses and offering sparse grazing to camel and sheep-owning nomads. The population is about 25,000 and the only towns are Villa Cisneros and El Aaiún (pop. 5,000) the newly built capital. The discovery in 1963 of rich deposits of phosphate may attract investment and allow of some economic development in future years.

Ifni is an enclave of just under 1,000 sq. miles extending some 20 miles inland from a cliffed coastline 50 miles long near the southern boundary of Morocco. The country is arid and the small crops of cereals, vegetables and dates depend mainly on irrigation from the numerous small streams which gash the coastal cliffs. Most of the population of about 50,000 live in the north where uplands averaging 2,000 feet come down to the sea. The capital is Sidi Ifni.

CANARY ISLANDS

In the Atlantic some 60 miles west of the northern boundary of Spanish Sahara lies the group of seven islands and six uninhabited islets forming the Canaries. The seven islands are Tenerife, Grand Canary, Palma, Hierro, Gomera, Lanzarote and Fuerteventura. All are of volcanic origin, the lavas being mainly basaltic. The first five islands are peaks of mountains rising abruptly from a great depth of ocean and reaching up to over 12,000 feet above sea-level. The islands are heavily populated, having 908,700 people on an area of only 2,900 sq. miles and much of it mountainous.

The islands benefit from their maritime situation in possessing a warm and pleasant climate where the great heat of the Sahara is modified and the range of temperature reduced. Las Palmas has an annual range of only 11°F (February 63°F, August 74°F) and the average diurnal range is even less. Summer winds are generally from the north-east and are responsible for a good deal of sea cloud. In the winter the hot, dry levante, a south-east wind from Africa, is occasionally experienced. Rainfall is light, except at the higher elevations, but around the coast reaches between 10 and 15 inches. The range of altitude within a limited

area set in sub-tropical latitudes favours a considerable variety of vegetation types, many of them exotic. On the lower ground up to 1,000 feet
date-palms, bananas, citrus fruits and sugar-cane supplement the xerophytic species common throughout the North African Mediterranean
littoral. Above, to about 2,800 feet, south European vegetation prevails
and the vine is grown. Higher still evergreen laurels, oaks and olives
thrive, to give way in turn to deciduous and then coniferous species.
About 7,000 feet, scrubby heaths of flowering broom predominate.

The volcanic soils are very fertile provided that water is available.
Irrigation makes possible a prosperous agriculture with emphasis on
early vegetables and tomatoes as supplementary exports to the main
trade, which is the production and export to Europe of the indigenous
small sweet banana. The mild and sunny climate has favoured the growth
of a substantial tourist trade, the two main centres being Santa Cruz
(pop. 130,000) in Tenerife and Las Palmas (pop. nearly 200,000) in
Grand Canary which is also a port of call for ocean liners.

References

1   T. Chipp, 'The vegetation of the central Sahara', *Geog. Journ.*, 76 (1930), p. 131
2   R. F. Peel, 'The Tibu peoples of the Libyan Desert', *Geog. Journ.*, 100 (1942),
        p. 83

Selected Bibliography

Oxford regional economic atlas: *The Middle East and North Africa* (Oxford, 1960)
R. Capot-Rey, *Le Sahara Français* (Paris, 1953)
E. F. Gautier, *Sahara: the great desert* (New York, 1935)
R. J. Harrison Church, *West Africa* (New York, 1961)
S. G. Willimott and J. I. Clarke (eds.), *Field Studies in Libya* (Durham, 1960)
UNESCO (ed. L. D. Stamp), *A History of land use in arid regions* (Paris, 1961),

E. Blackwelder, 'The insolation hypothesis of rock weathering', *Am. Journ. Science*,
        26 (1933), 97–113
J. I. Clarke, 'Economic and political changes in the Sahara', *Geog.*, 46 (1961)
        102–19
J. Despois, 'Le Sahara et l'écologie humaine', *Ann. de Géog.*, 70 (1961), 577–84
R. F. Peel, 'The landscape in aridity', *Trans. Inst. Brit. Geog.*, 38 (1966), 1–23
B. E. Thomas, 'Modern trans-Saharan routes', *Geog. Rev.*, 42 (1952), 267–82

J. I. Clarke, 'Oil in Libya: some implications', *Econ. Geog.*, 39 (1963), 240–59

W. B. Fisher, 'Problems of modern Libya', *Geog. Journ.*, 119 (1953), 183–99

A. T. Grove, 'Geomorphology of the Tibesti region', *Geog. Journ.*, 126 (1960), 18–31

R. J. Harrison Church, 'Problems and development of the Dry Zone of West Africa', *Geog. Journ.*, 127 (1961), 187–204

R. J. Harrison Church, 'Port Etienne: A Mauritanian pioneer town', *Geog. Journ.*, 128 (1962), 498–504

K. S. Sandford, 'Western frontiers of Libya', *Geog. Journ.*, 99 (1942), 29–40

PART VI

The Nile Basin and Horn of Africa

The Sahara stretches its barren wastes across North Africa to the Red Sea. Yet in its north-east quadrant, where it cradles the great basin of the River Nile and extends towards the mass of the Ethiopian highlands, it offers a surprising diversity of terrain that has provided a home for man since the earliest recorded time. Today the peoples of this part of Africa are a mixture of Caucasian stock with the black or Negro race. Here was the threshold across which Hamitic and later Semitic peoples entered the continent from Arabia to displace the Negro peoples, the purest of whom are now to be found in West Africa. Ancient Egyptians were probably a fusion of the Hamite and Semite, later becoming diluted with Negro elements from the south. In the seventh century A.D. Semitic Arabs conquered Egypt and spread up the Nile valley, while others crossed the Red Sea into Ethiopia and the Sudan. Gradually these became merged with the indigenous peoples, but Arab culture, language and religion now extend firmly from the Mediterranean to the northern limits of the Sudd and from the Indian Ocean into the foothills of the Ethiopian highlands.

22

Geology, Relief and Drainage

STRUCTURE AND GEOLOGY

The basin of the River Nile is delimited on the east by the Red Sea and Ethiopian highlands, in the south by the East African highlands north of Lake Victoria, whence the Nile issues, and to the west the less-well-defined watershed between the Nile, Chad and Congo basins trending north-west to include the Marra Mountains of the Sudan, the Gilf Kebir plateau and Libyan desert to the Mediterranean.

Structurally and geologically this part of Africa includes three distinctive major elements. Much of the area, particularly in the Sudan, is floored by the Crystalline Basement Complex; to the north of the Sudan and into Egypt increasingly younger sedimentary rocks bear witness to succeeding incursions and withdrawals of the sea (Fig. 46); south and east of the Sudan the highland masses represent a period of disturbance and uplift with rifting and much vulcanicity.

Rocks of the Archaean Basement are exposed at the surface over more than 50 per cent of the Sudan and 10 per cent of Egypt. Outcrops of these igneous and metamorphic rocks in the Nile valley account for the cataracts. In the Sudan they are partly masked by recent deposits, some of continental origin arising from weathering under arid conditions and others of alluvial character mainly from the vast semi-inland drainage centre of the Sudd. The Crystalline Basement rocks extend in a long tongue from Ethiopia and the Sudan northward along the Red Sea coast as far as the Gulf of Suez, and form the highest mountains in the south of the Sinai Peninsula; they are continued across the Red Sea in Arabia. West of the Nile they are less prominent, but form a basement for the Tertiary lavas, mainly basalts, which make up the Jebel Marra and are responsible for Mount 'Uweinat in south-west Egypt.

The Nubian Sandstone is the product of very long periods of continental weathering and denudation of the Archaean Basement rocks. The great thicknesses of sandstones (in places of more than 1,500 feet) also contain occasional beds of clays, marls and conglomerates. These unfossiliferous rocks range in age from the Carboniferous to the Cretaceous and cover about 25 per cent of the Sudan and 30 per cent of Egypt. They derive their name from the district of Nubia in the northern Sudan and extend

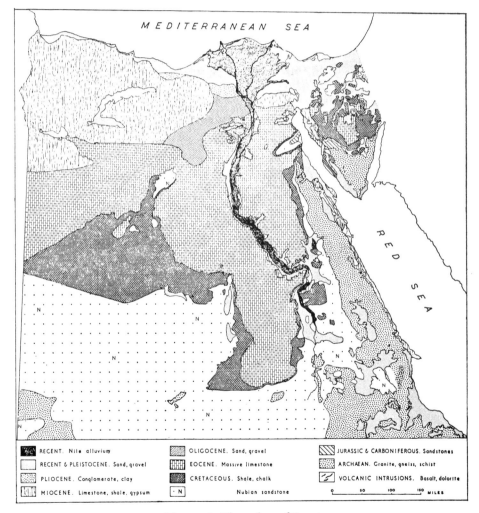

RECENT. Nile alluvium	OLIGOCENE. Sand, gravel	JURASSIC & CARBONIFEROUS. Sandstones
RECENT & PLEISTOCENE. Sand, gravel	EOCENE. Massive limestone	ARCHAEAN. Granite, gneiss, schist
PLIOCENE. Conglomerate, clay	CRETACEOUS. Shale, chalk	VOLCANIC INTRUSIONS. Basalt, dolorite
MIOCENE. Limestone, shale, gypsum	· N Nubian sandstone	0 50 100 150 MILES

Figure 46 *The geology of Egypt*

widely across the Sahara. They possess the valuable property of being aquiferous and convey northward much of the precipitation falling on the Darfur-Ennedi-Tibesti highland. Following the Archaean rocks they dip gently to the north and provide water for wells at a number of oases in the Western and Libyan deserts. To the north, in Egypt, these sandstones provide the base upon which later marine and fluvial deposits were laid down. The sinking of the land to the north during the later Cretaceous allowed an advance of the sea, followed in succeeding geological periods by alternate uplifts and subsidences affecting the northern two-thirds of Egypt. The Cretaceous Sea penetrated 600 miles from the present coastline and left thick calcareous deposits. These were in turn succeeded by Eocene limestones. These are the most widespread of the marine deposits in Egypt, extending over the central section of the Western desert and, because of a warp of the underlying older surface, forming a deep embayment west of the Nile to just south of the latitude of Aswan. They form the northern part of the Eastern desert between the Nile and the Red Sea highlands and part of the central plateau of Sinai, representing a striking plateau of massive limestone cut into by the Nile for over 400 miles from near Esna to Cairo. It is this formation that has provided most of the building stone used in the valley and delta.

The crustal movements of the Alpine mountain-building period began near the close of the Oligocene with the formation of the Red Sea Basin and uplift of its bordering mountains. A considerable uplift of the Crystalline Basement rocks of the Ethiopian highlands had taken place rather earlier, probably towards the close of the Eocene, but the real shaping of the Horn of Africa as we know it occurred with the great displacements and fracturings of the Oligocene-Miocene period when the creation of the Red Sea trough and Gulf of Aden severed Africa from Arabia. This period of crustal disturbance had much influence upon the evolution of the River Nile and led to the cutting of the great trench of the Nile valley in a broad syncline paralleling the anticline of the Red Sea highlands. This was completed during the Pliocene.

The incursion of the Pliocene sea was more local, mainly affecting the Nile syncline and the Red Sea trough, where fluviatile conglomerates, gravels and sands were deposited. The deposits of the Quaternary include the oolitic limestones of the coastal strip west of Alexandria; the gravels, sands and Nile mud of the delta and Nile valley; and the drifted sands of the Western desert formed by aeolian action upon disintegrating bedrock. In the Pleistocene, contemporaneous with the Ice Ages in

Europe, Egypt experienced pluvial periods. Torrential river flow of these times accounts for sands, gravels and large pebbles which form the basement of the present cultivated alluvium of the delta. This alluvium is very recent (probably it has been deposited during the last 16,000 years) and is derived mainly from the weathering and erosion of the volcanic rocks of the Ethiopian highlands.

Much detailed work has yet to be done on the geology and geomorphology of the Ethiopian highlands, but the general pattern is understood and its structural relationship with the East African highlands appreciated. There is, however, evidence of far more vulcanicity than in East Africa. Much of the lofty plateau of the Ethiopian highlands has been built up on massive lava sheets, which issued from both fissures and volcanoes that accompanied the series of tectonic adjustments affecting this zone of instability. Archaean crystalline rocks again form the basement upon which Mesozoic seas transgressed. They deposited sandstones and limestones, particularly in the east of the present upland mass. Towards the end of the Eocene, but before the main Alpine movements, considerable uplift took place. For example, some of the Jurassic sediments are now resting at 9,000 feet above sea-level. While there were some deformations, a general uniformity of uplift is apparent in the wide expanses of near-perfect plateau. The uplift was accompanied by the upwelling of magma and the ejection throughout the rest of the Tertiary period of vast quantities of lava, mainly basalts and trachytes sometimes several thousand feet thick, upon the Mesozoic surface or the Crystalline Basement.

The great crustal adjustments accompanying the Alpine orogenesis produced the striking series of rifts from Syria through Ethiopia to south-east Africa (see Chapter 1). Colossal fracturing and displacement occurred (often of up to 6,000 feet) which by the creation of a major rift valley aligned south-south-west towards Lake Rudolph here splits the highland mass into two unequal parts: the Ethiopian Plateau to the north-west and the Somali plateau (sometimes called the Central plateau) to the south-east. Renewed vulcanicity accompanied these great movements and the younger volcanic series (as it is termed) produced not only great lava sheets, but also a large number of volcanoes. The Crystalline Basement extends through Danakil to the Red Sea and in the east through Ogaden into Somalia. Less disturbed, and without lava cappings, the gneisses and schists are here responsible for sandy plateau country descending from 5,000 to 1,150 feet above sea-level.

The great mass of the Ethiopian highlands (Fig. 57), rising abruptly from surrounding deserts, dominates the geography of north-east Africa. This highland mass averages 7,000–8,000 feet in height, but its rolling upland tracts are deeply scarred by fissures (often of fault origin) and overlooked by lofty bastions 13,000–15,000 feet in elevation. The main ranges flank the rift valley and then bifurcate, the Harar highlands swinging to the east through northern Somalia to constitute the 'horn' of Africa, while the major range on the northern side swings due north, its 8,000-foot escarpment overlooking the Danakil scrub desert. Heavy rainfall and steep slopes produce powerful rivers which cut deeply into the volcanic rocks dividing the plateau into semi-isolated blocks. The highest peaks are in the Simen ranges in Amhara. These run north-east from Lake Tana and comprise a number of peaks, sometimes snow-covered, over 12,000 feet high, culminating in Ras Dashan, 15,160 feet.

The rift valley from the neighbourhood of Lake Rudolf is a clearly defined trench and contains a chain of lakes, some of considerable size (Lake Abaya is 50 miles long). The northern third of the rift is drained by the River Awash issuing from the Shoan uplands west of Addis Ababa and then, 50 miles from the coast, losing itself in the more arid funnel-shaped low plateau into which the rift has widened. Only a few short streams flow eastward, in turn also to peter out in the Danakil desert or in salty marshes short of the coast. The effective drainage of the mountain limb south of the rift valley is by a number of streams which unite in Somalia to form the River Juba. They rise on the Archaean rocks and flow, deeply incised, over Triassic and Jurassic strata to the coast.

The principal drainage of the highlands, however, is to the Nile Basin by means of three principal rivers; the Sobat, the Blue Nile and the Atbara (Takkaze). These three rivers account for four-fifths of the entire drainage. The Sobat gathers its waters from a number of streams rising in the south-west corner of Ethiopia. These tributaries descend in great falls (Boro Falls, 3,000 feet in 45 miles) and are unnavigable until the eastern edge of the Sudd is reached. During the flood (June–December) the river is navigable by steamer from Gambela to the junction with the White Nile.

The Blue Nile rises in the Gojjam highlands, flows north into the

Graham Finlayson

3 Papyrus boats beside Lake Chad

4 Tississat Falls on the Blue Nile near Lake Tana, Ethiopia

shallow Lake Tana (6,000 feet) and then out again by a series of rapids
and falls (Plate 4), plunging into a deep gorge, in places 4,000 feet below
the general level of the plateau. It flows first in a south-easterly direction
and then swings round to flow west and then north-west through the
Sudan to join the White Nile at Khartoum. Most of its water comes from
its torrential tributary streams (rather than from Lake Tana), themselves
the product of heavy seasonal rainfall. The Atbara's principal headstream,
the Takkaze (the Terrible), rises among the high peaks of Amhara and
flows north in a spectacular gorge to join the Atbara in the Sudan, which
in turn flows into the Nile nearly 200 miles below Khartoum. In the
Ethiopian highlands mountain glaciers were responsible for much erosion
and some deposition during the Pleistocene. They have dwindled away
with the onset of warmer conditions but helped to initiate many of the
gorges now being deepened by powerful rivers and proving so obstruc-
tive to communications but advantageous to local rulers and local
loyalties.

In contrast to Ethiopia the relief of the Sudan is low and relatively
uniform. Half the Sudan is below 1,500 feet and constitutes the plain
of the River Nile; only about 2 per cent is over 3,500 feet. Most of the
republic is included in the Nile Basin and mainly comprises vast clay
plains and extensive sandy areas of low undulations, emphasised in a
few localities by isolated granite hill masses such as the Red Sea highlands,
the Nuba Mountains of Kordofan in central Sudan and the Jebel Marra
of Darfur province.

The Nuba Mountains comprise a number of isolated granitic hill
masses, most rising abruptly from a detritus-strewn pediment of rocks
of the Archaean Basement Complex. Elevations of nearly 5,000 feet are
attained, which is about 3,000 feet above the surrounding plain and
sufficient for a rather heavier and more reliable rainfall, although not
enough to nurture permanent streams. The Jebel Marra in western Darfur
are volcanic masses mainly of basalt, also resting on the Archaean Basement. The range is not extensive, being about 70 miles north to south
and 30 miles east to west. It attains 10,073 feet. An upwarping of the
basement along the Lake Chad-Nile divide here gives a general elevation
of about 3,000 feet to the plain proper. The Red Sea highlands, also
formed of Crystalline Basement rocks, are a northward continuation of
the hills of northern Ethiopia; elevated during the Alpine orogeny, the
uplift was accompanied by faulting (the Red Sea rift being formed)
and some vulcanicity. In the south, Nubian Sandstone locally preserved

under lava flows suggests that this formation has now been eroded from the Red Sea highlands. These average 4,000–5,000 feet and are much dissected, offering steep escarpments to the Red Sea.

Highlands continue to flank the Red Sea in Egypt, presenting a tangled arid upland mass heavily faulted and dissected and exhibiting a wide range of rock types with granites predominating. The ranges extend northward over 500 miles to the Gulf of Suez. A number of peaks rise to over 6,000 feet, the highest being Gebel Shayeb (7,150 feet). These hills constitute over a third of Egypt's Eastern desert, the remainder being the platform of sedimentary rocks sloping to the Nile; mainly Nubian Sandstone to the great Nile bend and massive Eocene limestone farther north. It was the drainage from the Red Sea Mountains in more pluvial periods that accounts for the acute dissection of these sedimentary rocks, making the character of the Eastern desert very different from that of the Western desert. This Western desert is indeed the eastern part of the Sahara proper. It is a massive plateau of sedimentary rocks, mainly limestone, resting upon the Nubian Sandstone and Archaean Basement. Few parts exceed 1,000 feet and slopes are gentle except in a few deep basins, such as the Qattara Depression and the oasis depressions of Kharga, Dakhla, Baharyia, Farafra, Faiyûm and Siwa.

THE RIVER NILE

The greater part of north-east Africa is drained by the Nile, the father of African rivers. By its anomalous behaviour the Nile long troubled the ancients, who advanced delightful theories to account for this great river flowing for 1,500 miles across a desert and rising to a flood in the summer, contrary to all experience in their Mediterranean world. Exploration up the Nile was much obstructed by the cataracts and then the marshy Sudd and it was not until 1862, when Speke and Grant penetrating north from East Africa met at Gondokoro Sir Samuel Baker travelling south from Cairo, that the origin and course of the river became verified.

The Nile is estimated to be over 4,100 miles long from its source at the head of the Luvironza river which flows into Lake Victora. Its south-to-north flow, reaching the Mediterranean on almost the same meridian as its source, marks it off from other major African rivers which mainly trend east and west. In all, it flows through 35 degrees of latitude (3°50′S to 31°50′N) and consequently through the range of climates from equatorial to Mediterranean. The long profile of the river (Fig. 7) shows four distinct sections and serves to emphasise other anomalous features. The first section is that within the Lake plateau of East Africa, comprising a number of headstreams and lakes that feed the White Nile. This issues from Lake Victoria by the Ripon Falls (now submerged by the lake formed behind the Owen Falls Dam just to the north) and passes through the swamp vegetation of the shallow Lake Kyoga into Lake Albert via the Murchison Falls. From Lake Albert the river, now called the Bahr el Jebel (river of the mountains), falls at first gently but later by a series of rapids from the plateau to the swampy Sudd Plains.

The second section as far as the Sabaloka (or Shabluka) gorge is one of very low gradient. The river passes through the Sudd, accepting the Bahr el Ghazal (river of gazelles) from the west, the Sobat to the north of the marshes and then the Blue Nile at Khartoum. The Sobat floods in summer as a result of the Ethiopian monsoon and causes widespread inundations over the 200 miles of plains though which its middle and lower course passes before joining the White Nile. These widespread marshes delay the arrival of the high level at the White Nile junction by as much as three months. In this stretch of the White Nile the gradient is no more than 1 : 19,000.

From the sixth cataract at Sabaloka, 50 miles north of Khartoum, for the next 1,200 miles as far as Aswan the river bed alternates between gentle stretches and series of rapids where outcropping crystalline rocks provide the famous cataracts. Below Aswan the fourth section is of low uninterrupted gradient to the sea, with the river generally incised into the sandstone and limestone surface rocks. Just below Cairo, about 100 miles from the Mediterranean, the river bifurcates and flows in two distributaries, the Rosetta and Damietta branches across the level funnel-shaped delta to the sea.

Evolution of the River Nile

The alternation of graded and ungraded sections in the long profile suggests that the present river is relatively young and represents the amalgamation of a number of formerly independent systems. Tertiary earth-movements are thought to be the principal cause of adjustments in the drainage pattern.

In the mid-Tertiary times the proto-Nile was a much shorter stream draining little more than the present Egypt and flowing into the Tethys whose shoreline was as far inland as Cairo. By the end of the Miocene, rejuvenation caused the river to cut back into the newly uplifted Sabaloka ridge and subsequently to gain the Atbara as one of its headstreams. South of Sabaloka stood the vast inland drainage basin of Lake Sudd which grew in size as other independent systems to the south in turn emptied into it as a result of earth-movement. The series of falls on the rivers within the East African plateau are relatively recent links between formerly independent drainage basins. The Lake Edward drainage became linked with Lake Albert, which in turn following a faultline emptied via the Nimule-Gondokoro rapids into the Bahr el Jebel. From the east the Blue Nile also found its way into this great Lake Sudd.

The breaching of the Sabaloka ridge and the release of these waters to the north may well have occurred no more than 20,000–25,000 years ago in the late Pleistocene, when the waters from yet another independent East African system, that of Lake Victoria-Lake Kyoga, found an escape northward into Lake Sudd. Shorelines around Lake Victoria 300 feet and 100 feet above the present lake-level give support to these theories; the first representing the lake-level before the breaching of the Ripon Falls and union with Lake Kioga (in the Pliocene), and the second (much more recent) when the Murchison Falls were created by the Lake Kyoga waters finding an escape north into Lake Albert and the Sudd. With these great accretions of water, and additional sedimentation over a long period, the level of Lake Sudd rose, filled the course of a small tributary flowing south from the Sabaloka ridge, spilled over to the north and began the cutting of the overflow channel now called the Sabaloka gorge. The overflow waters linked the two major parts of the Nile system and the great river as we know it is therefore but a baby in terms of geological time.

23

Climate and Vegetation

Since the basin of the River Nile extends for some 2,000 miles from the Mediterranean to the East African plateau, and we add for our present purpose also the whole highland mass of Ethiopia and the dry Horn of Africa, it is clear that a number of distinctive climates may be discerned. Virtually the whole of the north-east quadrant of Africa experiences tropical climate. Marine influences are remarkably limited and it is relief that introduces variation into otherwise model climatic transitions related to changing latitude. Much of the region is part of the far larger desert belt of Africa and Arabia, dominated all the year round by cTs air (see Figs. 9 and 10).

During the northern winter when the ITC is far to the south, dry north and north-easterly winds penetrate deep into Africa and almost the whole of the Nile Basin is rainless. In the northern summer the ITC usually moves as far north as the central Sudan; then the southern part of the Nile Basin, including the highland mass of Ethiopia, experiences air-masses of mE type drawn from the south-west to the monsoonal centres of Ethiopia and India. These moist air-masses behind the ITC are responsible for the characteristic summer rainfall alternating with winter drought in the Sudan. It is these moist airstreams impinging upon the mountain-masses of East Africa and Ethiopia that release heavy rainfall (over 60 inches) and nurture and sustain the Nile in its 1,500-mile sinuous traverse across the Sahara.

Nowhere within the Nile Basin is true equatorial or true Mediterranean climate experienced. The plateau character of Uganda and Tanganyika modifies the equatorial climate; and the southern shores of the eastern basin of the Mediterranean, being 5 degrees farther south than those of the western basin, are but little affected by the winter depressions which move eastward along a more northerly course. The Mediterranean therefore has but limited effect; it cools the northern shores and grants a few inches of rain to a very narrow fringe of the Nile delta in winter. The Red Sea, almost entirely enclosed, is hot at all seasons and also has only local influence upon the surrounding even hotter shores.

CLIMATIC REGIONS (Fig. 47)

1. *The Somalia coastlands and lower plateau* Somalia is hot and dry throughout the year. With the northward advance of the ITC, marine

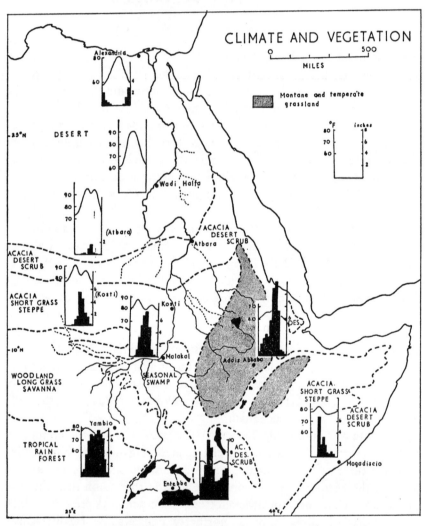

Figure 47 *Nile Basin and Horn of Africa, climate and vegetation*

Table 6

Station	Alt. (feet)		J	F	M	A	M	J	J	A	S	O	N	D	Year	Temp. range
Mogadiscio	59	Temp. °F	77	79	81	82	80	77	75	76	76	77	76	77	78	7
		Rain in.	—	—	—	7·0	2·2	3·5	2·0	0·6	0·5	0·7	0·4	—	16·9	
Berbera	31	T.	76	76	78	82	87	96	98	97	91	83	79	77	85	22
		R.	0·1	0·3	0·7	0·5	0·4	—	0·1	0·1	—	0·1	—	0·1	2·4	
Addis Ababa	8,005	T.	60	63	65	65	66	64	62	61	61	62	59	59	62	7
		R.	0·4	1·3	3·0	4·7	5·0	3·5	5·1	6·3	3·7	1·4	0·6	0·4	35·3	

tropical air from the Indian Ocean impinges upon this part of Africa, having been deflected eastward on crossing the equator. These airstreams flow parallel with the coast across the gently rolling low plateau of Ogaden and the Haud (1,000–3,000 feet), from the north-east in winter and south-west in summer. In the winter months no rain at all is recorded and the summer rainfall is light. The sudden arrival of the moist south-west winds brings a monsoonal 'burst' to Mogadiscio in April, when nearly half the annual 17 inches falls (Table 6).

In the summer off the east coast of Somalia the sea is several degrees cooler than in the open ocean because of the upwelling along the coast of water from the ocean depths (p. 62). This leads to frequent fogs between June and August and is a further contributive cause of the aridity of the littoral. This east coast is much cooler (10–15°F) than the north coast opposite the Gulf of Aden. Much of Somalia consists of the intermediate plateau country between the narrow coastal plains and the Ethiopian highlands. The light rainfall (about 15 inches) and average temperature at 4,500 feet of 60°F January to 75°F July make this a region of semi-arid thorn-bush grazing.

Thus Somalia, peripheral to the massive upland of Ethiopia, experiences desert and semi-desert conditions. Its highest rainfall in the Ogaden is only 18 inches. The prevailing vegetation is grass with thorn bush and numerous species of acacia. As is frequent in tropical latitudes the appearance of the countryside changes markedly with the seasons, dry brown grasses and leafless tree thickets during the dry season giving way to astonishing growth and verdure with the arrival of the rain.

2. *The Red Sea hills and coastlands* The narrow strip of land flanking the Gulf of Aden and the Red Sea, frequently backed by fault scarps, is one of the hottest regions of the world. Rainfall is very scanty (3 to 5 inches) and differs from that of Somalia in being winter rain. This comes from the north-east winds which give mists and light rains on the hills behind the coast. Virtually no summer rain is experienced, for the ITC normally only just attains latitude 20°N and consequently summer temperatures are not mitigated by rainfall. Temperatures of over 100°F are recorded daily in August. At Berbera the mean temperature for the summer months exceeds 90°F and in July the mean temperature is 98°F. Even the coolest month at Berbera has a mean temperature of 76°F (Table 6). Much of this is desert; at best vegetation is limited to

sparse herbs and scrubby bushes from which gums and resins are collected and which offer frugal pasture for sheep and goats.

3. *The Highlands of Ethiopia* Masses of mE air blowing from the south-west, and possibly supplemented by the indraught from the Indian Ocean, give heavy rainfall farther inland upon the Ethiopian highlands. This rain is heaviest in the south-west of the plateau where in places it exceeds 70 inches and gives at least 40 inches over most of the plateau above 6,000 feet. Most of this part of the highlands is drained by tributaries of the Nile. The rains begin in early April but become heavy and consistent in July, August and September. The heavy downfalls run off the crystalline rocks with great rapidity and torrents of red-brown floodwater sweep down the deep gorges on their way to Egypt and the Mediterranean. The rift valley being partially in the rain shadow receives about 25 inches, but the Danakil plateau, full in the rain shadow and receiving the descending winds, is hot and arid.

Ethiopians divide their country climatically and vegetationally into three altitude levels. The first is the *kolla*, the lower land up to 5,000 feet: mainly valley bottoms which are hot, sticky and in parts still malarial. Secondly, there is the *woina dega* (wine highland), 5,000–9,000 feet and the most attractive part for settlement with good pastures and well-cultivated fertile volcanic soils. At Addis Ababa the warmest month has an average temperature of 66°F and the coolest, November, 59°F. The rainy season of May to September is regarded as winter; the dry season as the summer. The third zone is the *dega* (highland), comprising all above 9,000 feet where conditions of heavy rainfall and cold do not favour settlement. It will be seen that despite its tropical latitude the plateau enjoys a mild temperature throughout the year. Diurnal range, in fact, is greater than annual range, for the mean diurnal range for the year in many parts of the plateau is 20–30°F, whereas the difference between the means of the warmest and coldest months is only of the order of 6°F. With a mean annual temperature at Asmara of 65°F and at Addis Ababa of 62°F this climate has been termed one of perennial spring (Table 6).

The great range of climate with varying altitude means that almost all forms of African vegetation are found in the Ethiopian highlands. The deep valleys of the *kolla* are forested with a range of tropical trees including ebony, bananas, rubber vines and bamboo, while the indigenous coffee shrub flourishes. The more open plateau tracts at 5,000–6,000 feet in the interior provide open park land with few trees although in the moister south-west there is greater tree growth. In the cool middle highland, *woina dega* (up to 9,000 feet) wooded or park savanna prevails, grassland with thorny trees but no extensive woodland—indeed wide views over great distances are possible. In this zone species of fig and native juniper thrive as do Mediterranean fruits and cereals. The higher and colder *dega* contains more grass but fewer trees and shrubs. Broadly these correspond to Alpine pastures but include great thistles and giant lobelias some of which attain 20 feet in height.

4. *The Rainlands of the southern and central Sudan* Throughout the Sudan, climatic conditions reflect the lack of notable physical barriers obstructing the airstreams from the Mediterranean to the East African plateau; this means that climatic conditions can change gradually with the latitude. No rain falls during the period of these north-easterly winds (cT type) and vegetation is dominated by the two-season character of the year, one rainy the other dry. All vegetation is tropophilous, in response to this climatic regime. In the extreme south the dry season is short, lasting from December to February, and is the hottest period of the year. Being within 5 degrees of the equator the annual range of tempera-ture is low (Juba: March 85°F, August 77.5°F, rainfall 38 inches). By the latitude of Khartoum the dry season lasts eight months and the mean annual rainfall is 5 inches. The rainfall totals in the south reflect both the increasing relief and proximity to the equator, for over 40 to 50 inches—with two maxima, associated with the overhead passage of the ITC—are experienced annually along the Sudan–Uganda border, but this amount diminishes steadily northward. Conditions at Khartoum are semi-arid and true desert occurs immediately to the north.

In the central Sudan three seasons are generally recognised: (1) the hot and very dry, early summer (March–June); (2) the hot rainy period (July–October); (3) the cool dry winter. In June daily temperature at Khartoum reaches 94°F, for the north wind (cT air) blows off the Sahara and dust storms are frequent. The rain comes with the south-west winds and temperatures fall perceptibly (Khartoum, August mean daily temp. 87°F). The rainy season lasts three to seven months according to latitude and the progress of the ITC. It is followed by the cooler and dry winter when skies remain cloudless and temperatures vary between 70° and 80°F (Table 7).

The prevailing vegetation in its character, height and thickness can be correlated closely with the amount of rainfall, the major variable factor in the climate. Consequently, a series of zones changing from south to

Table 7

Station	Alt. (feet)		J	F	M	A	M	J	J	A	S	O	N	D	Year	Temp. range
Khartoum	1,280	Temp. °F	70	74	79	86	91	92	89	87	88	88	80	72	83	22
		Rain in.	—	—	—	—	0·1	0·3	1·6	2·2	0·7	0·2	—	—	5·1	
Cairo	98	T.	55	57	63	70	76	80	82	82	78	74	65	58	70	27
		R.	0·4	0·2	0·2	0·2	—	—	—	—	—	—	0·1	0·2	1·3	
Alexandria	105	T.	58	60	63	67	72	76	79	81	79	75	68	61	70	23
		R.	2·2	0·9	0·5	0·2	—	—	—	—	—	0·3	1·4	2·6	8·1	

north may be observed (Fig. 47). In the extreme south are a few limited areas of evergreen tropical forests, but with the gradual extension of the dry season as one moves north the prevailing vegetation of the southern Sudan is rather open wooded savanna containing broad-leaved deciduous trees with grasses attaining 5 feet or more as the dominant ground herb. Nearly 100,000 sq. miles of the south-central Sudan comprises the Sudd or Flood Region. This consists of numerous rivers with floating vegetation amid marshy, reedy swamp zones and slightly elevated interfluves supporting perennial grasses and herbs.

Farther north, as the dry season lengthens and the total annual rainfall diminishes, the grasses become shorter and the trees sparser and lower. Below 20 inches thorny and more drought-resistant species appear. In general the grasses in the central Sudan are sweet and many of the shrubs are also browsed: the acacia short-grass steppe provides an important cattle-rearing region. This vegetation degenerates to steppe or semi-desert below the 15-inch isohyet. The sparse stunted trees and scrub woodland exhibit water-storage devices such as fleshy leaves and waxy surfaces to reduce transpiration. Prominent among them are various species of acacia and here and there the majestic baobab.

5. *The desert of Egypt and the northern Sudan* North of the 5-inch isohyet is true desert which extends northwards almost as far as the Mediterranean coast. The principal characteristics are aridity, a considerable temperature range (both seasonal and diurnal), a dry atmosphere and a high amount of sunshine throughout the year. The desert is not entirely bereft of vegetation, for here and there sparse scrub vegetation and tussocks of coarse grass may appear among wadi floors—especially in the east and on the flanks of the Red Sea highlands. Within this Saharan zone summer temperatures surpass 100°F (Aswan, mean daily max. June, 107°F), the sun burning down from a cloudless sky. At night, a fall of 25–30°F takes place. Rainfall is meagre and very irregular. Years may pass without any precipitation and then a sudden storm may give one or two inches. In the spring sporadic depressions from the Sahara traverse eastwards to the Delta of Egypt and are responsible for excessively dry southerly winds which sometimes bring dust and sand storms (khamsin) and which may persist for three to four days. During the winter, temperatures drop substantially (the January mean being 55–60°F) but frosts are unknown in the Nile valley and plant growth continues. The Egyptian year therefore is one of somewhat monotonous climatic conditions where two seasons

only are clearly distinguishable: the hot summer from May to October heralded by the khamsin, and the cooler winter from November to April.

6. *The Mediterranean coastlands*   The climate of the Mediterranean coast for a few miles inland differs from that of the rest of Egypt since it experiences a small winter rainfall (4–8 inches), milder winters but slightly lower summer temperatures (Alexandria, January 58°F, August 81°F. Table 7) as a result of the tempering effect of the sea and a prevailing onshore wind from the north-west. Winter depressions along the Mediterranean bring to this limited area strong winds, cool weather and short but heavy rains. The Delta shares the characteristics of both Mediterranean and Saharan climates, having a small winter rainfall (Alexandria 8 inches diminishing southwards to 1·4 inches at Cairo), mild winter temperatures and hot dry summers (Cairo, January 55°, July 82°F).

24

Nile Hydrology, Conservation and Irrigation

This century has seen the establishment of a series of large-scale irrigation works on the Nile that has radically transformed the Nile valley of Egypt and the Sudan to permit it to support nearly 35 million out of the 45 million living in the Nile Basin. Immense study of the whole river has had to be made; as a result, our knowledge of the character and regime of the Nile is probably greater than that of any other major river in the world and already the Nile is controlled and harnessed to a very high degree for the benefit of humanity. An apparently anomalous situation, perpetuated and expanded throughout historic time, is that now some 25 million live beside the river within the Sahara desert and therefore must rely utterly upon the rains that fall to feed the Nile in the tropical zone some 1,500 to 2,000 miles away. These people, in Egypt, therefore have an urgent interest in hydrological knowledge and conservation measures throughout the whole Nile Basin.

Comprehensive conservation schemes propounded soon after World War II might well have led to the establishment of a Nile Valley Authority (cf. TVA) for the mutual benefit of all the riparian states, but, lack of interest on the part of Ethiopia, suspicion and fear in Egypt and a general air of procrastination left the plans in abeyance. After 1952 the new revolutionary and nationalistic government in Egypt recognised the seriousness of mounting pressure of population and determined, at enormous expense, on the creation on Egyptian soil of the largest artificial dam in the world, the High Dam at Aswan.

The annual discharge curve of the river showing the contributions of major tributaries is demonstrated in Fig. 48. The diagram makes clear the overwhelming part that the Blue Nile plays in bringing the river to its great flood in August, September and October in Egypt and demonstrates the small flooding capacity of the White Nile. This is because the White Nile headstreams lie in regions receiving rain all through the year; further, the sequence of lakes and the Sudd through which it flows serve as regulators and even out moderate fluctuations of discharge. There is a tremendous loss of water by evaporation in the Sudd; the greater the rains the more the loss, for greater inundation follows, so increasing the surface of water subject to evaporation. The White Nile (Bahr el Jebel) enters the Sudd at Mongalla with an average flow of 27 billion cu.m. per annum and leaves it at Malakal, where the average flow is only 14 billion cu.m. per annum. In other words only half the water passing Mongalla reaches the junction with the Sobat; one is also led to conclude that much of the summer rain of the southern Sudan never reaches the Nile at all. In the south Sudan the flood begins in April but it does not reach Aswan in Egypt until July; similarly in the south the flood wanes by November but in the north not until January.

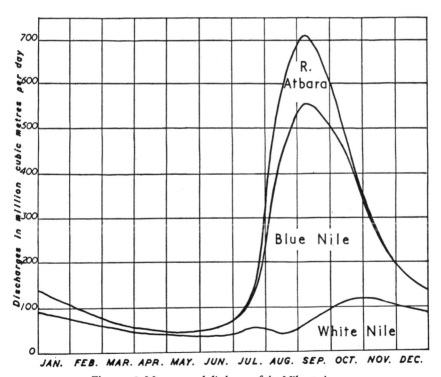

Figure 48 *Mean annual discharge of the Nile at Aswan*

The great flood of the Nile, so beneficial to Egypt, is the result of the torrential summer monsoonal rains of the Ethiopian plateau which sweep down through deep gorges to swell in chocolate-coloured flood the Blue Nile and Atbara. The Blue Nile is a perennial stream but the Atbara shrinks to a series of pools in the dry season, January to June. An analysis of the Nile flow at Aswan reveals that at maximum discharge in early September the White Nile accounts for 10 per cent of the discharge, the Blue Nile for 68 per cent, the Atbara 22 per cent; the total discharge being about 700 million cu.m. per day. In early May when Nile discharge is at a minimum it is made up as follows: White Nile 83 per cent, Blue Nile 17 per cent; the total discharge being only 45 million cu.m. per day. In the average year 84 per cent of Nile water at Aswan comes from Ethiopia and 16 per cent from the East African lake plateau.[1]

NILE CONSERVATION AND IRRIGATION

Throughout much of the Sudan and practically the whole of Egypt agriculture necessarily relies upon irrigation. This reliance is partial in the Sudan but total in Egypt and is based almost entirely upon the waters of the Nile. The use of the Nile for irrigation in Egypt may be traced back to the dawn of history, when seed was sown in the mud left after the annual flood waters had subsided. With the passage of time this became refined with the division of the land by earth banks into a series of large basins in which the silt-laden waters were allowed to stand for about forty days before being permitted to drain back to the river. Seed was still sown in the fertile surface layer of mud; the crops grew throughout the winter and were reaped in April and May when the land remained fallow and parched until the next August flood. This form of basin irrigation is still practised on about 700,000 feddans* of Upper Egypt. The provision of masonry regulators between the distributary canals and the basins is an innovation that allows more positive control of the water. The disadvantage that only one crop per year can be grown on basin land (unless well water is available to supply a summer crop) becomes more onerous as the number of mouths to be fed in Egypt grows more rapidly. As a consequence, basins are being gradually converted to perennial irrigation as more Nile water becomes available.

This form of irrigation, while fitting the annual regime of the river, is at the mercy of the year-to-year fluctuations in the size of the flood

* 1 feddan = 1·038 acres

(hence the 'seven fat and seven lean years' of the Old Testament), and as numbers grew it became imperative to adopt a more sophisticated, albeit far more expensive, irrigation system. Perennial irrigation which now serves most of Egypt's farmland is much more complicated, involving great storage reservoirs both in Egypt and in the Sudan, a system of barrages (or large weirs) across the river to raise the level of the water to feed a comprehensive system of distributary canals and an intricate drainage system to carry the used water to the sea.

Perennial irrigation began in Egypt about 1820 when Mohammed Ali attempted to extend the area under summer crops (and especially cotton) by creating a system of canals in the Delta. This was unsuccessful, for the Nile was too low at this season, and in 1843 Muhammad Ali agreed to the building of a barrage across the Nile at its bifurcation at the head of the Delta. This was intended to pond back the river to raise the level of water upstream for the supplying of the canals. Engineering techniques were then inadequate and full success did not attend this ingenious scheme until long after Muhammad Ali's death. It was not until 1890, when British engineers completed a major work of reconstruction, that the Delta Barrage functioned properly and made possible the spread of perennial irrigation throughout the Delta.

The British occupied Egypt after 1882 and put in hand an ambitious irrigation programme (Fig. 49). This led to the building of other barrages across the Nile and to the construction of two vast reservoirs at Aswan (completed 1902 and enlarged in 1912 and 1934) and Jebel Aulia in the Sudan (1937), for it became clear that the only way to supply plentiful water during spring and early summer when the Nile was low would be by conserving surplus water from the previous flood. In this way the great annual fluctuation of the river could be reduced somewhat and early summer water guaranteed. Thus perennial irrigation in its present form in Egypt has been developed only during this century.

In practice the sluice gates of the dams and barrages are opened during the flood and the great rush of water cleanses them of silt. As the flood begins to subside the sluice gates are closed, the dams fill up (November–December) and the barrages once more control the river level. The stored water is released in the low Nile period February–July. Major canals take off from above each barrage and supply lesser canals from which the peasants (fellaheen) take their water, sometimes by raising a small sluice for a permitted period or by lifting the water on to the land by shaduf or sakia.

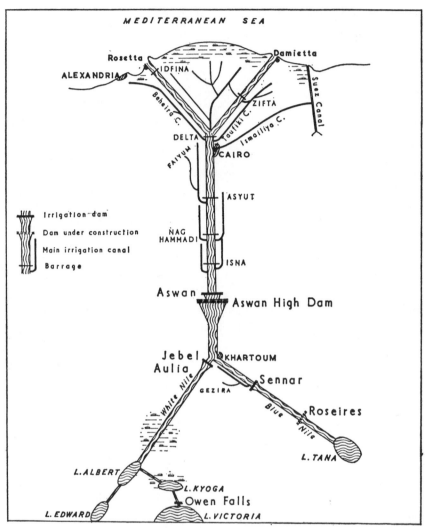

Figure 49 *Diagrammatic representation of the Nile Conservation works*

The Aswan High Dam

The water stored in the two dams is used to the utmost but still more water is urgently needed in order to reclaim and put into use potential farmland in and beside the Delta, such is the present pressure of population. There is also the danger of the occasional high Nile which may burst the banks and flood large areas of densely populated land, and of the very low Nile when it might not be possible to fill the reservoirs completely. Further, every year a great amount of Nile flood water carrying rich silt from the Ethiopian highlands flows out to the Mediterranean unused. It was to solve all these problems that one of the early acts of the revolutionary government of Egypt was to support the proposal for, and subsequently to set about the construction of, the Aswan High Dam. The site of the new dam is 4 miles above the old Aswan Dam. The new one is of colossal size, and its capacity will be 130 milliard cu.m. (twenty-five times the capacity of the old Aswan Dam) which will be retained by a dam wall 3 miles long. After 1970, when the dam is completed, the lake formed behind this retaining wall ('Lake Nasser') will extend 90 miles into the Sudan.

The enormous capacity of the Aswan High Dam allows it to fulfil several rôles. The danger of slow accumulation of silt can be regarded with equanimity; a capacity of 30 milliard cu. m. has been written-off to silting and this will require several centuries. A further 30 milliard cu.m is earmarked for flood protection, so that when the Nile flood is high and dangerous much of it can be held back in the reservoir. The dam capacity allotted to water for irrigation will be 70 milliard cu.m. Here the dam differs from those already existing on the Nile: they are dams for seasonal storage but the High Dam's capacity will be so great that it will provide over-year storage and surplus from good years will no longer flow to the Mediterranean but be held back for use in low Nile years. The extra water that will be available from the new dam will allow 2 million more acres of land to come under cultivation; it will supply enough water to permit all the existing basin-irrigated land to be converted to perennial irrigation; and it will allow an increase in rice cultivation in the Delta. Also vast quantities of hydro-electric power will be generated; the total capacity of the power houses will be 2,100 megawatts, making this one of the biggest hydro-electric schemes in the world.

Irrigation in the Sudan

The Sudan also makes use of the Nile for irrigation, but on a much smaller scale than Egypt. The total area under pump or gravity irrigation is about 2·4 million feddans. One reason for this is that the irrigable areas of fertile soil are much more limited and that summer rains are enjoyed; reliance upon the Nile is not absolute therefore, and diminishes towards the south. The principal area of perennial irrigation in the Sudan is the clay plain interfluve between the two Niles, south of Khartoum, called the Gezira. This became possible in 1925 with the completion of the Sennar Dam on the Blue Nile 150 miles above Khartoum (Fig. 49). Whereas the Jebel Aulia Dam in the Sudan on the White Nile reserves water for Egypt, the Sennar Dam was constructed for the Sudan's own use. It has a smaller capacity than the other two Nile dams (0.8 billion cu.m.) but serves two purposes: it raises the river level to feed the Gezira canal system and it stores water which is available for use after 1st January when by treaty all the Nile water (then at its lowest) until 1st July is reserved for Egypt. The cultivation of the Gezira has been strikingly successful (see p. 319) although it was found that modifications of the Egyptian irrigation methods were necessary: the clay soils are less permeable than the silt-augmented soils of Egypt and it is necessary to exercise a very close control over the amount of water released, even down to the individual holding. Evaporation losses are high but are somewhat balanced by reduced loss from percolation. Extension of the cultivated area in the Gezira proceeds slowly until the 1959 Nile Waters Agreement with Egypt can be implemented, when further Nile works will make more water available for the Sudan. In 1958 the Manaqil extension of the Gezira comprising 200,000 feddans came into use.

Pump irrigation, both under government and private schemes, is also practised on the Main and White Niles (Fig. 55), and basin irrigation in the Shendi and Dongola districts on alluvial terraces of the Main Nile north of Khartoum. These basins are less satisfactory than the much older ones in Egypt. Their surfaces are less even, with less deposition of silt; and, since they depend solely on the height of the Nile, the area inundated varies from year to year.

The 1959 Nile Waters Agreement was made between Egypt and the Sudan to replace one made in 1929 when Britain ruled or controlled most of the Nile Basin. The old agreement recognised Egypt's overwhelming reliance on the Nile by allotting her annually some 48 billion cu.m. and only 4 billion cu.m. to the (then) rather backward Anglo-Egyptian Sudan. The new agreement became necessary with the attainment of independence by the Sudan, her increasing use of Nile water for expanding irrigation schemes having already reached the limit of her water allotment, and also because the projected Aswan High Dam would conserve much more water. Although the Aswan High Dam is located in Egypt it will permit extended irrigation in the Sudan, for whereas after the flood the Blue Nile waters had been entirely reserved for Egypt (while the Sudan relied on the Sennar Dam and certain pumps), in future the Sudan can make use of the Blue Nile water in this season, Egypt making good this amount from the over-year storage in the new reservoir. Consequently the new agreement allotted Egypt 55½ milliard cu.m. and the Sudan 18½ milliard cu.m. The Sudan has been enabled to proceed with further irrigation projects which include a new storage dam at Roseires, to allow further perennial irrigation of the clay plains south of the present Gezira, and conversion to perennial irrigation of the basin areas in the north. The possibility of irrigation from the Atbara is being investigated; one scheme at Kashm el Girba has been put in hand and has been settled by peasants from Nubia whose homes will be covered by the waters of the Aswan High Dam.

Earlier conservation plans

The comprehensive and international plans for Nile conservation published in 1946 were based upon the use of certain of the East African lakes as natural reservoirs, far larger than any man could create. It was calculated that a dam which raised the level of Lake Victoria by one metre would retain the equivalent of twelve and a half times the capacity of the Aswan Dam at a very low cost. Other dams or regulators were proposed for Lake Kyoga, Lake Albert and Lake Tana, thus putting man in firm control of the Nile headwaters. The regulators would retain water in good years and allow the supply to be made up in low Nile years. For example, a high year on the Blue Nile would allow the White Nile works to reduce output down to navigation level and store the excess; in other words virtual storage of Blue Nile water in Lake Albert. The White Nile would generally be held back to about one-third of annual supply during the summer when there is plenty of water coming from the Blue Nile, and increased to send down two-thirds of the annual supply during the early months of the year when the natural level of the Nile is very low.

A further proposal, carefully investigated, was for the construction of a diversion canal 180 miles long from Jonglei near the southern end of the Sudd directly north to the Nile near the junction with the Sobat at Malakal, thus bypassing the worst of the Sudd swamps and consequently considerably reducing the loss by evaporation. The merit of these plans (which included other projected works) was that all the riparian states might gain some benefit (particularly since the dams would include hydro-electric power plants) and that it might be a first step to the integrated development of the whole Nile Basin. In fact, only the Owen Falls Dam at the outlet of Lake Victoria was built, by the British in 1954, and the remaining works may be delayed for many years as a result of the construction of the Aswan High Dam.

25

Egypt

Egypt, or the United Arab Republic, has a distinctive and un-African personality. Proud of its ancient heritage as one of the earliest cradles of civilisation, conscious of its agelong ties with the Mediterranean world, nevertheless it keeps kindled the burning flame of the desert and in more recent years has come to regard itself as a leader of the Arab world and the champion of Arab political advancement and Arab unity. As a consequence it now looks west to the Maghreb as well as east, and attempts to capitalise its central position amid this great sweep of Arab states stretching from the Atlantic to the Indian Ocean. Moreover, it no longer keeps its back turned on the rest of Africa but loses no opportunity of making its voice heard as a senior member among a mass of newly independent states. Yet the country's economic position is highly precarious: its daily bread depends upon the River Nile, and excessive and growing increase of population necessitates new and highly expensive irrigation works, while its political rôle, identified with hostility to Israel, leads to heavy armament expenditure. The mass of Egyptians live in acute poverty.

Most of Egypt is desert. With the exception of a few oases in the Western desert the habitable part of Egypt is restricted to the Nile valley and delta—a mere 13,500 sq. miles out of a total of 386,200. Habitable Egypt is, in fact, one 700-mile-long oasis made up of the triangular delta north of Cairo and the narrow ribbon of the Nile valley, rarely more than 10 miles wide. Throughout, the contrast between the desert and the sown is abrupt and dramatic. In this continuous oasis live 96 per cent of Egypt's 30 million people. For much of the period after A.D. 868 Egypt nominally recognised the suzerainty of Turkey. The basis of the modern state was laid by Muhammad Ali (1815–49), an Albanian who seized power after the expulsion of Napoleon, vigorously restored the country's economy and established the dynasty that ended only with the expulsion of King Farouk and his son in 1952 and 1953. Britain's communications with India and the Far East made use of Egypt even before the cutting of the Suez Canal. River boat was used from the Mediterranean to Cairo and then a desert caravan to the Red Sea, whence steamships completed the journey. Britain's purchase of the bankrupt Khedive's shares in the Suez Canal in 1874 made the link firmer and in 1882 a revolt and massacre of Europeans at Alexandria led to Britain landing an army, effectively becoming the protecting power and doing much to restore the country's economy. The Protectorate was ended in 1922 when the Sultan of Egypt became hereditary ruler. Ineptitude and intrigue by a corrupt ruling class were ended in 1952 when a group of young army officers under General Neguib and Colonel Nasser seized power and, in 1953, declared a republic. In 1955 British forces, then solely in the Canal Zone, were withdrawn from Egypt.

GEOGRAPHICAL REGIONS

An examination of the geography of Egypt is helped by the country's falling conveniently into four distinct physical divisions: the Western desert, the Eastern desert, the Sinai Peninsula and the Nile valley and delta.

THE WESTERN DESERT comprises nearly three-quarters of the republic. It forms the north-east corner of the great Libyan desert and stretches south from the Mediterranean to the Sudan border and from the Nile valley west to the borders of Libya. The greatest altitude is attained in the extreme south-west where the Gilf Kebir plateau surpasses 3,000 feet and the outcropping Archaean rocks of Gebel 'Uweinat reach over 6,000 feet. From Gilf Kebir the sandstone tableland slopes gently north to depressions, probably due to aeolian action, in which lie the Kharga and Dakhla oases. On their northern side a marked escarpment indicates the southern edge of the great limestone plateau where, in more northerly depressions, lie the oases of Farafra and Baharyia and, nearer the Nile, the large oasis of El Faiyûm which is below sea-level and irrigated from the Nile. Nearer the Mediterranean and in still younger limestones lie the depressions of Siwa and Qattara. The Qattara is the largest depression, with a floor over 400 feet below sea-level, which contains salt lakes and marshes and is uninhabited. The surface of the desert is stony or sandy in character. The absence of drainage lines is notable, as is the great area of sand dunes forming the Great Sand Sea which extends from Siwa oasis to Gilf Kebir. The gentle northward descent of the strata from the Ennedi-Tibesti divide and the wide mass of pervious rock resting on the impervious Basement series are conducive to the provision of underground water supplies. Aquifers in the sedimentary rocks are tapped by wells in the depressions and cultivation becomes possible. Except in these favoured oasis areas and in a few small settlements along the Mediterranean coast the wide sandy plains and occasional rocky outcrops are repellent to all but a few of Egypt's nomads, the majority of whom prefer to move with flocks and herds in the Eastern desert. The oasis communities are mainly self-sufficient, growing vegetables and cereals and usually selling dates (Siwa also sells olive oil) in exchange for manufactured goods. Experiments in extending the cultivable area are taking place near Kharga and Dakhla oases where artesian supplies are being tapped. Plans to utilise these waters to reclaim 100,000 feddans of desert land by 1970 have been formulated in what is termed the New Valley project. Kharga and Siwa are linked with the Nile valley by railway and motor road respectively, but the other oases are more remote.

THE EASTERN DESERT extends from the Nile valley eastwards to the Gulf of Suez and the Red Sea and consists essentially of an easterly chain of rugged mountains, the Red Sea highlands, flanked on the north-east and west by considerably dissected limestone and sandstone plateaux. This region of much scarred upland averages 2,000 feet but includes some peaks over 7,000 feet in height. Narrow and deep wadis trending both east to the Red Sea and west to the Nile carve the upland into detached blocks. The fractured and uptilted Crystalline Basement rocks in the northern third are overlain with sedimentary sandstones and limestones, but to the south Archaean rocks, mainly granites, are widely exposed in a wilderness of sharp peaked ranges. Here Gebel Shayeb attains 7,150 feet. The drainage from these mountains in more pluvial periods accounts for the complexity of wadis which emphasise the great contrast with the easily traversed plateau land west of the Nile.

Water resources, although sparse, are more plentiful than in the Western desert, although structural dislocations prevent the presence of extensive artesian supplies. The greater elevation causes a small rainfall and water can be found in sheltered hollows, beneath dry stream beds and from occasional springs. Nomadic shepherds roam these uplands and there are no permanent settlements. Settlement is confined to villages along the Red Sea coast and mining camps. Phosphates are worked near Safaga and Quseir and oil is obtained from wells in the sedimentary rocks at Ras Gharib and Hurghada.

THE SINAI PENINSULA is separated from Egypt proper by the isthmus of Suez. It is an irregular plateau, lofty in the south where the core of the peninsula is formed by a complex of old crystalline rocks, a continuation of the Red Sea hills. The northern two-thirds of the peninsula is a severely dissected limestone plateau. The gravel-covered central part known as the Wilderness of Tih ('the Wandering') averages 3,000 feet; its highest part in the south, the Egma plateau, attains 5,400 feet. The Sinai Mountains of the south, a mass of sharp peaks, gorges and ravines, are the highest in Egypt and culminate in Gebel Catharina, 8,650 feet. They are composed of metamorphic and igneous rocks, predominantly red in colour, from which the Red Sea takes its name. A series of fault scarps on the south-west drops down to the Gulf of Suez and the coastal plain is very limited. To the south-east bold fault faces overlook the Gulf of Aqaba. To the north, however, the country is more open and drains by shallow wadis to a dune-covered coastal plain and the Mediterranean. Rainfall is scanty, about 6 inches per annum in the north but less than 3 inches in the south, and this, coupled with inaccessibility, explains why the sparse population remains almost entirely in the north. The wadis here are broad and pockets of cultivation surround wells and springs such as at el Arish and Nekhl, for the plateau is waterless for most of the year. Elsewhere nomadism prevails. Mining takes place in the west; manganese is exploited at Um Bogma 15 miles from the ore port of Abu Zeneima and a number of small oilfields are exploited at Sudr, Asl, Wadi Feirain and Bala'eem. Much has yet to be learned of the mineral resources of the peninsula, for both exploration and development are retarded by inaccessibility.

THE NILE VALLEY AND DELTA   From the Sudanese frontier north to Cairo the Nile flows in a relatively narrow flat-bottomed groove, sinuous in outline. It is cut deeply into the Nubian Sandstone as far as the crystalline outcrop at Aswan; from near Isna the valley broadens between cliffs of white limestone. At Cairo the valley opens into the delta of the Nile with the land surface sloping gently to the sea and falling some 52 feet from Cairo in a very gentle gradient of 1 in 10,000. The delta comprises an infilled gulf of the Pleistocene Mediterranean and is composed of silt brought mainly from the Ethiopian highlands. The average thickness of the silt is 65 feet. In the north along the coast are shallow brackish lagoons and salt marshes: Lakes Mariut, Edku, Burullus and Menzaleh. Low sand belts separate the last three from the sea but limestone ridges intervene between Lake Mariut and the Mediterranean and the lake level is kept at 9 feet below sea-level by pumping. This allows a steeper gradient for the drainage channels carrying seawards the used irrigation water. This belt of 'Barari' or barren land is so near sea-level that drainage by free flow is impracticable and considerable washing and pumping operations are necessary to reclaim it to agricultural land; hence progress depends upon the future availability of Nile water. In the first century A.D. Strabo recorded the Nile as having seven delta distributaries; today these have become controlled and consolidated into two, known as the Rosetta and Damietta Branches from the small ports at their mouths.

Some 96 per cent of Egypt's population is located in the Nile valley and delta. From the earliest times this was the home of man where the reliable flooding and automatic renewal of fertility contrasted with the enclosing desert. Today this narrow trench of fertility and the delta plain contain some of the most densely settled agricultural land in the world, with population densities averaging 2,000 per sq. mile. It is not easy for those living under the highly artificial conditions of an industrial society removed from the land fully to comprehend what these numbers mean in terms of living conditions. Although there is a growing import of basic food grains, most fellaheen live substantially upon their own produce. With land scarce and too many desiring to farm it, land prices and rents (despite government attempts at control) are remarkably high; and with so many labourers available, wages are all too low. The result is very great poverty, malnutrition and disease among the mass of the peasantry.

The grey mud-brick huts huddle together in villages every one or two miles, the surrounding level land a mosaic of carefully tended small plots (Fig. 50). Shadufs and sakias creak as they lift precious irrigation water from the small distributary canals on to the ribbed and furrowed plots. It has been said that the Egyptian fellah spends at least one-third of his working life lifting water.

In Upper Egypt (i.e. south of Cairo) there are few towns other than the provincial capitals with their market and administrative functions, but within the delta are to be found nearly all the major towns and cities, the bulk of the country's industry and two-thirds of the total population.

Alexandria, lying west of the mouth of the Rosetta Branch (and thus avoiding silting up, for the longshore drift is from west to east), is the republic's principal port and formerly, owing to its more moderate summer temperature, was the summer seat of the administration. The only other large port, concerned mainly with the Canal transit trade, is

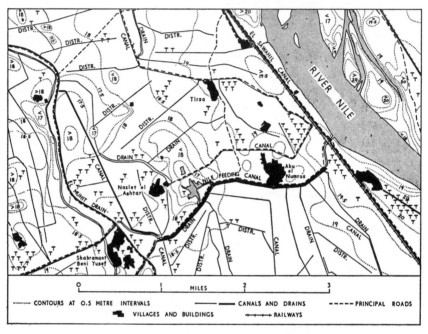

Figure 50 *Extract from Sheet 80/630, Survey of Egypt (1:25,000)*
The area is about 5 miles south of Cairo. Note how the land falls away from the banks of the Nile, and the complex system of irrigation canals and drains

Port Said at the Mediterranean end of the Suez Canal. The northern and eastern parts of the delta are marshy wastes awaiting reclamation, so that the narrow Canal Zone is separated from the delta proper. Only limited areas of it are irrigated, for example around Ismailia, for fresh water is scarce and still largely depends upon the Ismailia or Sweetwater canal which carries water from the Nile to this sterile isthmus.

SOCIAL AND ECONOMIC CONDITIONS

The strictly limited amount of farmland in Egypt and the increasing millions who struggle to live off it are potent in the shaping of both social conditions and the economy. Egypt is still essentially an agricultural country with over 60 per cent of its labour force engaged in farming, but the great strides taken in industrialisation since World War II owe much to the spur of population pressure, as does the growing import of food grains and the small but growing export of manufactured goods.

The excess of population in the rural areas shows in massive under-employment. Too many hands for a given number of jobs means irregular employment, low wage rates and a perpetuation of labour-intensive methods of production. Without changing the techniques in use, it is probable that some 10 million fellaheen could be withdrawn from agriculture without any fall in the volume of production. This is a measure of Egypt's population problem and bears some responsibility for the very low standards of living within the Nile valley. This unfortunate situation is worsened by the ill-health of the majority of the population. Living conditions are highly insanitary. The fellaheen live in houses or huts of mud-plastered sticks or mud bricks: and these (usually two-roomed) hovels at night also house the water buffalo, goats and poultry the family possesses. Animal dung collected by wives and children is used for fuel and adds to the dirt inseparable from a mud-built, clay-floored, fly-infested house. Progress is being made in providing pure drinking water to the villages, but it is an enormous task. Until it is accomplished drinking from, washing and excreting in, the water of the nearest canal or drain will continue. Water-borne diseases are a major scourge of the rural population, the two worst being the worm diseases bilharzia and ankylostoma (hookworm). Over 50 per cent of the rural population suffers from these debilitating diseases which engender apathy and sap the vitality. Malaria, eye diseases and tuberculosis are also prevalent. Greater provision of health centres and the use of insecticides are slowly bringing improvements. Under-nutrition and malnutrition are prevalent: the diet shows a deficiency of proteins and fats and an excess of starch from cereals (mainly maize), which are the mainstay of the peasantry.

The rhythm of daily life is the same in practically every Egyptian village. Dawn heralds the call of the muezzin for morning prayers and the village comes to life. Work follows immediately, for much is accomplished in the cool of the morning, and by sunrise most men and boys are heading towards the fields with their cattle and tools. By broad daylight the village seems almost deserted. Sunset sees the roads to the village crowded as villagers and cattle return home raising the great clouds of dust that characterise the country roads. Later there is an exodus of women and girls from the village to the Nile (or neighbouring canal) to fill their water jars while the men sprawl outside their houses in comfortable gossip or listen in the public square to Cairo Radio.

The unequal distribution of land ownership in Egypt was a prime cause of social unrest. Until 1952 two-thirds of the land was owned by 6 per cent of landowners, whereas 2 million peasants owned only 13 per cent in plots of less than a feddan each and another 2 million were landless. The large estates were usually let and sublet in smaller plots on a share-cropping basis and many of the big landowners were absentees living, often ostentatiously, in Cairo or Alexandria. When the revolutionary government came into power in 1952 it passed a Land Reform Act limiting family land holdings to a maximum of 300 feddans. The surplus was expropriated and allotted in small plots to landless peasantry. A further move in 1961 reduced maximum holdings still further, to 100 feddans. These moves were designed as much to break the power of the feudal landlords as to improve the lot of the landless peasantry, for inevitably there is not enough land to satisfy more than a small proportion of them.

That such a large population can live on so small an area is due principally to the inherent richness of the alluvial soils (now heavily supplemented with artificial fertilisers), the sunny climate, the reliable water supply derived from one of the world's most elaborate and efficient irrigation systems, the unremitting toil of a population skilled at gardening rather than farming, and a degree of poverty not readily comprehended in the West.

AGRICULTURE

Agriculture supplies, either directly or processed, about 85 per cent of all exports. Thanks to the irrigation system already outlined, Nile water is now conserved and so distributed that the greater part of Egypt's farmland receives adequate water during the early summer months when the Nile is at its lowest and the land otherwise would be parched. This means first that both summer and winter crops may follow one another on the same ground, although generally rotations are practised so that three crops are grown in a two-year period. The usual rotation is as follows. First year—November to May: cereals (wheat or barley), bersim (Egyptian clover), beans, onions. June to July: fallow. July to November: maize. December to January: bersim or fallow. Second year—February to November: cotton. In the north-central delta rice is a summer crop and sugar cane replaces some cotton in Upper Egypt. It will be seen that the land is only fallow for four months in twenty-four, and that the crop area each year is greater than the arable area (Table 9). Secondly, it is possible to grow cotton which needs most moisture during the summer months and therefore could not be grown on any scale before the introduction of perennial irrigation.

For years cotton has been Egypt's foremost crop. In any one year it occupies one-fifth of the crop area and the yield of high-quality medium-long and long-stapled cotton is around 500 lb. (or one bale) per acre, the highest in the world. Cotton exports have been the mainstay of the economy for decades and now contribute 65–70 per cent of export revenue. Egypt's competitive advantages in the world market arise from her highly suitable soil and a sunny climate where the amount of water can be closely controlled. Cotton growing demands a considerable labour supply, but in Egypt labour skilled in cotton growing and tending is plentiful and cheap. Further, the crop is inedible and has therefore been much favoured by absentee landlords who leave production in the hands of a hungry peasantry. World prices of cotton are higher than those for grain crops and cotton is therefore a far more remunerative and 'safe' crop to grow. Over the years the research station at Giza has introduced a succession of improved cotton varieties. During the between-war period the Sakellarides variety was paramount; after the last war Ashmouni came to the fore but has now been surpassed as a medium-long staple cotton by Menoufi. Among the longer staple (over $1\frac{3}{8}$ inches) Karnak is the foremost, and is also a post-war introduction. In order to maintain high-quality production the government controls the issue of cotton seed and also broadly determines the annual acreage, for cotton demands more water than all other major crops except rice. Egypt's growing textile industry now uses 30 per cent of the annual cotton crop and the raw cotton exports supply the greater part of the world market for long staples. The fine, strong silky cotton has special uses, for typewriter ribbons, high-quality dress and shirt materials, bookbinding, and windproof clothing, for example. Few of the small-holding peasantry grow cotton; they prefer food crops. It is the larger landowners and new co-operatives who grow this specialist crop.

The other principal crops are maize (a summer crop mainly grown in Lower Egypt), its counterpart millet (grown in Upper Egypt), wheat, bersim, rice (a summer crop of the central part of the delta), barley, lentils, beans and, in Upper Egypt, sugar cane. The rice acreage varies from year to year dependent upon forecasts of the Nile flood and in low Nile years the acreage is much reduced. Much of the rice is exported. The only other export crop of note is onions, grown chiefly in Upper Egypt. The yields of crops in Egypt are among the highest in the world. Dates are grown throughout the Nile valley but other fruits have a very limited acreage in a country urgently needing bread grains. Some citrus fruit and grapes are grown in the delta.

PASTORALISM   The pressure on the land for human food production precludes fodder crops and livestock rearing plays a minor part. The apparently high cattle and water-buffalo population is kept principally for draught purposes; meat production is low. The animals, usually in poor condition, are kept on bersim, chopped straw and maize fodder. Lean sheep and goats are found in most villages and the keeping of poultry is widespread. Fishing rather surprisingly also plays only a small part in the economy. Sardines and sponges are caught off the Nile delta and there is some fishing in the delta lakes and Lake Moeris in the Faiyûm, but the contribution of fish to the Egyptian diet is remarkably small.

MINERALS

Mineral resources are still comparatively little exploited owing to incomplete survey and problems of inaccessibility. Crude oil, phosphate, manganese, natron (natural soda), salt and iron ore are the principal minerals worked (Table 8). Production of crude oil now surpasses 7 million tons annually. The production from the older oilfields at Ras Gharib and Hurghada on the Red Sea coast is declining and most of the output comes from newer fields in Sinai at Sudr, Asl, Wadi Feiran and Bala'eem. In most of the refined products Egypt is now self-sufficient and in some, such as fuel oil, she can make a modest export. Oil exploration proceeds, particularly in the Western desert. Phosphate rock is mined along the north-east coast of the Red Sea but principally at Quseir, and most is exported to countries in the Eastern Bloc. Manganese is obtained from western Sinai and is mainly exported to Western Europe. Iron ore is now mined from the haematite deposits (c. 50 per cent Fe.) just east of

Aswan. This ore supplies the small iron-and-steel works established at Helwan near Cairo in 1958.

MANUFACTURING INDUSTRY

It is not generally realised that Egypt is the most industrialised country in Africa after the Republic of South Africa. Most industrial development has occurred since 1939 although the real beginnings may be traced to 1930 when tariffs were first imposed on manufactured imports. The spur of population pressure, the need to diversify the economy and so satisfy aspirations of nationalism have contributed to these developments. One reason for a slow expansion of manufacturing industry was the lack of capital, for it was far more profitable to invest money in land where a high return was assured. Other reasons were the small home market, for the mass of the people are too poor to satisfy more than minimal requirements of manufactured goods; the dearth of technical and managerial skills and generally high cost production by small units, whereby economies of scale did not accrue and better-quality imported goods maintained their market.

Industry received a fillip during the war when Egypt was a major allied base but cut off from European industry. Many new plants were established and others enlarged. Many of the less efficient of these establishments went out of business in the early post-war period and investment once more swung to land and agriculture. By 1952, when the revolution took place, manufacturing industry contributed barely 10 per cent of the national income. The revolutionary government invested public money in utilities such as roads, railways and power supplies upon which any growth of industry relies and after the seizure of the Suez Canal (1956) the government gradually took more and more industry into its grasp by seizing foreign business, banks and insurance and then nationalising or partly nationalising first the large and then the smaller Egyptian industrial concerns. These measures were designed to give the government greater control over industry and investment and to reduce the power of wealthy industrialists. They may prove harmful to the economy since they include the confiscation of property and seizure of assets of many of Egypt's growing commercial middle class, which numbers Syrians, Italians, Greeks, Lebanese, etc., who provide the business men, managers and entrepreneurs so urgently needed if industrial expansion is to go on.

Table 8   *Egypt: Industrial and Mineral Production*

(In '000 met. tons)	1939	1952	1954	1956	1958	1960	1962	1964
Extractive inds.								
Crude oil	749	2,379	1,972	1,828	3,184	3,319	4,504	6,979
Phosphate	578	527	534	615	558	566	682	594
Manganese	120	195	178	201	112	286	106	182
Iron ore	—	—	—	—	178	239	461	507
Manufactures								
Cotton yarn	24*	56	64	75	88	102	121	138
Cotton fabric	20*	43	48	52	60	64	78	89
Refined sugar	233	210	262	287	261	338	333	400
Superphosphate	20	106	114	170	179	188	164	252
Nitrate of lime	—	111	123	208	221	257	270	278
Cement	368	951	1,237	1,351	1,510	1,093	1,693	1,733
Tires and tubes ('000s)	—	—	—	220	289	485	433	1,201
Steel products	—	—	—	—	11	113	132	—

* Large factories only
Source: Federation of Egyptian Industries

Textiles are by far the largest industry of Egypt and include the spinning, weaving, dying and printing of cottons, wool, silk and rayon. A wide variety of fabrics, knitwear and furnishings is produced; indeed, the entire home demand is now satisfied. Exports of yarn and fabrics to the Sudan and other Arab states, Western Germany, Eastern Bloc states and Cuba now approach £20 million per annum. There are over 1·25 million cotton spindles installed and much of the output comes from large modern factories situated in the two textile towns of the delta, Mehalla el Kubra and Kafr el Dawal (Plate 3B). In all, the industry employs 115,000 workers. Other industries derived from local agricultural or mineral raw materials are sugar refining and milling (five mills in Upper Egypt and a refinery near Cairo), brewing, oil-seed crushing, vegetable preserving, and the manufacture of boot, shoe and leather goods, alcohol, soap, glass and cement. Large cement works at Cairo and Alexandria now have a considerable export trade. Two oil refineries at Suez have been enlarged to permit the start of petro-chemical industries, while artificial fertilisers (urgently needed by Egyptian agriculture) are manufactured at Helwan and near Suez and the small iron-and-steel plant at Helwan near Cairo produces about 220,000 tons of steel per annum.

Other manufactures include rubber tires, paper and cardboard, a range of consumer goods and motor-vehicle assembly.

There is a high concentration of industry upon the two main cities, Cairo and Alexandria. These two centres and adjacent areas include nearly three-quarters of the total number of industrial establishments, employing 70 per cent of the industrial labour force. The agglomeration of industry in and around these cities reflects the disproportionate pull of the few locations in underdeveloped countries, where public utilities such as electricity, gas, pure water, telephones are available and where there is a provision of labour and an effective market. On social and political grounds attempts are now being made to deflect some new industrial growth into the Canal Zone. There is practically no industrial development at all in Upper Egypt.

Egypt possesses no coal (coke is imported for the steel works) and this has helped to retard industrial development until more recent years when oil production has increased and is now the country's main fuel. Much of it is converted to electricity, which is supplemented (since 1960) by the generation of power at the Aswan Dam. It is this power that supplies the El Khattara fertiliser factory and new pump irrigation schemes in Upper Egypt. The vast increase of electrical power available when the Aswan High Dam is completed should be significant to Egypt's industrial expansion, although the cost of transmitting much of this power to the delta will be high.

POPULATION AND SETTLEMENT

Egypt has a major population problem that now has deep repercussions upon her economy. The population is over 30 million (1967) and increases by 600,000 yearly: a far greater rate of increase than ever before. This marked increase after the last war is the result of the notable drop in death rates (particularly infant mortality); birth rates remain as high as ever (Fig. 21). At 43 per 1,000, the crude birth rate is one of the highest in the world but the crude death rate has dropped in twenty-five years from 28 to 16 per 1,000. As a result Egypt's population has practically doubled in the last thirty years, whereas the habitable area has altered very little and population pressure has become intense (Table 9). Some 65 per cent of the population is in Lower Egypt (delta) and the Canal Zone, but some of the highest densities are in Upper Egypt: Sohag, with over 2,600 per sq. mile, is the most thickly populated entirely agricultural governorate of Egypt. As in the other North African states, recent demographic trends are expressed in a relatively young population: two-thirds of Egypt's peoples are under thirty.

Table 9　Egypt: Population, Cultivated Area and Crop Area, 1897–1960

Year	Total population	% increase per decade	Cultivated area (feddans)	Crop area (feddans)
1897	9,715,000	—	5,099,070	6,871,700
1907	11,287,000	16·2	5,357,640	7,624,620
1917	12,751,000	13·0	5,307,534	7,724,980
1927	14,218,000	11·5	5,529,756	8,606,340
1937	15,933,000	12·1	5,333,330	8,362,340
1947	19,022,000	19·8	5,797,600	9,138,570
1960	26,578,000	30·5	6,100,000	10,367,730

1 feddan = 1·038 acres
Areas are the mean of five years centred on every fifth year

Most Egyptians live in hamlets and villages but the proportion of town dwellers increases and now about one-third lives in towns of over 25,000 inhabitants. The two major cities overshadow all others and increase at a faster rate. *Cairo* (pop. 3·5 million) and *Alexandria* (pop. 1·6 million) have each increased by at least two-thirds during the last fifteen years. Cairo was founded in A.D. 960, located on high ground near the 700-foot escarpment of the Mokattam hills (Fig. 51). The Nile, then broader and uncontrolled, flowed farther east than now and here had islands which facilitated a crossing. With its famous Citadel, built A.D. 1176 by Saladin, the city occupied a position ideal as a market and commanded both valley and delta. In the old city today the craft divisions of this period remain—alleys of the Musky (or Bazaar quarter) devoted to goldsmiths, coppersmiths, pottery makers and so on. Modern Cairo really dates from Ismail's rule (1863–79). Railways were built, the Suez Canal constructed and a new Cairo laid out beside the Nile at the foot of the old. Fringing marshlands were reclaimed, wide avenues laid out and government offices moved to new buildings from the Citadel. This century has seen a northward and westward expansion with satellite towns developing west of the river and connected by bridges to the main city. Giza is now a busy industrial suburb with a quarter of a million

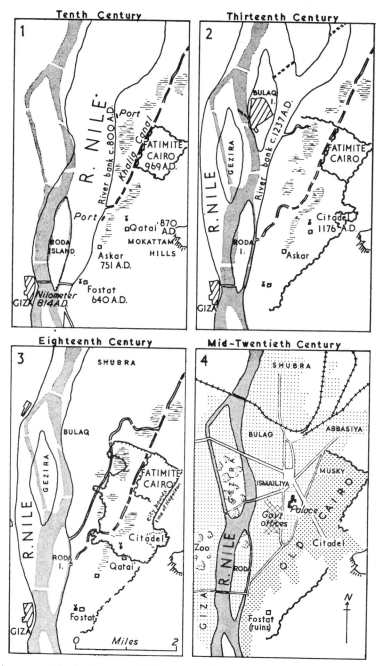

Figure 51 *The development of Cairo* (after Platt & Hefny). The present course of the Nile is indicated by shading on all four maps. In map 4 the built-up area is represented by stippling

population. The dormitory towns of Heliopolis, Ma'adi and Helwan are linked by electric railway.

The city is the administrative, business and now industrial centre of Egypt. In its busy wide main streets with their department stores and stylish shops European dress mingles with the gown and tarboosh of the East, but away from the tall ferro-concrete hotels, shops, offices and apartment houses thousands live in tortuous alleys of old mud-brick houses.

Alexandria is less of a market centre, having its hinterland limited by the brackish Lake Mariut, but it is Egypt's foremost port, handling 80 per cent of the total trade. The city was founded in 332 B.C. by Alexander the Great, mainly as a naval base, being clear of the Nile silt and protected by the Pharos island. The gradual silting of a mole across to the island has created an isthmus half a mile wide, now partly occupied by the modern city. This isthmus divides eastern and western harbours, the main port lying on the west side. Cotton ginning, rice milling and cement manufacture are important activities connected with the export trade. There is an oil refinery, textile factories, and cigarettes are manufactured from imported tobacco.

COMMUNICATIONS AND TRADE

In contrast to her habitable area, Egypt has a very good transport net with a particularly good railway system (nearly all standard gauge, double track) supplemented by roads and water. The first railway completed in 1856 connected Cairo with Alexandria. Now there are 2,700 miles of the railway, state owned and operated, which serve all parts of the Nile valley as far south as Aswan. These lines are supplemented by light railways which serve the Faiyûm and parts of the delta, and the Kharga oasis is connected to the Nile valley by a narrow-gauge line.

Until recently roads have generally been neglected, partly owing to strong competition from state-owned railways. Most of the roads are of packed earth, suitable for farm animals and carts but not modern motor traffic. From 1952 road development received priority and the main roads were widened and surfaced. The Nile and major canals are used for the transport of bulky goods such as cotton, pottery and some grain. Most of the waterways are open all the year but low water level at the end of the winter prevents boats being loaded to full capacity.

Political differences with the West during the 1950's, particularly over the financing of the Aswan High Dam project, and the seizure of the Suez Canal caused a disruption of a customary trade pattern and the deflection of much trade to the communist countries, who advanced loans and concluded agreements. In recent years the Soviet Bloc has taken about 45 per cent of Egypt's exports (mainly raw materials); North America and Western Europe take 30 per cent (mainly foodstuffs and oil products) and the rest of the world, principally the Arab countries, up to 25 per cent (foodstuff and manufactures). The Eastern Bloc supplies about 30 per cent of imports (mainly iron and steel products and timber) and Western Europe about 40 per cent (machinery, vehicles and fertilisers). Egypt's principal exports include raw cotton and its by-products, cotton piece goods, rice, onions, phosphate and manganese ores, mineral oils and cement. Imports are of wheat and flour, fertilisers and chemicals, industrial machinery, iron and steel wares, vehicles.

THE SUEZ CANAL

The Suez Canal breaches the isthmus between the Mediterranean and the Red sea and by shortening sea routes between Europe and the East has become the world's most important sea canal. Basically it is a ditch excavated in sandy soil, which makes use of the depressions of Lake Timsah and the Bitter Lakes (Fig. 52). It was proposed by Ferdinand de Lesseps in 1854, work began in 1859, and it was completed in 1869. The Canal is 100 miles long and is at sea-level throughout. When first opened, at certain points the depth of channel was only 18 feet. A succession of improvement schemes has both deepened and widened the Canal over the years, keeping pace with the increasing size of vessels. Deepening and widening continues, the present depth permitting passage of vessels of 38-foot draught. The Canal was owned and operated by an international company (in which the British Government was an important shareholder) and by a Convention of 1888 it should be open to vessels of all nations and free from blockade. The Company's concession was due to expire in 1968 but Egypt seized and nationalised the Canal in 1956, paying some compensation.

The graph (Fig. 53) reveals a remarkable increase in traffic through the Canal since the last war. There has been both an increase in the number of vessels and also in their size. Whereas in any year during the 1930's an average of about 5,800 vessels used the Canal, the average number during the early 1960's was 18,000. Oil tankers form just over

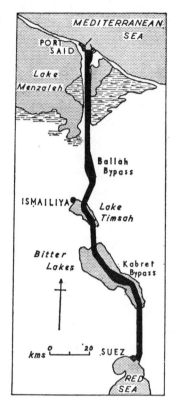

Figure 52 *The Suez Canal*

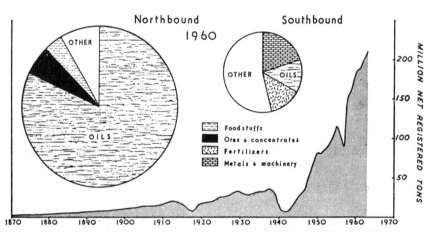

Figure 53 *Cargo in transit through the Suez Canal, 1960, and the growth of Canal traffic 1870–1964*

half the vessels involved, and with the movement of oil from the Persian Gulf to Europe the south to north tonnage exceeds the north to south by nearly 5 to 1. The Canal shortens the sailing distance to India from the United Kingdom by 4,400 miles and to Kuwait by 4,800 miles; to Singapore by 3,600 miles and to Melbourne by 900 miles. The route through the Canal to India and Australasia forms a major sea artery of the British Commonwealth and British ships have always been the most numerous of those using the Canal; the proportion, however, is declining. In 1913, 60 per cent of the shipping was British; in 1938, 50 per cent and in 1965, 17 per cent.

Port Said (with *Port Fuad* on the eastern side) has become the third largest town in Egypt. Most of its business is with vessels in transit through the Canal. Oil-bunkering services are available and ships are repaired. At the southern end, *Suez* and *Port Tewfig* have also grown. Here two oil refineries are established and fertiliser factories. A pipeline carries oil to Cairo. The Canal is of little significance to Egypt's own commerce but her hold on such a strategic waterway enhances her international standing, gives her a further source of revenue (although much goes back in the improvement schemes) and, against the 1888 Convention, allows her to deny passage to Israeli vessels.

CONCLUSION

The revolutionary government in Egypt makes strenuous efforts to grapple with the population problem. Great hopes are placed in the Aswan High Dam which will make available enough water ultimately to add a further 2 million feddans to the cultivable area and increase the annual crop area to about 12 million feddans. Much of this extra land will become available with the reclamation of the marshes and parts of the lagoons in the delta. The water will also allow the development and expansion of El Tahrir ('Liberation Province') on the desert edge west of the delta, where small but costly reclamation and settlement schemes are being carried out. Another possible expansion of habitable Egypt is in the 'New Valley', a general name given to the series of oasis depressions in the Western desert. Here it is hoped to expand substantially the cultivated area and population by means of new deep wells and better communications with the Nile valley and delta. These schemes, however, will not go far if the present rate of population increase continues or, as is likely, even increases. Industrial development can only offer limited help in employing future excess millions, for the growth of the home market is likely to be slow and the range of manufactures suitable for export is small. As with most underdeveloped countries with an excessively high rate of population increase, the only real long-term solution is a reduction in fertility. Unless this occurs in Egypt the standard of living of the mass of the people is likely to remain low.

26

The Sudan

The term Sudan is frequently used to indicate the broad belt of savanna country stretching from the Atlantic to the Ethiopian Mountains; the name (from the Arabic) is commonly regarded as indicating 'land of the blacks'. The eastern Sudan, however, is also a political unit, and since 1956 an independent republic. For much of the nineteenth century the north Sudan was under Egyptian rule. Attempts with British assistance to suppress the slave trade met with some success but fired off the Mahdi revolt which expelled the Egyptians and their British advisers. The Sudan was retaken by Sir Herbert Kitchener (later Lord Kitchener) in 1898 and a joint British and Egyptian administration was established under the title Anglo-Egyptian Sudan.

The area of the republic is 967,500 sq. miles and the population in 1965 was estimated to be 13,540,000. Of these about 70 per cent are Moslem Arabs and Nubians living in the north; the remainder in the south are Nilotic and Negro peoples. This draws attention to a most significant factor in the geography of the Sudan, its position, encompassing a number of climate and vegetation belts and including peoples of very different ways of life, language and religion. The republic extends from the heart of the Sahara on the Egyptian border south to the foothills of the East African highlands. Three east-west trending divisions may be used to aid geographical treatment.

GEOGRAPHICAL REGIONS (Fig. 54)

The Northern Sudan This is a part of the Sahara, an extension of the Libyan desert and stretches from the boundary with Egypt (a straight line across the sand waste at about 22°N) to where steppe vegetation appears with the light summer rainfall at about latitude 16°N. Three sub-divisions are the desert, the Nile valley and the Red Sea hills. West of the Nile the land surface consists of sandy or gravelly plains with occasionally well-dissected hills of the Nubian Sandstone. Towards the north-west are areas of sand dunes, outliers of the Great Sand Sea of Egypt's Libyan desert. A few water-courses debouch to the river from the outcrops of the Archaean Basement rocks south of the great bend of the Nile; these are seasonally supplied by the light and variable summer rainfall (2 to 4 inches). East of the Nile and partially contained within its great bend is the Nubian desert. Most of it is developed on the igneous and metamorphic Archaean rocks of the Basement Complex. Outside the Nile valley, oases are few and seasonal water-courses, except near the Red Sea hills, are rare. These arid areas support small parties of Arab nomads with camels, sheep and goats; a settled way of life is impossible. Towards the Red Sea in the broken hill country rainfall is low and irregular, pastures are poor. Hamitic people, the Beja, predominate and combine poor cultivation in seasonal stream beds with nomadic pasturing of camels and sheep, some of them descending to the narrow coastal plains in the winter.

A settled way of life is limited to discontinuous stretches of the palm-fringed Nile valley, particularly where the river has cut a broad trench in the Nubian Sandstone. Between Khartoum and Wadi Halfa this is usually flanked by river terraces. Except locally this part of the Nile is not navigable, since it contains five of the cataracts. Around Shendi and Dongola are irrigated basins beside the river that once were a part of its bed; many of these flood naturally and some by simple channels. In some cases pumps have been installed, converting them to perennial irrigation. Agriculture rarely extends as much as two miles from the river and a number of villages marks these more fertile stretches. They include Shendi, Atbara (at the confluence of that river with the Nile), Berber, Abu Hamad, Merowe, Dongola and Wadi Halfa on the border with Egypt. In these villages nomads trade animals and goatskins for grain and pulses. On the border with Egypt is Wadi Halfa. This is the northern terminus of the Sudan railway and there is a river connection with the southern terminus of the Egyptian railways at Aswan. All this part of the Nile valley will be flooded when the Aswan High Dam fills. Wadi Halfa will be submerged and the artificial lake will extend 90 miles up the river into the Sudan. Egypt paid compensation towards the resettling of the 50,000 Nubians rendered homeless. They have been resettled at Kashm el Girba on the Atbara near the Ethiopian border.

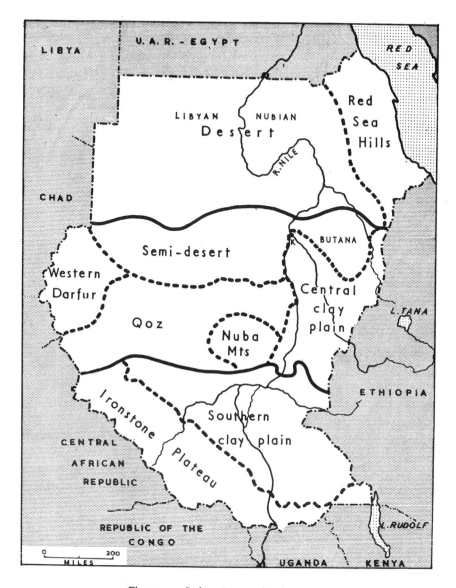

Figure 54 *Sudan:* Geographical regions

Central Sudan

Between latitudes 16°N and 10°N, this provides an intermediate zone between the desert and the long-grass savanna and swamp of the better-watered Negroid south. The title Central Rainlands emphasises the characteristics of this area which is the most productive and most populous part of the republic. A number of subdivisions based on soil, climate and vegetation may be distinguished. In the north is semi-desert steppe land, in the west the higher western Darfur, in the centre the Qoz and the Nuba Mountains and east of the White Nile the clay plains.

THE SEMI-DESERT STEPPE, west of Khartoum and Butana to the east, offers sparse grazing to a number of nomadic camel and sheep-owning Arab tribes. The rainfall (from 4 to 8 inches) lasts only through three summer months and largely conditions the movement of the tribes who, for nomads, are reasonably well off. The rains are generally reliable and if below average, a more southerly pasture-seeking movement is possible by arrangement with neighbours. Each tribe has a number of base areas with watering points where they will have concentrated by the end of the dry season and in which small areas of millet are hopefully sown. From these they move southwards with the onset of the rains, dividing into small family groups. With the rains a northerly circuit is followed between June and November visiting known waterpoints and wells until finally, all other pasture used, they return to the winter grazing ground (Fig. 55). Here gum is collected from small incisions in acacia bushes, the skins are prepared, camel and goat hair and wool are spun and rugs made. Annual visits to market towns such as Omdurman, El Obeid, and En Nahud enable them to trade animals, gum arabic, rugs and saddlery for grain, cloth, sugar and tea.

WESTERN DARFUR   West of the Central Rainlands, the land rises to culminate in the volcanic range of the Jebel Marra, 10,073 feet. Here in western Darfur rocks of the Basement Complex provide the plinth for these volcanic, mainly basaltic rocks. The plateau of these old rocks, an undulating peneplain, varies between 2,000 and 3,000 feet and is emphasised here and there by isolated hills (inselberge) and ridges. Rainfall is more plentiful—up to 30 inches over a good deal of the uplands—and the vegetation varies from thorn bush on the thin soils of the upland to denser woodland savanna in the south. Streams radiate from the upland; some are perennial for their first 5 to 10 miles but surface flow beyond these limits occurs only during the wet season (May to September). Except in the drier north where nomads and semi-nomads move with sheep and goats (the stony country is unsuitable for camels), most of the

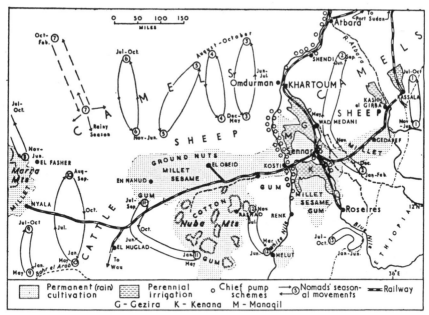

Figure 55 *Economy of the Central Sudan* (after K. M. Barbour). The Kenana irrigation scheme was projected only and was to be started after 1966 after the Roseires Dam was completed. Numbers refer to the following tribes: 1. Beni Āmer. 2. Rufāa esh Sharq. 3. Hawawîr 4. Kabābīsh. 5. Hamar 6. Kawahla. 7. Meidob. 8. Zaghawa. 9. Habaniya. 10. Rizeiqat. 11. Mesiriya Zurug. 12. Awlad Himeid. 13. Ingessana

population of western Darfur clusters round the upland and beside the stream beds, for even in the dry season the water table is not far below the stream beds. Silty alluvial fans and river terraces provide the principal areas of settlement and cultivation of the Fur. Millet, groundnuts, sesame and maize are the principal crops and in some of the larger villages tree fruits—mangoes, citrus, bananas—are grown. Rather poor-quality cotton is indigenous and is used locally for cloth making.

THE QOZ East of Darfur and stretching to the White Nile is the very different terrain of the Qoz: a great stretch of undulating sand, once a southward lobe of the Sahara and now fixed by short grass and acacia scrub vegetation. This has always been a zone of movement between the desert and the swamps, and particularly since the Moslem conversions has become the pilgrim route from West Africa to Mecca. The landscape is somewhat monotonous, the undulating surface being clothed with grasses, herbs (sweet veld) and scattered low trees. To the south the trees become larger and more numerous with increasing rainfall. Semi-nomads move over the borders into the Qoz both in the north and the south and serve as a reminder that until this century agriculture here was subsidiary to pastoralism. The prevailing pattern of settled agriculture has developed during the last half-century and is still evolving. It has arisen as a result of firm government, improving communications and establishment of market towns, and a great programme of water reservoir development. The spine of the settled area has become the railway, extended from Sennar to El Obeid in 1911 and continued to Nyala in Darfur in 1960, supplemented by the road from El Obeid to El Fasher. The rail link from the Nile valley at Atbara to Port Sudan was completed in 1905. Deeper and more productive wells were bored in the railway zone with modern appliances and people became encouraged to settle permanently, cultivating millet, sesame and groundnuts during the rainy season; sowing with the rains in July and harvesting in December in the dry season. Sheep and goats are kept to provide milk, meat, skin, hair and wool. The railway has now become an important artery of trade. Lorries bring grain, groundnuts, sesame, cotton, gum, arabic and melon seeds into the stations.

The improvement of rural water supplies is basic to further develop-ment of the Central Rainlands; since the war a number of measures to create water storage facilities for the six-month dry season have been quite successful. Foremost among them has been the use of modern earth-moving machinery to excavate *hafirs*. The *hafir* was a small hand-excavated cistern or tank, usually related to seasonal streams, which could store some water for most, if not all, of the dry season. The new *hafirs* are much larger and with access roads have helped to open or consolidate settlement over considerable areas. Several hundred *hafirs* have now been made, a large number being in the areas surrounding the Nuba Mountains and impounding run-off from the hills. Many areas have thus come under cultivation and cotton has been successfully introduced as a cash crop. In this most southerly section of the Qoz, around and among the Nuba hills, the nomadic Baggara tribes are found. They winter along the Bahr el Arab and move north to the sweeter grasses of the Qoz with the coming of the rains and floods. A growing number are gradually turning to agriculture, some attracted by high cotton prices.

THE CLAY PLAIN   From the junction of the White and Blue Niles and
east from the Nuba Mountains to the Ethiopian border stretches a mono-
tony of clay plain. Amazingly level, the deeply cracking clays in the
north are well adapted to irrigation agriculture, necessary because of the
limited rainfall. Numerous irrigation schemes here, headed by the famous
Gezira Scheme, have completely altered the landscape and way of life
of thousands. The plain between the two Niles (Gezira = island or
peninsula) slopes down to the north and west and thus facilitates the
flow of irrigation water impounded in the Sennar Dam on the Blue
Nile. The Main Irrigation Canal is on the east side of the Gezira and its
distributaries now serve nearly a million acres, mainly in the east. It has
been found that some of the soils nearer the White Nile are too poor
to repay irrigation. The Gezira Scheme was a successful venture in
co-operation between European management and African cultivators
and still continues, although few Europeans now remain. When the
original concession lapsed in 1950 the Sudan Government established a
Gezira Board to take over the function of the original private Gezira
Syndicate.

The scheme operates as a triple partnership between government, who
provide land and water and take 42 per cent of the net return, the Board,
which takes 10 per cent for its management (the syndicate took 20
per cent), and the tenant, who receives 44 per cent plus 4 per cent in
social services. Land allocations have been on a princely scale in comparison with peasant holdings in Egypt, tenants holding approximately
40 feddans in four fields. An eight-year rotation is cotton, fallow, millet
(dura), fallow or lubia (fodder legume), fallow, cotton, fallow, fallow;
thus cotton is grown only one year in four. This whole system is lavish
of land and underlines the light pressure of population in comparison
with Egypt. In the more recent Manaqil extension of the irrigated area
holdings are reduced to about 15 feddans. Of this 5 are under cotton
within a three-year rotation: cotton, dura millet and lubia fodder ($2\frac{1}{2}$
feddans each), and fallow (5 feddans). Tenancies in the Gezira when
they fall vacant are now being reduced to 20 feddans each. A prime
object of the scheme was to produce an export crop and provide a source
of revenue to aid the government in the development of the country.
It has proved highly successful: medium-long staple cotton (over $1\frac{3}{8}$
inches) is grown and its export provides 60–70 per cent of all export
receipts.

The Manaqil extension (completed in 1962) has added 800,000

feddans in the middle of the Gezira under perennial irrigation. Other extensions of perennial irrigation are being developed using the greater share of Nile water (agreed with Egypt in 1959) including a dam (completed 1966) on the Blue Nile above Roseires. This will supply the later phases of the Manaqil extension and further massive additions (the Kenana extensions) south-west of the Sennar Dam. The potential for extension of irrigation in the Sudan is very great and lies mainly in the clay lands south of Khartoum and beside the Atbara farther east.

South of the irrigated Gezira are many villages whose inhabitants depend upon unirrigated cultivation supplemented by water from the Blue Nile: wells or *hafirs* allowing sesame, maize, millet to be grown. Nomadic tribes also move regularly across the southern clay plain. The Baggara astride the White Nile use the grasses that grow beside it after each summer's inundation and move a short distance from the river during the rains and flood period. Other nomads such as the Rufaa el Hoi in the southern Gezira traverse more than 200 miles, wintering in the south as the marshes dry out and moving north with the onset of the rains to avoid the scourge of flies and mosquitoes in the southern marshy areas.

The Southern Sudan

This comprises the southern part of the pear-shaped clay plains and the fringing uplands to the west and south. The clay plain is exceedingly flat. The gradient of the Nile passing through it is only 1 : 13,000; consequently the great volume of additional water during the rainy season cannot be accommodated by such level rivers and widespread flooding occurs. Thus during the rainy season almost the entire plain becomes a swamp, impassable except by boat along the main rivers (Plate 5). The waters recede and evaporate with the dry season until permanent water is confined to the main rivers and some areas of permanent swamp supporting the tall reed-like papyrus (*Cyperus papyrus*) whose extent was overestimated before aerial reconnaissance revealed that it rarely extended more than 8 miles from the permanent channels. The general term *sudd* (Arabic = barrier) applied to this area derives from the great masses of floating vegetation that occasionally block the navigable channels. Grass fires sweep much of the area in the dry season and this, with the clay soil, helps to account for the paucity of trees. The lack of shade and dryness do not favour the tsetse fly and cattle rearing is the main occupation.

5 Dinka tribesmen in the Sudd area of the Sudan

6 The Uluguru Mountains, Tanzania

The Nilotic tribes, mainly Shilluk, Nuer and Dinka, adapt their mode of living to these conditions. As the floods rise they move their beasts and possessions to the few islets of interfluves upon which they crowd and to the surrounding unflooded land, particularly in the west on the edges of the laterite uplands called the Ironstone Plateau (Fig. 56). Here, in fact, are their permanent conical thatch-roofed huts and cattle byres, the former often built on piles to allow fires underneath to smoke

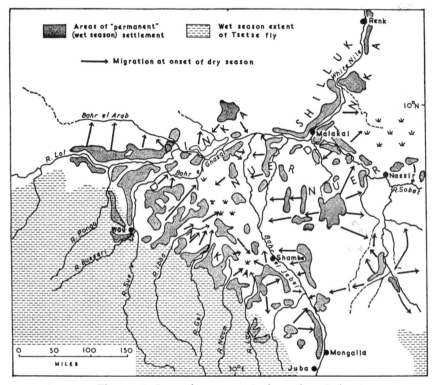

Figure 56 *Seasonal movements in the southern Sudan*

out flies and mosquitoes. Tiny patches of sorghum millet, maize and vegetables are grown, often scarcely enough for subsistence. Fishing is an important pastime, but cattle are the real interest. They become lean on the very limited grazing during the wet season but fatten up as the young men move them back over the young grass as the waters recede. The families are reunited when the harvest has been reaped. Cattle camps close to the permanent channels or swamps are left with the first rains in April. Such migrations may be from 10 to 50 miles.

The only town in the region is Malakal (pop. 10,000); a dry-point settlement east of the Nile, the centre of administration and a local market. Difficult and poverty-stricken though their way of life is, these Nilotic peoples have shown very little disposition to explore other ways of living. The long-term plans for Nile conservation which will lead to considerable control over the White Nile system will here reverse the season of main flow (p. 291–2). This will necessitate considerable changes in the traditional way of life of the Nilotic people and will present an enormous task to inculcate new ways of living to about a million people who already distrust their masters in the Arab north.

THE ECONOMY

The Sudan is a country of great plains; about one-third of its total area is suitable for cultivation or grazing, mineral resources so far as is known are negligible, industrial development is only beginning. Thus the main activities and wealth of the country are agricultural and pastoral. The customary African dual division of the economy into a subsistence and money section prevails. The subsistence sector is based on rain-fed growth of food crops under primitive methods, the money economy on commercial growing of irrigated cotton. The areas of commercial production are in the Khartoum-Gezira area and along the river and rail lines, mainly in the north-eastern quadrant of the country. Subsistence production occupies more than half the population and uses 80 per cent of the cultivated area. Grazing is principally left to the nomadic tribes peripheral to the Central Rainlands. The subsistence area of the Rainlands holds a great potential; much of the produce of this sector could be expanded for consumption and export if transport and markets were available. The extension in 1959 of the railway from El Obeid to Nyala and in 1962 southwards to Wau, and from Sennar to El Roseires (1955) may prove important catalysts in this transformation.

Industrial development has made some progress since the war; naturally it is concerned mainly with the processing of agricultural products. Tanneries, soap works, cotton ginneries and breweries exist in a number of urban centres. A cement works was established at Atbara in 1949 and another at Rabak in Blue Nile Province in 1964; a meat-canning works at Kosti in 1952; textiles mills at Nazara in 1950; two aluminium-working plants and a glass factory in Khartoum-Omdurman. At Wad Medani a cigarette factory was started in 1958. Much foreign capital is invested in these enterprises, which for the most part are located in the east-central Sudan and underline its economic dominance.

The Sudan's economic growth has been largely related to the expansion of cotton production and its export. Cotton and its products account for about 65 per cent of total exports; oil seeds (15 per cent), gum arabic (10 per cent), and animals and animal products (6 per cent) are the only other exports of note. Principal imports are textiles, petroleum products, vehicle and transport equipment, metals and machinery, coffee, tea and sugar. The United Kingdom is both the best customer and supplier.

POPULATION, COMMUNICATIONS AND SETTLEMENT

The first National Census of the Sudan was taken over several months during 1955–6. The total population was recorded as 10,255,912. There is a high rate of natural increase which is likely to grow as the death rate becomes reduced with the application of better medical knowledge. In 1965, the population was estimated at 13,540,000. Some 90 per cent of the population is rural but the few urban centres provide the centres and mainsprings of administrative, political and economic activity. *Khartoum* is by far the largest town. In fact, the agglomeration here comprises three towns: Khartoum, Omdurman and Khartoum North enclosing the confluence of the Blue and White Niles. The population is over 300,000. Khartoum is a modern town laid out by the British after Kitchener's reconquest; Omdurman and Khartoum North (formerly Halfaya) are African market towns. *Port Sudan* has grown in importance with the increase of trade, of which it handles 80 per cent. It now has a population of about 50,000 and has half a mile of quays, warehouses, petrol-storage installations, a salt evaporating works and a cotton ginnery.

The recent economic history of the Sudan underlines the importance of modern means of communication. These make possible the expansion of the modern commercial sector of the economy upon which the future economic growth of the republic depends. Railways came to the Sudan with Kitchener in 1898, for his army constructed the desert line from Wadi Halfa to Atbara and Khartoum. The need for establishing a revenue-earning sector of the economy quickly led to the rail link from Atbara to the Red Sea at Port Sudan. Other lines were built to Sennar and to El Obeid (1911). Later the Kassala and Gashe cotton-growing areas were connected with Port Sudan and with Sennar. Since the attainment of independence there has been an upsurge of railway building. In 1955 the line southward to Sennar was extended to El Roseires and in 1959 the line through the Central Rainlands was extended 435 miles to Nyala in Darfur, with a branch line reaching Wau on the western margin of the Sudd in 1962. Until this branch was completed the only permanent link between the northern and southern parts of the country was by river steamer—shallow stern-wheel ones are used. The White Nile and Bahr el Jebel are navigable all the year as far south as Juba (where roads link with Uganda) but the Blue Nile is only navigable as far as Roseires in the high-water season. Few roads have yet been constructed. Most existing roads are merely cleared tracks that become impassable in the wet season.

The main problem facing the Sudan Government is to fuse more closely the north and south of their country: the watery southern clay plains with their Nilotic inhabitants are a different world remote from Khartoum and the Central Rainlands. Improvement of transport between north and south may hold few economic incentives but politically it is becoming increasingly urgent.

27

Ethiopia and Somalia

Between the highlands of East Africa and the gash of the Red Sea stands a massive mountain bastion. On its south-east attendant plateaux and plains drop down to the Indian Ocean. The bulk of the area is included in the Empire of Ethiopia with the new state Somalia on its east. A torrid sparsely populated zone severs Ethiopia from the East African highland and this, with the arid Eritrean coastlands, completes a zone of drought which encircles the mountainous uplands. Ethiopia has a long history and an independent outlook that is intimately related to its mountain isolation. For sixteen centuries the greater part of the country has been Christian; and from the seventh century almost isolated by the conquests of Islam which closed the Red Sea and encircled the mountain mass. Except for a brief period in the sixteenth century when Portugal assisted in repelling the Moslems, the country remained cut off from the Western world until the nineteenth century when travellers, merchants and missionaries made gradual penetration, to be followed by treaties with the Great Powers. Italy, who possessed Eritrea in the north and Somalia to the south-east, invaded and annexed Ethiopia in 1935, but British forces restored the country to the Emperor Haile Selassie in 1941. The former Italian colony of Eritrea was transferred to Ethiopia by the United Nations in 1952 and became an autonomous unit within the new Federation of Ethiopia and Eritrea. Ethiopia is an empire derived from a combination of a number of formerly separate kingdoms and the Emperor, or Negus, was recognised by them as their king of kings. Now these former kingdoms, such as Kaffa, Shoa, Gojjam, Tigré, have the status of provinces, for since the time of Theodore (1865–8) the emperors have increased their power and centralised the government.

The area of Ethiopia is nearly 400,000 sq. miles. Within it a number of distinctive regions may be identified for geographical treatment: these are shown in Fig. 57.

THE HIGHLANDS, split into two unequal portions by the rift valley, present a rolling upland area averaging 8,000 feet but with many of the higher parts over 13,000 feet. Within part of the rift itself and on its eastern margins these highlands are bounded by spectacular escarpments. The mountain areas are particularly distinguished from the lower interior plateaux by the greater rainfall they enjoy and the milder summer temperatures. Many of the highest areas are snow-covered for a short time each year and a rainy season, mainly between June and October, in sympathy with the Indian monsoon, gives over 40 inches. The driest months, when only a few showers fall, are confined to November to January in the south but the period becomes longer in the north. These highland areas extend from 5° to 17°N, about 800 miles. The main mass flanks the rift valley for over 300 miles but tapers to the north; the highest parts lie to the east, centre and north where considerable areas above 12,000 feet are common. South of the rift valley the Somali-Harar highlands drop down steeply to the south-west, the highest peaks (nearly 14,000 feet) overlooking the rift.

The heavy run-off feeds powerful rivers that cut deep gorges in the volcanic rocks, often being guided by rifts and fissures. These break up the uplands into a series of *ambas* or flat-topped mountains, sometimes their tops protected by resistant strata, which possess water, grass and arable land, and are natural strongholds. Eighty per cent of Ethiopians live in the highlands, mainly in tight little independent villages of round wattle huts beneath gum-tapped eucalyptus trees. They obtain their livelihood by agriculture and stock rearing. Frost is unknown and tropical vegetation thrives in the *kolla*: the hot lower slopes of the highlands and the valleys below 5–6,000 feet. Bananas and coffee are the more important products, coffee being an important export crop: *arabica* coffee is believed to have orginated in Ethiopia. Nearly 90 per cent of Ethiopian coffee grows wild. Most grows between 5,000 and 6,500 feet in the south-west of the highlands in the provinces of Kaffa (whence the name 'coffee'), Gamu and Harar south of the rift. The output could

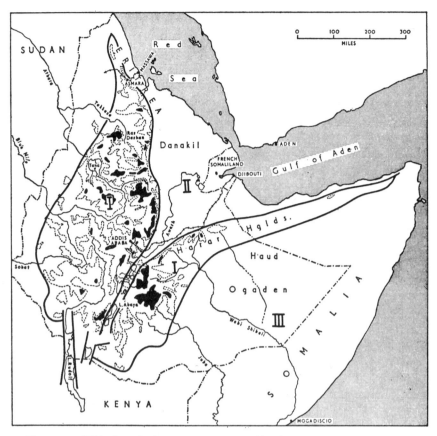

Figure 57 *Ethiopia and adjacent regions.* I. Highlands. II. The Red Sea littoral and Danakil lowlands, continued to the south-west in the rift which splits the highlands in two. III. Low plateaux and Somali coastlands

be substantially expanded if cultivation and marketing became more systematic. Annual exports of coffee average 55,000 tons and account for over 50 per cent of the country's export revenue. Most of the highland population lives in the *woina dega*, the middle highlands between 6,000 and 9,000 feet. Here cereals are grown and tree fruits such as the orange, apricot and fig are produced. Sheep and cattle are kept.

Ethiopians in the highlands recognise two principal types of soil: black and red. Black soils occur in areas liable to waterlogging in the wet season, for example shallow valleys and basins. Red soils are found on the better-drained slopes and are less fertile than black soils. Cereals (the tiny-seeded grass *t'eff*, wheat, barley, rye, sorghum and maize) and pulses (chick peas, green peas, beans and lentils) are the principal crops grown. Up to 8,000 feet *t'eff* and wheat are most important; above this barley and wheat predominate. Simoons records the cultivation of wheat, barley, rye and flax at 11,000 feet on Ras Dashan.[1] In the highlands two crops a year are frequently grown in succession in the same field, for the heavy rainfall makes certain the maturing of the second crop. Rotations vary from place to place but a typical one of the black soils is first and second year *t'eff*; third year *nug* (a yellow-flowered oil plant); fourth year *t'eff*; fifth year chick peas and sixth year *t'eff*. The black soil is so fertile that it is seldom fallowed. On the red soil a fallow year comes when yields fall, often every third year, and a typical rotation then is first year *t'eff*; second year millet and third year fallow.[2]

The ox-drawn plough was first introduced by the Amhara and is now used all over the highland area. The hoe, the digging stick and the sickle are the other principal implements, the first two being used more at lower altitudes where fields are cleared by slashing and burning and some shifting cultivation takes place. In the upland areas of settled farming domestic animals, mainly sheep and cattle, graze the fallow fields, their droppings helping to restore fertility to the soil. The stock population is heavier in the drier north than in the south of the highlands.

Above 9,000 feet is the *dega* proper: here the hardier cereals will grow, but it consists mainly of open short grassland offering abundant pasture for animals. There is very little bush except in sheltered places and few trees except introduced eucalyptus, grown beside almost every habitation. Here population is sparse but transhumance is less general than might be expected. Altitudinal movement of herds is local only; cattle may be sent upwards under the supervision of boys and young men during the rainy season to avoid mud and flies, a small seasonal fee being paid to the chief controlling the grazing areas. Goats and sheep are rarely moved. In the north the cattle are the humped zebu type, in the south a long-horned zebu type. Cattle are valued highly in Ethiopia and a man's wealth is often measured by the size of his herds. Hides and skins serve a variety of household and agricultural uses and also provide a substantial export.

THE INTERIOR PLATEAUX, including the rift valley, stand as independent features mainly to the south of the highland mass. Here they drop down through Ogaden to the Somalia littoral. The lower altitude of this *kolla* zone (3,000–5,000 feet) is responsible for the greater heat and marked diurnal range of temperature. Rainfall is also less, much of the area having under 20 inches. The great heat is somewhat mitigated by the fact that the valleys are broader here. In better-watered parts, such as the Awash valley in the rift, sugar cane and oilseed crops are grown, including castor, sesame, groundnuts and sunflowers, but much of this area is pastoralist country.

THE RED SEA LITTORAL In the east the highlands are girt by the arid lower land flanking the Red Sea. The parched, hot and treeless coastal plain is narrow (10 to 50 miles) and backed by low hills in Eritrea and French Somaliland and by the more substantial prolongation of the Harar highlands overlooking the Gulf of Aden. Between the Ethiopian highlands and the Eritrean coast lies the burning Danakil desert, in places below sea-level. There is little settled life in so arid an area and most of the population is nomadic, rearing animals and collecting gum arabic. Although the Red Sea is rich in fish, fishing is little developed.

Since antiquity, in common with other parts of the Middle East and East Africa, Ethiopia has suffered the scourge of the desert locust. Periodically these descend to destroy crops in the arid areas and less frequently do great damage in the highlands. Ethiopia is free from the tsetse fly. Little mineral wealth has yet been proved: there is a small gold production, some potash salts are worked in the Danakil plains and salt is also produced. Exploration for oil is being carried out in Ogaden. Industrial development is yet in its infancy—most is located at Addis Ababa. Textiles, cement, bricks and tiles are made and sugar is milled.

POPULATION AND SETTLEMENT

No census has yet been held in Ethiopia, so that the official population total of over 20 million is but an estimate. A further consequence is that no vital statistics are available and therefore there is no accurate knowledge of the rate of increase of the population. Undoubtedly as medicine and hygiene become more practised, as in other parts of Africa, the death rate will fall and a more rapid population increase is likely. The position of Ethiopia between the Middle East and Negro Africa and a long history of invasions explains why the Ethiopian population is made up of a number of separate ethnic communities. Ethiopia has provided the meeting ground for many peoples and in its mountain fastnesses many languages and cultures have been preserved. Some seventy different languages are spoken but the official language is Amharic and at least one-third of the people are the Amhara, commonly called Ethiopians. They inhabit the central Ethiopian highlands and to their north are related peoples, the Tigréans. These peoples are of mixed Semitic and Hamitic origin but Christians; the Emperor claims descent from King Solomon and the Queen of Sheba, who herself was Ethiopian. They are proud and warlike and although in numbers a minority they have been the ruling people in Ethiopia for many hundreds of years. These people kept in touch with Western Christendom and civilisation; their priests preserved a formal system of education only now supplemented by state schools. They brought in the plough and extended cultivation at the expense of woodland. The coastal areas flanking the Red Sea, Gulf of Aden and Indian Ocean and the uplands of the Horn of Africa which they contain are the home of Hamitic peoples originally from southern Arabia. The Galla and Somali are the most important, the majority of them being Moslems.

Addis Ababa, the capital, has nearly half a million inhabitants and excepting Asmara (the capital of Eritrea) is the only large town. Much of the capital's growth has been in recent years. It became the capital in 1889 and for the next twenty years consisted of little more than the royal palace and one or two African villages set in eucalyptus woodland on a broad but ravine-scarred bench, a fatiguing 8,000 feet above sea-level. The capital, with its unmade rutted roads and jumble of squalid buildings, was not far advanced from the African village stage when the Italians took over in 1935. The real advance has come during recent years when, with the spread of independence throughout Africa, the city was modernised to become a fitting capital for the doyen of Africa's independent rulers. Old streets were widened, asphalted double carriage-way roads, new hotels and ministries were constructed; a new international airport was completed and new façades attached to dilapidated shops and residences. In 1961 the Emperor inaugurated a magnificent building complex known as Africa Hall, erected especially to provide an Assembly Hall and Secretariat building for the United Nations Economic Commission for Africa. It provides a meeting place, and home of the permanent secretariat, of the independent states in Africa. The city's population is most diverse: there is a substantial body of several thousand Yemeni merchants as well as Greeks, Armenians, Syrians, Indians and some 15,000 Europeans and Americans. The city is connected by railway with the coast at Djibouti in French Somaliland (486 miles). There are three trains in each direction weekly.

Through the fields the thrice-weekly train from Djibouti laboured the last few miles to the capital, puffing more frantically as its wheels turned faster, slipping on the steepening gradient. As the road ran down through the last fields and sisal estates, the villages became fewer and more primitive, a line of mud huts holding the thorn scrub back from the road for a few yards. The smarter huts had tin roofs, and some were decorated with gaudy posters advertising soap or razor blades. There was an air of sleepiness about the villages: hardly a woman was to be seen, and the men sat at the front of their houses or leant against the posts, not talking, just watching.

Outside the villages, the life these people led became more apparent, men clothed in a brown length of cloth falling from one shoulder watched over their herds of cattle, crackling their way slowly through the dry bush. Thin and straight backed, with tight-curled heads held proudly, the men carried spears. Two little boys held up a young deer for sale. A Galla woman, her back bent under a load of firewood, was walking to some market that might be as much as 3 days away. She would get a dollar (2s. 10d.) for her six days' toil. Over her head there danced a thick black spiral of flies, attracted by the smell of the rancid butter with which she had anointed her hair.[3]

Perched in the highlands on an outmoded defensive site, Addis Ababa gives one a feeling of isolation and remoteness out of keeping with the overwhelming tasks of bringing communications and economic development to the rest of the potentially rich upland country. The only other railway is that between Agordat and Massawa via Asmara (191 miles) in Eritrea. This addition to the empire, although arid and poor, has a rather different personality, for it reflects sixty years of Italian occupation. There are roads, towns and two ports, Massawa and Assab. Good roads are being constructed, but so far these total no more than 5,000 miles and away from them transport is by pack animals: mules, donkeys, horses and camels. This paucity of modern means of communication retards economic development. The transport system is still that of a backward people engaged in subsistence farming, although the recent development of air transport linking Addis Ababa with foreign capitals and a number of internal towns must be noticed. Foreign trade is quite small, totalling no more than $170 million per annum. Coffee is the only important export; imports include textiles, vehicles, oil products and machinery.

Much is now being done under the guidance of the Emperor to speed the emergence of Ethiopia as a modern state. Democratic institutions have been introduced and a whole system of education from primary schools to a university at Addis Ababa has been established. A technical college has been built at Bahar Dar, at the southern end of Lake Tana, the forerunner of an industrial centre to arise when the falls of the Blue Nile (Plate 4) are harnessed for hydro-electric power. The geography of Ethiopia poses many difficulties to such speedy development: communications are poor and difficult and the mass of the people is out of touch with the surge of feeling and enthusiasm for change engendered in the administrative centres. Their daily lives of subsistence production and limited opportunity continue much as before: great potentiality lies untapped until the means for an easier flow of ideas, people and products becomes possible.

THE SOMALILANDS

The Somali peoples are dispersed over the Horn of Africa, throughout the new Somali Republic, in the south-east of Ethiopia and also in the north-east of Kenya. Their republic attained its independence in 1960 and comprises the peninsula of the former Italian and British Somali territories, the one facing the Indian Ocean, the other the Gulf of Aden. The small enclave of French Somaliland still remains under the control of France. In the north there is practically no coastal plain, for the prolongation of the Harar highlands brings 7,000-foot mountains close to the Gulf of Aden. On the Indian Ocean side the plateau descends from Ethiopia in a number of escarpments to a final one a few hundred feet high overlooking, between Mogadiscio and Kismayu, an alluvial plain watered by the seasonal Webi Shibeli which, in fact, does not reach the sea.

The area of the Somali Republic is 246,000 sq. miles and the whole of it is hot, semi-arid or outright desert. Some of the highest area in the north receives a little over 10 inches of rain annually, and a limited area along the south-east coast around Mogadiscio (the capital and roadstead port) receives more than 15 inches, but otherwise sparse grazing and scrub desert prevail, the aridity enhanced by the permeability of the limestones and sands comprising much of the surface rock. Pastoralism is the mode of livelihood of 80 per cent of the population, most of them being nomadic or semi-nomadic, paying little attention to boundaries and in the north moving up into Ethiopian Ogaden and the Haud in summer. Sheep and goats are their principal animals and the collection of gums and resins from the scrubby desert bushes brings in a small supplementary income. Agriculture is limited to a few better-watered areas such as the valleys of the Juba and Webi Shibeli where former Italian estates produce sugar cane, bananas (the main export) and cereals. On the coast, fishing and salt evaporating give some employment.

The population of the Somali Republic is estimated at between 2 and 3 million. The capital is *Mogadiscio* (pop. 120,000) and there are no other towns of any size. *Djibouti*, capital of French Somaliland (pop. 45,000), is of greater importance, for it is the principal outlet and inlet for 60 per cent of Ethiopia's trade (the railway to Addis Ababa was completed in 1913) and a port of call for ocean shipping. Traffic on the railway has increased by a third since 1950.

The attainment of independence by a majority of the Somalis has stirred up those outside the bounds of the new state, for Somali peoples are divided between four political units. Frontiers are ill-defined and generally disregarded by the predominantly nomadic people as they roam the steppe grazing. Kenya with her new independence is loth to part with her national territory, desert though it may be, and Ethiopia has no liking for a strong Moslem state expanding on her borders. Thus the impoverished, ill-endowed young state, so urgently needing to turn attention inwards to her own improvement, has become a focus of unrest born of religion and nationalism which may yet upset the Horn of Africa.

References

1 F. J. Simoons, *Northwest Ethiopia: Peoples and economy* (Madison, 1960), p. 66
2 *ibid*, 73
3 M. R. Melville, 'A journey in Ethiopia', *The Times*, March 30, 1950

Selected Bibliography

Oxford regional economic atlas: *The Middle East and North Africa* (Oxford, 1960)
J. Ball, *Contributions to the geography of Egypt* (Cairo, 1939)
K. M. Barbour, *The Republic of the Sudan* (London, 1961)

W. B. Fisher, *The Middle East*, esp. Ch. XIX (London, 1956)

A. Gaitskell, *Gezira: a story of development* (London, 1959)

Y. Abul-Haggag, *Physiography of Northern Ethiopia* (London, 1961)

H. E. Hurst, *The Nile* (London, 1957)

J. Lebon, *Land use in Sudan* (Bude, 1965)

A. B. Mountjoy, *Industrialisation and Under-developed Countries*, esp. Ch. 9 (London, 1966)

J. D. Tothill (ed.), *Agriculture in the Sudan* (London, 1948)

United Nations, *Structure and growth of selected African Economies* (New York, 1958)

J. Lebon, 'On the human geography of the Nile Basin', *Geog.*, 45 (1960), 16–26

A. B. Mountjoy, 'Egypt's population problem', *Trans. Inst. Brit. Geogr.*, 18 (1952), 121–35

A. B. Mountjoy, 'The development of industry in Egypt', *Econ. Geog.*, 28 (1952), 212–28

A. B. Mountjoy, 'Land and the Egyptian peasant', *Geog.*, 40 (1955), 194–6

A. B. Mountjoy, 'The Suez Canal at mid-century', *Econ. Geog.*, 34 (1958), 155–67

G. Murray, 'Water from beneath the Egyptian Western Desert', *Geog. Journ.*, 118 (1952), 443–52

G. Murray, 'Land of Sinai', *Geog. Journ.*, 119 (1953), 140–54

N. el Nasr, 'Land use in the Nile Delta', *Geog.*, 40 (1955), 178–90

K. M. Barbour, 'The Wadi Azum', *Geog. Journ.*, 120 (1954), 174–82

K. M. Barbour, 'Irrigation in the Sudan', *Trans. Inst. Brit. Geogr.*, 26 (1959), 243–63

K. M. Barbour, 'North and south in Sudan', *Ann. Assoc. Am. Geogr.*, 54 (1964), 209–26

H. R. J. Davies, 'An agricultural revolution in the African tropics', *Tijdschrift v. Econ. en Soc. Geog.*, 55 (1964), 101–8

G. Hamdan, 'Growth and functional structure of Khartoum', *Geog. Rev.*, 50 (1960), 21–40

W. Hance, 'The Gezira', *Geog. Rev.*, 44 (1954), 253–70

P. P. Howell, 'The equatorial Nile project and its effects in the Sudan', *Geog. Journ.*, 119 (1953), 33–48

J. Lebon and V. Robertson, 'The Jebel Marra, Darfur, and its region', *Geog. Journ.*, 127 (1961), 30–49

J. Oliver, 'Port Sudan: the study of its growth and functions', *Tijdschrift v. Econ. en Soc. Geog.*, 57 (1966), 54–61

C. Brooke, 'The rural village in the Ethiopian Highlands', *Geog. Rev.*, 49 (1959), 58–75

D. Buxton, 'The Shoan plateau and its people', *Geog. Journ.*, 113 (1949), 157–72

J. W. Pallister, 'The geomorphology of the Northern Region Somali Republic', *Geog. Journ.*, 129 (1963), 184–7

A. Beeby Thompson, 'The water supply of British Somaliland', *Geog. Journ.*, 101 (1943), 154–60

PART VII

East Africa

The great plateau area of East Africa has considerable geographical unity, although it is now divided politically into three (originally four) independent states all within the British Commonwealth. These states and the dates of their independence are Tanganyika (1961), Uganda (1962), Zanzibar (1963), Kenya (1963). Prior to the granting of independence Kenya was a British colony, except for a small coastal portion belonging to Zanzibar. This part and Zanzibar were both under a Sultan and were British Protectorates. Uganda was a Protectorate and Tanganyika (formerly German East Africa) was first a mandated territory and then a United Nations trusteeship territory administered by Britain. British commercial interests began trading in East Africa towards the close of the nineteenth century; subsequently the British Government assumed responsibility for agreements with the Africans and brought to a successful conclusion many years of attack on the Arab-organised slave trade. To develop Uganda and free her from the slave traffic a rail link from the coast through Kenya was begun in 1895. The Africans were not attracted to such labour and the line was built by labourers brought over from India, many of whom remained in East Africa as the forbears of the present thriving Asian population. The railway reached Kisumu on Lake Victoria in 1901 and proved a vital factor in increasing economic development in both Uganda and Kenya. In 1885 Germany took Tanganyika from the Sultan of Zanzibar who claimed suzerainty over it. 'German East Africa' was conquered by Britain in the First World War.

East Africa displays a microcosm of the problems of the whole continent. We find here native Africans at all stages of economic and social development from pastoral nomads to wealthy cotton growers, while plantations and large European farms contrast with overcrowded native subsistence farming. Malaria-bearing mosquitoes, the tsetse fly and locust all take their toll and the bitter problems of plural society—black, brown and white—are worsened by inter-tribal enmity.

In 1965 the population of the East African states was estimated at 27 million, of whom about 100,000 were European and 400,000 Asian. East Africa is an ethnological mixing ground where three great ethnic groups are found. In northern Uganda are the southernmost of the pastoral *Nilotic* tribes; on the Kenya-Tanganyika border are the *Half Hamites* of whom the Masai are the principal tribe; elsewhere the *Eastern Bantu* are the dominant peoples, divided into many tribes and attaining their highest level of development in Uganda. Arabs and Asians are most numerous in the coastal belt and in Zanzibar where Swahili is the lingua franca. Other Asians are spread widely in urban and commercial employment.

In 1948 an East African High Commission was established to provide and administer certain services common to the three mainland countries. These included defence, a common customs service and the operating of a variety of social, research, scientific and economic services. In that year also an East African Railways and Harbours Administration assumed, on a unified basis, control of the railways and chief ports and the operation of lake, river and some road services. With independence there is a body of East African opinion that would like to see this system extended finally to embrace a Federation of the separate territories. Both geographically and economically there is a strong case for such a development, towards which the independent governments have pledged themselves. The union of Tanganyika and Zanzibar to form Tanzania in 1964 may point the way.

28

Physical Geography

With the offshore islands, the total area of East Africa is 682,800 sq. miles spread between 12°S and 5°N. Within this area practically every variation of physical feature from arid desert to snow-capped peak is demonstrated. Much of the present-day East African topography owes its origin to the substantial earth-movements during the Tertiary period. In East Africa they resulted in a sequence of uplift and downwarp, the foundering of large areas to form a chain of rift valleys and the spewing out of much lava, which continued into the Quaternary period. Much of the region comprises Pre-Cambrian igneous and metamorphic rocks of the Basement series which form the great plateau masses. The highest land (except for Ruwenzori) is formed by the later outpourings of volcanic materials. Sedimentary rocks are limited in area and sporadic in occurrence, being confined mainly to the coastal zone and the north-east of Kenya.

East Africa is really a country of plateaux representing a series of planation surfaces. They are dominated by some of Africa's highest mountains: Kilimanjaro (19,340 feet), Kenya (17,058 feet), Ruwenzori (16,794 feet). These mountains, related to the rifting, are all on or near the equator, yet they are snow-capped and possess glaciers. The rift valleys (see also Chapter 1) are aligned in one Main or Eastern Rift system which passes from Ethiopia and Lake Rudolf through the heart of Kenya and Tanganyika into Malawi, and a Western Rift branching off to form the deep trench now occupied by Lakes Albert, Edward, Kivu and Tanganyika. Lake Tanganyika is the world's second deepest lake, with a maximum depth of 4,706 feet.

PHYSICAL REGIONS (Fig. 58)

THE COASTAL PLAIN is low and narrow (10 to 40 miles wide) and is composed of Quaternary sediments fringed with coral reefs. It is hot and, except in the extreme north, humid with mangrove swamps in the estuaries. Soils vary considerably from fertile alluvium of the river estuaries to extensive infertile spreads of coral shag. The plain is narrow throughout most of Kenya but broadens out behind Dar es Salaam to include the lower course of the Rufiji river. The western limit of the coastal plain is indicated by a series of minor escarpments or steps of successively older sedimentary rocks which lead on to the threshold of the massive plateaux that cover the greater part of East Africa.

THE NYIKA   Behind and above the coastal plain stretches the Nyika (Swahili = wilderness) of Kenya and northern Tanganyika. It is a planation surface of end–Tertiary age rising gently inland and averaging 2,000 feet in height. The surface is broken here and there by relict hill masses and inselberge and dissected by a number of small rivers, including the Tana, Galana, Pangani and Rufiji, which empty into the Indian Ocean. This low plateau is nearly pinched out by the Pare-Usumbara Mountains, but further south widens into the South-East Plateau of Tanganyika. This is a semi-arid countryside which becomes desert in the north-east of Kenya where the annual rainfall is under 10 inches. In the west the Nyika is bordered by hills and ranges such as the Matthews Range and Kitui hills in Kenya and the Nguru Mountains and Southern highlands of Tanganyika. These introduce the true East African plateau.

THE EAST AFRICAN PLATEAU   This great upland mass, comprising the greater part of Tanganyika and Uganda and nearly half of Kenya, is composed mainly of the Basement rocks which attain heights of around 7,000 feet in Kenya and northern Tanganyika. Here bevelled remnants and accordant summit levels are related to planation from the pre-Miocene period. Within this great plateau area a number of sub-divisions may be made. An outstanding feature occurring in this plateau is the *Eastern or Main Rift Valley*. This passes through these uplands south from Lake Rudolf to Lake Malawi. Within southern Kenya it varies from 40 to 50 miles in width and is flanked by mountain buttresses in places over 3,000 feet high. The floor of the valley is quite high, ranging from about 1,300 feet in the north to 6,250 feet at Lake Naivasha in the centre and dropping to 2,000 feet at Lake Manyara in Tanganyika. Farther south the rift loses the trough-like character it exhibits in Kenya and becomes less of a topographical feature, the western boundary appearing as a cliff of varying height, the eastern face rarely prominent.

Nevertheless, it guides the line of the upper Great Ruaha river within the Southern Highlands where its floor rises to over 3,000 feet. Within these highlands the Eastern and Western Rift systems unite. They pass beneath volcanic hills attaining over 9,700 feet, part of the Kipengere Range,

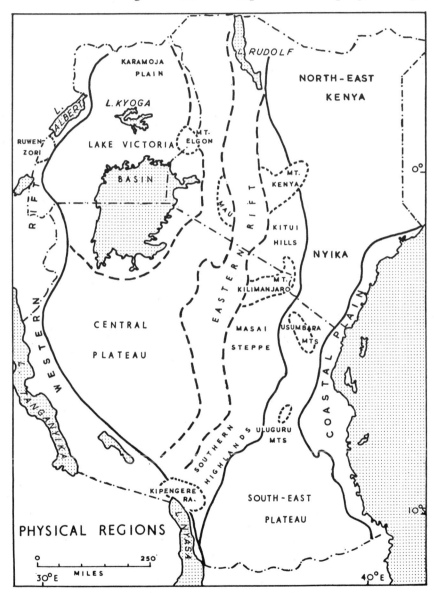

Figure 58 *The physical regions of East Africa*

cradle Lake Malawi and direct the course of the Shiré river to the Zambezi and the sea.

Flanking the rift from Lake Rudolf to Lake Manyara in northern Tanganyika are higher masses and mountains composed of Tertiary to recent volcanoes and associated lava flows. These form extensive and massive bastions and peaks rising strongly above the general level of the plateau: notably Mount Kenya (17,058 feet,) the Aberdares (to 13,000 feet) and the Mau uplands (to 10,000 feet), all in Kenya, and Kilimanjaro (19,340 feet) in Tanganyika. The soils derived from the decomposition of volcanic rocks are here more fertile than those formed on the Basement series. This fertility, coupled with the mitigation of the climate with greater altitude, made these areas favourable for white settlement which led subsequently to the general term 'the White Highlands', now less appropriate since land ownership there is no longer restricted to Europeans.

The East African plateau bears in its centre the *Lake Victoria Basin*. All the plantation surfaces in East Africa show evidence of warping, especially between the rifts where a great structural downwarp or sag contains the relatively shallow Lake Victoria and marshy Lake Kyoga to its north, both part of the Nile drainage system. This depression and a number of other downwarps in central Tanganyika are conveniently called the Lake Victoria Basin. It includes much of Uganda, much of the Nyanza district of Kenya, and part of the lake province of Tanganyika. Most of this area is a little below 4,000 feet and in the lower parts Pleistocene sediments have accumulated and mask the old crystalline rocks.

South of the Lake Victoria Basin and including about half of Tanganyika is the *Central Plateau*. Like the rest of the great plateau area it is composed of crystalline rocks of the Basement series, but is at a rather lower elevation, averaging little more than 4,000 feet. The rather monotonous undulating landscape for much of the year is brown and parched.

THE WESTERN RIFT VALLEY AND HIGHLANDS terminate the plateau in the west. The highlands flank the edge of the western branch of the rift valley, generally repeating the pattern already noted with the eastern branch. The rift extends in an arc from Lake Albert to Lake Tanganyika and also contains within it Lakes Edward and Kivu. The floor of this rift is generally between 2,000–3,000 feet, somewhat lower than its eastern counterpart. Again great peaks and masses tower above the rift valley in such mountains as Ruwenzori (16,794 feet), a great horst of Archaean rocks (the highest non-volcanic mountain in Africa), and the Mfumbiro chain of active volcanic peaks which crosses the rift from the Congo Republic to Rwanda and Burundi and forms the water parting between drainage northward to the Nile and that to Lake Kivu and the Congo system. Several of these peaks surpass 14,000 feet.

Drainage

Most of the drainage of East Africa flows to the Mediterranean via the Nile system or to the southern Atlantic via the Congo system. Drainage to the Indian Ocean is limited in amount and in Kenya several rivers crossing the Nyika are seasonal, being reduced to a series of muddy pools during the dry season. The Tana and Galana are the only two perennial streams, descending by falls from the plateau of the Basement rocks. Neither is navigable. Tanganyika has few permanent rivers, for much of her Central Plateau has a dry season of five to six months when very little rain falls. The main rivers flowing into the Indian Ocean are the Pangani, fed by the snows of Kilimanjaro, the Ruvu, the Rufiji, which receives many tributaries from the Southern Highlands, and the Ruvuma which forms the republic's southern boundary with Portuguese East Africa. Of these only the Rufiji is navigable for 60 miles from its extensive delta. A number of other streams flow into Lake Victoria, Lake Tanganyika and Lake Malawi; thus Tanganyika contains the divide separating the headstreams of the Nile, Congo and Zambezi. A fourth division of the drainage is into inland basins. In Kenya there are a number of lakes in the floor of the rift such as Lakes Rudolf, Nakuru, Magadi and in Tanganyika Lakes Natron, Manyara and Eyasi.

CLIMATE

The East African states extend between latitudes 4°N and 11°S and are therefore mainly equatorial. However, the compact mass of uplands and the great elevations attained locally are responsible for climates ranging from those of the tropical coastal belt with temperatures around 80°F all the year and a high humidity, to temperate climates within the highlands where mean temperatures lie between 70° and 50°F with diurnal ranges of as much as 30°. Uganda with more uniform relief exhibits less marked climatic variation, mean temperatures generally being between 75° and 70°F, with daily ranges nowhere greater than 20°F. Rainfall also shows a great range of variation, from 5 inches or less on the Somalia border to as much as 100 inches in some of the mountainous areas.

The climates experienced over East Africa are somewhat complex and so far the meteorological processes responsible are not fully understood, so that causation must still be dealt with tentatively. East African climates owe much to three factors: an equatorial location; the presence of so much high land; and, in particular, monsoonal influences. The character and direction of flow (tending to parallel the coast) of the major air-streams over East Africa account for the seasonality and the generally low rainfall experienced in an equatorial area, and give East African rainfall a considerable degree of variability from the norm.

During the southern summer in the period November to April the ITC moves far to the south, and behind it northerly and north-easterly airstreams flow over East Africa. In Kenya, Uganda and northern Tanganyika these winds are of cT type and dry, arriving from Arabia and the continent of Asia. In southern and eastern Tanganyika, additional influx of mT air from the Indian Ocean gives rise to sporadic rains. With the northward movement of the ITC in the southern winter, mainly southerly airstreams blow over East Africa, including the mT air of the South-East Trades of the Indian Ocean, and also mE air from an Atlantic source which passes over the Congo towards Ethiopia. The mT air loses much of its moisture over Madagascar and, like the northerly (winter) winds, does not deposit much rainfall over East Africa; while most of the precipitation from the south-west flow of mE air falls more to the north over the south-west Ethiopian highlands. East Africa experiences most rain in the transition months during the passages of the ITC. During these periods the winds become weak and variable, and the rainfall is small for an equatorial region. These rainy transition months are February to May and October to December. Most rain falls in the former period, known as the 'maize rains'; the lesser rains later in the year being called the 'millet rains'.

The coastal zone south of Mombasa experiences over 40 inches and the higher plateau elevations surpass that figure. Much of the lower and middle plateau areas receive under 30 inches which, under conditions of equatorial heat, is inadequate for arable farming. It is in fact necessary to distinguish between rainfall and *effective* rainfall (Chapter 5). Most rain is experienced on the south-facing mountain slopes and those relating to the Western Rift such as Ruwenzori. The highest of the volcanic mountains may well receive up to 100 inches.

Rainfall is of great economic significance, for the vast mass of the East African population depends on agriculture and pastoralism for a livelihood. Over considerable areas mean annual amounts of rain are marginal, and this situation is worsened by the unreliability of much of the rain. The year-to-year variation is large: many stations have recorded maximum annual rainfall more than four times the minimum and seasonal drought of six months or more affects nearly two-thirds of the area. Most of Tanganyika experiences a southern hemisphere régime, with one rainy season of five to six months and the rest of the year dry. Much of Kenya and Uganda, being nearer the equator, has a two-season rainfall, the longer of these periods lasting about three months. In the extreme north of Kenya and Uganda a northern hemisphere régime of one wet season becomes apparent, but the amount of rain in northern Kenya is so reduced that desert conditions are experienced.

Typical equatorial temperatures, practically constant at around 80°F, are confined to the coastal plains near the equator where temperatures within 2-3° of the mean annual of 78°F are recorded. These are not high temperatures; it is the high humidity that makes this climate very unpleasant and enervating. Away from the coast, altitude tempers the heat: above 4,500 feet is considered suitable for white settlement. Nairobi at 5,500 feet has a mean of 63°F, rather like that of an English summer month. However, the small annual range characteristic of equatorial latitudes persists and at Nairobi is only 7° (Table 10). Temperature throughout the year is pleasant but monotonous and the real variation is not seasonal but diurnal. Nights are cool with rapid radiation and a difference of up to 25° or more between daily maximum and minimum is common, giving support to the saying 'night is the winter of the tropics'. Frost is frequent above 8,000 feet, limiting agriculture, and snow occurs above 14,000 feet.

The marked influence of topography upon East African climate facilitates a division into climatic regions closely coincident with the physical regions already outlined, but modified according to latitude. The coastal belt, except in the extreme north, is hot and damp with rainfall of up to 50 inches. From Mombasa south to Dar es Salaam is the strip exhibiting the nearest approach to equatorial conditions, although the annual total of rain (Mombasa 46 inches) is somewhat low. The temperature range is from 82°F (March) to 75°F (July), only 7°F. The

Nyika and Jubaland on the Somalia border are sparsely peopled, dusty brown, parched areas of desert and steppe. The annual rainfall, varying from 20 inches in the south probably to as little as 5 inches on the northern border with Ethiopia and Somalia, falls mainly on permeable rock.

Inland with increasing altitude temperatures become lower and rainfall increases. The most favoured regions of the middle and upper plateau stretch from central Kenya into Uganda. The greater rainfall is also more reliable and here is to be found the greater proportion of the population of the two countries. Whereas the highest area, flanking the Eastern Rift, receives well over 50 inches, the rift valley itself (generally 2,000–3,000 feet lower) is in the rain shadow of the plateau and around Lake Naivasha receives about 30 inches. This diminishes to about 10 inches at Lake Rudolf in the north and to 20 inches over much of central Tanganyika to the south. Thus the greater part of the Eastern Rift offers only poor grazing.

In south-eastern Uganda the proximity of the equator and presence of the vast water surface of Lake Victoria bring near-equatorial climatic conditions; Entebbe beside the lake at 3,800 feet has an annual temperature range of only 2° and receives 58 inches, with rain every month and maxima in April and December. Humidity is high, and although malaria and other tropical diseases are coming under control, Uganda has never been attractive to Europeans (Table 10).

One botanist returning from Uganda has described the conditions as, 'like being encased in warm moist dough'. The highest rainfall is experienced on the north-eastern and western lake shores, probably related to the paths of the prevailing winds recharged in their passage over the lake. One result is that the Lake Basin in particular and Uganda generally offer a green and more verdant aspect than most of East Africa, which for much of the year is brown. Much of the interior of Tanganyika has rather less than 30 inches of rain and a southern hemisphere régime of summer fall and a five-month dry season.

THE SOILS

East Africa with its varied rock types, relief and climates has developed a considerable range of soils. Climate is the most important formative factor, since it affects the character and rate of the weathering and the growth of vegetation and bacteria. Both rainfall and temperature affect the rate of weathering, which becomes greater with higher temperatures;

Table 10

Station	Alt. (feet)		J	F	M	A	M	J	J	A	S	O	N	D	Year	Temp. range
Mombasa	50	Temp. °F	80	80	82	81	79	77	75	76	77	79	80	80	79	7
		Rain in.	0·8	0·7	2·5	8·0	12·6	4·0	3·5	2·3	2·0	3·3	4·2	2·0	46·0	
Dar-es-Salaam	43	T.	82	81	81	78	76	74	74	74	75	77	79	81	78	8
		R.	3·3	2·1	4·8	11·9	7·4	1·1	1·7	1·1	1·1	1·2	2·9	2·7	42·3	
Nairobi	5,450	T.	64	65	65	64	64	62	59	59	62	65	64	62	63	6
		R.	1·9	3·6	4·2	8·9	5·6	2·2	0·9	1·1	1·2	2·3	5·3	2·8	39·9	
Entebbe	3,863	T.	71	71	71	70	70	70	70	69	70	70	70	70	70	2
		R.	2·6	3·6	5·8	9·7	8·5	5·1	2·9	3·1	3·1	3·5	5·0	5·1	58·0	

lateritic soils (see p. 83) are widespread, and the occurrence of hard iron-pan layers often gives little depth of workable soil, even where higher rainfall and high temperatures might otherwise lead one to expect deep soils. Much of the parent rock in East Africa is crystalline, and the nature of the soils formed depends principally on the amount of quartz in the parent material. Sandy soils are derived from granites and sandstones, but parent rocks low in quartz—such as lavas—produce rather more fertile clayey soils.

The most highly developed lateritic soils are associated with the planation surfaces; on slopes, frequent erosion makes for youthful soils. Deep, mature, well-drained, fertile soils are limited in extent, mainly being confined to areas of rolling topography from 4,000 to 10,000 feet, where rainfall is not less than 40 inches, and where the parent rock is volcanic. Such soils can retain a high proportion of the seasonal rainfall for the use of crops and vegetation during the dry season. It will be deduced, then, that most East African soils are easily leached, lack humus and often show chemical deficiencies. The better soils are in the volcanic highlands of Kenya, where rainfall is also high and reliable. Most of the soils of Tanganyika are sandy in character and the valleys become seasonally waterlogged ('mbugas'), mainly because of perched water tables where the gradient is very small during the rainy season, and in some cases because of iron-pan horizons, the only exceptions being the dark clays and clay-loams of the southern highlands. Uganda has useful clay and clay-loam areas on the north and west coasts of Lake Victoria, but in southern Uganda many valleys are permanently waterlogged and papyrus-filled. Farther north the waterlogging becomes more seasonal and to the north-east soils become more sandy and arid.

VEGETATION

East African physical conditions engender a great range of vegetation. This variety and diversity depends primarily upon rainfall and altitude. The relatively low rainfall and the extensive area above 4,000 feet create conditions in striking contrast with those of the Congo Basin to the west. Although astride the equator, equatorial forest is rare (it is found on the northern shores of Lake Victoria), and except for coastal and montane forests most of East Africa is clothed with varying forms of savanna. In the narrow coastal areas coconut-palm and casuarina flourish, as do mangroves in the river estuaries and deltas. Inland, conditions become drier and in the Kenya Nyika thorn woodland, the grotesque baobab and drought-resistant thorny scrub become dominant. Farther south, in Tanganyika, with slightly better rainfall grasses improve. Over the whole area both domesticated and wild animals find sustenance, and the thorn-bush pastures of the north, although poorer, have the advantage of being free from the tsetse fly.

On the plateau proper of Kenya, Uganda and central Tanganyika, where rainfall averages 30 inches per annum and exhibits a marked seasonal régime, open savanna prevails. The density of tree growth and height of grasses increase with the greater frequency and abundance of rain: from scattered trees with *Hyparrhenia* and other grasses 3–6 feet high, to savanna woodland with intermittent evergreen thickets and taller grass, such as elephant grass (*Pennisetum purpureum*) up to 12 feet high. In Tanganyika large areas of savanna woodland are called Miombo woodland, where *Brachystegia* canopy trees, evergreen thicket and tall grasses mingle. In Kenya, on the richer soils in the volcanic area between 3,500 and 5,000 feet, the vegetation provides a valuable pastoral region and Kikuyu grass (*Pennisetum clandestinum*) is a valuable grazing grass above 6,000 feet, thriving in rich newly cleared forest soil. The mountains and the high plateau country demonstrate a vegetational zoning with altitude, reflecting the increasing and reliable precipitation and the lower temperatures. Above 5,000 feet evergreen trees are more conspicuous; *Croton megalocarpus* and cedars predominate before merging into temperate rain forests above 6,000 feet with cedars, podocarp, juniper and camphor trees. Much of this woodland has been cleared either by native shifting agriculture, after which it reverts to bush, or for coffee and tea plantations.

Between 9,000–10,000 feet on the moister mountains is a well-defined zone of mountain bamboo, *Arundinaria alpina*. This forms dense thicket growths with a height of 30 to 50 feet, but above 10,000 feet gives way to sub-Alpine and then Alpine vegetation. The sub-Alpine belt includes tree heathers, tussock grasses and patches of heathland, and merges into a zone of short Alpine grasses with a mingling of bulbous and leguminous plants and giant *Lobelias* and *Senecios* where there is sufficient moisture. A few of the highest peaks surpass the snow-line, which is at about 15,000 feet.

AGRICULTURAL POTENTIAL

The wide range of conditions has been noted, but not all are beneficial to human settlement and means of livelihood. As with all communities

relying upon farming for a living, rainfall and water supply are of paramount importance. Here in East Africa rainfall amount and reliability
are decisive in affecting the type of farming undertaken. Experience has
shown that there is little chance of successful cereal cultivation where
the reliable rainfall is under 30 inches. Consequently the 30-inch rainfall
reliability line serves to distinguish the pastoral from the arable lands
and is also a useful guide in determining prospects for agricultural
expansion.

Other factors also interact with rainfall reliability in restricting farming;
they include environmental and physical obstacles, technical and organisational difficulties (among them are soils, tsetse fly, communications,
manpower and level of skills). In most areas, however, it is the rainfall
that is decisive. It is more than unfortunate that whereas climate and soil
conspire to make part of Kenya and most of Tanganyika into potentially
great pastoral countries, the presence of the tsetse fly renders this impossible. Kenya has 10 per cent of its area subject to the fly, Tanganyika
60 per cent and Uganda about 32 per cent. Not all the affected areas
would be suited only to pastoral pursuits; much of that affected in
Tanganyika has a fair prospect of sufficient rain to support arable farming.
Consequently much of the future economic development of East Africa
hinges upon success in the battle with the fly and there are no prospects
of any immediate triumph.

A series of techniques has been evolved that offers some success in the
eradication of the insect and the diseases it transmits. Insecticides to kill
the fly itself, bush clearing to destroy its natural habitat, or the destruction
of game whose trypanosome-infected blood forms the food supply of
the fly, are three directions of attack. Research continues into methods
of immunisation for both men and cattle. Progress is slow and expensive,
but so long as the fly is paramount, mixed farming will be impossible
and agriculture will remain retarded over considerable areas.

An examination of the rainfall reliability map (Fig. 59) and Table 11
reveals that approximately half of East Africa (including one-half of
Tanganyika and over four-fifths of Kenya) has little prospect of receiving
a reliable 30 inches of rainfall each year and therefore on this count
must be classified primarily as pastoral. In fact, rather less than a quarter
of East Africa enjoys a high reliability (nineteen years out of twenty) of
a 30-inch rainfall (which generally makes arable farming possible) and
most of this is already well settled. It will be seen that Kenya has little
of this land, Uganda much of it, and Tanganyika lies between these

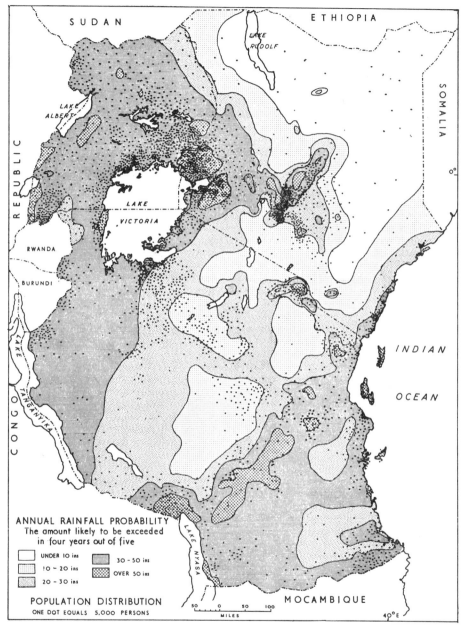

Figure 59 *East Africa:* Rainfall probability and population distribution

extremes. In Kenya the only lightly populated areas of this good agricultural land are in the 'White Highlands'; the native areas are heavily
settled. Uganda has much potentially good agricultural land away from
the Lake Victoria area that is still lightly populated. Tanganyika has one
lightly populated potentially good farming area in the south, from Lake
Malawi extending north-east towards Morogoro, including the Kilombero river valley; most of the area, however, is subject to tsetse fly.

Table 11   *Rainfall probability in East Africa*

Percentage of land area receiving selected amounts of
annual rainfall in four years out of five

Rainfall	Kenya	Uganda	Tanzania	East Africa
Less than 20 in.	72	12	16	35
20–30 in.	13	10	33	20
30–50 in.	12	72	47	41
Over 50 in.	3	6	4	4

Source: Natural Resources of East Africa (Nairobi, 1962), p. 79

The limitations of the bulk of the pastoral zone must be recognised.
Much of this land in northern Kenya and central Tanganyika is too arid
for satisfactory development and is likely to remain the home of hardy
nomadic camel and cattle men who exist only with great difficulty. In
the better savannas (such as the Masai and Kamba land units, the Mkata
Plains, the grassy Southern Highlands of Tanganyika, Karamoja and
Ankole in Uganda) economic animal husbandry may become possible—
given fly eradication, the provision of water and education in animal
and pasture management. These areas, however, are small and widely
scattered and their development is likely to be slow. In viewing East
Africa as a whole the maldistribution of the fertile areas becomes plain
and the East Africa Royal Commission drew attention to the choice
that lay before the three territories: to develop independently on a
separate territorial basis or to develop jointly for the benefit of all three
territories. The latter course is the more difficult, owing to strong racial
and political divisions, but would be advantageous in the pooling of
resources.

In the north-western corner of the region artificial political boundaries carve into three unequal divisions the geographical and ecological unit of the Lake Victoria depression. This area is a single economic unit and constitutes a region of the greatest potential economic growth in East Africa. Individual development by the three independent states is likely to produce uneven and unco-ordinated progress and might well cause Tanganyika's small portion, isolated because backed by marginal areas, to remain undeveloped. Co-ordinated development would enhance Kenya's entrepôt activities, lift the Tanganyika area with its neighbours and raise agricultural income in Uganda. The undeveloped fertile land in south-west Tanganyika can only become productive if the difficulties of communications, testse fly and lack of capital for irrigation and other works are overcome. Some UN or World Bank external assistance may become available, but more progress might occur if the local resources were pooled in a co-operative regional approach by and for East Africa as a whole. This pinpoints a great issue now faced by the three newly independent territories: whether in the light of geographical, economic and political circumstances Federation is necessary and desirable and, if so, how best to bring it about.

29

Kenya

The State of Kenya was granted independence in 1963 after sixty-eight years of British rule. It has an area of 225,000 sq. miles and a population of 8·63 million (1962 census), of whom 8·3 million are Africans, 56,000 of European descent, 176,000 Asians (Indians, Pakistani and Goanese) and 34,000 Arabs. Kenya's natural resources are very limited; her greatest is her soil, from which the livelihood of nearly all her people is obtained and almost her entire export revenue earned. The country exhibits such a variety of natural conditions, rising from sea-level to 17,000 feet, and ranging from desert to mangrove swamp, that practically any crop can be grown in some parts of the country, from strawberries to coconuts, from potatoes to cassava. Nevertheless the productive area of Kenya is much restricted by a number of physical factors; the greatest of which (as we have seen) being the amount and reliability of rainfall. Two-thirds of the country is arid and serves to support a relatively few Hamitic and Nilo-Hamitic pastoralists; the greater part of the population concentrates in the better-watered highlands of the south-western quadrant and the narrow coastal strip.

SETTLEMENT ON THE LAND

When, in 1901, the railway had been pushed across the uplands to Lake Victoria, Sir Harry Johnston reported: 'Here we have a territory (now that the Uganda railway is built) admirably suited for a white man's country, and I can say this, with no thought of injustice to any native race, for the country in question is either utterly uninhabited for miles and miles or at most its inhabitants are wandering hunters who have no settled home. . . .'

The railway opened these apparently empty highlands to European penetration; the settled African peoples were in the high rainfall area bordering Lake Victoria and on the slopes of Mount Kenya, the Aberdares and the hills of Ukambani. Between these well-watered fertile areas were extensive upland plains receiving rather less rainfall and grazed over by the pastoralist Masai. It was into these empty plains that white settlers moved and succeeded in obtaining good agricultural returns with their better techniques and equipment. In a series of enactments the Masai were restricted to definite areas and were finally allotted a large Reserve on the border with Tanganyika; inter-tribal struggle on the uplands thus came to an end. Later, objections were raised to the white settlement; in some cases tribal land that took its turn under shifting agriculture had been alienated and in other cases Africans took advantage of the peaceful conditions to move into the land no longer supporting Masai herds, such as on the Mua hills. Here they met Europeans who had been allotted the land by the government. Similarly the early triangle of white settlement between Emali–Nairobi–Fort Hall was a no-man's-land between the Masai to the south, the Kamba on the better-watered Ithanga hills and the Kikuyu on the lower slopes of the Aberdares. This land between 5,500 and 7,000 feet receives between 30 and 50 inches of rain and the rolling country is underlain by deeply weathered rich volcanic soil. It now contains two-thirds of all European-owned coffee plantations in Kenya and also supports tea estates and dairy herds. In this way considerable areas of the highland above 5,000 feet became settled by Europeans who were allotted and sold land by the Crown which was not owned by the African tribes. By law African lands were made secure against white settlement and in 1939 the white settled areas were secured against African settlement. One result of British rule was a considerable increase of population and in 1961 the status of the 'White Highlands' was changed and Africans were allowed to purchase land and farm in those areas. Loans and grants were made available to assist the better African farmers to do this.

It was the construction of the railway from Mombasa to Kisumu that made possible the settlement and economic development of the Kenya highlands as well as of Uganda. Numerous branch lines were added and in 1928 the railway was extended north of Lake Victoria to Kampala. Less than one-fifth of the over-30 inches annual rainfall area was alienated to Europeans and Asians but it is this land which produces two-fifths of the gross agricultural production and no less than 85 per cent of the agricultural exports of the country. The much larger area farmed by

Africans is responsible for the remaining three-fifths of the gross agricultural production and for 15 per cent of the exports. This great difference
is not because they hold inferior or too little land. 'Africans own or can
utilise over four-fifths of all the land with a rainfall of more than 30
inches per annum, and within this segment, if the cream of the land
were to be counted—that with a rainfall of 45 inches per annum or over,
falling in two seasons with deep fertile soil and with temperatures sufficiently high to permit the taking of two good crops a year—it will be found
that Africans occupy practically all of it and always have occupied it, with
very small pockets available to Europeans or Asians, which were uninhabited for one reason or another when land was originally alienated for
settlement.'[2] It is patently not true that Africans have had only the left-
over land in Kenya.

LAND CONSOLIDATION

The reasons for the poor African farming output lie elsewhere, in their
system of land tenure and their unscientific farming. African land in
the settled area is normally held communally according to tribal law and
custom although gradually private tenure or ownership has become
accepted. The indigenous system of tenure and inheritance has led to
fragmentation and poor land use, for on heavily fragmented land it is
impossible to farm properly. 'It is, for instance, quite impracticable to
make efficient use of 43 fragments aggregating 8 acres in extent and
situated up to 8 miles from the owner's homestead; but if consolidated
this represents a holding capable of providing a full subsistence plus
£200 per year, or a net profit of £25 per acre, whereas fragmented the
net profit would not exceed Shs. 30/– per annum at best.'[3]

These lands are usually densely peopled and most males go out to work
in towns and farms leaving the bulk of the cultivation to the women. A
tremendous potential of increased production is locked up in these lands,
as land consolidation in Kikuyuland has shown. The Kikuyu Land Unit
is at the eastern edge of the Kikuyu highlands north-west of Nairobi. It
is hilly (over 5,000 feet) and much dissected by streams flowing to the
Athi and Tana rivers. A fertile red volcanic loam covers much of the
plateau. There, in the Central Province, after the Mau Mau troubles the
Kenya Government imposed radical land reform with excellent results.
Land consolidation is not new in Kenya, for it was started over twenty-five
years ago in the Kericho district among the Kipsigis, but since it was a

Kenya Information Services

7 (A) Former Governor General of Kenya Malcolm MacDonald helps weed vegetable patch at Wanjohi/Kipipiri Settlement Scheme, near Nakuru, Kenya

7 (B) A lesson on livestock nutrition at Lietego Settlement Scheme, Kisii, Kenya

Kenya Information Services

8 The resettled village of Kapsowar on the lip of the rift valley in Kenya, where new practices include strip cropping and contour farming

voluntary process its extension has been limited. Kikuyu holdings in the Consolidation Scheme average 4 to 5 acres that may have been formerly in up to thirty scattered pieces; and the farmer and his wives would have had to trudge from one to the other to work them. Under the new policy every piece of land was measured and mapped and each man received the same total land as before, but in one piece. Much of the land is composed of long, narrow, parallel ridges and usually plots are designed to run from ridge top to valley bottom. When the new apportionment was done the farmers were given registered titles to their farms, which is security for a commercial bank loan to develop the land. Time saved in walking to many plots can now be devoted to better husbandry; holdings are large enough to plan properly for crop rotations, terracing and trials of new crops. As a result yields have increased threefold and more valuable cash crops such as coffee, tea and pyrethrum, are being grown. Land consolidation is gradually being carried out in other tribal areas. Other advantages also accrue, for example in central Nyanza where over 80,000 acres of high-quality irrigable land cannot yet be irrigated because of the restrictive native customs of tenure and inheritance which make it impossible to lay out sound irrigation schemes. Everywhere land consolidation has been followed by improved land use.

A corollary to these operations in Kikuyuland was the collecting of the Kikuyu into villages. These Bantu agricultural people live scattered in isolated family groups, their huts standing on their holdings (*shambas*). During the Mau Mau emergency they were forcibly grouped into villages so that they could be better controlled. Unpopular at first, village life was found to have attractions and although some farms are now set up on the larger newly consolidated holdings, small-holders and those with only garden plots remain in the villages, either finding work on a larger consolidated farm or in the village, or even in Nairobi. The villages and small townships are a part of the new agricultural order and have become a permanent feature of the Kikuyu landscape, while health and educational measures have been able to make greater and quicker impact. Today large villages perch on every hilltop and a pattern of more productive land use may be discerned in the fenced fields, orderly rows of crops, trees and broad terraces that run with the contour round the hillside (Plate 8). All these changes in African land ownership and farming are being accomplished within the broad framework of the Swinnerton Plan, proposed in 1954.

Misgivings were aroused in 1961 when the first farms in the White

Highlands were acquired by the government and resold in small plots to African, mainly Kikuyu, cultivators. Where fleets of tractors with four-furrow ploughs once turned the soil, African peasant farmers moved in. Nearly 1·5 million acres, or over a third of the mixed farming land that had been worked by Europeans, were bought from the Europeans by the Kenya government (with British and international financial aid) for division among landless African families. Most of the new holdings are included in a 'high density' scheme, where farms, averaging about 10 acres, are expected to provide subsistence and, after loan repayment, an income of about $70 a year. While there is less population pressure, a smaller number of larger African holdings form a 'low density' scheme. Great advances are taking place: the new free-holders have to learn quickly to grow new crops and to employ new techniques. They have twenty years to pay for their farms and to repay initial loans, and this can only be accomplished by revolutionary changes in their traditional agriculture.

These developments underline Kenya's growing agrarian problem. Kenya's African population is beginning to increase at a rapid rate and presses ever more strongly upon the limited agricultural land. The schemes for providing land in the former White Highlands are expensive and cannot absorb more than a fraction of the landless people; much will have to be done to improve the output of traditional agriculture. Early doubts as to whether the new smallholders could produce as great a return from the land as the large-scale, highly capitalised European farmers are gradually being set at rest as new lessons are learnt and the intensive character of the farming bears fruit. The new settlers have to join co-operatives for seed and fertilizer provision, for coffee processing and pyrethrum drying, for marketing. In some cases the large-scale character of certain ex-European farms is being maintained by co-operative farming managed by the Department of Settlement, but there is no doubt that Kenya will be primarily a land of smallholders in the future.

AGRICULTURE

Agricultural regions

There are three important farming areas in Kenya: on parts of the coastal plain, on the highlands flanking the rift valley, and in Nyanza Province beside Lake Victoria (Fig. 60).

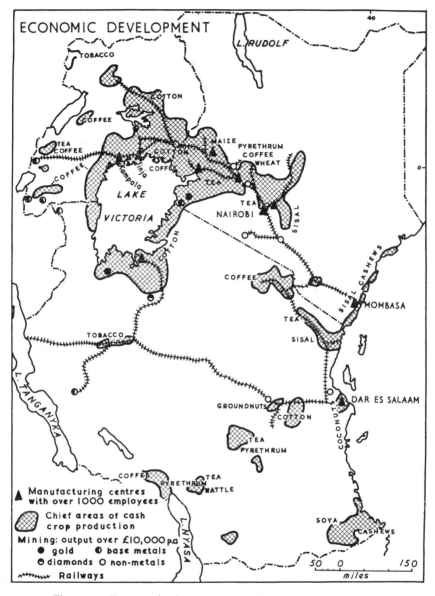

Figure 60 *Economic development in East Africa* (after T. J. D. Fair)

THE COASTAL PLAIN   The well-watered southern part of the coastal plain is mainly under subsistence crops: maize, cassava, yams and rice in some of the river estuaries. Coconuts, sugar and cotton are native grown and offer some commercial return; Europeans operate a number of sisal plantations. Inland and to the north, the poor grass, scattered acacia trees and scrub of the Nyika are of little value except to Somali and Galla camel and cattle nomads. Farther inland on the plateau, first on the Basement Complex and then on the richer red-soiled volcanic rocks, where rainfall is assured population density increases and agriculture is firmly established, although before British rule the virile and aggressive Masai pastoralists ranged widely over these grasslands preventing their permanent occupation by agricultural tribes.

THE HIGHLANDS European farmers in the highlands produce coffee, tea, sisal and pyrethrum. Wheat is a major cereal crop and high-quality cattle and dairy herds have been built up. Cattle and sheep ranching takes place in the somewhat drier parts of the Central Rift. It is these efficient mixed farming areas that have traditionally fed the urban areas of Kenya and must continue to do so no matter what form the farming takes. African production is mainly for subsistence and maize is most important. The growing of the cash crops coffee and pyrethrum by Africans is spreading. Most of Kenya's forested areas lie in the higher parts of the central and rift valley provinces between 6,000 and 12,000 feet above sea-level. Their greatest contribution to the economy is water, for they protect the main water catchment areas of the country and only a small proportion of the forests is used commercially.

NYANZA To the east of the Lake Victoria Basin is Kenya's third agricultural region, principally Nyanza Province. Here there has been little alienation of land to white settlers. This is a densely peopled region of thriving African agriculture. There are three major structural subdivisions: north of the Kavirondo Gulf a plateau rising to over 7,000 feet in the east and up to Mount Elgon (14,178 feet) in the north. Much of this sloping up from the lake shore is part of the undulating Kavirondo peneplain on the Basement Complex; to the north this merges with the Tertiary volcanic rocks of Elgon. In the centre is the Kavirondo Rift, a trough that trends 80 miles east from the Kavirondo Gulf. To the south are the Kisii highlands, a deeply dissected area of broad valleys and steep ridges reaching more than 6,000 feet.

The soils north of the lake are sandy brown on the granitic areas and richer and deep red on the Elgon volcanics. Those of the Gulf lowland, mantling the nearly level rift floor, are black calcareous 'cotton' soils (although cotton cultivation is not restricted to these soils) and to the south and east, towards Kericho, there are extensive grassy areas on deep red volcanic soils. The climatic influences of the equatorial location and of Lake Victoria are apparent in the distribution and amount of rainfall. A highly reliable rainfall varying from 30 inches in the Gulf to over 60 inches on the uplands helps to make this a region of most productive agriculture. It has often been called the 'granary of Kenya', mainly because maize production, especially north of the Gulf, exceeds local needs and allows of export. However, a great variety of crops is grown, matching the diversity of the physical conditions, though much of this is due to European influence and the introduction of new crops. Cotton was introduced with the arrival of the railway to Kisumu, for a commercial crop was needed to provide the line with freight. It was slow in becoming accepted. A ginnery was set up at Kisumu in 1908; at first most of its intake was from Uganda but gradually cotton growing spread throughout central and southern Nyanza. Coffee growing on the Kisii highlands began about 1935. In order to maintain quality, coffee in Kenya could only be grown under licence and expansion of the coffee acreage here was slow until restrictions were eased after 1960. Rice was another crop introduced both as a famine-prevention measure and a cash crop and, with bananas and sugar-cane, demonstrates the great variety of crops grown. Farther east the Kericho district is the major tea-growing area of Kenya, but most of these plantations belong to Europeans.

Agricultural Problems

Kenya relies heavily on her agriculture, which provides about 90 per cent of her export trade. The gross agricultural output is around £80 million: of this European and Asian farmers' produce accounts for £34 million and Africans about £46 million. Exports are about £33 million a year out of total exports of £37 million. European and Asian farmers account for 85 per cent of these exports, Africans for 15 per cent. Nevertheless the share of Africans in exports is rising rapidly with consolidation and the spread of individual land tenure, the untiring work of agricultural teachers and demonstrators and the Cash Crops Policy Plan designed by the government to extend cash-crop production among African producers and to improve yields. From these figures the importance of the settler population in Kenya is manifest, but this also indicates the dual economy so noticeable elsewhere in Africa. Poverty is widespread among the African population where the net annual income per head is estimated at £12 and the growing problem of a high rate of population increase has now to be reckoned with. As with most of the newly independent African states highly dependent on agriculture, these years are seeing great efforts to move the economy from subsistence to market agriculture whereby higher income may be obtained, and effective home demand for manufactured products engendered, which in turn will support manufacturing industry and urban occupations. Kenya has some advantage here in that her geographical endowment does not limit her to a single export crop, but to several in which both Africans and Europeans participate. Not all her people are moving along the new path together, for some tribes such as the Kikuyu are more responsive and hard-working than others such as the Masai, whose economy is based upon cattle keeping and who are falling behind in this march of progress.

INDUSTRY

Industrial development in Kenya, while more advanced than amongst her neighbours, is still in its infancy. It is mainly confined to the processing of agricultural produce such as cotton ginning, sugar milling, drying and hulling of coffee and the pressing of oil from cotton-seed and ground-nuts. There is some fruit and vegetable preservation, preparation of pyrethrum extract for insecticide and wattle extract for tanning. Lorry and bus bodies, cement, building materials of clay, wood and metal are made. Among consumer goods manufactured locally are beer, cigarettes, footwear, textiles and clothing, soaps, household metal products. The market for these goods is mainly domestic although some export of aluminium hollow ware, footwear and cigarettes to other parts of Africa has begun. The potential market for home-manufactured goods is very large and will be realised as improving agriculture raises the rural Africans' income. Well over 100,000 are now employed in manufacturing industry and although there is a high labour turnover (most Africans regard urban and industrial areas as places of temporary employment), the beginning of a permanent urban African population is tending to develop at Nairobi and Mombasa.

The two major centres of manufacturing industry are at Nairobi and Mombasa, the two principal towns (the capital and chief port), where a sound infrastructure of public utilities and transport facilitates manufacturing, and a pool of labour and effective markets exist. Both towns have chemicals, glass, cement and paint works and numerous small consumer goods industries; in addition, Nairobi manufactures textiles. Many of the firms are subsidiaries of great industrial concerns like Unilever, ICI and Portland Cement. At Limuru, Bata have established a large footwear plant, and textiles are made at Nakuru.

East Africa lacks coal and much industrial power is electrical, derived from hydro-electric sources or from thermal stations using imported fuels. Kenya is poor in hydro-electric potential but has small plants on the Maragua, Tana and Thika rivers. Some power is also obtained from the Owen Falls Dam in Uganda. Mombasa has thermal plants but obtains some hydro-electric power from the Pangani Falls in Tanganyika. East Africa's first oil refinery was opened at Mombasa in 1964. Except for cement, brewing and flour milling, most of the industrial plants are small, making lighter demands on capital, managerial and organisational expertise, clerical and accounting personnel. However, lacking economies of scale they are often high-cost producers.

The export trade of all three mainland territories is shown in Table 13, where it will be seen that three crops (coffee, sisal and tea) supply 54 per cent of Kenya's exports. Principal imports are manufactured goods such as rubber tires, newsprint, cotton-piece goods, iron and steel products, chemicals, machinery and vehicles, mineral fuel and lubricants. The geographical distribution of the trade of East Africa as a whole is shown in Table 14.

COMMUNICATION, POPULATION AND SETTLEMENT

Kenya's sole great port is Mombasa, with its spacious harbour of Kilindini. From this port the trunk railway through Nairobi to Uganda was completed to Lake Victoria in 1901. A number of branches and extensions were made to it sometimes in order to attract settlement and sometimes to serve existing settlements, such as white settlement in the Trans-Nzoia in 1921. The whole pattern of the white settlement and opening-up of Kenya devolves from the construction of this railway line by the British Government. It cost $15 million and took five years to build; it was very much a speculative venture, for there was no worthwhile freight to be carried to the coast at that time. The objects of the line were both strategic and humanitarian. British control of the interior in the face of German activity in Tanganyika had to be made more effective and depended upon good communications; further, the construction of the railway obviated the carriage of goods by men and put an end to the lingering slave trade. The story of development can be measured in terms of freight and passengers: in 1902 the railway carried 13,000 tons of freight and 73,000 passengers; in 1947 the railway carried 1,818,000 tons of freight and 3 million passengers.

The largest city in the four territories is *Nairobi* (5,500 feet), the capital of Kenya. It received a royal charter in 1950 and has a population of over 300,000 (including 100,000 Asians and 25,000 Europeans). The whole history of Nairobi is included well within the spell of a lifetime. It dates from 1899, when the railway from the coast reached this spot on the great Athi Plain and a main workshop and depot were constructed there. It began as a railway construction camp, but with a position in the midst of early 'empty' upland attractive to white settlers, it soon grew in size and importance. It is now the transport focus of East Africa and the headquarters of many firms trading in East Africa. Its most remarkable growth has been since 1945, in which time its population has quadrupled. One result has been the emergence of an ugly but lusty town sometimes reminiscent of the immature towns of America's Middle West. Many of the multi-racial city population know little of the real Africa:

> They know the bus routes better than the jungle tracks, and are most at home among the crowded, unhygienic Indian bazaars, wide plate-glass fronts of the department stores, and motor-car showrooms in the macadamised, tree-lined main streets, where thousands of parked cars, wing to wing, line the pavements all day. Urbanised Africans in all stages of western civilisation, their comfortable nakedness ex-changed for European-style clothing, mostly second-hand and often incredibly dilapidated, have begun to forget the peace and contentment of the family holdings . . . In the half-light between Africa's historic darkness and the glare of the strange modern world, they know mainly the pressure of the new economic system into which they have been born, the frustrating emptiness of the leisure hours of the uneducated and uncultured in overcrowded 'locations', and the absence of the social security provided by the family unit in a tribal society.[4]

MOMBASA is an old Arab centre, built on an island in a coastal inlet. Deep water on its western side forms the magnificent harbour of Kilindini, reckoned the finest on the east coast of Africa. It handles over 3 million tons of cargo annually, three times that of its nearest rival, Dar es Salaam.

Kenya's 8·6 million population is concentrated in the three productive regions already discussed: the coastal zone centred upon Mombasa; the central province where Kikuyu, Meru and Embu Land Units cluster among the Aberdare and Mount Kenya foothills (some areas here such as Fort Hall have a population density of over 400 per sq. mile); and Nyanza Province (Fig. 59). The rate of increase of Kenya's population can only be estimated, but in 1962 it was about 2·25 per cent per annum, a rate which would be sufficient to double the population in thirty years.

30

Uganda

The former British Protectorate of Uganda became a fully independent member of the British Commonwealth in 1962. It was in 1894 that the British Protectorate was declared over the Kingdom of Buganda and certain adjoining territories when Britain assumed the administrative responsibility of the British East Africa Company. Uganda consists of a number of independent kingdoms, of which Buganda is the largest, now existing in a Federal relationship. The Baganda, who inhabit Buganda, are among the most advanced African peoples. They had a well-developed political system of king, ministers and parliament and a flourishing agricultural economy when the Europeans first arrived. This was preserved under the British system of indirect rule. Until recently the province of Buganda was recognised as a native kingdom under a 'Kabaka', with the title of 'His Highness'. The districts of Bunyoro, Ankole and Toro also have had hereditary rulers.

Uganda has a total area of 94,000 sq. miles (about the same as the British Isles) of which 15 per cent is water; this includes parts of Lake Victoria and Albert, the whole of Lake Kyoga and the Victoria and Albert branches of the River Nile. The population is 7·5 million (1965) and includes 70,000 Asians but only 10,000 Europeans, mostly administrators, educationalists and technicians. Among the Africans just over 1 million are Baganda. The average density of population at over eighty per sq. mile is very high for Africa; in the most populous parts, around the shores of Lake Victoria, density approaches 300 per sq. mile.

PHYSICAL BACKGROUND

The greater part of Uganda constitutes a shallow downwarp in the Basement Complex with upland around the edges; Lake Victoria fills the centre of the depression. Along the eastern frontier with Kenya, Mount Elgon attains 14,176 feet and farther north the boundary is the watershed between Lake Rudolf and the Nile drainage. Other mountains, including those in Karamoja stand along the northern boundary with the Sudan. To the west is the extensive mountainous mass flanking the Western Rift valley, including parts of Toro, Ankole and Kigezi districts. The bulk of Uganda consists of plateau between 3,500 and 4,500 feet above sea-level. Near Lake Victoria the plateau (of the mid-Tertiary) is dissected into numerous tabular hills with an amplitude of 500–600 feet between hill top and valley bottom. Farther away the country is one of gentle undulations through which Nile waters slowly drain through a labyrinth of swamps that constitute Lake Kyoga. Navigable channels are maintained through the swamp vegetation and the lake is used as a waterway by those farming the surrounding fertile countryside.

Although Uganda is on the equator, its climate avoids the full equatorial heat and rainfall, thanks to the tempering effect of altitude and the considerable areas of lake water. In a sense the climate comes midway between that of the Congo Basin and of the arid heat of eastern Kenya. Except in the extreme north-east, rainfall on the plateau varies from 30 to 60 inches, the heaviest being experienced on the north shores of Lake Victoria, on the slopes of Mount Elgon and on the upland to the west and north-west (Fig. 61). A less reliable and rather lower rainfall is experienced in a discontinuous belt from the south-west to north-east. In the vicinity of Lake Victoria two maxima of rain are experienced, associated with the double transit of the ITC. The early maximum is usually the greater, but both play their part in making it possible to raise two crops from the same land in the year. In the north of the country, farther from the equator, a definite period of drought occurs which limits the productivity of the land. Along the north shore of Lake Victoria the probability of obtaining optimum water requirements for crops twice a year is as high as 74 per cent, whereas at Gulu, 200 miles to the north, the probability is only 4 per cent.

Thus in the north the year divides into a warm, wet season and a hot, dry season, but near Lake Victoria the annual range of temperature is compressed almost to vanishing point. Elevation reduces temperatures but the year-long humid heat so bountiful to plant growth is disliked by Europeans, and this helps to explain the small number of Europeans and even smaller number of European settlers in Uganda. The areas of reliable rainfall and general fertility favour plantation agriculture and a

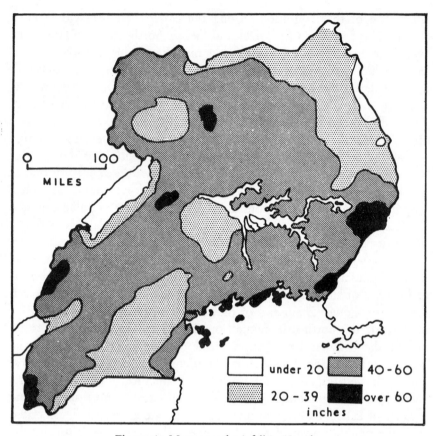

Figure 61 *Mean annual rainfall in Uganda*

few Europeans settled before World War I, but the enervating climate
and the incidence of such insect-borne diseases as sleeping-sickness
discouraged settlement; since 1916 the alienation of freehold land to
non-natives has been prohibited, although Asians manage sugar and tea
estates near Jinja.

The vegetation reflects the two main climatic zones based on seasonality
of rainfall and it is climate also that has paramount influence upon agriculture. Modified tropical forest is found in southern Buganda and Busoga
near the lake shores, but much of it has been cleared and the prevailing
vegetation is elephant grass (*Pennisetum purpureum*) with scattered trees.
This forms a belt round the northern shores of the lake, narrow in the
west, widest (up to 50 miles) in the north. This gives way in the drier

area of west Masaka and north-east Mengo to short grass with scattered low trees.

AGRICULTURE

Climatic zones are reflected in distinctive crops and agricultural practices. There is a particular contrast between the high and low rainfall regions, for in the former the food supply is mainly derived from planted crops, principally the plantain (or cooking banana), sweet potatoes and cassava, whereas in the remainder of Uganda sown crops predominate, notably finger millet, maize and pulses. This distinction is not absolute, for some seed-bearing crops are grown in the high-rainfall region, and some planted crops, notably sweet potatoes, are grown elsewhere. The low rainfall (short grass) zone is favourable for cattle keeping but not the

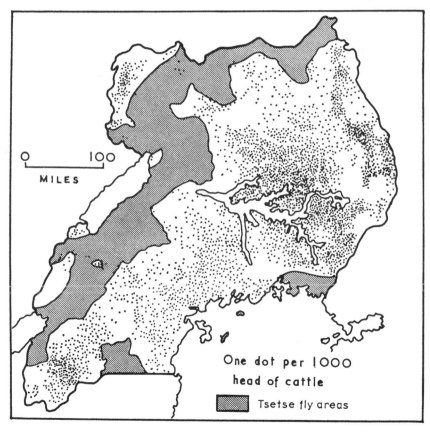

Figure 62 *Distribution of cattle and tsetse fly in Uganda*

wetter elephant-grass country, and although some cattle are kept they are grazed away from the cultivated areas and often herded by hired tribes-men from the drier cattle country. Tsetse fly, bringing human sleeping-sickness and ngana, still infests parts of the Lake Victoria northern shores especially in Busoga (Fig. 62). Cultivation of the banana is easy and in-volves little toil. The plant sends out suckers so that a typical family grove contains about twenty stems in varying stages of maturity, able to provide food all the year round. The foliage of the tree acts as an umbrella against the rain, excessive soil leaching is prevented and the dead leaves form a useful mulch.

The main cash crops grown in the high-rainfall zone are cotton and robusta coffee. The introduction of cotton in 1904 resulted from a combination of circumstances and policies: the need to find freight to make viable the newly opened Kisumu–Mombasa railway, a movement in the United Kingdom to lessen Lancashire's dependence on USA cotton supplies, and the need to get the Africans to produce a cash crop in order to earn tax money upon which administration and development depended. The main response came from the Baganda, who already had a higher standard of living than their neighbours and who found that cash-crop production enabled them to satisfy their relatively sophisti-cated needs for good cloth, house utensils and paper. Early on, the East Africa Company had been warned that the usual trading rubbish would not do for Buganda. In 1905 cotton production was 241 bales worth £1,089; in 1910, 13,378 bales worth £165,412, or more than half the total exports of the Protectorate. Climatic conditions are not ideal for cotton, for there is an excessive production of foliage and the ripening season is not quite hot enough. Nevertheless conditions are such that the crop cannot fail: a sizeable harvest is assured.

The success of cotton growing in Uganda has been particularly important in demonstrating the possibility of export crop production by Africans on their own fields and without direct European supervision. Since the end of World War II coffee growing has increased to vie with cotton for first place, while a new crop, cacao, has been successfully introduced. Both coffee and cacao take several years to become estab-lished, but are then more than twice as profitable per acre to the peasant than cotton and less demanding of labour. In this region also, particularly near the lake, sugar is grown and there are a number of tea estates (Fig. 63).

In the 'short grass' zone, where rainfall is usually below 45 inches per annum and more seasonal in distribution, farming is typical of much of

Africa, being based on hoe cultivation of annual crops with livestock included in the farming in non-tsetse-fly-invaded areas. The main subsistence crops are finger millet, sorghum, beans, sweet potatoes and cassava. The most important cash crops are cotton and groundnuts. On the higher fringes of the zone arabica coffee is grown and in parts of Ankole, Toro and West Nile districts it is the foremost cash crop. Government-sponsored tea estates are increasing. Cattle keeping is more

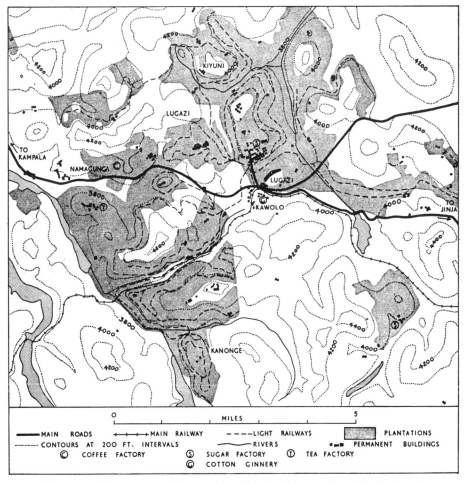

Figure 63 *Extract from Sheet 71/11, Uganda (1:50,000), 2nd ed. (1959), Directorate of Overseas Surveys.* Lugazi lies midway between Kampala and Jinja, and 10–20 miles from the shore of Lake Victoria. Mean annual rainfall at Lugazi is 53 inches

general, although in places there is no great integration of crops and stock. In the drier areas of the Karamoja districts of the north, and the Ankole district west of Lake Victoria, cattle keeping is the major occupation and few crops are grown. In the higher mountain areas above 6,000 feet on Mount Elgon and in parts of the western province, where a number of Europeans have settled, more temperate crops can be grown, including pulses and the English potato. The cash crop, although not produced in large quantities, is arabica coffee.

The best cattle in Uganda are the big-horned animals from the high grasslands of Ankole. Generally cattle are of a poorer quality on the humid lowlands where considerable areas are still subject to tsetse fly. The excessively starchy diet of Africans in the high-rainfall region leads to malnutrition, particularly protein malnutrition of young children (called Kwashiorkor). Goats, poultry and fish give some animal protein and variety but beef and milk tend to be luxuries, and tribal taboos are a hindrance to progress in varying the diet.

MINERALS AND INDUSTRY

Uganda is not well endowed with minerals in economic quantities and mineral production is virtually confined to copper from the Kilembe Mine in the Ruwenzori Range. The mine was opened in 1956 following the completion of a 208-mile western extension of the railway from Kampala, constructed for the purpose. Transport problems have undoubtedly hampered mineral development in Uganda, but that is not the sole reason, for much of the country has now been surveyed and no significant deposits have been located other than the copper of Kilembe. In the volcanic and metamorphosed rocks of Mount Elgon-Nyanza, and flanking the Western Rift, a multitude of minerals has been discovered, but usually the deposits are small and scattered or larger and spread thinly so that for the most part economic development is precluded. The completion of the western extension to the railway will make survey and exploitation of any new discoveries in the Ruwenzori area easier, but no high hopes are held of great discoveries. Much of Uganda is covered with red laterite which, while containing some iron ore, has not sufficient concentration of bauxite to warrant commercial exploitation. The long distance to the coast (over 800 miles) adds considerably to the cost of any production.

A cement and asbestos-cement industry is now well estabished at Tororo based upon the local limestone, hydro-electric power from

Jinja, 80 miles to the west, and asbestos from Rhodesia. The annual capacity is 150,000 tons and the location is proving favourable for sales also in Kenya and Tanganyika. Other minerals worked and exported in small quantities are wolfram, tin and phosphates.

Agriculture and livestock form the basis of Uganda's economy and occupy 90 per cent of the population. The industries that exist are mainly derived from the processing of agricultural produce, although a number of rather different industrial activities have recently been begun at Jinja, beside the Owen Falls. The main agricultural industries are cotton ginning, sugar milling, cigarette manufacture, vegetable-oil extraction, coffee and tea preparation; most of these are located in the producing areas near Lake Victoria, especially in the Kampala-Jinja area. A wider spectrum of industry has been attracted to Uganda with the development of hydro-electricity at Jinja where the Nile leaves Lake Victoria by the Owen Falls. The town's population is now 30,000 and it has become a focus of modern industries. The generating station, opened in 1954, has an installed capacity of 120 MW and space has been left for two more turbines which will raise capacity to a maximum of 150 MW. A power grid has been built and this has allowed industrial expansion in Kampala and Tororo as well as at Jinja. Power is also exported to Kenya.

The largest electricity user at Jinja is the copper smelter which refines Kilembe copper, producing over 15,000 tons per annum worth nearly £4 million. A cotton-textile factory was set up at Jinja in 1956 followed by another in 1965. Also at Jinja, brewing, vegetable oil production, sugar refining, flour milling, paper and match making, cigarette and tobacco manufacture take place. A plywood factory, a rubber tire factory and a steel rolling mill now operate. Plans for the manufacture of paper bags and nitrogenous fertilisers have been prepared.

Export crop production and industrial development are concentrated mainly in Buganda and parts of the eastern region, areas widely accessible owing to road and rail facilities and directly profiting from the power station at the Owen Falls (Table 12).

Table 12

Factories registered with Uganda Labour Department

	Buganda	East	West	North
1960	836	515	109	62

This is creating a number of problems, for the growing opportunities and greater wealth in the south raise discontent elsewhere and act as a spur for population movement into the favoured areas. The Uganda Government is taking steps to reduce such inequalities. One method is by setting up Lint and Coffee Marketing Boards which buy cotton and coffee at fixed prices irrespective of the distance they have to be moved to the coast after processing. In this way they subsidise the more remote producers and lessen the incentive for people to migrate to Buganda to grow cotton.

ECONOMIC PROBLEMS

Uganda is a well-endowed country: its agricultural output is greater than that of either Kenya or Tanganyika but the value of its manufactures is much less than that of Kenya. It is favoured by climate and soil, but also suffers from its inland position and from the tsetse fly. Its people, however, are active and intelligent, and economic development since the first coming of the railway has been spectacular. The growing interest in cash-crop production allied to the growing rate of population increase is beginning to raise a number of agricultural problems, particularly the shorter fallowing periods. In the low-rainfall region where rotations take place this is not so serious but in the high-rainfall region where one or two plants are cropped regularly the land is beginning to deteriorate. Further, growing wealth, especially in Buganda, is resulting in much more travelling about, often leading to the neglect of the banana gardens.

Uganda's transport system is efficient and well developed. In addition to good roads her rail system is being enlarged. The western extension to Kasese (1956) is financially successful; another line has been extended northwards to Gulu and a further extension to serve the West Nile district is planned. These are significant developments that will further the opening up of lightly populated areas suitable for commercial farming and stock rearing.

Uganda's chief economic difficulty arises from her heavy dependence upon the two principal cash crops, coffee and cotton, and upon copper (Table 13). In 1961 these accounted respectively for 35, 42, and 7 per cent of total export earnings. World prices for primary products fluctuate considerably from year to year and revenue derived solely from them does not form a firm basis upon which to develop an economy. There is a tremendous potential in agriculture, in which investment should bring substantial returns. In the period 1945–60 only £15 million went into agriculture, whereas £32 million was invested in electricity development and £2 million alone in the Nyanza textile industry. Agriculture employs 5 million whereas the textile industry employs about 2,500. The Owen Falls scheme may have been over-ambitious (even now the maximum demand is only about 60 per cent of installed potential). Certainly the fanciful plans for an 'African Detroit' at Jinja have become muted and the industrial development there is modest in comparison with earlier hopes. Uganda's real wealth lies in her agriculture and much remains to be done to improve its productive capacity. There are physical problems of soil erosion and tsetse-fly infestation to be overcome, and ways must be found to ease credit facilities to the small producer, to further the spread of agrarian education, to foster the diversification of crops, and improve transport and marketing facilities. In this way favourable natural conditions may be used more fully and living standards will continue to improve.

31

Tanzania

Tanganyika became an independent state within the British Common-
wealth in 1961 and adopted a republican form of government in 1962.
In 1964 it entered into a political union with Zanzibar and the name
Tanzania was adopted.

TANGANYIKA

Tanganyika is the largest but also the poorest of the four East African
states. In 1891 this part of East Africa, nominally under the suzerainty of
the Sultan of Zanzibar, was taken over as a Protectorate by Germany.
For many years the history of German rule was one of disturbance and
bloodshed as tribes rebelled and were suppressed. The country was conquered in World War I and subsequently divided as mandated territory
between Belgium and Britain; the Belgians received Ruanda and Urundi
(now Rwanda and Burundi) and Britain the rest. The area of the republic
is 361,800 sq. miles, or larger than Kenya and Uganda together.

The greater part of Tanganyika is plateau. Lower land flanks it on the
coast and around Lake Victoria; higher land in the Kilimanjaro-Pare-
Usumbara Mountains of the north-east, the Southern Highlands and
the mountains forming the Western Rift valley system. The Eastern
Rift zone, although a geomorphological division throughout most of
Tanganyika, has little geographical significance.

FARMING REGIONS

THE COASTLANDS Tanganyika has about 500 miles of coast and the
plain bordering it for the most part varies between 10 and 40 miles in
width. It extends from the Kenya border at 5°S to Tanganyika's southern
border along the Ruvuma river at 11°S. All the coastal zone receives more

than 30 inches of rainfall and from the Rufiji river north generally over 40 inches. Mangrove swamps abound in the estuaries, usually backed by a belt of coconut-palms. With the presence of cooler upland close behind the coast in the north, it was not surprising that the development of the north-east of the country should receive most attention from the Germans who laid particular emphasis upon establishing plantations and settling Europeans. Some sugar, spices and rice are grown in the coastal zone but sisal (transplanted from the Yucatan, Mexico, in 1893) is the principal cash crop grown in European or Indian-owned plantations.

Sisal exports account for nearly a third of Tanganyika's total export by value and Tanganyika is the world's largest supplier.

THE NORTH-EAST HIGHLANDS These include the mighty Kilimanjaro (19,340 feet), the highest mountain in Africa, Meru (14,979 feet), and the discontinuous upland appendage that trends to the south-east, including the Pare Mountains and culminating in the Usumbara Mountains (8,428 feet). Kilimanjaro and Meru are of volcanic origin and associated with the formation of the rift valley to their west; the rest of the uplands are uptilted parts of the Crystalline Basement Complex. The upper parts of the Usumbara, Kilimanjaro and Meru receive over 60 inches of rain annually, but on their north-west sides in the rain shadow are areas which receive little more than 20 inches. On the whole, however, this upland region is more distinctive in its relief, its greater rainfall, more luxuriant vegetation and European influence than the surrounding plateau.

These highlands, especially between 5,000 and 6,000 feet, were attractive to European settlement and a variety of crops was tried on them, including rubber (at rather lower levels), sisal and coffee. The Germans quickly started building a railway inland from Tanga, passing along the western side of the highlands. They had planned to build the railway across to open up the reputedly rich lands around Lake Victoria, but when the British line from Mombasa reached the lake first they abandoned their plans and eventually, in 1911, made Moshi the western terminus (in 1929 extended to Arusha). They then turned their attention to the construction of a central line from Dar es Salaam across to Tabora and Kigoma on Lake Tanganyika (1914); a spur north to Mwanza on Lake Victoria was completed in 1928. These well-watered uplands nourish the greater part of Tanganyika's forests, including valuable cabinet woods such as African mahogany and cedars. A great deal of this woodland was cleared for plantations early in the century. Coffee of the arabica variety has proved the most satisfactory crop of Kilimanjaro but yields are poorer on the more siliceous soils of Usumbara. From 1923 further alienation of land to Europeans was forbidden and this has now become one of the more densely populated parts of the republic. The Kilimanjaro area is in the hands of the Chagga, who are now among the foremost and wealthiest native coffee producers.

THE INTERIOR PLATEAU comprises the greater part of Tanganyika and includes the Masai steppe, the rift zone and the Central Plateau. The altitude varies between 3,000 and 4,500 feet, the topography is gently undulating, broken here and there by residual hills. This is an unfavoured area: pest-ridden, frequently drought-ridden and of poor soil. Much of the central part of this plateau receives little more than 20 inches of rain per annum, while to east and west rather more than 30 inches are enjoyed in an average year. Unfortunately there is a high variability of rainfall from year to year: in the centre it is very rare to receive 30 inches, in the better-watered east and west three years in ten may not produce that amount of rainfall. This makes arable agriculture hazardous and relegates most of this vast area to pastoral uses. For much of the year this is a brown country of dried-up open savanna; the heat is very great, the atmosphere dry; the rainless season becomes more definite and more prolonged as one moves south. The yellow-brown plateau soils hold little humus and in places are seasonally waterlogged, especially where an iron pan has formed in the subsoil. Large areas of the plateau, particularly the south-west quadrant, are only lightly inhabited and scarcely utilised, for a combination of light uncertain rainfall, poor soils, tsetse-fly and remoteness militate against utilisation whether by Africans or Whites.

Over large parts the semi-nomadic ranching of cattle, sheep and goats, often combined with rudimentary shifting agriculture, is almost the sole activity. Pastures are poor throughout the long severe dry season and relatively abundant for the usually shorter rainy season. Tsetse-fly hinders the movement of stock in search of better grazing (Fig. 64). The carrying capacity of the pastures is small but herds are often large; for example it is often thought that the more stock one has, the more beasts are likely to survive the next drought.

Crops grown include millet, cassava, maize and groundnuts, but these are uncertain and poverty is widespread. Commercial production is small, but some European settlers have successful sisal plantations and profitable cotton growing around Kilosa and Morogoro in the Central railway zone and within 200 miles of Dar es Salaam. Farther west Dodoma and Tabora, once ivory and slave-caravan centres, remain local market centres of some importance, being on the main route to Dar es Salaam. Tabora is at the junction of the branch line north to Mwanza on Lake Victoria that taps this richer area after passing through the diamond field at Shinyanga.

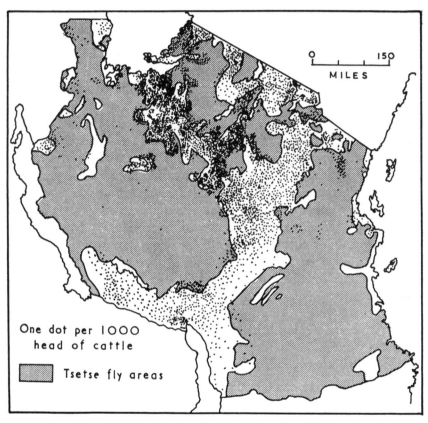

Figure 64 *Distribution of cattle and tsetse fly in Tanzania*

THE SOUTH-EAST PLATEAU A good deal of the southern part of the plateau between Lake Malawi and the coast is rather better watered although still lightly populated and subject to the tsetse fly. Local irrigation in the basin of the Rufiji river makes cotton growing successful and tobacco and cotton feature in the local crops, especially around Songea. Had the ill-fated groundnut scheme directed its main attention to this region rather than to Kongwa and Urambo in central and western districts, more success might have attended the venture.

The Groundnut Scheme resulted from erroneous forebodings that the wartime shortage of edible fats and oils would be prolonged into the post-war years. A mission sent out to East Africa in 1947 made a hurried survey (much of it by air) lasting nine weeks, and recommended enthusiastically an enormous scheme of wholesale bush clearing and large-scale groundnut and sunflower growing, both valuable oil-giving crops. Originally a total area of 3,210,000 acres was suggested, most in Tanganyika but some in Northern Rhodesia and in Kenya. Farming units of 30,000 acres were envisaged, in other words the creation of whole counties of continuous arable agriculture. Both Kongwa and Urambo are near the central railway line and therefore more accessible than Nachinwea in the slightly better-watered south. The whole scheme was based upon a misplaced trust in capital: the view being that, given sufficient capital investment, human and physical difficulties can be overcome or avoided. Haste ruled the planning; no time could be spared at Kongwa for primary reconnaissance and survey, for soil investigation and mapping, for adequate investigation of meteorological data. No pilot schemes were undertaken. An astounding collection of machinery (much secondhand) was assembled and put to work in clearing the matted tangled vegetation and then ploughing the exposed soil. The machines were inadequate for the tasks since special machines to cope with those conditions had yet to be invented. The mass of vegetation at times was almost impenetrable; the hard pan of iron or the lateritic soils rendered useless the first ploughs, and the machines, far from replacing man, needed his attention both for maintenance and operation.

With no highly skilled industrial population to draw on, second-best had to do and at one time three-quarters of all the machines were out of action. The areas eventually cleared and cropped were ridiculously small compared with the initial plans. A series of dry years, the over-compacting of the sandy soil by the heavy machinery, lack of particular chemical constituents in the soils, made the harvests pathetically small. Further, such large-scale mechanised farming demands a considerable and highly expensive framework, or infrastructure, of roads, railway, power stations, water supplies and, in the south, a port. In economically developed° countries these costs do not fall on a single enterprise but are widely shared. Here they fell on a very limited range of crops and the costs were prodigious. In all £36 million was eventually written off by the British Government when the original scheme was abandoned in 1951.

In the south a huge area around Nachinwea, 100 miles inland, was marked for development. This meant the construction of a railway, of a pipeline for petrol and a deep-water port—the first between Mombasa and Durban. The port site was Mtwara, 40 miles south-east of the established shallow port of Lindi. With the collapse of the groundnut scheme the cleared area was taken over by the Tanganyika Government and run as African small-holdings and experimental farms. The southern province, however, offered further possibilities given the link to the coast. To the north of the railway line on the Rondo plateau a lumbering industry was successfully begun and possibilities of cashew nut, tobacco and coffee production by smallholders persuaded the government to keep open the railway and port. The southern province is of high agricultural potential, but is isolated. It produces the bulk of the cashew, cassava and sesame marketed in Tanganyika and also grows tobacco, coffee and sisal. However, the volume of freight never became enough to pay the cost of operating the railway; it was closed and the line lifted in 1962. Growing competition from road transport was another reason for its lack of success.

THE SOUTHERN HIGHLANDS, trending north-east from Lake Malawi and reaching up to Kilosa, offer extensive rolling upland country 3,000 feet or more above the general level of the surrounding plateau. Rainfall is also well above 30 inches in most years, yet the area is very lightly settled. The two great drawbacks are the tsetse-fly, a menace to both man and animals, and remoteness, for there are few good roads and no railways to the rest of Tanganyika and the coast. The long road haul to railhead limits freight to high-value, low-bulk commodities that can stand the high cost of transport. Non-African estates send out by road to the railhead at Dodoma or Itigi coffee, tea, pyrethrum and tobacco. The chief estate areas are around Iringa (where Greeks and Indians specialise in tobacco growing and curing), Njombe and Tukuyu. Experimental sugar growing is taking place in the Kilombero valley. African settlement is very sparse, perhaps as a result of the German suppression of rebellions early in the century. Around Njombe wattle planting by Africans for tanning extract is being encouraged by the government, but such schemes are extremely limited while this area of great potentiality is so poorly served with communications. This also prevents the working of the extensive coal deposits east of Lake Malawi, the Ruhuhu coal field and other deposits near its head.

THE LAKE VICTORIA LOWLANDS of north-west Tanganyika are densely settled and better watered, although the rainfall is less than that of the Uganda north coast of the lake. Most of the littoral enjoys 40 inches and the coastlands of Bukoba on the west of the lake have over 60 inches. The main subsistence crops are millet, cassava and pulses, with cotton as the principal cash crop. In Bukoba coffee growing is increasing at the expense of cattle rearing, formerly a well-integrated feature of the farming that has helped to maintain soil fertility. With an increasing population and diminishing fertility of the land the Tanganyika Government here faces a problem of growing seriousness.

MINING AND INDUSTRY

Minerals played a small rôle in Tanganyika's economy until relatively recent years. More than two-thirds of the republic's surface is composed of Archaean crystalline and metamorphic rocks favourable to mineral formation. Much detailed prospecting has yet to be done. Minerals now provide nearly 15 per cent of Tanganyika's export earnings, most coming from diamonds. Small discoveries of diamonds have been known for many years but in 1940 a major discovery was made at Mwadui by a Dr J. T. Williamson and most of the country's output now comes from the Williamson Mine in which the government acquired a half-share in 1958. Production is worth about £5 million a year. Another important mineral is gold—from east of Lake Victoria, the Musoma gold field; south of Lake Victoria, Mwanza gold field; the Iramba plateau in Central Province; and the waning Lupa Mines of south-western Tanganyika. Annual production is about £1 million. Other minerals produced in smaller amounts are lead, tin and mica. Industrial development is less advanced than in Kenya and Uganda. The only significant centre of manufacturing is Dar es Salaam, where textiles are made and milling, brewing, soap manufacture, meat processing and packing also take place.

POPULATION AND TRADE

The estimated population of Tanganyika in 1965 was 10,180,000 including about 17,000 Europeans and 111,000 Asians. There are over 100 tribes within the country, most Bantu, but some Hamitic and Nilo-Hamitic. *Dar es Salaam*, the capital and chief port, has a population of over 130,000. Its trade has increased fivefold since 1939 and is now over 1 million tons a year. This necessitated the construction of deep-water berths, opened in 1956 (previously it was a lighterage port). Much of the domestic hinterland of the port is unproductive and some of the produce from the richer Lake Victoria areas finds its way to Mombasa via the Kenya railways. Tanga, to the north, serves the coffee and sisal estates of the north-east highlands. The central railway and Dar es Salaam provide one of the outlets for the Congo Republic and newly independent Burundi and Rwanda (see Chapter 50). This transit trade has varied greatly during the years when Belgium ruled the Congo; for example, before the opening of the Lobito rail route in 1931 a good deal of Katanga copper was exported via Dar es Salaam. Today coffee is the principal transit export.

Although she possesses the greatest area and highest population of the East African countries, Tanganyika is poorer than her neighbours. She relies almost entirely upon her primary productions, notably sisal, cotton, coffee, which account for nearly two-thirds of export revenue. Her only other product of notable value is diamonds—now worth about £5 million a year. A major share of her trade is with the United Kingdom (Tables 13 and 14).

Table 13   *East African Exports 1960—Principal Commodities*

Commodity	Value £'000			East Africa	Percentage total value East Africa
	Kenya	Uganda	Tanganyika		
Coffee	10,260	16,990	7,240	34,590	26·3
Cotton, raw	840	14,930	8,830	24,600	18·7
Sisal fibre	4,570	50	15,440	20,060	15·2
Tea	4,410	1,450	1,150	7,010	5·3
Hides and skins	1,760	1,150	1,840	4,740	3·6
Diamonds	—	—	4,620	4,620	3·5
Copper and alloys	450	3,690	—	4,140	3·1
Other	12,900	3,330	15,910	31,900	24·3
Total	35,190	41,590	54,820	131,600	100·0

Table 14   *Directions of East Africa Trade 1960*

(Expressed as a percentage of total exports and imports)

	E.A. exports %	E.A. imports %
United Kingdom	24·3	34·6
Remainder of Commonwealth	24·3	14·3
EFTA (exc. UK)	2·1	3·0
EEC	23·6	18·0
Japan	4·3	11·3
USA	10·7	4·5
Rest of world	10·7	14·3
	100·0	100·0

THE FUTURE

All the East African countries face serious difficulties in raising the level of living of their peoples. Tanganyika in many ways is even less well endowed than her neighbours. It has been said that her 'trinity of priorities' consists of food, water and communications. Her water supplies are particularly deficient, for some 60 per cent of Tanganyika is virtually waterless and consequently uninhabited. Only about 10 per cent is regarded as well watered, and this area holds over 60 per cent of the population. Tanganyika has few rivers and even fewer amenable to irrigation schemes. Her communications problems are particularly severe. The main arteries upon which a transport net may grow are the railways. Until 1962 Tanganyika had three (now two) separate lines running east-west from the coast to the interior. Between these lines are large stretches of territory unserved by railways and poorly served by roads. Further, the best agricultural areas (over 30 inches reliability zones), except for parts of the north-east highlands, are not served by these railways. The great central line passes through hundreds of miles of arid bush and waste, but to its south the upland areas of great potentiality towards and beside Lake Malawi are ignored. There is neither railway nor an all-weather road between Nairobi and any part of Tanganyika. The failure of the Mtwara–Nachingwea line is a serious setback for those seeking investment for the opening up of southern Tanganyika. Railways are costly to build and here there is no assured freight, only the expectation that given a railway link to the coast, export crop farming will expand.

The Nachingwea line did not penetrate far enough inland to the better farming areas, so that much freight came by lorry to the railhead and subsequently, rather than break bulk there, went all the way by lorry to Mtwara or Lindi.

Upon advice given by the International Bank for Reconstruction and Development, a first Development Plan was carried out in the period 1961–4. One quarter of the expenditure of £24 million was devoted to agriculture: to develop water resources and irrigation, to modernise methods of husbandry, to fight pests and diseases and to improve the pastoral industry. A five-year plan, the first of three and involving the expenditure of £246 million, was announced in 1964 and again put emphasis upon general agricultural improvement; it included schemes for further settlement and development of the Kilombero and Pagani-Wari river basins.

Environmental hazards and shortcomings in Tanganyika limit the scope for agriculture, but over wide areas a more productive pastoral industry is possible. The map (Fig. 64) shows the very uneven distribution of cattle in the republic, reflecting certain diseases (Trypanosomiasis and East Coast Fever carried by tsetse-flies and ticks respectively), and lack of permanent water supplies. The areas with most cattle are the semi-arid parts of the country free from the chief pests and diseases but where water supplies are available. Cattle concentrate in the northern half of the country and down the length of the Southern Highlands. Some of the pastoral tribes such as the Masai of the northern border are nomadic. There is much scope for improvement. Communal land ownership but unrestricted grazing by large individually owned herds result in low productivity and deterioration of pasture. Pastures are not 'managed'; there is little effort to arrange for rotational grazing and resting of pastures. The result is over-stocking, low productivity and the growth of man-made desert, for where the grazing is removed the soil washes away and erosion sets in, the water table is affected, springs dry up and the herdsmen move on to ruin other areas.

Similar problems face all the three East African mainland countries. A harshness of environment that so far has meant poverty and hardship for the mass of the population must still be overcome. To attain greater income per head requires great capital investment for improving education, health, communications, water supplies, agricultural credit and so on. Since the annual income per head of the East African people averages only £20–30 there is little scope for saving or for much of the needed capital being generated at home. These countries, like most of those of Africa, will depend for a long time upon grants, loans and investment by overseas countries.

The Royal Commission that investigated the economic and social problems of East Africa (1953–5) made a number of recommendations that still serve as a general guide for the governments of the newly independent countries. It emphasised that the road to better living was through specialisation of production, the move away from subsistence agriculture and to the necessary expansion of markets. This in turn required improved communications. Individual land tenure and owner-ship was a mechanism whereby credit might be made available and incentive to betterment could be inculcated. Again, this would be related to an expansion of education particularly in its agrarian application. The real wealth of East Africa lies in its land, which so far is thoroughly underdeveloped. Industrial growth is never likely to be other than limited and related to the domestic market.

ZANZIBAR

In 1890 the islands of Zanzibar and Pemba were placed under British protection by the Sultan. In 1963 the islands resumed their independence within the British Commonwealth, becoming a republic and entering into a union with Tanganyika in 1964. They were keen to point out that they were not a British-created African nation: Zanzibar was independent when the English were fighting the Wars of the Roses. They have a proud sense of identity, of Arab roots and Islamic culture, and have a longer history than any African state except Ethiopia. However, times have changed. No longer does Zanzibar hold parts of the mainland and no longer is the island the centre for trade (mainly in ivory and slaves) undertaken by Arabs across East Africa. With the development of the mainland economies and of the great ports of Mombasa and Dar es Salaam, Zanzibar's commercial functions have lessened; she is no longer the Venice of East Africa. The republic consists of Zanzibar Island (640 sq. miles) 22 miles off the mainland and Pemba Island (380 sq. miles) 25 miles to the north-east. The population is increasing rapidly and the 1965 estimate was 320,000 (Zanzibar 180,000, Pemba 140,000). The islands are the meeting ground for Arab, Indian and African, and during the period of British protection a high degree of co-operation between the races was achieved. The revolution in 1964 that deposed the Sultan put the African majority into power.

The climate is akin to that of the adjacent mainland coast but somewhat wetter, for the islands stand in the path of the saturated mT airstream originating as the South-East Trades across the Indian Ocean. Most of Zanzibar Island receives 60 inches and much of Pemba over 80 inches. Some rain falls in most months of the year but there are two rainy seasons, the first March–May and the second in November when the north-east winds blow from the Arabian Sea. High temperatures are experienced all through the year owing to the latitude (6°S) and low elevation. Marine effect may reduce temperatures by one or two degrees compared with Tanga and Mombasa. The range of temperature through-out the year is quite small. These conditions of humid heat for much of the year favour a growth of a more luxuriant vegetation than on the main-land coast. The natural vegetation was dense forest but over the centuries most has been cleared for agriculture and at the same time other tropical plants from India, Madagascar and the East Indies were introduced.

Cultivation in the islands is intensive and there is much concentration on the two cash crops, cloves and coconuts. Here is produced 60 per cent of the world's supply of cloves, actually the unopened buds of the clove tree which was introduced from the East Indies early in the nineteenth century. Disease during the post-war period cut back production in Zanzibar Island and there is now a greater concentration in Pemba. In all, the islands have about 3 million clove trees. There are about the same number of coconut-palms and copra is an important export. These two commodities and derived products provide the base for almost the entire economy; much food is imported (Table 15):

Table 15

Exports, 1960	£ thousands	Imports, 1960	£ thousands
Cloves and clove oil	3,656	Food	1,672
Copra	310	Spirits, beverage and tobacco	207
Coconuts	136	Machinery	370
Coconut oil	274	Textiles	516
Oil cake	58	Fuels and oils	340
Fibres	201	Vehicles, bicycles	193
All other exports	133	All other	1,717
Total domestic exports	4,768		
Re-export	845		
Total exports	5,613	Total imports	5,015

Most of the clove plantations are Indian or Arab owned, but some have been subdivided into peasant holdings. Some of the labour needed on the plantations comes from Tanganyika and Moçambique. Experiments at commercial production of cacao and citrus fruits are now being undertaken and there is some hope of greater revenue from tourism.

References

1 H. H. Johnston, *Report by His Majesty's Special Commissioner in the Protectorate of Uganda*, Cmd. 671 (1901), 7
2 L. H. Brown, 'Agriculture and Land Tenure in Kenya Colony', in E. W. Russell, *Natural Resources in East Africa* (Nairobi, 1962), 104
3 L. H. Brown, *ibid*, 105
4 'Royal Charter for Nairobi', *The Times*, 30.3.50

Selected Bibliography

Atlases of Tanganyika, Kenya and Uganda (1956; 1959; 1962)
East Africa Royal Commission, *Report 1953–5*. Cmd. 9475 (1955)
Economist Intelligence Unit, *Power in Uganda 1957–70* (London, 1957)
H. Fearn, *An African economy: Nyanza Province of Kenya* (London, 1961)
H. C. G. Hawkins, *Wholesale and retail trade in Tanganyika: a study of distribution in East Africa* (New York, 1965)
J. Hill and J. Moffett, *Tanganyika: A review of its resources and their development* (Dar es Salaam, 1955)
E. Huxley, *Forks and hope* (London, 1964)
International Bank, *Economic development of Tanganyika* (Baltimore, 1961)
International Bank, *Economic development of Uganda* (Baltimore, 1962)
International Bank, *Economic development of Kenya* (Baltimore, 1963)
D. N. McMaster, *A Subsistence crop geography of Uganda*, World Land Use Survey, Occasional Papers No. 2 (1962)
D. Malcom, *Sukumaland, an African people and their country* (London, 1953)
J. K. Matheson and E. W. Bovill (eds.), *East African agriculture* (London, 1950)
A. M. O'Connor, *An economic geography of East Africa* (New York, 1966)
C. Wrigley, *Crops and wealth in Uganda* (Kampala, 1959)

T. D. Fair, 'A regional approach to economic development in Kenya', *S. Afr. Geog. Journ.*, 45 (1963), 55–77
B. Hoyle, 'Recent changes in the pattern of East African railways', *Tijdschrift v. Econ. en Soc. Geog.*, 54 (1963), 237–42

N. C. Pollock, 'Industrial development of East Africa', *Econ. Geog.*, 36 (1960), 344-54

R. W. Steel, 'Land and population in British Tropical Africa', *Geog.*, 40 (1955),

E. B. Worthington, 'East Africa and her neighbours', *Geog. Journ.*, 121 (1955), 417-28

N. S. Carey Jones, 'The decolonization of the White Highlands of Kenya', *Geog. Journ.*, 131 (1965), 186–201

W. T. Morgan, 'The "White Highlands" of Kenya', *Geog. Journ.*, 129 (1963), 140–55

E. S. Munger, 'Water problems of Kitui district, Kenya', *Geog. Rev.*, 40 (1950), 575–82

F. F. Ojany, 'The physique of Kenya: a contribution to landscape analysis', *Ann. Assoc. Am. Geogr.*, 56 (1966), 183–96

N. C. Pollock, 'Agricultural revolution in Kikuyuland', *S. Afr. Geog. Journ.*, 41 (1959), 53–8

S. J. K. Baker, 'Buganda: a geographical appraisal', *Trans. Inst. Brit. Geog.*, 22 (1956), 171–80

B. Hoyle, 'Economic expansion of Jinga, Uganda', *Geog. Rev.*, 53 (1963), 377–88

D. N. McMaster, 'Bukoba District, Tanganyika', *Geog. Rev.*, 50 (1960), 73–88

J. F. Middleton and D. J. Greenland, 'Land and population in West Nile District, Uganda', *Geog. Journ.*, 120 (1954), 446–57

W. Hance and I. van Dongen, 'Dar-es-Salaam', *Ann. Assoc. Am. Geog.*, 48 (1958), 419–35

C. Gillman, 'A Vegetation-type map of Tanganyika', *Geog. Rev.*, 39 (1949), 7–37

E. S. Munger, 'African coffee on Kilimanjaro', *Econ. Geog.*, 28 (1952), 181–5

PART VIII

The Eastern Islands

A number of islands lying in the Indian Ocean off the coast of Africa claim certain geographical connections with the continent. By far the largest is Madagascar, the fourth largest island in the world. Although the Mascarene Islands, comprising the Seychelles, Mauritius and Réunion, are minute in comparison, their combined population numbers 1 million, nearly one-sixth that of Madagascar.

32

Madagascar

The island of Madagascar is one of the less-well-known parts of Africa. Its location in the South Indian Ocean, away from major shipping routes since the opening of the Suez Canal, has been partly responsible for limited contact with the European world; and the 250-mile-wide Moçambique Channel effectively separates it from the African mainland. It possesses characteristics which distinguish it from any other part of Africa—the language and culture of its native peoples, the widespread intensive cultivation of rice, and the absence of tsetse fly, for instance—yet physiographically it has definite links with the adjacent continent. The island measures nearly 1,000 miles from north to south, and with 241,000 sq. miles exceeds France in area. Its size, mountainous character and isolated position were among the factors that delayed exploration of its interior until the 1860's, though the island was known to the Portuguese in the sixteenth century.

It is now generally thought that Madagascar was peopled originally by East Africans, who brought over a predominantly pastoral economy; much later, Indonesians arrived, importing an Eastern-type culture and paddy-rice cultivation. Today there are some eighteen different tribes in the island, all of whom understand one basic language—Malagasy. The largest tribe, now numbering over 1 million, is the Merina (or Hova), who, long before the advent of any European colonists, had established a highly organised society and economy in the central highlands, with their capital at Tananarive. The first European colonists on the island in the seventeenth century were French. This eventually led to a rather vague French Protectorate over the island in 1885. The formal annexation of Madagascar as a French colony under General Gallieni followed in 1896.

The existence of the magnificent harbour of Diego Suarez was the reason for British invasion of the island in World War II, to prevent this strategically valuable base from falling into Japanese hands, for the local government of Madagascar sided with Vichy France. After the war the island returned to French rule; economic development progressed, and the varied resources of the island became better appreciated. In 1960 French rule came to an end, and the independent Malagasy Republic was born. It still, however, retains its links with the other African members of the French Community, and France still purchases nearly two-thirds of its exports.

The present population numbers more than 6 million, of whom 98 per cent are Malagasy. Numbers of French have declined since 1960, when there were about 70,000, since many officials were replaced by Malagasy. Few parts of the island are densely peopled. The principal areas of close settlement are some highland basins, and it is also in the highlands that the capital, *Tananarive*, the largest settlement (pop. 270,000) is situated. Overall, the rather low population density of twenty-five per sq. mile resembles that of tropical Africa generally. The population is, however, increasing rapidly, due to improved health measures and disease control: malaria, for instance, has now been practically eliminated. The rate of expansion is about 2·5 per cent per annum, whilst there is a remarkably high proportion of young people—40 per cent are under fifteen years of age.

RELIEF AND STRUCTURE

It is possible that Madagascar was joined to Africa as part of the former continent of Gondwanaland until approximately Jurassic times. The eastern two-thirds of the island, including the highlands, consist of Pre-Cambrian igneous and metamorphic rocks, similar to the foundation rocks of the African continent (Fig. 65). On the west is a series of sedi-mentary rocks, from upper Carboniferous to Tertiary and Quaternary in age, dipping gently towards the Moçambique Channel. The lower part of this series consists of the continental Karroo System, whose accumula-tion was brought to an end by the major marine transgression of the middle Jurassic.

The highlands of Madagascar (Fig. 65) are really a dissected plateau, whose flat-topped interfluves and hill summits fall most commonly in the range 4,000–5,000 feet above sea-level, comparable with some major plateau surfaces in southern Africa. In places the mountains rise much higher, especially in the Tsaratanana massif of the north (up to 9,450 feet) and in the volcanic Ankaratra group (maximum 8,675 feet) south of

Tananarive. As the coastline is near, dissection of the highlands by rivers has been rapid. Within the highlands there are a number of small alluvial basins, tapped by rivers, but in a few cases still containing lakes, such as Lake Alaotra.

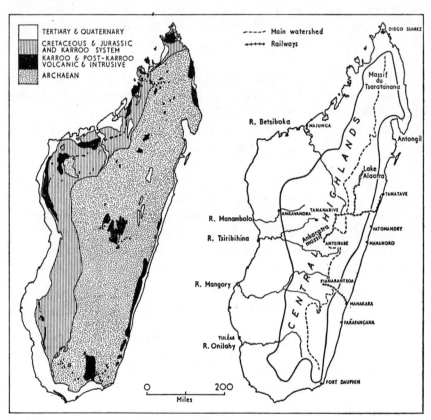

Figure 65 *The Malagasy Republic.* The left-hand figure shows the geology of the island; the right-hand indicates some features of the island's relief and drainage, together with railways, principal settlements and ports

On the east, the highlands end in escarpments overlooking the coast-lands. Behind Tamatave there are two such escarpments, the lower one rising abruptly to 3,000 feet and, behind a bench at this level, a further one rising to 4,500 feet. The eastern coastlands themselves are rarely more than 20 miles wide, except locally behind Farafangana. They consist partly of a flat sandy littoral, with a series of lagoons and swamps.

West of the central highlands lies a series of plains and low plateaux, formed of the westward-dipping sedimentary formations. Cuestas and strike vales are a characteristic feature; for instance, a discontinuous depression in lower Trias, over 300 miles in length and flanked by an escarpment in upper Trias on the west, has been etched out by rivers between Ankavandra and the Onilahy river. The broad flat plains next to the west coast consist of Tertiary and Quaternary sediments.

The coastline of Madagascar is for long stretches lacking in indentations, while most of those that do occur suffer from heavy silting by rivers draining into them, or else are exposed to the prevalent winds. Consequently, the island possesses few good natural harbours. Diego Suarez, the one exception to this, has its value greatly diminished by its location in the extreme north, away from any areas of commercial importance. The straightness of the east coast from Antongil Bay to Fort Dauphin is the result of faulting; the only modern port along this stretch is Tamatave, artificially constructed. The west coast, since it faces Africa, is less exposed, but all possible harbours are shallow and need constant dredging.

CLIMATE, VEGETATION AND SOILS

The climate ranges from humid tropical on the east coastlands to semi-arid tropical in the south-west. The most pleasant climate is on the highlands, where altitude mitigates the temperature and where there is also a pronounced division in the year between dry season and wet season. In the past, malaria has been the curse of the coastlands and many other parts, but an intensive campaign of DDT spraying has now practically eliminated it.

In summer the ITC lies along the north of the island; the north coast is bombarded by the mE air from the north, and the eastern coast and highlands by equally moist and unstable air from the east or north-east together with regular tropical hurricanes which may do great damage on the coast. This is the season of heaviest rainfall in all parts of the island, with a great deal of thunder. In winter the whole island comes into the mT airstream of the South-East Trades, which have a long trajectory over the Indian Ocean and meet the highlands at right angles giving the maximum orographic effect; thus, the east coast and eastern highlands receive further heavy rainfall, but the western half of the island lies in rain shadow and often under the influence of dry easterly föhn winds. The winds on the east coast at this season are unusually strong and persistent.

Total rainfall varies from 128 inches at Tamatave and over 100 inches on the island of Nossi-Bé in the north-west, to less than 15 inches in the south-west (where the dry season occupies eight or nine months of the year). Most of the central highlands receive 40 to 80 inches, with a five-to six-month dry season. Temperatures on the coastlands are high in summer, monthly means reaching 80°F or more, and only a little cooler in 'winter'. On the highlands between 4,000 and 5,000 feet, temperature conditions compare closely with the Rhodesian uplands.

Forest formerly covered most of the central highlands, but burning for native agriculture and extension of grazing land left it occupying only one-tenth of the island. The principal forest areas are on the steeper eastern slopes of the highlands and on parts of the eastern coastlands. Mangroves fringe parts of the east and west coasts. In the central highlands savanna and steppe are now dominant, with only a few patches of woodland. As well as regular burning and grazing, the five- to six-month dry season helps to retard regeneration of the forest. In the south and south-west of the island, where conditions verge almost on semi-desert, scrubland is characteristic, with xerophytic types of plants including cacti.

The soils appear to be mainly lateritic and of limited fertility, except in some basins or coastal areas of recent deposition. There are also a few regions of richer volcanic soils, as around Lake Itasy and Antsirabe in the centre of the island. Soil erosion in the highlands is an acute and wide-spread problem, due to the high rate of rainfall and the prevalence of steep slopes; deforestation and overgrazing are primarily responsible for the initiation of the process, leaving the red earth without sufficient protection from the intense thunder showers.

FARMING

The great majority of the Malagasy depend on their animals for their livelihood. Here there are none of the restrictions which the tsetse fly imposes in many parts of tropical Africa. There are probably no fewer than $7\frac{1}{2}$ million cattle in the island, mainly African breeds and of poor quality. Their excessive numbers have given rise to overgrazing and problems of soil erosion in some areas. In the drier south-west a nomadic way of life is encountered. Superimposed on this pastoral base are other forms of agricultural activity, ranging from shifting cultivation, which is mainly found in the east, to intensive production of rice and various cash crops. Though only a fraction (about 4 per cent) of the island is cultivated, yet it is from this small part that the most important Malagasy products are

Table 16

Temperature and rainfall at selected stations

Station	Alt. (feet)		J	F	M	A	M	J	J	A	S	O	N	D	Year	Temp. range
Tamatave	20	Temp. °F	80	80	79	77	74	71	70	70	71	74	77	79	75	10
		Rain in.	14·4	14·8	17·8	15·7	10·4	11·1	11·9	8·0	5·2	3·9	4·6	10·3	128·2	
Tananarive	4,500	T.	70	69	69	67	63	60	59	58	62	67	68	70	65	11
		R.	11·8	11·0	7·0	2·1	0·7	0·3	0·3	0·4	0·7	2·4	5·3	11·3	53·4	
Tuléar	20	T.	82	80	79	76	72	71	69	69	72	75	78	81	70	13
		R.	3·1	3·2	1·4	0·3	0·7	0·4	0·1	0·2	0·3	0·7	1·4	1·7	13·5	

derived. Rice is the most extensive crop, occupying more than 1·5 million acres or a third of the cultivated area. Its cultivation as the primary food crop is one of the most distinctive features of Madagascar, sharply differentiating the island from any other part of Africa. It is found in most parts of the country except the south-west, though the alluvial highland basins, such as those of Lake Alaotra and around Tananarive, are the areas of most intensive production. As well as providing a fundamental item of the Malagasy diet, a surplus is normally available for export. The actual amount exported each year, however, fluctuates considerably, for only the top-grade rice is easily saleable; but it normally represents about 10 per cent of the total export trade. Its production could undoubtedly be further expanded without difficulty—a point of significance when the rate of population increase is considered—and its cultivation is ideally adapted to help conserve the soil in hilly lands where terracing is practised. Other food crops include manioc, maize and groundnuts, as in tropical Africa.

Easily the most important cash crop is coffee, providing about 35 per cent of the exports. During the years following World War II its production remained rather static at about 25,000 tons, but since 1952 there has been a definite though irregular increase, reaching 50,000 tons in 1961. The coffee, mainly of the robusta variety, fares best on the hill slopes above the eastern coastlands, where rainfall and drainage are favourable and where there are patches of volcanic soil. In the Ankaratra massif, young volcanic soils support some better-quality arabica coffee.

Other cash crops, of which there is a considerable variety, are of much less importance economically. Vanilla production has diminished greatly since the 1920's, due to competition from synthetic vanillin; tobacco production, on the other hand, is rising steadily—the 1958 output was double that of 1938. The cultivation of cloves is also on the increase, especially since disease afflicted many of Zanzibar's producing areas. The list of agricultural products is a long and varied one: space precludes more than passing mention of sugar (there is a large new plantation on the lower Mahavavy river), sisal and cotton (in the western provinces of Majunga and Tuléar), but in many cases production tends to be erratic and the future not easily predictable.

MINING

The mineral resources of the island are not yet fully known but appear to be rather meagre. Although Madagascar is one of the world's chief graphite producers, both graphite and mica, the two most important minerals obtained, account for a mere 2 per cent of the island's export trade. Graphite is mined on the east coast of Tamatave; owing to technical developments in metallurgical processes, world consumption has diminished and the annual production of 12,000 tons from Madagascar is not always easy to market. The island also possesses rich deposits of thorium sands; an undisclosed quantity of uranium and thorium compounds is now mined around Behara in the south. The only solid fuel resources are represented by the small Sakoa coal field in Tuléar Province. Reserves probably amount to 3,000 million tons, but the coal is ashy and of low carbon content.

MANUFACTURING

There is very little manufacturing industry in the island, and almost all that which does exist is concerned with the processing of the local agricultural produce—the milling of rice, production of starch and tapioca from manioc, refining of sugar, meat canning and rum distillation, for example. A textile works at Antsirabe relies on local cotton. There are, however, two factors distinctly favourable for industrial development: the quite considerable potential for hydro-electric power, hardly yet touched, and the fact that the Malagasy in general provide more efficient labour than do the Bantu Africans. At present there are eight small hydro-electric installations (e.g. on the rivers Mandraha and Tsiazompaniry), compared with twenty-five thermal electric plants; but given the necessary capital, hydro-electricity could be much more highly developed. Unfortunately, in common with so many other African countries, capital is scarce; nor will the remote position of the island and the limited market represented by its population encourage any rapid industrial development.

TRANSPORT

The rugged and mountainous nature of most of the island presents great difficulties for the construction of modern forms of surface communication; it is therefore not surprising to find that there are only two railway systems totalling no more than 500 miles, and that there is only the same length of metalled road, but on the other hand, that there have been impressive developments since the last war in airfield construction. The island now boasts over 100 major airfields, with regular flights operating between all the chief towns. Railways carry a relatively small proportion of Malagasy trade—only one-fifth of all exports, for instance—since the centres of production are so widely scattered throughout the island. The first railway was completed in 1913 between the capital and the east coast; it has branches tapping the rich agricultural regions of Lake Alaotra and Antsirabe. The line from Fianarantsoa to the coast, opened in 1936, illustrates very clearly the problems of engineering involved in climbing from the eastern lowlands on to the central highlands. In 100 miles, it possesses forty-nine tunnels, and forty-seven bridges and viaducts. In the years following World War II the French made great progress in railway modernisation; the lines are now amongst the most efficiently run in Africa, and use diesel or diesel-electric locomotives only.

An unusual feature of the transport network in the island is the Pangalanes Canal. This connects a series of natural lagoons along the east coast, protected from the prevalent east winds by sand and shingle bars. Available for 30-ton barges between Tamatave and Vatomandry, and for 5-ton barges to Mahanoro, it is not yet linked directly with the harbour at Tamatave. The lack of direct loading facilities from ships at Tamatave greatly reduces its value.

PORTS AND TRADE

Without a doubt the finest natural harbour is that of *Diego Suarez*, a volcanic bay second only in size to Rio de Janeiro. Though important as a naval base, especially in the last war, it provides an outlet for only the northern tip of the island, and possesses only a short deep-water quay. The only large modern port in the island is *Tamatave* (pop. 49,000). Situated on the exposed and reef-girt east coast, the harbour is artificially enclosed; it is far from satisfactory, for during severe storms, unfortunately common in these parts, so much wave motion develops that ships have to put out to sea. Nevertheless, Tamatave is Madagascar's chief port, handling about half the total port traffic of the island. It is the proposed site of an oil refinery with a capacity of 600,000 tons, large enough to supply the island's current needs. *Majunga* (pop. 52,000) on the north-west is the island's second port, handling about half the volume of Tamatave's traffic. It has a more sheltered harbour but lacks a deep-water quay. In spite of this, many imports pass through it, for it is on the side of the island facing Africa and subject to less stormy weather than Tamatave. Furthermore, it possesses a good road connection to Tananarive, 380 miles distant. The only other port of significance is *Tuléar* (pop. 29,000) with some deep-water facilities, serving the south-west.

The general level of trade is low. The islands of Mauritius and Réunion (see next chapter) together export as much as the Malagasy Republic. The five principal agricultural products—coffee, rice, vanilla, tobacco and cloves—account for two-thirds of the export trade. The island is still heavily dependent on France, which takes over half of all exports and provides nearly three-quarters of all imports; and there is a considerable trade deficit, imports exceeding exports by as much as 30 per cent. The situation has deteriorated in recent years, as growing internal demand, partly resulting from a rising population, reduces the surplus available for export; at the same time, the republic is being forced to purchase more raw materials, capital goods and fuel in order to lay the foundations of a more modern economy, less heavily dependent on the sale of a few cash crops which are not always easy to market.

33

The Mascarene Islands

Separated from Madagascar by a broad basin of the Indian Ocean, whose floor here lies at depths of 15,000 feet or more, is the Mascarene Ridge (Fig. 66). Only its highest peaks break the ocean surface to form a number of islands, from the Seychelles in the north, to Mauritius and Réunion in the south.

THE SEYCHELLES

The ninety-two Seychelles Islands are mostly small and the majority uninhabited. They were visited by the Arabs in the twelfth century, later by the Portuguese, and first colonised by the French from 1756 onward. In the Napoleonic Wars a British force took over the islands, which became a British dependency in 1814. The population today is of both European and African descent, the Africans being brought over as plantation labourers until the abolition of slavery in 1824. The present population numbers over 46,000, of whom 80 per cent live on the largest island, Mahé (55 sq. miles). Mahé has granite peaks reaching nearly 3,000 feet, but the other small islands are considerably lower and some entirely of coral formation. The hills are clothed in forest, while coconut-palms fringe the shores. The climate is maritime and equatorial, for the islands lie within 5° of the equator. Rainfall approaches 90 inches a year; temperatures are usually around 80°F. with little seasonal variation. Unlike Mauritius and Réunion, hurricanes are very rare. The islanders depend on the sale of copra (there are large coconut plantations), cinnamon bark and oil, guano and salted fish. There are hopes of expanding the tourist industry, for the islands offer beautiful scenery, a warm climate, fishing and bathing.

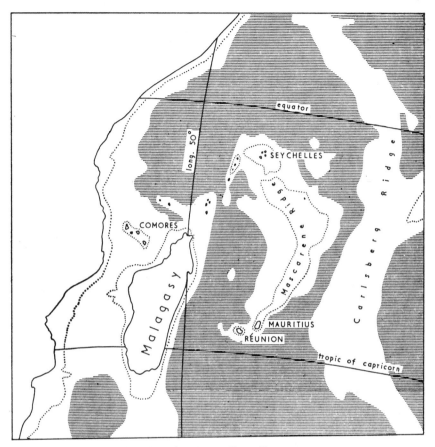

Figure 66 *The relief of the Indian Ocean floor off East Africa, and the position of the Mascarene Islands.* The shaded area lies at depths greater than 2,000 fathoms. The 1,000-fathom line is also shown

MAURITIUS

'The initial impression of Mauritius is of an island that is bizarre and slightly improbable. Grotesque pinnacled mountains rise up in groups around the dome-shaped central upland; going inland from Port Louis, one passes in a matter of miles from a coastland as dry as the Transvaal in winter to a mossy inland as green as Ireland and characteristically shrouded in cloud.'[1]

The jagged peaks rising to 2,700 feet are in fact all that remain of a volcanic caldra of mid-Tertiary age. The central uplands represent, a series of shield volcanoes of more recent date. The island's more southerly situation (latitude 20°), compared with the Seychelles, results in a more moderate maritime tropical climate, mean monthly temperatures on the coast ranging from 68° to 80°F. The climate is dominated by the South-East Trades, bringing nearly 200 inches of rain to mountains on the east and centre; the north-west of the island is, however, in rain-shadow, with as little as 30 inches, and here are to be found all the main towns except Mahébourg. There are two rainy seasons, the principal one December to June, and a lesser one in August. Hurricanes are unfortunately a regular feature, occurring with greatest frequency during the main rainy season. Even moderate storms do great damage to buildings and the sugar-cane plantations on which the island's economy depends. A particularly disastrous hurricane was that of February 1960 when wind speeds reached 160 m.p.h.

Known to both Arabs and Portuguese, and uninhabited when visited by the Portuguese in 1505, Mauritius was first settled by the Dutch in 1598. After the foundation of their more important Cape Colony in 1652, their interest in the island declined, and they abandoned it in 1710. The French were next on the scene, occupying the island until the arrival of a British force in 1810 during the Napoleonic Wars, for French pirates were preying too successfully on British traders returning from India. Mauritius was formally ceded to Britain in 1814.

The population now numbers over 750,000. Since the island measures only 40 miles by 30 miles, in places population densities rise to 2,400 per sq. mile (the average is nearly 1,000). About half are of Indian extraction, Chinese account for about 4 per cent, about 20,000 are French-speaking, and the remainder mostly of mixed European-African blood. It would be hard to find a greater diversity of people on such a small area anywhere else in the world. When the slave trade was abolished the French planters on the island were left without a ready source of labour to work the sugar plantations, so, like the planters in Natal, they brought over thousands of Indians (mainly from Madras) and Chinese. Between 1834 and 1925 the net Indian immigration amounted to 300,000. One-third of the population lives in the overcrowded towns such as the capital *Port Louis* (pop. 107,000), *Curepipe* (36,000) and *Mahébourg* (12,000). Port Louis has a sheltered harbour, though large vessels have to anchor half a mile off-shore. Mahébourg borders a lagoon enclosed by a coral reef; the lagoon floor is exposed at low tide so that it is useless except for small pleasure craft. A network of railways connects all the main towns.

The island's economy rests heavily on sugar-cane. Plantations cover 220,000 acres (48 per cent of the island's total area), and sugar provides 99 per cent of the exports. Consequently, abnormally low rainfall or the incidence of hurricanes can have devastating results. The 1960 sugar crop amounted to 236,000 tons, compared with more than double that amount the previous year. The sugar industry is now secured against losses due to hurricanes under a government insurance scheme. Crops other than sugar, comparatively unimportant, include tea and tobacco.

The main problem for the island is the upsurge in the population (a 25 per cent increase between 1952 and 1962) set against limited resources. A very delicate situation arises from almost total dependence on sugar monoculture; sugar acreage has been expanding recently, but as this has taken place with very little additional labour, unemployment on the island is rising steadily. If the present rate of increase continues, the population could reach the million mark in the next decade, with disastrous consequences for the economy of the island.

RÉUNION

Only slightly larger than Mauritius, this island is much more mountainous, with peaks reaching 9,000 feet, and one, the Piton des Neiges, 10,000 feet. These highest points receive snow in winter, and there are signs of Pleistocene glaciation. The present climate is similar to that of Mauritius; both islands are menaced by hurricanes in the wet season.

The early history of European settlement and occupation followed much the same pattern as in Mauritius, but whereas the latter was confirmed in British hands in 1814, the island of Réunion was restored to France. The population (400,000) is largely African, or mixed European and African, with a minority of French officials and, in contrast to Mauritius, only a few Indians. The density of population is not so high as in Mauritius, but there is nevertheless considerable pressure on the land. Most settlements are on the narrow coastlands, including the capital *St. Denis* (pop. 42,000). The chief port is Pointe des Galets, or 'Le Port', on the north-west, linked to St. Denis by rail. Sugar-cane is, as on Mauritius, the principal crop, occupying 90,000 acres and yielding 200,000 tons of sugar in 1960. Most sugar plantations lie between 2,000 and 4,000 feet, above which the sharply rising slopes are covered with forest up to about 6,000 feet.

References

1 H. C. Brookfield, 'Pluralism and geography in Mauritius', *Geog. Studies,* 5 (1958), 3–19

Selected Bibliography

G. Bastian, 'La politique économique de la République malgache', *Cahiers d'Outre Mer,* 14 (1961), 323–38

G. Donque, 'Le développement de la culture cotonnière à Madagascar', *Cahiers d'Outre Mer,* 15 (1962), 255–70

G. Grandidier, 'Madagascar', *Geog. Rev.,* 10 (1920), 197–222

W. A. Hance, 'Transportation in Madagascar', *Geog. Rev.,* 48 (1958), 45–68

H. Isnard, 'Les plaines de Tananarive', *Cahiers d'Outre Mer,* 8 (1955), 5–29

J. D. du Rau, 'Le sisal dans le Sud malgache', *Cahiers d'Outre Mer,* 7 (1954), 51–83

J. D. du Rau, 'La situation économique de Madagascar', *Cahiers d'Outre Mer,* 12 (1959), 174–209

M. Sarremejean, 'La vie agricole dans les plaines de Tananarive', *Cahiers d'Outre Mer,* 14 (1961), 349–71

V. Thompson and R. Adloff, *The Malagasy Republic: Madagascar today* (Stanford, 1965)

B. Benedict, *Mauritius: problems of a plural society* (New York, 1965)

H. C. Brookfield, 'Problems of monoculture and diversification in a sugar island: Mauritius', *Econ. Geog.,* 35 (1959), 25–40

H. Isnard, 'La Réunion et la Martinique', *Cahiers d'Outre Mer,* 9 (1956), 58–69

J. E. Meade and others, *The economic and social structure of Mauritius* (London, 1961)

R. M. Titmuss and B. Abel-Smith, *Social policies and population growth in Mauritius* (London, 1961)

PART IX

The Zambezi-Limpopo Lands

The Zambezi river basin is the fourth largest in Africa. A well-marked drainage divide separates it from the Congo Basin, a divide adopted by Wellington as the northern limit of the sub-continent of southern Africa. An equally prominent watershed separates the Zambezi and Limpopo catchments in Rhodesia. As in many other parts of Africa, physical and hydrographic dividing lines conflict seriously with the political boundaries, which it would obviously be impracticable to ignore. The area considered in this chapter therefore represents a compromise. Physically it is bounded on the north by the Congo-Zambezi watershed; on the west by the less-well-defined edge of the Kalahari; and on the south by the Limpopo depression. Politically, this section is concerned with Rhodesia, Zambia and Malawi, and Portuguese East Africa (Moçambique). The term 'Central Africa' has often been used to refer to the area of the former Federation of the Rhodesias and Nyasaland. This usage is a well-known and long-established one, but it is not descriptively accurate.

THE HISTORICAL AND POLITICAL BACKGROUND

The occupation by white settlers of Southern Rhodesia, originally Mashonaland and Matabeleland, began in the 1880's, most of the settlers coming from or through South Africa, as had many of the earlier explorers and mineral prospectors. Rhodes in 1889 founded the British South Africa Company to open up more of the territory whose native population at the time was less than half a million, and the Company in fact administered the Rhodesias until 1922. Following white elections in Southern Rhodesia, this country became a self-governing British colony in 1923 in preference to joining the Union of South Africa. Northern Rhodesia was taken over as a British Protectorate in 1924. The charter of the British South Africa Company does not expire until 1986, but it has no governmental responsibility today and relinquished its mineral

Table 17   *The population of the Zambezi–Limpopo lands*

Country	Year	Total (to nearest hundred)	European	African (estimated)	Asian and Coloured	Density per sq. mile
Rhodesia	1961 (non-African Census)	3,855,900	221,500	3,616,600	17,820	25
Zambia	,,	2,514,800	74,640	2,430,300	9,840	9
Malawi	,,	2,921,100	8,750	2,900,200	12,120	80 (excluding lake areas)
Moçambique	1960 Census	6,593,000	103,000	6,436,000	54,000	22

rights in Northern Rhodesia when the latter attained independence in 1964. Nyasaland, first explored by Livingstone in the 1860's, became a British Protectorate in 1891 after Sir Harry Johnston had negotiated a series of treaties with the African chiefs and suppressed the Arab slave trade.

In 1953, following long discussions and a white referendum in Southern Rhodesia, proposals to link the Rhodesias and Nyasaland in a Federation were approved in the British Parliament and a new major political unit created in this part of Africa. The secession of first Nyasaland and later Northern Rhodesia brought Federation to an end in 1963. During the ten years of its existence it became clear that there were many economic advantages to be derived from the union of the three territories, which together covered an entirely landlocked area approximately the size of the Republic of South Africa, and dependent on Portuguese facilities for most of its overseas trade. Within Southern Rhodesia (now known simply as Rhodesia) and Zambia (formerly Northern Rhodesia) there are more than 300,000 European settlers (70 per cent are in Rhodesia) making this one of the chief areas of European settlement in tropical Africa. Of the white population, nearly half is of South African origin, though more English-speaking than Afrikaans. This white population increased threefold between 1941 and 1961. Malawi, formerly Nyasaland and roughly equivalent in land area to Scotland and as long as Great Britain from north to south, has few white people, but almost as many Africans as Rhodesia. In 1964 both Zambia and Malawi attained total independence. The Rhodesian white minority government unilaterally declared independence from Britain in 1965, but neither Britain nor the United Nations has recognized this state of independence. Rhodesia has a considerably larger number of white settlers than any other country in tropical Africa apart from Angola.

The territory of Moçambique (about twice the size of Rhodesia) is a Portuguese overseas territory, where Portuguese settlement dates back to 1505. Moçambique and, on the west of Africa, Angola, are Portugal's chief overseas possessions, amounting to 7 per cent of the area of Africa and making her the largest remaining colonial power in the world. Moçambique (like Angola) is administered simply as a province of Portugal, and government is from Lisbon through a Governor-General. Of the total population (now over 6 million) about 120,000 are classed as full Portuguese citizens and entitled to the vote; but only 5,000 of these are Africans, few of whom can reach the necessary standards of literacy or wealth.

34

Physical Geography

GEOLOGY AND STRUCTURE (Fig. 67)

Except for the coastal plain of Moçambique, the greater part of the area is underlain by various rock groups of Pre-Cambrian age. Of these, the Archaean granites and gneisses are the most extensive. Of later Pre-Cambrian age are certain sedimentary formations; the Katanga System of Zambia (corresponding to part of the Transvaal System in South Africa) contains valuable mineral deposits, particularly of copper ore. Rhodesia is crossed by a major Pre-Cambrian intrusion known as the Great Dyke (an offshoot of the Bushveld Igneous Complex) which, appearing as a range of hills running north-north-east for 330 miles, also contains many important minerals. The most recent Pre-Cambrian rocks are the quartzitic sandstones of the Melsetter highlands.

The Karroo System consists of continental-type sediments (sandstones, shales, etc.) laid down on the eroded surface of Pre-Cambrian rocks, and, at the top of the system, great thicknesses of basalt lavas. Owing to later denudation it is now found mainly in downfaulted areas such as the middle Zambezi and Luangwa troughs. The Ecca beds of the Karroo System contain thick coal seams worked at Wankie; the upper Karroo basalts, equivalent in age to the Stormberg basalts of Lesotho, are well displayed in the gorges below Victoria Falls.

The Cretaceous period saw extensive marine deposition in Moçambique—sandstones, shales and limestones—and this phase continued into the Tertiary. Searches for oil in these strata are in progress. Continental equivalents of the marine Cretaceous have been found in the Luangwa and Malawi troughs, attesting the great age of these features.

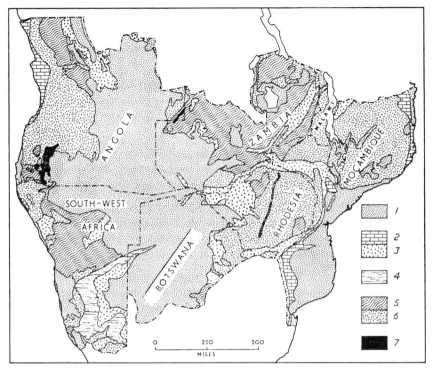

Figure 67 *The geology of the Zambezi lands and South-Western Africa*
1. Quaternary and Tertiary continental. 2. Mesozoic and Tertiary marine.
3. Karroo. 4. Palaeozoic (other than lower Karroo). 5. Younger Pre-
Cambrian. 6. Older Pre-Cambrian or Archaean. 7. Post-Karroo eruptive and
intrusive rocks

RELIEF AND DRAINAGE (Fig. 68)

Rhodesia and Zambia are characterised by some of the most perfect planation surfaces in the world. Vast expanses of apparently level land at heights
of 4,000–5,000 feet dominate much of the territories. Cutting across these
upland plains are the fault troughs occupied by the middle Zambezi and
Luangwa rivers. In more detail a number of distinct physical divisions
can be recognised. In the south the *Limpopo-Sabi lowlands* lie below 3,000
feet. Structurally this is a downfaulted region floored mainly by Pre-
Cambrian igneous and metamorphic rocks. A few outliers of later sedimentary and volcanic rocks rise above the plain. The River Limpopo
follows a winding course on the surface of the plain until it reaches the

Tolo Azimé rapids at about 1,500 feet near Messina, where it becomes
incised and falls more steeply down to the Moçambique Plain. The
Rhodesian uplands consist of a broad zone along the watershed between the Zambezi and Limpopo-Sabi tributaries, bevelled at heights
between approximately 4,000 and 5,500 feet. The exceptional evenness of
the planation surfaces over large areas may be partly due to the fact that
they are mostly cut in granite. Even the Great Dyke fails to form a major
feature, rising in the Umvukwo Range no more than 1,500 feet above the
surrounding plateau and usually less. River valleys are shallow, but usually
well defined; there are few areas of impeded drainage. In the east the land
surface stands at over 5,000 feet, and where it ends in the Great Escarpment overlooking the lower country of Moçambique, the Melsetter and
Umtali Mountains marking outcrops of quartzitic and intrusive rock reach
8,000–8,500 feet. Away from the central watershed zone, the land falls below
4,000 feet and becomes much more dissected by rivers. In these lower
parts, the older (Tertiary) planation surfaces have been largely destroyed.

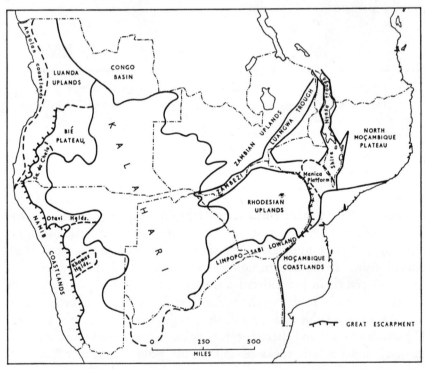

Figure 68 *Physical regions of the Zambezi lands and South-Western Africa*

The Zambian Uplands are also cut by extensive planation surfaces varying in height (possibly as a result of later warping) from 3,500 feet near Livingstone to over 5,000 feet in parts near the Congo border and in the Muchinga Mountains. In detail the surfaces are even flatter and less well drained than their counterparts in Rhodesia. The main surface in the Copperbelt is the mid-Tertiary or African surface at about 4,200 feet; a few isolated hills rising to 4,600 feet are the last remnants of the older Gondwana surface. The planation surfaces of the uplands sink to 3,500 feet on the Kalahari border, and farther west disappear beneath a covering of Kalahari Sand and other deposits. On the northern side of the Zambian-Congo border, the landscape becomes less monotonously flat; the development of hills and ridges indicates the deeper incision of the Congo drainage which is cutting back into the Zambian plateau. The surfaces are of great significance in the human geography of the Zambezi lands; their elevation has modified the climate and encouraged white settlement, while their level nature has greatly facilitated agriculture and the development of modern communications over large areas.

The Middle Zambezi and Luangwa Troughs are downfaulted areas containing Karroo beds, extending from the south-west of Wankie to the Tanganyika border. Details of the faulting are complex; structurally, the region is part of the East African rift valley system. It should be emphasised, however, that the present troughs are the result of denudation acting on the soft infilling of Karroo and post-Karroo strata. The floors of the troughs may lie up to 3,000 feet below the adjacent plateaux; sections of the trough floors are fairly flat, and in places terminate at the foot of imposing escarpments, e.g. the 3,000-foot Mavuradona Escarpment north of Salisbury. The River Zambezi in the trough flows mainly over Karroo rocks, but in a few places, notably Kariba gorge, it has cut through these to become superimposed on the underlying Pre-Cambrian. *The Malawi-Shiré trough* continues the East African rift valley system directly southward. The rift containing Lake Malawi is deepest in the north between the Livingstone Mountains and the Nyika plateau. Here the lake is over 2,300 feet deep and possesses virtually no bordering plain. Farther south, the lake has a fringe of flat land up to 30 miles wide behind Kota Kota. The lake level averages 1,550 feet; it is known to fluctuate by 24 feet largely because vegetation periodically blocks the shallow outlet. From the outlet downstream to Liwonde the Shiré river falls only 6 feet, but below this the river drops 1,400 feet in the Murchison Rapids which are spread over 70 miles. The Shiré is navigable below Port Herald. Around Lake Malawi the highlands of Pre-Cambrian rock rise to 8,700 feet in the Nyika plateau, only 9,000 feet in the Livingstone Mountains and in Tanganyika, to 10,420 feet in the volcanic cone of Mount Rungwe. Isolated in the south, Mount Mlanje stands east of the Shiré river and attains 9,840 feet (Plate 8B).

Northern Moçambique consists of a platform built almost entirely of granite and metamorphic rocks, with a narrow coastal fringe of Cretaceous and Tertiary marine sediments. The surface slopes eastward from heights of 6,000 feet and over in the uplands near Lake Malawi, and from nearly 8,000 feet in the Namuli Mountains to about 1,000 feet at the plateau edge. The coastline is probably a faulted one. The rivers drain east and north-east, the Ruvuma forming the border with Tanganyika.

The Manica Platform in central Moçambique represents the work of river planation, producing a surface sloping from 3,000 feet at the foot of the Great Escarpment (Umtali–Melsetter highlands) to 500 feet near the coast. It extends up the Zambezi valley to the Quebrabasa gorge. *The Moçambique coastal plain*, broad in the south, rises very gradually inland to about 500 feet, except where it is interrupted by the Sheringoma plateau (1,100 feet, north of Beira). The plain is underlain by Cretaceous and Tertiary limestones and sandstones. Coastal sand-dunes are of great size in places, blocking river exits. Inland, the river courses are often ill-defined, so that vast inundations may follow the rains.

THE RIVER ZAMBEZI. The river rises in Zambia at about 4,500 feet. After passing through part of Angola, it enters the flat basin area of Barotseland, which it floods in the summer. From Sioma to Victoria Falls the gradient steepens and rapids occur where the river encounters Karroo basalts. At Victoria Falls the river plunges over a drop of 355 feet. Sixty-five miles below the falls there begins the lake impounded by the Kariba Dam (water-level 1,600 feet, almost the same as that of Lake Malawi). On the left bank below the dam the Kafue and Luangwa rivers enter. The Quebrabasa rapids in Moçambique mark the limit of navigation on the lower Zambezi, about 390 miles upstream from the delta. The great economic significance of the Zambezi lies not in the navigability of some stretches, however, but in the Kariba hydro-electric scheme, in a proposal for a similar power development at the Kebrabasa gorge in

Moçambique, and in the possibilities for irrigation in certain areas. On the other hand, the very size of the Zambezi is an obstacle to communication; only two railways cross the river at present—at Livingstone and Sena. The bridge at Sena is no less than 2¼ miles long. At Tete, where there is a road ferry, the river is still nearly half a mile wide. Between this point and Livingstone the only road crossing, apart from that at Kariba Dam, is at Chirundu, where the Great North Road on its way between Salisbury and Lusaka passes over the Otto Beit Bridge.

CLIMATE

Except for the south of Moçambique, the area lies within the tropics, reaching latitude 9° in the Abercorn highlands. But over most of the uplands, temperatures are rarely excessive due to the modifying influence of altitude. Temperatures of 90°F are exceptional at 5,000 feet, and the average temperatures of the warmest month at places over 4,000 feet are in the seventies. Mean monthly temperatures at Salisbury resemble those at Cape Town. On the other hand, in the Limpopo valley and the low-lying parts of Moçambique, maximum temperatures may reach 110°F. It will be seen that the annual range of temperature is relatively small— 10° only on the Moçambique coast, 15° on the uplands. Rainfall is a more important factor in the differentiation of the seasons.

Fig. 69 shows the mean annual rainfall, decreasing to the south and south-west. Areas with more than 50 inches are restricted to highlands (e.g. Umtali, Mlanje), and to parts of Moçambique. In the Limpopo valley the total rainfall is barely 15 inches. However, maps such as this conceal much vital information, for the rainfall is markedly seasonal; it also varies in amount from year to year, and its geographical distribution is not constant. As examples of these two last points, the recorded rainfall at Mazabuka on the railway south-west of Lusaka was 18 inches in 1923 and 52 inches in 1924. Differences in rainfall between neighbouring farms in Rhodesia of 12 inches in one year, with reversal of the amounts in the following year, have also been noted.

The rain is associated with mE from the north, as the ITC moves south across the territories. The first sporadic rains occur in September in the north, November in the south, but precipitation is not at all reliable till a month or so later. Just before the rains break it becomes excessively hot and oppressive in the lower areas; finally, the

Table 18

Temperature (°F)

Station	Alt. (feet)	J	F	M	A	M	J	J	A	S	O	N	D	Year	Range
Salisbury	4,831	69	69	68	66	61	57	57	60	66	70	70	69	65	13
Lusaka	4,191	70	71	70	69	65	61	61	65	71	76	74	71	69	15
Tete	456	82	82	80	80	77	72	70	74	79	85	85	84	79	15
Nkata Bay (Lake Malawi)	1,600	77	76	77	75	72	68	67	69	74	77	80	78	74	13
Moçambique	49	82	82	81	80	76	73	72	72	75	78	82	83	78	11

rains arrive and for several months it may rain for short periods almost every day, turning the red dust into red mud. The rains fall in thundery showers, the rate sometimes reaching 6 inches an hour, so that much water fails to soak into the ground and the usefulness of the rainfall for plant growth is much reduced. Rainfall of this intensity is also highly conducive

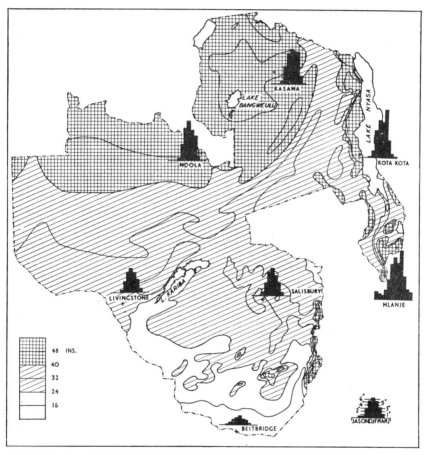

Figure 69 *Mean annual rainfall in Zambia, Rhodesia and Malawi, together with its seasonal distribution at selected stations*

to soil erosion. Further, the rainy season begins generally in the warmest period of the year when evaporation losses are greatest. In between the downpours, the clouds clear, and days with less than three hours' sunshine are infrequent.

The rains continue until March or April, and occasionally unreliable showers until May. The winter season (May to August), the most pleasant time of the year, is generally dry, with mild sunny days and frost on the higher parts at night. From the middle of August temperatures rise rapidly until the first thunderstorms of the rainy season break. This concentration of rainfall into the summer season is repeated at most stations in this part of Africa. Beira, with 56 inches a year, and Lourenço Marques, with 32 inches, both have more than 85 per cent of their rainfall in six months. The proportion at Livingstone on the Zambezi is 95 per cent, which indicates the reason for the great variation in flow of the river throughout the year. The average discharge of the Zambezi at Livingstone ranges from 500,000 acre-feet in November to more than 5 million acre-feet in April.

SOILS AND VEGETATION

No comprehensive survey of the soils of the whole area is yet available. In Rhodesia work so far has indicated a fairly close relationship between soil type and parent rock. In Zambia a more genetic classification forms the basis of a recently published map. From the viewpoint of agriculture other factors, such as accessibility and climate, often take precedence over soil type.

Granite, the most common rock, produces rather poor sandy soils, but these nevertheless have been widely cultivated in Rhodesia in areas where transport facilities are reasonable. Some of the schists, gneisses and intrusions provide richer loams. The Karroo beds develop a variety of soils, of which those formed on limestone appear most valuable. In areas of relatively high rainfall and peneplained surface, strong lateritic tendencies are noticeable in soil formation, with reddish colouring in the upper horizon and iron-rich concretions. Generally speaking, the less highly laterised and more potentially fertile soils are found on the plateau margins where dissection is in progress and drainage better.

Various forms of savanna characterise much of the area. All types are to be found, from closely forested areas mainly in the valleys and on hill slopes, to open grassland with scattered trees on the level planation surfaces. According to the length of dry season and the amount of moisture available, trees may be evergreen or deciduous. One of the most widespread savanna forms is characterised by the tree species *Brachystegia*. It thrives on the plateau areas of 3,000–5,000 feet, but is less common on

Table 19

Precipitation (inches)

Station	Alt. (feet)	J	F	M	A	M	J	J	A	S	O	N	D	Total
Kasama	4,544	10·7	9·9	10·9	2·8	0·6	0·1	0·1	0·1	0·1	0·8	6·4	9·5	51·5
Livingstone	3,161	5·7	6·0	4·3	1·0	0·3	0·1	0	0·1	0·1	0·9	2·9	5·2	26·5
Bulawayo	4,405	5·6	4·3	3·3	0·7	0·4	0·1	0·1	0·1	0·2	0·8	3·2	4·8	23·4
Nkata Bay	1,600	8·1	12·4	13·2	11·6	3·3	2·4	2·2	1·1	0·3	0·4	0·9	8·6	64·5
Moçambique	49	8·9	8·7	5·6	3·2	1·2	1·2	0·6	0·5	0·4	0·4	1·2	5·5	37·4

the lowlands. In the drier warmer valleys of the interior the *Mopani* tree is dominant. Acacias and the baobab tree also favour drier areas. The savanna is useful for extensive grazing; in the early summer, when the grasses have withered before the rains, tree foliage can sometimes supply feed for animals, and the trees themselves provide useful shade. On the higher lands of eastern Rhodesia (Melsetter–Inyanga) and of Malawi, savanna is replaced by mountain forest on the wetter parts (generally around 5,000 or 6,000 feet), including the magnificent cedar forests of Mlanje Mountain. Elsewhere in these highlands areas of grassland occur.

Along the coast of Moçambique there extends a belt of tropical forest a few miles in width, where the short dry season and rainfall of up to 50 inches encourages the growth of dense bush and evergreen forest, with palm trees, and occasional patches of mangrove swamp, as in the Zambezi delta.

35

Rhodesia

Lying between the Zambezi and the Limpopo, this is one of Africa's smaller countries with an area (150,333 sq. miles) less than half that of Tanganyika. Yet it has one of the largest white populations (225,000 in 1965) of any country between northern Africa and South Africa, and about half the land is alienated to white settlers. The remainder is the home of over 4 million Africans whose chief tribes are the Matabele and the Mashona. Two generations ago, when the white man first came to Rhodesia, the Africans probably numbered fewer than half a million; their society was then entirely tribal, existing by subsistence farming and cattle herding. The Mashona of the moister northern areas were primarily cultivators, while the Matabele, arriving somewhat later from the Transvaal and occupying the southern and western areas, were a more warlike people, primarily cattle folk, who obtained grain and other crops from the weaker Mashona by raiding. With the advent of white settlers, and the pacification and subdivision of the country into white and African areas, the Matabele cattle herders turned increasingly to cultivation. In the African areas the traditional economy and way of life have remained to some extent undisturbed, but elsewhere, the more advanced economy of the white settlers has been superimposed. There is thus a dual society and economy in Rhodesia, as in many other formerly colonial areas in Africa.

FARMING

African farming and way of life

The African, living in his village within a tribal framework, cultivates his crops mainly (sometimes exclusively) for consumption within the family or village. With the simple techniques employed, the lack of crop rotation and the lack of fertilisers, the soils seldom permit more than three or four successive harvests from the same piece of land. Shifting and bush fallowing provided the traditional answer to this problem; only a few areas of richer alluvium in valley bottoms allowed more continuous cropping. Such methods of cultivation have proved extremely wasteful of land; Prescott[1] calculates that a man with one wife would need over 30 acres of arable land, and points out that as most men have two or three wives their arable needs are greater. It is in fact the women who are the main cultivators, for a large proportion of the younger adult male population is absent in the towns for long periods, working in European factories or mines, or employed on European farms.

As well as cultivation of maize and other food crops, cattle are herded. There are 3·5 million head of cattle in Rhodesia, of which by far the larger number belongs to Africans; characteristically the animals are of poor quality. To the African, wealth has for long been assessed in the numbers of cattle owned. Since villages are located near water, the cattle drink in the morning and are then driven out on to the common veld grazing. They are seldom driven far, and accordingly graze the same areas until these are bare. The denuded areas gradually extend until vast tracts of land are impoverished and become liable to erosion. Thus, together with the practice of shifting cultivation, deterioration of the land has been encouraged over wide areas.

In 1926 the Department of Native Agriculture was established, and the government began attempts to limit shifting cultivation, to improve methods of farming, and introduced soil- and water-conservation projects. But already another problem was looming—the high rate of native population growth. Prior to European occupation the landscape was characterised by a low density of villages or kraals, separated by wide stretches of open savanna which provided both grazing and firewood. But since then European settlers have taken over large tracts of the better land, especially along the higher and flatter parts of the uplands. In the Native Reserves (Fig. 70) the African population has risen steadily. Today most of the land in the Reserves is either in use, resting from cultivation, or too badly damaged by erosion. Thus serious problems of congestion have arisen in the native areas, due principally to the wasteful methods of farming employed. In an effort to grapple with this state of affairs the Native Land Husbandry Act of 1951 was passed to control land use and allocation, and thereby promote more efficient use of the land, particularly by limiting grazing per unit area and by arresting shifting cultivation. Since 1951 African farming has in many areas been completely revolutionised, though by 1960 the pace of change had become much slower as a result of increasing lack of co-operation between the Africans and the government.

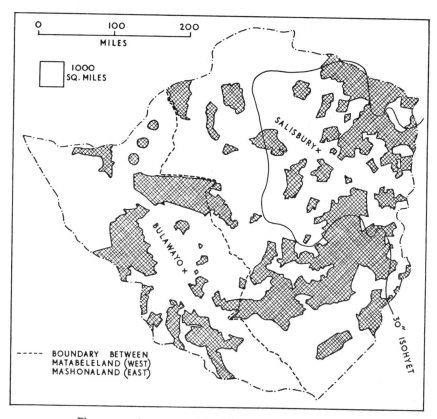

Figure 70 *Areas reserved for Africans in Rhodesia, 1964*

A typical example of change is Yafele's kraal, about 25 miles east of Salisbury, described by J. H. Beck.[2] Here the cultivated land is divided into permanent strips allocated to each family and recorded on maps at the Native Commissioner's Office. Each family has about 6 acres of strips, which are 20-yard-wide contour terraces designed to check run-off and soil erosion. Before the rainy season begins around October the strip fields are ploughed; in November they are sown with maize, the staple food crop, and leguminous crops such as groundnuts. Low yields are typical—half a bag of maize per acre, a small fraction of the yield obtained by European farmers. One reason for this is that though officially crops should follow a rotation, in practice it is impossible to enforce this because of the complexity and fragmentation of the strip pattern. Furthermore, 'many African farmers are still at the educational level where, if maize does well one year on a particular spot, they plant maize in the same ground the next year in the belief that a similar crop will result'.

But, very slowly, African farming is undoubtedly improving in many areas under guidance from local administrators. Under the Native Land Husbandry Act land rights must be registered, land consolidation has begun and agrarian education is provided. Numbers of cattle are being controlled, and even reduced, while overall crop production is definitely rising. The value of maize, beans and groundnuts sold by Africans as surplus to their subsistence requirements has risen from £1·5 million in 1948 to £5 million ten years later, and about one-third of all the maize grown for sale in Rhodesia is now produced by black African farmers.

European farming

The congested native areas stand in direct contrast to the spacious lands of the European farmers, who cultivate some 800,000 acres of the best land in the country. On the uplands above 4,000 feet there is plenty of relatively flat and undissected land, a pleasant climate with 25 to 35 inches of fairly reliable rainfall, and a shorter dry season than in many other parts of the Zambezi lands. But the Rhodesian uplands have not only their physical attractions for the European farmer but also economic advantages, for along the watershed zone runs the main railway, completed about the turn of the century, and linking the region now with the port of Beira, with the mining regions of Zambia, and with the Republic of South Africa. Costs of transport are vital in the development of commercial agriculture, and, as in many other parts of Africa, distance from railhead or main road plays its part in helping to determine the type and pattern of land use.

Tobacco is the most valuable cash crop. After its introduction to Africa by the Portuguese or Arabs it was cultivated by natives in small patches around their villages. Tobacco planting by European farmers on a commercial scale dates from about 1910, since when Rhodesia has risen to become one of the world's leading Virginia-type tobacco exporters, prior to the imposition of British economic sanctions in 1966. In 1945 tobacco surpassed gold as Southern Rhodesia's principal export, and subsequently became the mainstay of the country's economy (51 per cent of the total value of agricultural production in 1960). There were 41,000 acres under tobacco in 1935, compared with 219,000 acres in 1962-3.

The most important tobacco areas lie between 4,000 and 5,000 feet, with 32 to 36 inches of rainfall, though the actual limits are 3,000 to 5,000 feet with not less than 28 inches. Within such areas the detailed distribution of tobacco farming is governed by the pattern of European-owned land, and access to a railway. Expansion has been particularly rapid since World War II. Some marginal districts have increased their acreage fivefold, whilst the greatest absolute increase has been in the Salisbury–Marendellas–Makoni districts. Of the total number of European farms in Rhodesia about half count tobacco as their principal crop. On an average tobacco farm tobacco occupies less than 5 per cent of the total farm acreage, yet furnishes three-quarters of the farm income. Fertilisers and crop rotation are essential to maintain good yields and high quality. The rotation nearly always includes maize, which is itself an important crop, grown for animal feed or for sale. Tracts of woodland are kept to supply timber for the tobacco smoke-curing process.

The main tobacco area in Rhodesia extends from Umtali and Marendellas (Fig. 71), past Salisbury and Hartley, to Darwin in the north and the Lomagundi–Urungwe districts in the north-west. Minor production comes from the Melsetter, Victoria and Gwelo districts. One of the main problems retarding expansion is labour supply. Labour is needed both in the field and in the curing process, and about two-thirds of the labour is supplied from outside Rhodesia—indeed, many farms depend wholly on non-Rhodesian migrant labour. About half of this migrant labour comes from Moçambique, one-third from Malawi and the remainder from Zambia. The supply is inadequate, and efficiency low. In fact, it is labour supply which, at the present time of high tobacco prices, is controlling the future development of tobacco growing, and not physical conditions, for there are probably 2 million acres of European-owned land potentially suitable (Plate 14A).

Maize, often grown in rotation with tobacco, occupies much greater areas of land—about 400,000 acres overall. It is produced under a variety

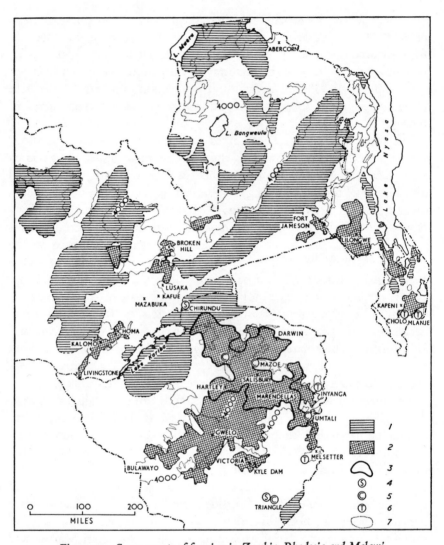

Figure 71 *Some aspects of farming in Zambia, Rhodesia and Malawi*
1. Areas infested with tsetse fly. 2. Areas of tobacco farming. 3. Main tobacco-farming region of Rhodesia. 4. Sugar-cane plantations (irrigated). 5. Citrus orchards (irrigated). 6. Tea-producing areas. 7. Contour at 4,000 feet

of conditions, but generally needs at least 25 inches of rain, and does best on the heavier red clays and loams. Yields are generally low compared with the United States or Argentina, since it is given little attention as a crop and rarely supplied with fertiliser. The most important European maize-growing areas are in the Salisbury region. Production (nearly 4½ million bags in 1962–3) is rising, but high transport costs limit the sale of the gradually increasing surplus to countries such as Malawi which so badly need it.

Other crops produced in Rhodesia are of comparatively minor importance as yet. *Sugar-cane* is grown on irrigated planations such as the Tate and Lyle estates at Chirundu in the Zambezi valley, and the Triangle and Hippo Valley estates in the Lundi valley. Those in the Lundi valley are irrigated from the new Kyle and Bangala Dams on the Mtilikwe river near Fort Victoria. At present Rhodesia imports large quantities of sugar, so that expansion of these sugar-growing areas is planned. With further reservoirs, at least 100,000 acres could be made available. *Citrus fruit* orchards, limited in scope as yet, are also to be considerably extended in the Lundi valley. The Limpopo valley railway to Lourenço Marques (1955) and its branch to Hippo Valley (1964) are providing a new outlet for this part of Rhodesia. Other fruit-growing areas include the British South Africa Company's citrus estates irrigated from the Mazoe Dam, and some deciduous fruit orchards in the Melsetter-Inyanga highlands. Finally, among the cash crops *tea* should be mentioned. It is, of course, restricted to the eastern areas of high rainfall. Although of far greater importance in Malawi, production in Rhodesia is expanding, especially with the development of the new estates at Inyanga.

STOCK REARING by European farmers in Rhodesia involves much greater areas than crop growing. Many European farmers have been turning to livestock to reduce an overdependence on maize-tobacco farming. Unlike Zambia, most parts of the Rhodesian uplands are free of tsetse fly, while rinderpest, a great scourge since the earliest days of white settlement, has been brought under a measure of control. Large beef-cattle ranches are now a feature of the landscape; with exports of beef and skins in 1963 valued at £5 million, Rhodesia is today the main meat producer of tropical Africa. Dairy farming is not far behind in importance, being well established wherever there are railways to link with the urban centres and the major creameries at Bulawayo, Gwelo and Salisbury.

IRRIGATION has enabled new areas for agriculture to be opened where drought, erratic rainfall or flooding have so far precluded agriculture. Mention has already been made of the irrigated sugar-cane and citrus-fruit estates. In the Sabi valley an irrigation scheme for African farmers was begun as long ago as 1932. A survey in 1947 of this valley indicated that over 250,000 acres were potentially available, and the irrigated land has since been extended. The soils have proved very productive, and African farmers obtain good yields of maize, wheat, legumes and cotton grown in rotation on 2- to 4-acre plots. Further reservoirs are being built in the upper reaches of the Sabi. The Kariba scheme on the Zambezi will be considered in the next chapter; here it may be noted that it is hoped to irrigate about 200,000 acres below the dam. About two-thirds of this area will be in Moçambique. In all these irrigation projects the primary need is a storage reservoir which is able not only to supply water through-out the dry season in excess of evaporation losses but also able to contain the floods in summer. On the Zambezi, for instance, the maximum flow at the Kafue confluence, before the Kariba Dam was constructed, was about forty times the minimum.

MINING

Rhodesia is fortunate in possessing the second-largest worked coalfield in Africa at Wankie, first reached by the Bulawayo railway in 1904. The coal occurs in thick seams in the lower Karroo beds over considerable areas of territory (Fig. 67), and reserves are immense. The Wankie coal-field, with that of Natal, is the only sizeable deposit in the whole of Africa of good-quality coking coal. Output at present is about 3 million tons a year, and is in fact diminishing. Until 1960 Wankie coal was the main source of power for mining and industry in the Zambezi lands, and only limitations of railway capacity prevented expansion of coal output. Now electricity from Kariba is available, and coal is consequently in less demand.

Apart from coal, more than thirty base minerals, both metallic and non-metallic, are exploited in Rhodesia. The Africans mined gold, and to a lesser extent silver, copper and iron, for centuries before the arrival of the white man. These early metal workers may well have been the people who built the Zimbabwe Ruins.

European gold mining dates from 1890. The main gold-bearing rocks are Pre-Cambrian and lie on either side of the Great Dyke, worked by many small and scattered mines. Recently interest has revived, and the larger mining companies are now taking a more active part in development. Que Que is the main centre. The Great Dyke contains valuable deposits of asbestos and chrome. Indeed, Rhodesia's production of asbestos is second only to that of Canada, and of very high quality. The chief producing area is around Shabani, on the through-railway to Lourenço Marques. There are extensive deposits of high-quality iron ore, ample for the needs of the expanding iron and steel industry.

Table 20   Value of mineral production (£ million) from Rhodesia

Mineral	1939	1952	1963
Asbestos	1·09	6·65	6·00
Gold	6·23	6·52	7·10
Chromite	0·19	4·28	1·98
Coal	0·43	1·82	3·08
Others	0·20	0·88	5·57
Total	8·14	20·15	23·73

MANUFACTURING INDUSTRY

One of the most spectacular features in the economic development of Rhodesia since World War II has been the growth of manufacturing industry. Gross industrial output in 1965 was nearly 10 per cent of that of the Republic of South Africa, whereas in the early post-war years the figure was under 5 per cent. Several factors have contributed to this expansion. The mining industry has provided much of the capital. The very considerable white immigration since World War II has been extremely important: Rhodesia has experienced the most rapid increase in white population in the history of the whole British Commonwealth, and many of the immigrants have been industrialists. The Act of Federation, in 1953, by bringing together varied resources of minerals, agricultural produce and labour, also helped to encourage industrial investment. Much more recently, the completion of the Kariba Dam has provided a new major source of electrical power for secondary industry.*

* A discussion of the Kariba scheme and its implications will be found in the section on Zambia.

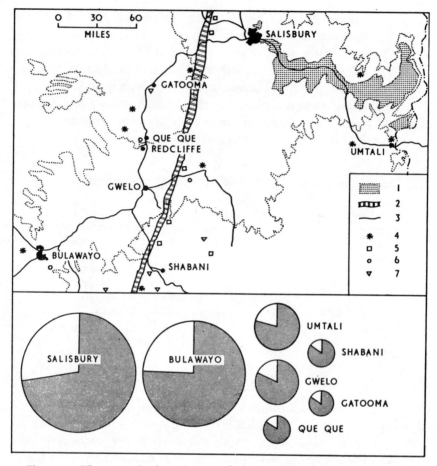

Figure 72 *The principal industrial centres of Rhodesia.* The relative population of the towns is shown by circles; the shaded segments of these circles represent the proportion of non-Europeans

1. Land over 5,000 feet (the 4,000-foot contour is also shown as a dotted line). 2. The Great Dyke. 3. Railways. 4. Mines producing copper ore. 5. Mines producing chrome ore. 6. Mines producing iron ore. 7. Mines producing asbestos

Gold mines are too small and too numerous to be represented on this scale

There is growing awareness of the potential markets for basic consumer goods in tropical Africa, and of the need to found the economy on a more substantial basis than that provided by tobacco and minerals. Already the several major towns along the railway in Rhodesia from Bulawayo to Salisbury are forming the nuclei of an industrial region, second only in importance in southern Africa to that of the southern Transvaal. Although a quarter of the industrial output comes from food-processing industries, the iron and steel industry must receive first mention. At Redcliffe, eight miles from Que Que (Fig. 72), is the large modern steel works opened by the Rhodesian Iron and Steel Commission (RISCO) in 1948. Producing 91,000 tons of steel and 216,000 tons of pig-iron in 1961, these works draw on local iron ore and limestone, and purchase their coal and coke requirements from Wankie; new coke ovens on the site have recently been opened. Chrome ore is available from the Great Dyke nearby. The Que Que area is now the focal point for heavy industry in Rhodesia. At present steel production is only one-fifth of requirement, and expansion of the steel industry is high on the list of priorities. Another iron and steel works developed by RISCO is sited on Bulawayo. South of Que Que on the railway lies *Gwelo* (pop. 35,000), which has the advantage of being close to the new link with Lourenço Marques. Sited at Gwelo are the works of Rhodesian Alloys, producing ferro-chrome for stainless steel. Here, too, there are plans for enlargement since the factory was completed in 1951. The opening of the factory has relieved the chrome-ore mines which had hitherto been stock-piling due to congestion on the Beira railway. Also at Gwelo are asbestos works, and an important footwear industry. *Gatooma*, north of Que Que, was originally concerned like it mainly with gold mining, but has now become the centre of the Rhodesian cotton-textile industry. The first experimental cotton mill was opened here during World War II. Cotton spinning and weaving is now one of the basic industries of Rhodesia; about half the raw-cotton requirements are imported. Other works at Gatooma are concerned with engineering, and cement and brick manufacture.

At either end of the Rhodesian 'Midlands' stand the major cities of *Bulawayo* (pop. 196,000) and *Salisbury* (pop. 300,000). Bulawayo is Rhodesia's largest industrial town, with over 500 separate industrial establishments. Its proximity to the Wankie coal field has been an advantage, and it is also a main railway junction. The range of industries is considerable—machinery, textiles, clothing, furniture and soap are produced; there are grain and flour mills, sugar refineries, and other factories processing food. Salisbury has a similar range of industries, together with printing works, and tobacco factories and markets. It also possesses a large new fertiliser factory, relying on North African phosphates at present, but soon to use apatite from mines in the Sabi valley.

Rather separate from the main line of industrial towns from Bulawayo to Salisbury is *Umtali* (pop. 36,000). Its particular advantages for industry are proximity to Beira, and a plentiful water supply. It has developed as a centre for industries processing agricultural products, but more recently a paper mill has been located here, based on local afforestation schemes in the eastern highlands—about 200,000 acres of conifers have now been planted. At Umtali there is also a new British Motor Corporation vehicle assembly works, while engineering and metal-working industries, clothing and textile factories, have grown up. Nearby, at Feruka, an oil refinery with a capacity of 750,000 tons a year has been built at the end of a pipeline from Beira.

The political situation is the most important factor holding up further industrial development. Since 1965, trade with countries other than South Africa has been severely curtailed by economic sanctions imposed first by Britain and later by the United Nations. Many Rhodesian industries have in consequence had to curtail their production severely, either because of inability to sell in their usual markets, or because of lack of imported raw materials. The Umtali motor assembly plant, for instance, came to a complete standstill in 1967, and the pumping of oil through the Beira pipeline was suspended in late 1965.

Once the political conflict over Rhodesian independence is resolved and economic sanctions are removed, the main problems in the further expansion of secondary industry in Rhodesia will be threefold. First, the market represented by the African population is very limited in purchasing power, while that of the white population is small in size. Opportunities for the export of industrial goods appear limited, for there would be direct competition with the more highly developed South African industry, and several neighbouring territories in any case have their own plans for future industrial development. Secondly, labour needs to be more efficient and productive. There is tremendous waste in the use of migrant labour at present, with high turnover rates, while the colour bar has led to inefficiency and lack of co-operation from the Africans. The third problem is that of attracting capital. A high rate of investment in the post-war years and, under Federation, the high revenues from Northern Rhodesian copper mining have been the basis of existing industrial development. The extent of future investment in Rhodesia is impossible to assess.

36

Zambia

After many decades as a British Protectorate, Northern Rhodesia received its independence in 1964 and was renamed Zambia by the new African government. In contrast to Rhodesia south of the Zambezi the numbers of European settlers are relatively few, and more than half of them are concerned with mining in the Copperbelt. The African population is slightly smaller than that of Rhodesia, and since Zambia is a much larger country (290,300 sq. miles, approximately three times the size of Great Britain), one of the most striking features is its emptiness. Outside the Copperbelt the average population density is only seven persons per sq. mile. Yet Africans have lived in Zambia for centuries. Traces of ancient civilisation dating back 1,000 years before the advent of white settlers have recently been found in the Gwembe valley, 70 miles south of Lusaka; evidence of gold and copper working, cotton spinning and weaving has come to light from old burial grounds here.

Zambia gives an impression of endlessly undulating plateau country, lying mostly between 3,000 and 5,000 feet. Driving north from Livingstone (the capital before 1935) along the main highway to the Copperbelt, the road passes first through about 60 miles of dry sandy grassland, where trees are few and stunted. For the next 250 miles the road becomes more hemmed in by trees, though after Kalomo, European tobacco farms and fairly extensive cattle ranches make their appearance. Termite mounds 10 or 20 feet high are a regular feature of the landscape. In the midst of this European farming country lies *Lusaka*, the present capital. It stands on an open plateau at 4,000 feet; its history dates back to 1905 when a railway siding was built here. Its isolation and its multi-racial population (108,000 Africans, 12,000 Europeans and 2,000 Asians) are features in common with many other large settlements in tropical Africa. Its houses are mostly single-storeyed, and occupy large plots, giving the town a spacious appearance. A feature of the residential areas is the strict racial segregation, the European areas being on slightly higher parts of the plateau.

North of Lusaka the bush becomes progressively denser; hill tops support *Brachystegia* and *Jubernardia* with sparse grass while depressions contain tall grass and denser woodland. The tendency for tree cover to become denser over the plateau as one moves from south to north partly reflects increasing rainfall. The low-lying floors of the middle Zambezi and Luangwa down-faulted troughs are relatively dry and very hot; many parts have less than 25 inches of rain, the effectiveness of which is much reduced by its arrival during the hot season. On the northern and higher parts of the plateau up to 50 inches is experienced.

FARMING

European farming

European farming in Zambia is very restricted in extent compared with Rhodesia. Many factors contribute to this. The presence of tsetse fly over approximately half the country, but more particularly in the Zambezi, Luangwa and upper Kafue valleys, severely restricts pastoral farming to which large areas might otherwise be suited. Rainfall on the plateau is not deficient in total amount except possibly in the south-west, but is more erratic in its incidence than in Rhodesia, and strongly seasonal. Lateritic soils are extensive and possess the usual disadvantages for permanent cultivation. Land alienated to white settlers has been far less extensive than in Rhodesia, consisting principally of areas along the railway and in the Copperbelt and amounting to only 6 per cent of the total area. But for the European farmer the most important consideration is accessibility. European farms are largely located near the railway, particularly from about 35 miles north of Lusaka south-west towards Kalomo. Lusaka is the commercial hub of this farming area, which concentrates on the combination of maize and tobacco noted in Rhodesia, and on dairy farming and stock rearing. Another important European farming area exists at Mkushi, 190 miles north of Lusaka. Mazabuka and Choma are smaller centres.

In the extreme east of the country around Fort Jameson, and in the north-east around Abercorn, are much smaller areas of European farming, remote from railway and any large towns, which have declined considerably since their initial settlement. Fort Jameson was once important for tobacco. Before commercial farming can be further extended in Zambia, improvement of the transport system and especially the roads will be essential. At present the proportion of land cultivated by European farmers stands at less than 0·1 per cent of the total area. Maize is the most extensive crop planted, occupying about two-thirds of the cultivated ground, and yielding about 400,000 tons a year; but tobacco is much more important, being the primary cash crop of the territory in spite of the fact that it occupies only 16,000 acres (compared with over 200,000 acres in Rhodesia).

Again in contrast to Rhodesia there are no important irrigation works in Zambia, apart from the 7,000-acre sugar scheme of Tate and Lyle near Mazabuka. The old lake flats of the Kafue valley above Kafue town have often been considered for agricultural development; the principal necessity here is to control the river and prevent annual flooding. An experimental drainage and irrigation scheme, fostered by Rhodesian Selection Trust, has now closed down. Mixed farming was tried out, based on winter wheat or barley, summer rice and fodder crops in rotation, but both wheat and planted pasture were largely failures. The station was recently taken over by the Zambian government, and some sugar-cane is being grown successfully, with yields approaching 130 tons per acre.

African farming

Although in recent years African farming has in many areas been improving greatly, with better farming practices, increased use of fertilizers, and cultivation of cash crops, the general picture is still one in which subsistence cultivation dominates, and contrasts sharply with the activities of the European settlers. The more remote areas, particularly the northern plateau away from the railway, remain the stronghold of primitive shifting cultivation. In these areas methods of agriculture have changed little for centuries, and only the very beginnings of a cash-crop economy can be seen. Audrey Richards describes the typical practice of the Bemba, a large Bantu tribe who live in an area of about 37,000 sq. miles around Kasama.

The population is very dispersed. The average density is 3·9 per

square mile, and it falls as low as 1·7 in some areas. The villages are
scattered in clearings in the bush within reach of streams and are often
as much as 15 to 20 miles apart. The Bemba plateau is about 4,000 feet
high, covered with savanna forest of the Brachystegia type. The rains
occasionally fail, or are badly distributed from an agricultural point of
view, but usually they are heavy, giving an average annual rainfall of
51 inches. The soil of the plateau is generally poor.

The Bemba are shifting cultivators, but they practise a particular
form known locally as the 'chitimene' system. This is the burning of
circular piles of branches to form an ash-bed, and on this the seed is
sown. The main tree-cutting season [is] May and June. The branches
[are] fired in September or November. When the rains have started to
fall, a catch crop such as kaffir-corn or maize may be sown sparsely
over the seed bed. The main millet crop is not sown until December,
when the ground has been softened by rain. The seed is sown broad-
cast, without preliminary hoeing, and it is then covered with earth
thinly. The maize heads ripen in February and March, and are eaten
green. The main millet crop [ripens] in May. [After reaping] the millet
garden does not immediately revert to bush. It is used again for three,
four or even more years, according to the goodness of the soil and the
labour available for a sequence of crops. Thus the Bemba are shifting
cultivators, but they only shift to a limited extent. Then the gardens
are allowed to revert to bush and a new village is built somewhere in
the neighbourhood.[3]

Clearly the system is only suited to an area of low population density,
and government policy has been opposed to it. Before independence the
British authorities were disturbed by the destruction of the bush. Each
family requires up to 300 acres for its subsistence. The administration
found it difficult to visualise extension of social services, and particularly
of schools, while the villages are moving every four or five years. After
World War II the government did introduce peasant farmer schemes in
the Bemba country, but they proved costly and disappointing. Some of
the more enterprising Bemba have, however, been turning to commercial agriculture independently, in spite of their lack of capital resources.

There is a good example of a government-aided African farming
scheme at Chombwa near Mumbwa in Central Province. In this scheme,
mechanisation and European management are provided at cost and each

farmer is allotted 20 acres of land. In 1966, each farmer cropped 6 acres of cotton and 2 acres of maize. Yields of maize averaged 3 tons per acre, and of cotton 2,300 lb. per acre. The most successful African farmers in such schemes are usually those who have gained experience in nearby European farming districts.

In the upper Zambezi area of the west lies Barotseland, a kingdom of 300,000 inhabitants, and formerly a 'protectorate within a protectorate', its special status deriving from early treaties with Queen Victoria. Here among the periodically inundated grasslands is the home of great cattle-owning tribes such as the Lozi, for the area is free of tsetse. A type of transhumance is practised, the people with their cattle moving to higher ground when the rivers flood in February or March, and returning once the floods have subsided to cultivate their maize and pasture their cattle. Barotseland has two 'capitals', Lealui on the plains and Limulunga on the higher land, to which the King's court moves ceremoniously by royal barges and canoes when the rains come.

Another area of regularly flooded ground in Zambia occurs in the north-east. Lake Bangweulu was discovered by Livingstone in 1868, five years before his death there. The lake is shallow, fed by the Chambeshi, which forms a great swampy delta, the home of some 10,000 Africans. The water-level fluctuates seasonally; in the rainy season the people move to villages on higher mounds and cultivate cassava, while in the dry months the men live in fishing camps on the lake shore. But there are also longer-term cycles of changing water-level associated, as Debenham discovered,[4] with temporary blockage of some channels with vegetation. In high-water cycles villages were flooded and crops ruined, whereas in low-water years the black swamp soils proved fertile. With recent dredging and channel cutting, these fluctuations have been largely eliminated. The people trade the fish with surrounding Bemba tribes for maize, but they also sell quantities of dried fish to the Copperbelt where there is a large market for it.

There is thus a great diversity in farming in Zambia. Not only are there sharp contrasts between European farming and African subsistence agriculture, but—because of the variety of climate, soil and the distribution of tsetse fly—also great differences in the forms of agriculture on which the vast majority of the Africans depend for their livelihood.

In an area of less than 1,600 sq. miles on the Congo–Zambezi watershed lies the Copperbelt (Fig. 73), one of Africa's most valuable and highly mineralised zones, second only in importance to the Rand of South Africa. The production of copper is the key industry of Zambia, for copper is by far the most valuable export, second only in Africa to the export value of South Africa's gold. Under Federation, copper provided nearly 60 per cent of Federal export revenue. Though production of copper has fluctuated widely over the last few years, in 1960 Zambia (then Northern Rhodesia) was the world's second most important copper producer (standing next to the USA) and is thought to possess reserves of copper ore equal to those of the USA. Over the last five years its share of world copper production has varied between 11 and 16 per cent. The copper produced is, moreover, the cheapest in the world.

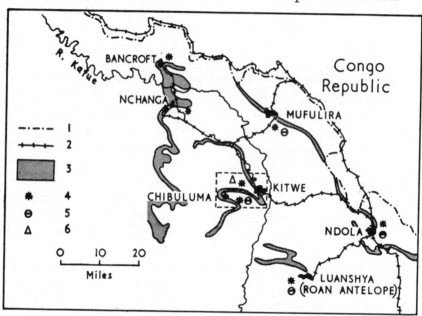

Figure 73 *The Copperbelt of Zambia*

1. Frontier with the Congo Republic. 2. Main railways. 3. Outcrops of the Lower Burana Mkubwa Series (Pre-Cambrian), in the shales and sandstones of which the copper-ore bodies are found. 4. Copper-producing areas. 5. Cobalt-producing areas. 6. Uranium-producing area

The rectangle enclosed by broken lines around Kitwe represents the area of Figure 74

The development of the Copperbelt has raised certain unique problems. The region is situated in the heart of the sub-continent of southern Africa, nearly 700 miles in a direct line from the nearest coast. Salisbury, the nearest major town, is 350 miles away (1,076 miles by rail). Before the 1930's the area of the Copperbelt, with its present six producing mines, busy towns, highways and airfields, schools and theatres, shops and factories, was one of isolation. It was thinly populated and agriculturally unproductive, due to a combination of poor soils, tsetse fly and primitive agricultural techniques. Roads were little more than tracks through the bush, rivers were crossed by rough ferries, malaria was an ever-present danger. It is estimated that there were less than 20,000 Africans in the region in 1931, compared with 300,000 in 1961.

British prospectors, attracted by reports of ancient African copper workings, first discovered the copper ores in the upper Pre-Cambrian rocks about the turn of the century, and the region was tapped by rail, from the south, in 1909. Because of the low grade of the surface ores, mainly copper oxide, the area aroused little interest; but in 1925 copper-sulphide ores were located at depths of about 100 feet below the surface. Invention of the flotation process in 1910 solved the problem of refining low-grade (3·5 per cent) sulphide ores economically, and working of these began in 1928. In 1931 the area produced 3,000 tons of blister copper (up to 99 per cent pure), production rising rapidly to over 100,000 tons in 1933. Since the mid-1930's electrolytic copper (99·95 per cent pure) has been produced in increasing quantities. By 1938 output had reached 220,000 tons; by 1958, 376,000 tons. In 1958 a new electrolytic refinery was opened at Ndola; production for 1964 reached the record level of 632,000 tons, of which three-quarters is electrolytically refined. Since World War II also there has been a phenomenal rise in the price of copper, with the exception of a temporary fall about 1958.

Table 21   *Production of copper 1945–64*

Year	Tonnage	Value, £ million
1945	194,000	11
1948	214,000	26
1954	379,000	91
1956	383,000	121
1958	376,000	70
1961	559,000	114
1964	632,000	149

Clearly it is unsound for the economy of Zambia to rely to the extent
that it does on the production of a metal whose value is liable to fluctuate
in this manner; hence the importance of the development of agriculture
and manufacturing industry in the territory, especially now that Federation with Rhodesia has ended.

The chief mines are located at Nchanga, Nkana, Mufulira and Roan
Antelope; newer ones are Chibuluma, Bancroft and Chambishi. The

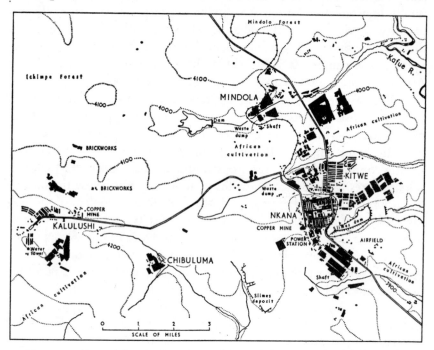

Figure 74 *Part of the Zambian Copperbelt around Kitwe and Chibuluma* (for
location of this map, see Figure 73). The contour interval is 100 feet. Only the
main roads are shown, but all buildings are indicated. Note the emptiness of
the land surrounding the Copperbelt towns, and, by comparison with Figure
73, the distances separating the mining centres. The total population of the
several towns on this map is about 110,000

first four form the nuclei of four main settlements. Ndola has been the
government administrative centre of the region since 1904, and its history
as a settlement goes back much further; still to be seen in the town is the
wild fig tree under which Arab and African slave-traders bartered human
lives. The other principal town of the Copperbelt, Kitwe, is of more modern foundation (1928) and is today slightly larger than its rival Ndola.

Table 22   *Population of major centres in the Copperbelt*

Town	(Non-African (Census 1961)	African (estimated)	Total, 1961 (to nearest 100)	Total 1939
Nkana–Kitwe	12,540	77,200	89,700	21,000
Ndola	11,570	73,100	84,700	18,000
Luanshya	5,910	51,100	57,000	24,000
Mufulira	6,840	61,200	68,000	18,000
Nchanga–Chingola	5,700	38,000	43,700	6,000
Bancroft	2,330	18,100	20,400	nil

These and other smaller towns of the Copperbelt contain well over half the European population of Zambia and one-eighth of the African population. Here, then, is a concentration of population which, apart from that of the southern Transvaal, has no equal anywhere else in southern Africa. The towns of the Copperbelt are linked to the railhead at Ndola by branch railways, while there is also a good network of tarmac roads. Ndola is the principal airport. The mining companies have made full use of copper profits to provide housing, medical and recreational facilities for both Europeans and Africans. Newly built mining communities are represented by neat rows of white houses shimmering in the heat haze.

Because of the situation of the Copperbelt, 1,200 miles by rail from the nearest port, it is necessary to refine the copper-ore in the mining area. In the past most of the electricity for this was supplied from thermal power stations at each end of the Copperbelt, receiving coal from Wankie in Rhodesia, 560 miles away. Wood has at times been used as fuel when coal deliveries were inadequate—owing to congestion on the railway from Wankie. The Copperbelt also purchased hydro-electricity from the Congo (up to one-third of its total electricity requirements). The completion of the Kariba Dam and transmission lines to the Copperbelt means that the problem of a dependable electricity supply has now been overcome. Today Kariba contributes the greater part, and coal from Wankie less than one-quarter, of the electricity needed.

Undoubtedly the principal problem which the Copperbelt has to face is that of transport. Even after refining, vast quantities of copper have to be sent by rail, and rail charges to the ports add one-third to the price of the copper. There is a choice of outlets—1,200 miles to Lobito on the west coast, 1,450 miles to Beira on the east—together with other possible routes little used for copper traffic at present, such as that to Lourenço

Marques (1,450 miles). The Beira route handled most of the copper traffic up to 1966. It is unfortunately a route which carries a great deal of other traffic, handling coal from Wankie (which made up nearly a third of the total tonnage of Rhodesian Railways in 1957), serving the industries of the Rhodesian Midlands (Bulawayo-Salisbury), and carrying much of the agricultural produce. It is, moreover, only a single-track line for the most part and was not designed for high speeds or loads. Congestion was particularly troublesome up to 1955, when the opening of the Lourenço Marques route relieved the position considerably, not by tak-ing copper, but by handling other items of Federal trade amounting to a million tons or 10 per cent of total North and South Rhodesian railway traffic in 1958. Further relief was afforded with the completion of the Kariba scheme which has greatly reduced the tonnage of coal travelling by rail from Wankie to the Copperbelt.

Prior to 1966, the Lobito route across Angola never took much Zam-bian copper in spite of the fact that the ocean route to the main markets is 3,000 miles less than that from Beira. This was because of long-standing agreements between Rhodesian Railways and the Copperbelt which did not expire till 1956. These laid down low rates for both copper traffic and coal from Wankie. In 1957, however, equal freight rates to either Beira or Lobito were agreed, and the amount of North Rhodesian copper mov-ing to Lobito built up to 120,000 tons a year; but early in 1960 the Federal Government imposed a limit of only 36,000 tons (7 per cent of current production) largely for strategic reasons: the Lobito route passes through the Congo and Angola where the political situation is uncertain. In 1966, with the worsening of relations between Zambia and Rhodesia, the trans-Angola railway again became a primary outlet for copper from the Copperbelt. The problem of transport is one which affects not only the Copperbelt but the whole of the Zambezi lands. Possible long-term solutions involving new railway and port construction are discussed in Chapter 38.

Other minerals that are present in the area are cobalt and uranium. Cobalt sales in 1963 were valued at just over £1 million, production being from Nkana and Chibuluma. Baluba is thought to have the largest undeveloped cobalt-ore body in the free world; investigations of the occurrence of uranium are in progress.

Apart from the Copperbelt, there is the well-known Broken Hill mining area, which was opened in 1906 with the coming of the railway from Livingstone. Lead and zinc are the principal minerals extracted, but more recently vanadium and cadmium have also been recovered. Total value of production was about £4 million in 1963.

INDUSTRY AND POWER

Industrial development here is still in its infancy compared with Rhodesia, but is concentrating on two areas—the Copperbelt and the capital, Lusaka. Industrialisation is highly desirable in view of the excessive reliance on copper at present, but competition from Rhodesia or South Africa will have to be faced; there is a shortage of both skilled and un-skilled labour, and the markets for many consumer goods are still small. The mines of the Copperbelt have provided the main stimulus in their demands for machinery and electrical equipment, for example. In Kitwe and Ndola there are now factories turning out such products on a small scale, as well as building materials, clothing and various minor articles. At Ndola, a new Land Rover assembly plant has replaced the former Willys factory at Lusaka. In *Lusaka* (pop. 122,000), the first tobacco factory in Zambia has opened. More recently still there has been a proposal to estab-lish an iron and steel industry here, relying on steel scrap initially, but eventually to be based on local iron ore and Rhodesian coking coal. The proposed steel mill will have only a small capacity—30,000 tons; in spite of this, it is by no means clear where sufficient steel scrap is to be obtained, and the viability of the project is highly dubious. Other indus-tries include grain milling, meat packing and a cotton ginnery; at Chil-anga, seven miles away, there is a large cement works. Industrial develop-ment in Zambia has, paradoxically, been stimulated by secession from the Federation, and is actively encouraged by the new African government.

The Kariba scheme

The supply of power to the Copperbelt has until recently been one of the most pressing problems, especially since sales of refined copper account for such a high proportion of Zambia's income. In 1955 the total installed capacity of power stations in North and South Rhodesia was about 450 MW. In the next ten years it is thought that the Copperbelt alone will need this amount, while industrial expansion in Rhodesia may demand another 1,400 MW. By 1957 the Copperbelt was being forced to purchase increasing quantities of electricity from the Belgian Congo— costing £1,500,000 in 1957 and equal to 20 per cent of total Federal consumption. Most of the remaining electricity was provided by power stations burning coal from Wankie; the main limitation on increasing the supply from this source has been congestion on the railway from Wankie.

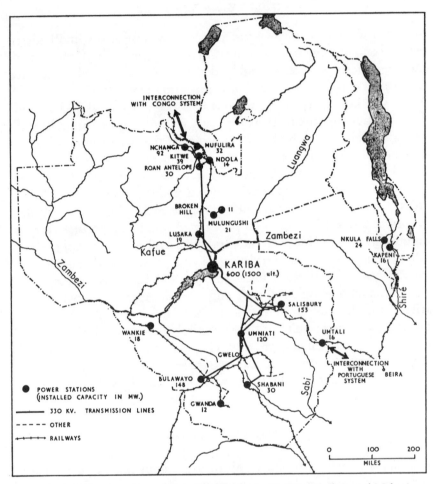

Figure 75 *Electricity generation and distribution in Zambia, Rhodesia and Malawi.* Power stations with less than 10 MW capacity are not shown. All except Kariba, Mulungushi and Nkula Falls are coal fired

The development of large hydro-electric schemes in the Zambezi lands had been under review for many years before the Kariba scheme was embarked on. The Victoria Falls themselves are known to possess a maximum power potential of about 500 MW, but the flow of the

Zambezi here is highly variable, from 15,000 to 200,000 cusecs,* and there is no possible storage site upstream to regulate the flow. The lower Kafue river has also been considered: in 22 miles of its lower course this river falls about 2,000 feet in a gorge, and a dam at the head of this could give 400 MW initially. However, the Kariba scheme on the Zambezi was chosen as more promising (Fig. 75), and the dam was completed in 1959, in spite of unprecedented floods on the river in 1956–7 and 1957–8. The dam is situated in the Kariba gorge, about 45 miles above the Kafue confluence; the gorge, cut through Karroo rocks into the Pre-Cambrian, narrows to 100 yards in its lower part, and its sides rise abruptly 1,500 feet above the river. The dam is 420 feet high, and the impounded water stretches up-valley for 175 miles (Plate 9). The powerhouse is underground (at present on the southern or Rhodesian bank) and has six generators of 100 MW each. Up to 1961 the maximum power demand was 400 MW, but to allow for future industrial expansion a second powerhouse is planned for 1970 to contribute a further 900 MW. A problem recently encountered has been corrosion of the turbines resulting from the high hydrogen sulphide content of the Kariba lake water. This probably arises from the submergence of so much vegetation.

One of the more costly items has been the construction of transmission lines to the Copperbelt (268 miles) and to the Bulawayo–Salisbury industrial area (total of 660 miles). Transmission is at 330 kilovolts; the first electricity reached the Copperbelt in December 1959, since when the generating capacity has been gradually stepped up, reaching its maximum in 1962. Power from Kariba now means that the Copperbelt is freed from restrictions on output due to inadequate power supplies. It also means that industrial expansion in both Zambia and Rhodesia can go ahead with the knowledge that an ample supply of electric power at reasonable rates is available. And, thirdly, the burden placed on the railways in transporting coal for power stations hundreds of miles from Wankie has been considerably eased. However, the cost of Kariba ($215 million) has been enormous (about one-third of the money was provided by the International Bank) and a considerable public debt has been accumulated. Further comparable development schemes are unlikely for some time to come, now that Federation has ended, at least until a stable political situation is achieved in each territory.

* One cusec = one cubic foot per second

37

Malawi and Moçambique

MALAWI

Malawi, formerly Nyasaland, stands in sharp contrast to Rhodesia and Zambia. It is small (46,100 sq. miles, one-quarter of the size of Rhodesia), mountainous and well watered and is densely populated. Its African population of 3 million is larger than that of Zambia. It has few natural resources other than the crops it can grow.

The dual nature of the farming economy, emphasised in Rhodesia and Zambia, is again apparent in Malawi. The bulk of the population engages primarily in subsistence agriculture, growing crops of maize, cassava and millet, with rice appearing on the lake fringe (Fig. 76). Along the shores of the lake the people supplement their diet by fishing from dug-out canoes. Yet Malawi cannot produce enough food for its people. In the first place a great deal of the land is too mountainous or too elevated for cultivation. Then the methods of cultivation employed are not those adapted to obtain the greatest yield from the cultivable land. Thirdly, the population is increasing, currently at a rate which will double it in twenty-five years.

Overcrowding is thus the cardinal problem. The population has steadily increased since the ending of the slave trade and the suppression of tribal warfare. The density of population long ago reached the point in the southern provinces where shifting agriculture could no longer be practised. In Chiradzulu district this density is well over 300 per sq. mile. Under such pressure and continuous cultivation the soil is noticeably deteriorating; hardier crops such as millet are gaining ground at the expense of maize. Early this century the government began encouraging the Africans to produce cash crops, such as cotton or tobacco. While these supplied an income, they only served to aggravate the situation as less land became available for food crops. One outlet for surplus labour, and a method of earning supplementary income, has for long been migration to work on farms in Rhodesia, in the gold mines of the Rand, or the copper mines of Zambia. Here the African can earn far more than he can in his homeland. Out of 400,000 young able-bodied males, some 170,000 at any given time are absent. Consequently, agriculture at home suffers; sometimes crops are wasted because of insufficient hands to help with their harvesting.

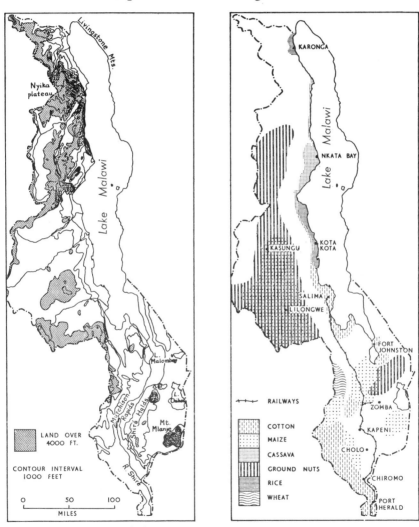

Figure 76 *Malawi:* relief, and the distribution of some crops. The principal cash crops of Malawi—tea and tobacco—are shown on Figure 71

Another outlet has been employment on European estates in Malawi. Only 2·5 per cent of the land is owned by Europeans, yet this 2·5 per cent produces more than half Malawi's total exports. Tea is the chief cash crop grown on European farms with African labour. It was introduced in 1878, and reached its present position of importance in the early 1930's at the time of the decline of coffee. It is concentrated in the southern areas of high rainfall—the Mlanje and Cholo districts. Even in these areas the rainfall is not always reliable: at Chisunga, for instance, the total for 1960 (35 inches) was 21 inches below the average for the previous eight years, resulting in a considerably reduced crop. At present Malawi yields about 25 per cent of Africa's tea. With a value of over £4 million in 1961 it was then the second most valuable agricultural export from the Central African Federation.

Cash crops grown mainly by Africans on their own plots of land include cotton and tobacco. Tobacco is generally found from 1,500 to 3,000 feet, but particularly on the Shiré highlands around Kapeni (formerly Blantyre) and Limbe, and on the Lilongwe highlands west of the lake. Production amounts to about 15 per cent of that of Rhodesia. Cotton is grown mainly along the lower Shiré valley, below 2,000 feet. Sugar-cane growing is being developed in the south; hitherto, Malawi has had to import sugar worth £1·5 million annually.

About one-fifth of Malawi is officially classed as woodland or savanna woodland, in spite of the fact that much of the natural forest has been destroyed. Remaining areas of forest are now carefully guarded, especially the Mlanje cedar forests (Plate 8B). The Mlanje cedar grows only in Mlanje and the adjacent Mchese Mountains. It is really a form of cypress, and as its wood is very durable and ant-resistant, it is highly valued. Afforestation schemes are now in progress in various parts of Malawi, using pines, eucalyptus and Mlanje cedar.

Malawi has very little manufacturing industry, as yet, to offer employment to its surplus population—only 160,000 of Malawi's 4 million people are in paid employment. Cotton ginneries, brick making, iron working and wood working are of relatively minor importance. The only mineral deposit of note in the country is the bauxite of Mlanje Mountain. Commercial exploitation of this is contingent on the Shiré valley hydro-electric project (Fig. 75), the first major development scheme which the country has seen since the coming of the railway. By constructing a minor barrage at Liwonde the flow of the Shiré river below this point has been regulated, and power is generated at the Nkula Falls, north-west of Kapeni, where the river drops 170 feet. Power developed in the first stages is about 24 MW, and it will also be possible to drain and irrigate areas of land in southern Malawi and in Moçambique for sugar, rice and cotton. The dam was completed in 1966, at a cost of $7 million. It will enable Malawi to reduce fuel imports, and it will encourage the development of light industry in addition to the production of aluminium from the local bauxite. The centre of such developments will probably continue to be Kapeni (pop. 63,000), the chief commercial town. The seat of government, hitherto at *Zomba* (pop. 18,000), is being moved to Lilongwe, which is in a more central position.

MOCAMBIQUE

Four and a half centuries ago the Portuguese came to Moçambique, but it is only in the last fifty years that this territory of 302,300 sq. miles has emerged from a history of neglect and stagnation. In the early part of this century the country was in fact offered for sale to Britain at a price of £3 million, but the bargain was refused. Moçambique's period of modern growth stems from the construction of railways across the territory to link her western neighbours with the ports of Beira and Lourenço Marques. The greatest changes in the economic life of the country have come, however, since World War II. Portuguese investment has been steadily increasing, especially with the Six-Year Development Plans (1953–8 and 1959–64), under which millions of pounds have been spent on ports, transport, industry and irrigation schemes. On the other hand, many parts have not yet been touched by these latest changes —towns such as Moçambique, the ancient capital of the north, or Quelimane, where Livingstone reached the sea after crossing the continent, have altered little through the centuries.

The population now numbers over 6·5 million, of whom all but 100,000 or so are African (Bantu) though with a considerable admixture of Arab blood. About 800,000 of the northern tribes adhere to Islam. The population is very unevenly distributed. The average density is twenty-two per sq. mile, but for large areas, such as the interior of the Northern plateau, the inner Zambezi valley and much of the coastal plain between Beira and the Limpopo, the figure is under five. Many areas were denuded in the past by the slave-raiding Arabs.

The Northern plateau is essentially a southward continuation of the South-East plateau of Tanganyika (see Chapter 28), bordered by Lake Malawi and the Malawi highlands in the west. The highest elevations are actually attained in the Namuli Mountains (7,980 feet); its eastward slope to the coastline is interrupted by minor steps. Only the higher parts are well-watered—over 60 inches on the Namuli Mountains and over 45 inches on the Malawi highlands; in the valleys and towards the coast the rainfall is less than 35 inches. The rainfall, moreover, is strongly seasonal and often erratic. Nevertheless, agriculturally this is an important region. Its eastern and south-eastern parts are relatively densely populated, though there is still enough land for shifting cultivation and bush fallowing to remain common practices.

The main food crops are cassava and rice; maize becomes more usual

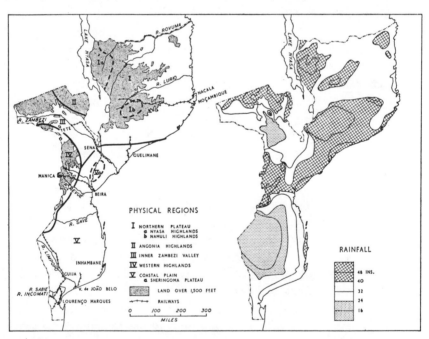

Figure 77 *Moçambique*: physical regions and mean annual rainfall. The shading on the rainfall map is designed to emphasise the wettest and driest zones respectively

in the interior. The outstanding cash crop is cotton. Its development has been relatively recent but it now ranks as Moçambique's foremost export crop (18 per cent of exports by value in 1963). About three-quarters of all the cotton produced in the territory comes from the north. Before cotton rose to its present position of importance, copra and sisal were the dominant products, coming mainly from plantations in coastal districts. Quelimane is reputed to have the world's largest coconut grove. On the wetter areas of the Namuli highlands tea is grown; it was introduced on a commercial scale in the 1930's and production is now about half that of Malawi. Tea accounted for 5 per cent of Moçambique's exports in 1963.

The Angonia Highlands isolated in the north-west are the home mainly of Bantu cattle folk, cultivating a little maize and other food crops. Apart from the south and the Malawi highlands, this is one of the few areas in Moçambique free from tsetse fly. *The inner Zambezi valley* is thinly inhabited and as yet economically undeveloped, though it is soon to be the site of a huge hydro-electric and irrigation project (see p. 451). At Sena, where the great river enters the coastal lowlands, there are sugar estates irrigated by the Zambezi. *The western highlands* belong to the Rhodesian uplands. The Great Escarpment rises sharply to heights of as much as 8,000 feet on the frontier; the Beira railway encounters it at Manica. There are a few European farms in this area, producing maize and tobacco. In the Zonue valley, just south of Manica, the government is sponsoring a small settlement scheme for Portuguese farmers.

The coastal plain is flat and often marshy; large areas are periodically inundated by the rivers. The alluvial soils of the river valleys are potentially highly fertile, but elsewhere there are vast tracts of poor sandy material. Agriculture and settlement have developed mainly south and south-west of Inhambane, as far as the Swaziland border, and to a lesser extent around Beira. Maize and rice are the principal food crops, sugarcane the chief cash crop. Sugar accounted for 11 per cent of Moçambique's exports in 1963; production is still small compared with Natal farther south, for instance, but is likely to expand considerably since climate and soil conditions are generally very favourable if irrigation can be provided.

Development of agriculture on the coastal plain hinges on both drainage and irrigation works, paradoxical though that may seem. Even though considerable areas are flooded at one period of the year, in the dry season water is completely inadequate for crops such as rice and sugar-cane. Total rainfall diminishes rapidly inland—from 40 inches at Inhambane to less than 15 inches within a hundred miles of the coast. In 1952 work was commenced on the Limpopo Irrigation Scheme. The Limpopo has now been dammed at Guija, 70 miles from its mouth, where the river is crossed by the Lourenço Marques–Rhodesia railway (constructed 1955). About 80,000 acres above Vilo de Joao Belo are to be irrigated for wheat, rice, millet, lucerne, cotton and sugar-cane. One of the main objects is to provide land for both Portuguese and African farmers in an area of rather unreliable rainfall. Eventually it is hoped to attract about 9,000 Portuguese families to the area: at present there are 5,000 Portuguese on small-holdings. The former mosquito-ridden swamp is now a patchwork of fields divided up by roads, irrigation canals and dykes. The families live in three-roomed cottages grouped in hamlets. Each red-tiled cottage has a cow byre attached and is reminiscent of rural homes in Portugal. Each family receives about 7 acres of irrigated land, and about 70 acres of pasture. An area near Chibuto has been set aside for African settlement.

A larger irrigation scheme (240,000 acres eventually) is planned for the adjacent lower Incomati river, just north of Lourenço Marques. There will be two associated dams, one on the Sabie river near the Transvaal frontier and the other where the Limpopo valley railway crosses the Incomati. The Sabie Dam will also generate electric power. Like the Limpopo scheme, the Incomati project is designed for Portuguese settlers as well as Africans, in the hope that some contribution will be made to the problem of rural overpopulation in Portugal.

MINING AND INDUSTRY

Mining is not important in Moçambique and is largely confined to small-scale coal working in the Zambezi valley at Moatize (near Tete), where the coal from Karroo beds is of good quality and plentiful. Most of the production, up to 120,000 tons a year, is used on the railways. Uranium ore was discovered in the Tete area not long ago, and has been worked intermittently. There are minor workings for gold, beryl and bismuth, and a search for oil in the Zambezi delta and adjacent coast-lands is in progress; the first oil was recently located at Dondo near Beira.

Industrial development is largely limited to factories processing agricultural products in the principal towns, especially Lourenço Marques and Beira. Cotton ginning, sugar refining, soap manufacture and tobacco preparation are the more important industries. Most electric power is generated by thermal stations burning coal from Tete or South Africa; the only significant hydro-electric scheme yet built is on the Revué river, where the power plant has a capacity of 13 MW, and sells surplus power to Umtali in Rhodesia. The Sabie Dam is to supply power to Lourenço Marques, while a second installation is under construction on the Movene river near the Swaziland border. A much larger project than any of these is the proposal to dam the Zambezi at Cahoro Bassa, at the downstream end of the Kebrabasa gorge, to create a reservoir stretching 150 miles upstream to the Rhodesian border. The hydro-electric potential is esti-mated at 4,000 MW, and over 3 million acres are thought to be suitable for irrigation from the dam. A further outcome of the project will be the creation of a navigable waterway from a point upstream of Tete to the coast, where a new seaport, Cuama, is planned. This would allow de-velopment of the considerable mineral resources in the Tete and other areas.

SOCIAL PROBLEMS AND FUTURE PROSPECTS

In their overseas territories the Portuguese have followed a unique racial policy which, in the light of recent developments in Angola, is proving less successful than had been hoped. In Moçambique there is no colour bar, and privileges of full Portuguese citizenship are available to any African who attains the necessary standards of literacy and wealth, and who accepts the Christian religion. Many Africans are failing to claim full citizenship even though they are qualified, since once they become 'assimilados' they also become liable for higher taxes and military service, and they have also to compete directly with Europeans for jobs.

The rise of African nationalism is apparent in Angola, and Moçam-bique can hardly remain immune for long. Until the last few decades Moçambique has been economically one of the most backward parts of the African continent; but in spite of limited finance Portugal has in recent decades made considerable progress in developing Moçambique. The first Six-Year Plan did much to improve the railways; under it, with the help of the Export-Import Bank, the Lourenço Marques–Rhodesia railway was financed; it opened in 1955. In the north the port of Nacala

has been modernised as a new outlet for this region, while in the south
the Limpopo Irrigation Scheme is providing valuable land for European settlement, reinforcing the white community in Moçambique,
and at the same time drawing off some of Portugal's excess population.
In 1965 the territory opened its first north-south major trunk road,
linking the two chief towns of Beira and Lourenço Marques. The
future economic prosperity of Moçambique will undoubtedly continue to rest on the valuable transit trade through Beira and Lourenço
Marques (see next chapter), and on the export of agricultural produce. Industrialisation on any significant scale is unlikely for some time
because of competition with cheap manufactured products available
from South Africa or Rhodesia, and the limited nature of the home
market.

38

The Zambezi Lands' Trade Outlets;
The Former Federation

Rhodesia, Zambia and Malawi are entirely landlocked states, dependent on their neighbours for trade outlets. By far the greater proportion of their trade passes across the border by rail into Moçambique, on its way to the two principal port outlets of Beira and Lourenço Marques.

The main railway system of the Zambezi lands developed about the turn of the century. By 1902 there was a continuous line from South Africa, entering Southern Rhodesia at Plumtree, passing through Bulawayo and Salisbury, and terminating at Beira. Seven years later the railway from Bulawayo through Northern Rhodesia reached the Copperbelt and the Congo border. The only important addition to the rail net since has been the connection to Lourenço Marques from Shabani (1955). The route chosen for this new line has the easiest gradient from coast to hinterland anywhere in southern Africa. The construction of the line and the completion of the Kariba project (which has lessened the need to transport so much coal from Wankie) have considerably relieved the pressure on the railways; moreover, since 1950, Rhodesian Railways have spent much on track improvements and on new rolling stock and locomotives. As a result, even though copper traffic alone was 500,000 tons in 1964 instead of the 200,000 tons before World War II, and in spite of the expansion of agricultural and industrial production, the railways since 1957 have been able to handle all the traffic offered with but little delay. The tonnage hauled rose from 8·5 million tons in 1954 to 11·5 million tons in 1960 of which 1·5 million tons used the Lourenço Marques outlet. Yet it may not be long before further economic expansion renders the situation critical again.

Two solutions to the problem are available. The first is continued railway improvement, such as the double-tracking and electrification of certain sections. The second solution is the construction of new rail links. One of the principal defects of the railway system between Beira and the Copper-belt is its circuitous nature. Passenger trains take four days to cover the distance (1,450 miles) and goods trains longer. Yet the straight-line distance is only 600 miles. A link from Lusaka to Sinoia would provide a much more direct route, but has been considered impracticable because of the steep grade of the northern valley side at the Zambezi crossing. Apart from its circuitous route, the Beira railway has not been well laid out: many curves are sharp, gradients reach 1 : 33 in the section crossing the Great Escarpment near the Moçambique border, and the lowland section in Moçambique is liable to flooding. In its second Six-Year Plan, however, the Portuguese Government is realigning and re-grading the whole of the line from Beira to the Rhodesian border. At the same time the Nacala–Cuambo railway is being extended to Lake Malawi. Nacala is considered to be the best natural harbour on the east coast of Africa, and one of the finest in the world; it has been recently modernised, yet it is little used. Its railway to Lake Malawi is well built and designed for heavy traffic. A more ambitious proposal under active consideration by Zambia, now that trade through Rhodesia is impeded, is a direct rail link between Zambia and Tanganyika via Kasama and Mbeya, to terminate at Mtwara (see p.379).

THE EAST COAST PORTS

For the Zambezi lands *Beira* (pop. 60,000) remains the chief exporting port, though not a very satisfactory one. Three-quarters of Beira's trade passes to or from Rhodesia. Since 1955 some of the pressure on Beira has been relieved by *Lourenço Marques* (pop. 184,000), which has a fine harbour and is one of the best-equipped ports in southern Africa (Fig. 78). Its first deep-water berth was actually opened one year before that at Durban. Now it has a minimum water depth in the approach channel of 27 feet, compared with only 11 feet at Beira. At Beira (Plate 14B) conditions for port development are much less favourable—marshy surroundings are difficult for building, a tidal range of 23 feet (compared with 14 feet at Lourenço Marques) makes crane operation sometimes impossible, and the channel is subject to silting. The hinterland of Lourenço Marques includes part of South Africa (especially the southern Transvaal mining and industrial region for which it is a most important port) and its rail link with the Transvaal is far better constructed than Beira's link with Rhodesia. The port is 100 miles nearer to Johannesburg than Durban is. And since 1955 it has also been drawing traffic from Rhodesia. It is thus not surprising that Lourenço Marques is now handling over 7 million tons of cargo annually, compared with Beira's 3·5 million tons. Lourenço Marques' share is likely to increase still further, for its potential capacity is over 7 million tons. On the other hand, Beira's facilities are being currently improved—20 per cent was added to its handling capacity in 1962, and more is planned by the Portuguese Government. In the case of both ports petroleum products form the biggest single group of imports—60 per cent of all imports for Lourenço Marques, which possesses a refinery of 600,000 tons capacity, built in 1961. Beira's principal exports up to 1965 consisted of copper (over one-third of the total tonnage), chrome ore and tobacco. In Lourenço Marques coal comes first and chrome ore second. Only a small part of the cargo handled at either port originates in Moçambique itself—about one-seventh of Beira's trade and one-sixth of that of Lourenço Marques.

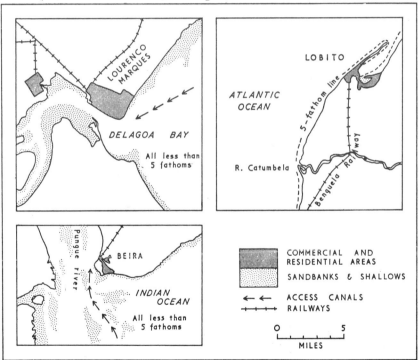

Figure 78 *The sites of Lourenço Marques and Beira in Moçambique, and Lobito in Angola*

Beira and Lourenço Marques are by far the most important cities in Moçambique. The southerly location of Lourenço Marques is a disadvantage for administration as a capital. But between them these two towns contain 60 per cent of all Europeans living in the territory, and both of them have a varied range of manufacturing industries. The revenue collected from traffic using these ports and their connecting railways is of vital importance to the economy of Moçambique as a whole. Other ports along the Moçambique coast, such as Moçambique itself, Quelimane or Inhambane, are of comparatively minor importance, dealing only with local traffic from the immediate hinterlands tapped by their respective railways.

A POSTSCRIPT ON THE CENTRAL AFRICAN FEDERATION

The Federation of Rhodesia and Nyasaland was ended in 1963 after a life of ten years. It was in several respects a unique political unit in Africa. Its landlocked position made it dependent on Portuguese facilities for its chief outlets, and the distance of the main centres of economic development from the coast had placed a severe strain on the transport system. The economic advantages derived from Federation between the three territories were considerable. There was a favourable balance of trade (Federal exports exceeded imports by 30 per cent in 1960), while the natural assets of the territories were varied and partly complementary— the mineral wealth of the Copperbelt and Southern Rhodesia, the agricultural products of Southern Rhodesia and Nyasaland, the immense reserves of native labour, and running through the heart of the Federation the Zambezi river, the site of one of Africa's major hydro-electric schemes. Industrial development thus rested on a broad base of natural resources, abundant power and cheap African labour, and the Federation consequently took first place in the industrial output of tropical Africa. Its prosperity could be judged from the fact that the total income of the Africans rose by 40 per cent between 1954 and 1960, and by 55 per cent for Europeans, while in the same period the gross national product increased by 60 per cent. The numbers of Europeans living in the Rhodesias increased at an unprecedented rate, and there was considerable urban growth (see Table 23) for the majority of the new white immigrants settled in the towns. By 1961 nearly half the European population of the Federation was in the two major cities and industrial centres of Salisbury and Bulawayo. And with the expansion of mining and industry, increasing numbers of Africans moved in to the towns to supply labour. The only major town to show a decline between 1953 and 1961 has been Wankie, entirely dependent on its coal mines.

Table 23   Changes in the European population of selected towns in the Central African Federation, 1956 to 1961

Salisbury	+ 43 per cent		Lusaka	+ 25 per cent
Bulawayo	+ 21 ,, ,,		Kitwe	+ 27 ,, ,,
Umtali	+ 27 ,, ,,		Ndola	+ 25 ,, ,,
Gwelo	+ 48 ,, ,,		Kapeni	
Que Que	+ 65 ,, ,,		(Blantyre)	+ 69 ,, ,,
Wankie	— 12 ,, ,,			

Source: G. T. Rimmington, *Geography 48* (1963), 321

The racial policy of the Federation was ostensibly 'partnership' between Africans and whites. Nevertheless, some aspects of racial segregation were as strongly marked as in South Africa—the colour bar in industry and on the railways, for instance. Now that Zambia and Malawi have achieved independence under African governments, greater equality of opportunity between white and black peoples is likely; in Rhodesia, still under white rule, the future is difficult to forecast.

Federation facilitated the system of labour migration, on which industry, mining and European farming chiefly depend. Due to the rate at which expansion of these has taken place under Federation, labour shortage has been and still is an acute problem. Manufacturing now employs more than mining—18 per cent of wage earners compared with 13 per cent. The main sources of migrant labour are within the area of the Central African Federation: it is estimated that about one-third of Malawi's able-bodied male population is absent, working in other areas, and about one-sixth of Zambia's. Moçambique does, however, make a small contribution to the labour supply, for about one-fifth of the African males employed in Rhodesia and about 1 per cent of those in the Copperbelt come from Moçambique. The Copperbelt is less dependent on extra-territorial labour than Rhodesia. In 1961 about three-quarters of all workers in the Copperbelt were Zambian (the largest single group being from the Bemba tribe), with most of the remainder coming from the contiguous territories of Malawi and Tanganyika. In recent years labour migration has begun to show signs of decreasing. This is actually one aim of Rhodesian policy, which plans eventually to eliminate labour migration by developing the Native Reserves and by establishing a permanent native labour force in the main industrial centres. Similarly, the mines of the Copperbelt have made a great effort to build up a stable labour force, with some success indeed, for the average length of service at some mines is now seven years. The broad picture of incipient decline in migrant labour, however, is also to be linked with the growth of commercial agriculture in African areas, and with the greater opportunities for local employment in the towns.

The economic effects of the break-up of the Federation are bound to be far-reaching. Malawi's economy has been gravely affected by secession, for Federal money, of which £35 million was made available between 1953 and 1963, no longer flows into the country. Malawi's export of labour to Rhodesia and Zambia may also be affected: hitherto, her migrant labourers have remitted an average of £2 million to £3 million annually to their families at home. An increase in the already high rate of unemployment in the country seems inevitable, and even though the Shiré valley hydro-electric project has been completed, there seems little hope of any significant industrial development for some time.

Zambia has equally pressing economic problems as a consequence of the diminution of trade with Rhodesia since 1965, and especially the problem of liquid fuel supplies with the stoppage of oil imports through Beira. Her heavy dependence on copper sales makes her economy highly vulnerable, for copper prices are liable to fluctuate widely and the mineral is by no means inexhaustible. Under Federation, Zambian copper sales supplied half the Federal revenue. For the future, expansion of Zambia's industry and agriculture will be essential, and there will have to be assurances that electric power from Kariba will continue to be made available by Rhodesia.

Rhodesia undoubtedly benefited most from Federation. It is symbolic that the existing installations of the Kariba power scheme, the most ambitious project tackled during Federation, lie on the south bank of the Zambezi, in Rhodesian territory. The expansion of manufacturing industry in the country since Federation was introduced has been emphasised already, and it is the prospect of continued industrial development, together with the broad base of numerous mineral resources and considerable agricultural potential which will assure Rhodesia's eventual viability as an independent state. But the immediate prospects are less happy. The breakdown of trade with Zambia in 1965 and the economic sanctions imposed by Britain and other countries are threatening the whole basis of the Rhodesian economy. Loss of confidence in the country's economy at present has resulted in a great diminution of capital investment, and whereas the early years of Federation saw large numbers of new white settlers arriving in Rhodesia, recent years have witnessed a shrinkage in the white population with emigration. Whereas there was a net inflow of 13,000 European settlers in 1956, diminishing to 1,500 in 1960, there was a net outflow of 1,400 in 1961 and of 5,400 in 1963. Undoubtedly if it had not been for generous assistance from the Republic of South Africa, especially over the supply of oil, the Rhodesian economy would have suffered complete collapse in 1966.

References

1 J. R. V. Prescott, 'Overpopulation and overstocking in the native areas of Matabeleland', *Geog. Journ.*, 127 (1961), 212–25
2 J. H. Beck, 'Yafele's kraal', *Geography*, 45 (1960), 68–78
3 A. I. Richards, 'A changing pattern of agriculture in East Africa: the Bemba of Northern Rhodesia', *Geog. Journ.*, 124 (1958), 302–14
4 F. Debenham, 'The Bangweulu swamps of Central Africa', *Geog. Rev.*, 37 (1947), 351–68
   F. Debenham, 'The water resources of Central Africa', *Geog. Journ.*, 111 (1948), 222–34

Selected Bibliography

F. Debenham, *Nyasaland: the land of the lake* (London, 1955)
A. I. Richards, *Land, labour and diet in Northern Rhodesia: an economic study of the Bemba tribe* (London, 1939)
J. H. Wellington, *Southern Africa: a geographical study* (Cambridge, 1955, 2 vols.)
S. Williams, *The distribution of the African population of Northern Rhodesia* (Lusaka, 1962)
M. Yudelman, *Africans on the land: economic problems of African agricultural development in Southern, Central, and East Africa, with special reference to Southern Rhodesia* (Cambridge, Mass., 1964)

S. J. K. Baker and R. T. White, 'The distribution of native population over south-east Central Africa', *Geog. Journ.*, 108 (1946), 198–210
H. C. Brookfield, 'New railroad and port development in east and central Africa', *Econ. Geog.*, 31 (1955), 60–70

G. M. Howe, 'Climates of the Rhodesias and Nyasaland according to the Thornthwaite classification', *Geog. Rev.*, 43 (1953), 525–39

J. R. V. Prescott, 'Migrant labour in the Central African Federation', *Geog. Rev.*, 49 (1959), 424–7

R. W. Steel, 'Land and population in British tropical Africa', *Geography*, 40 (1955), 1–17

B. N. Floyd, 'Land apportionment in Southern Rhodesia', *Geog. Rev.*, 52 (1962), 566–82

J. R. V. Prescott, 'Population distribution in Southern Rhodesia', *Geog. Rev.*, 52 (1962), 559–65

P. Scott, 'The tobacco industry of Southern Rhodesia', *Econ. Geog.*, 28 (1952), 189–206

P. Scott, 'Migrant labour in Southern Rhodesia', *Geog. Rev.*, 44 (1954), 29–48

D. S. Whittlesey, 'Southern Rhodesia—an African compage', *Ann. Assoc. Am. Geogr.*, 46 (1956), 1–97

M. M. Cole, 'The Kariba project', *Geography*, 45 (1960), 98–105

M. M. Cole, 'The Rhodesian economy in transition and the role of Kariba', *Geography*, 47 (1962), 15–40

M. M. Cole, 'Vegetation and geomorphology in Northern Rhodesia', *Geog. Journ.*, 129 (1963), 290–310

W. H. Reeve, 'Progress and geographical significance of the Kariba Dam', *Geog. Journ.*, 126 (1960), 140–6

R. W. Steel, 'The Copperbelt of Northern Rhodesia', *Geography*, 42 (1957), 83–92

F. B. Wells, 'Transport in the Rhodesian Copperbelt', *Geography*, 42 (1957), 93–5

E. Wilson, 'Lusaka—a city of tropical Africa', *Geography*, 48 (1963), 411–14

W. B. Morgan, 'The lower Shiré valley of Nyasaland: a changing system of African agriculture', *Geog. Journ.*, 119 (1953), 459–69

W. A. Hance and I. S. Van Dongen, 'Beira, Mozambique gateway to Central Africa', *Ann. Assoc. Am. Geogr.*, 47 (1957), 307–35

W. A. Hance and I. S. Van Dongen, 'Lourenço Marques in Delagoa Bay', *Econ. Geog.*, 33 (1957), 238–56

I. S. Van Dongen, 'Nacala, newest Mozambique gateway to interior Africa', *Tijdschrift v. Econ. en Soc. Geog.*, 48 (1957), 65–72

PART X

South Africa

South Africa, comprising the Republic of South Africa (472,400 sq. miles), the Kingdom of Lesotho (formerly Basutoland), and Swaziland, is in many respects a unique part of Africa. First and foremost, it is the principal area of European settlement in the continent. At present more than half the European population of Africa is found here, and settlement by Europeans has been continuous for more than 300 years. No other part of Africa possesses such an unbroken record of white settlement. The administration and government of the Republic have always been entirely in the hands of the Europeans, in spite of the fact that Africans outnumber Europeans by more than three to one. Economically, South Africa is distinguished by her wealth of mineral resources and, partly as a result of the profits derived from sales of minerals, by her relatively high level of industrial development. The Republic of South Africa is in fact easily the most industrialised country anywhere in the continent of Africa. South Africa accounts for 43 per cent of the entire mineral output of Africa, yet manufacturing industry now contributes as much to her national income as mining and agriculture combined. Nearly one-third of the income of the African continent is in fact generated in the South, while the national per capita income is twice the average for Africa.

The geographical, as opposed to the political, limits of South Africa are by no means easy to define, for the South African plateau is but the southern extremity of the continental shield as a whole. In very general terms the northern limits of the region are provided by the lower Orange river in the west and the Limpopo river in the east. In the centre there is no natural dividing line breaking the extent of semi-arid country known as the Kalahari. The political frontier in this region is particularly arbitrary and has no geographical merit. The problem of the location and definition of major regional boundaries is a constantly recurring one in Africa, due partly to the conflict between political frontiers and watersheds, and partly to the ill-defined nature of certain relief features and drainage basins.

39

Structure, Relief and Drainage

As in the greater part of Africa, the south is underlain by a platform of Archaean rocks. Over two-thirds of South Africa these ancient igneous and metamorphic rocks are, however, buried by later sedimentary rocks, of which three main groups only need concern us (Fig. 79).

The earliest group of rocks resting on the Archaean Basement is Pre-Cambrian. At the base of the group lies the Dominion Reef System. Above it is the famed Witwatersrand System, consisting of quartzites, slates and the 'reefs' or gold-bearing conglomerates. In the Johannesburg area this System alone is no less than 4½ miles thick. The geological sequence is continued by the Ventersdorp System, mainly volcanic, and then by the Transvaal System, with its extensive iron-ore deposits and limestones, providing two of the basic raw materials for the iron and steel industry. Finally, the Bushveld Igenous Complex, an immense intrusion of late Pre-Cambrian age, contains one of the world's most extraordinary assemblages of minerals, including platinum, chrome, gold, silver and asbestos. The lava and dolomites of the Ventersdorp and Transvaal Systems respectively are the most important water-bearing strata in South Africa, making a significant contribution to agricultural, industrial and domestic water needs in the southern and western Transvaal.

Secondly, in the south-west, a group of rocks of Silurian and Devonian age has been folded to form the Cape Ranges. At the base of the group the Table Mountain Sandstone is up to 5,000 feet thick, and is most important physiographically, forming massive plateaux, or the hard cores of the Cape Ranges. The succeeding Bokkeveld Shales give rise to valleys or lowlands in the Cape. The third member of the group, only surviving in a few places, is the Witteberg Series of quartzites and shales.

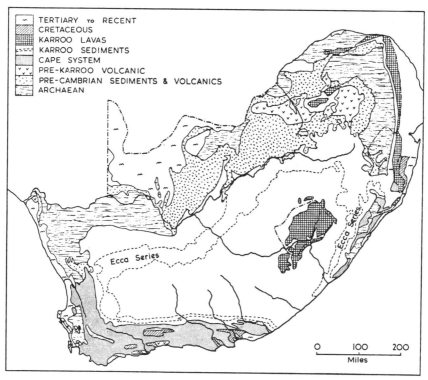

Ecca Series

Ecca Series

0   100   200
Miles

Figure 79 *The geology of South Africa*

Thirdly there is the Karroo System. Of mid-Carboniferous to lower Jurassic age, this has the most extensive outcrop of any formation in South Africa. It attains a maximum thickness of nearly 5 miles. At its base occurs an interesting series (the Dwyka) of glacial deposits and shales, which lie on the peneplained and glaciated sub-Karroo surface. Higher up in the Karroo System comes the Ecca Series, which contains vast coal reserves of inestimable value to South Africa. The most recent Karroo

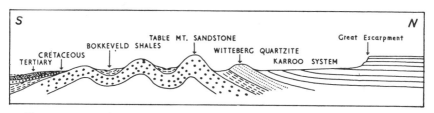

Figure 80 *A geological sketch-section from north to south through the eastern part of the Cape folded belt*

rocks are lavas, up to 4,500 feet thick in Lesotho, here capping the imposing Drakensberg Escarpment (Plate 10). A section (Fig. 80) from north to south through part of Cape Province shows that the Karroo System lies almost horizontally; only in the south does it become partially involved in the folding of the Cape Ranges.

RELIEF AND DRAINAGE

The essential physical framework of South Africa (Fig. 81) consists of a plateau, depressed in the centre, and terminated by bold escarpments which overlook the coastal regions. More than half of South Africa lies more than 4,000 feet above the sea; in the east, parts of the plateau attain heights of 10,000 feet or more. The plateau is drained principally to the west by the Orange–Vaal river system, though in the north a smaller portion feeds the Limpopo. The divide between the Limpopo and Vaal drainage (Fig. 81) runs approximately east-west through Johannesburg.

The escarpment edges of the plateau, overlooking the lower marginal or coastal zones, are collectively referred to as the *Great Escarpment*. Lying at distances of 35 to 150 miles from the coast, the Great Escarpment has thus a variety of local names; in the east and south-east it is known as the Drakensberg, whose crest-line rises to over 11,000 feet; traced westward, through Cape Province, it is variously known as the Stormberg, Sneeuberg, Nuweveld Reeks, Roggeveld Berge and Langeberg. The crest-line in the western sections is not usually higher than 5,000 feet. Wellington has described it as 'the most fundamentally important physical feature in the sub-continent'.[1] Its great size in the Drakensberg has already been noted. Essentially, it is an erosion scarp, formed by the headward erosion of steeply graded rivers flowing down to the coast. It is formed of a great variety of rocks; but it is most impressive in areas where alternations of hard and soft beds are present, or where there is a resistant cap-rock formation. Examples of such resistant strata in the east are the Stormberg lavas (upper Karroo age) and the quartzites of the Transvaal System. In areas of the Archaean granite or gneiss the escarpment is often less marked. The Great Escarpment is conceded to be a feature of considerable antiquity, and has been pushed inland from the coastline by erosion for distances up to 150 miles. According to L. C. King[2] it represents the gradual destruction of the Gondwana cyclic remnants (seen as the High Veld generally) by later cycles of erosion beginning in the early Cretaceous.

9 Kariba Dam on the Zambezi, completed in 1959. The dam is 420 feet high; the underground powerhouse is on the Rhodesian (left hand) side

10 The Drakensberg in Natal, a portion of the Great Escarpment of southern Africa, cut in horizontally bedded Upper Karroo lavas and sandstones

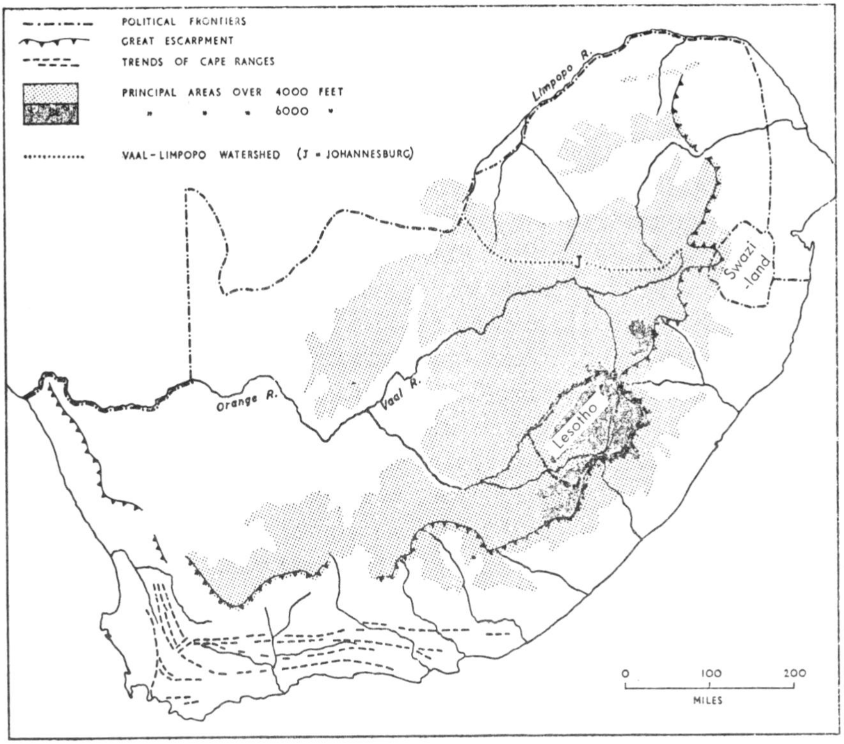
POLITICAL FRONTIERS
GREAT ESCARPMENT
TRENDS OF CAPE RANGES
PRINCIPAL AREAS OVER 4000 FEET
" " " 6000 "
VAAL-LIMPOPO WATERSHED (J = JOHANNESBURG)
Limpopo R.
Swazi-land
J
Vaal R.
Orange R.
Lesotho
0
100
200
MILES

Figure 81 *South Africa:* elements of relief and drainage

Beyond the crest of the Great Escarpment the country consists largely of extensive rolling plains dropping almost imperceptibly to 3,000 feet in the centre of the sub-continent. These upland plains are of erosional origin, but the widespread presence of nearly horizontal strata has also contributed to the general evenness of the landscape. Only in Lesotho does mountainous and broken country form part of the interior, rising to 11,425 feet on the crest of the Drakensberg, the highest point in South Africa. The underlying rocks in Lesotho belong to the Karroo System, horizontally bedded, and include great thicknesses of lava. The numerous rivers have carved deeply into the lavas and sandstones, producing the most beautiful and spectacular scenery in South Africa. At the Maletsunyane Falls there is a sheer drop of 600 feet. Nearly all the drainage of this high mountain country feeds into the Orange river, which escapes from the highlands in the south-west.

Surrounding Lesotho on the west and north is the plateau of the

High Veld. The term 'veld' may be used in both a botanical and an altitudinal sense. Thus, 'High Veld' may refer simply to land over 4,000 feet (cf. 'Low Veld' for land below 2,000 feet), or it may refer to an area of open grassland above 4,000 feet. The term is usually applied to the eastern interior plateaux of the southern Transvaal and the Orange Free State, where grassland is the dominant vegetation and where the undulating land surface lies mostly between 4,000 and 6,000 feet. The area is drained westward by the Vaal, Caledon and Orange rivers. Its northern limit is represented by the Witwatersrand 'ridge' on which Johannesburg stands at 6,000 feet. There is no topographical boundary to provide a western limit to the High Veld—only gradually increasing aridity. Except in the north, where older Pre-Cambrian rocks are exposed, the region is underlain by Karroo strata, almost horizontally bedded.

North of the Witwatersrand lies an area usually known as the *Transvaal Bushveld.* The name 'Bushveld' refers to a type of dry savanna vegetation characterised by open grassland with scattered trees and bushes. The region lies inside the great bend of the Limpopo valley, and in elevation is much lower than the High Veld, parts falling below 2,000 feet and the average being only 3,000 feet. The topography is complex in detail, but broadly consists of a central basin, drained by the Olifants and Crocodile rivers, surrounded by a series of broken ranges. Geologically it is an area from which most of the Karroo rocks have been removed by erosion, exposing the Pre-Cambrian formations which here include the Bushveld Igneous Complex.

West of the High Veld extends a vast expanse of semi-arid plateau, sometimes known as the *Upper Karroo,* reaching to the Great Escarpment on the south and west. Across it flows the Orange river, entrenched in a gorge below the Aughrabies Falls. The relief on the whole is subdued, consisting either of surfaces planed across the Karroo strata, or of the stripped sub-Karroo surface bevelling Pre-Cambrian rocks. The elevation drops steadily from the edge of the High Veld (at about 4,000 feet) and from the Great Escarpment crest in the south (at 4,000–5,000 feet) to about 2,000 feet in the region of the lower Orange river. Due to the aridity, drainage apart from the Orange river is intermittent, flowing only after occasional torrential downpours in the summer. It has been said of this area that if you fall into a 'river', you brush the dust off and walk along the bed until you are able to climb up the bank. But after a rainstorm the river may come down in spate so rapidly that travellers by car or wagon have sometimes been overwhelmed and carried away.

On the seaward side of the Great Escarpment there is a much greater diversity of landscape and relief. First there is the *Karroo*. The term 'Karroo' is derived from a Hottentot word meaning 'waterless'. The term has been applied in a geological sense (the Karroo System of rocks), in a botanical sense (referring to scrub vegetation), and in the topographical sense used here. This region consists of the Great Karroo, lying immediately below the Great Escarpment, and the Little Karroo, separated from the Great Karroo by the Swartberge. The Great Karroo is underlain by Karroo sandstones and shales, generally horizontally bedded, except towards the Swartberge where the Cape folding commences. The altitude of the Great Karroo Plains is between 1,500 and 2,500 feet. The Little Karroo is slightly lower; and it possesses some permanent rivers such as the Olifants and Gouritz, whereas on the Great Karroo intermittent stream flow is the rule.

Around the Karroo on the south and west stand the *Cape Ranges*. These are of folded structure, related to orogenic movements mainly in the Triassic, and built out of Silurian and Devonian rocks. The ranges fall into two sets. The first consists of the Cedarberg and Olifants Mountains, trending north-north-west to approach the west coast near the lower Olifants river; in the south this group of mountain ranges is cut off by the south coast around Cape Hangklip. The second set trends roughly east-west; it begins by crossing the first set around Worcester and the Hex River Mountains, producing an area of complex topography, and continues for nearly 400 miles until cut off by the coast around Port Elizabeth. It includes the Swartberge (already mentioned) and the Langeberg (not to be confused with the Langeberg forming part of the Great Escarpment in western Cape Province). These east-west trending ranges consist of multiple anticlines, while the intervening lowland strips are generally synclinal (Fig. 80). Most of the principal ranges are built out of Table Mountain Sandstone; and parts rise to well over 7,000 feet. The transverse portions of the rivers which cut across the fold ranges appear to have been superimposed from Jurassic and Cretaceous sediments, which were worn off the original mountain ranges after uplift, filled in the synclines, and provided a surface on which the rivers were initiated. Later the rivers re-exposed the fold ranges and cut gaps (known as *poorts* or *kloofs*) across them; subsequent tributaries extended themselves along the softer sediments still remaining in the synclines, in some cases capturing other streams. Thus the present almost rectangular drainage pattern has emerged.

From the foot of the Drakensberg across to the east coast extends a
belt of country most of which lies between 1,000 and 4,000 feet. Except
in Zululand (north-east Natal), a true coastal plain is very narrow or
entirely absent. Inland, the country has been greatly dissected by the
rivers flowing steeply to the sea from the Drakensberg. But in spite of the
broken character of the country a series of steps or planation surfaces has
been recognised, principally at 4,500, 2,500 and 600 feet. About two-
thirds of the region is underlain by Karroo strata. The one area where
the relief is relatively subdued is in the Lowveld of eastern Transvaal;
here, rolling plains below 2,000 feet are interrupted only by scattered
granite inselberge.

Between the Atlantic coast and the Great Escarpment on the west there
is a narrow belt of desert, a southward continuation of the Namib desert
in South-West Africa. The underlying rocks are of Archaean igneous and
metamorphic formation, except next to the coast where Tertiary and
Quaternary deposits occur. Behind part of the desert strip the Great
Escarpment rises to 5,600 feet in the Langeberg, but elsewhere is less
prominent.

40

Climate, Vegetation and Soils

General consideration of the position of South Africa (latitudes 23° to 35°) suggests a sub-tropical climate. A closer examination shows that there are in fact many varieties of climate within South Africa, from the warm humid region along the east coast to the cool conditions encountered in the Lesotho highlands, the highest parts of which support only a tundra-like vegetation. The variation of temperature experienced over South Africa arises from differences of elevation rather than of latitude. Thus, although Johannesburg is 8° nearer the equator than Cape Town, it is actually 3° or 4°F cooler as regards mean monthly temperatures, because of its altitude of nearly 6,000 feet (Table 24). This is in spite of the fact that Johannesburg is 300 miles from the nearest coast. Pella, on the lower Orange river, in a latitude 3° south of Johannesburg but only 1,500 feet above sea-level, has a mean January temperature 17°F higher than Johannesburg. In roughly the same latitude, but on the west coast, Port Nolloth has a mean January temperature of only 60°F (Pella 86°, Johannesburg 68°F), showing the influence of proximity to the ocean. A comparison of the annual range of temperature between Pella, 140 miles inland, and Port Nolloth is equally instructive: Pella 29°F, Port Nolloth 7°F. Temperatures on the west coast of South Africa are considerably affected by the cool Benguela current offshore, as the example of Port Nolloth has just shown. The east coast of South Africa is influenced by the warm waters of the Indian Ocean (Fig. 13): Durban, in a latitude 1° south of Port Nolloth, has a mean January temperature 15°F higher.

Most of South Africa lies beyond the tropic, and the relatively high elevation of many areas means that frost is likely to occur almost everywhere at times. The night temperature in July at Johannesburg may be

Table 24

Temperatures (°F) at selected stations in South Africa

Station	Alt. (feet)	J	F	M	A	M	J	J	A	S	O	N	D	Year	Range
Cape Town	40	71	71	69	64	60	57	55	57	58	62	66	69	63	16
Port Nolloth	23	60	60	60	58	57	55	53	54	55	56	58	59	57	7
Johannesburg	5,463	68	67	65	61	54	50	51	55	60	65	66	67	61	17
Durban	16	75	75	74	71	66	63	62	63	66	68	71	73	69	13
Kimberley	3,927	77	75	71	64	56	51	50	56	61	68	72	75	65	27

as low as 20°F. The lowest recorded temperature in the Republic of South Africa is 6°F, at Carolina in the eastern Transvaal at 5,600 feet. Even on the coastal areas occasional light frosts occur, especially in valley bottoms. The more severe and regular frosts of the higher parts provide definite limitations to certain crops, such as sugar-cane and citrus fruits.

Not only is there a close relationship between relief and temperature: relationship between relief and rainfall is equally apparent. Except for a very narrow coastal strip on the east, humid climates are coincident with the higher land (Fig. 82). Generally, the most arid parts of South Africa are located in the north and west of Cape Province, where the land drops below 3,000 feet. The wettest parts are to be found on the Drakensberg (annual averages up to 75 inches) and on some of the Cape Ranges: the Drakenstein Mountains south of Worcester rise to 5,000 feet and record

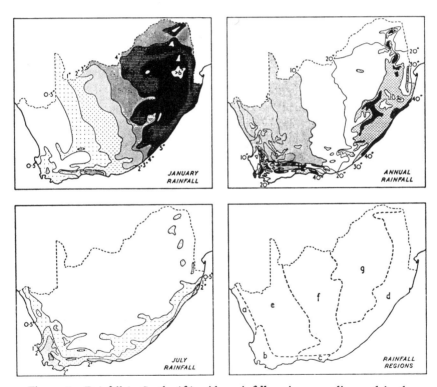

Figure 82 *Rainfall in South Africa* (the rainfall regions are discussed in the text). On the map of annual rainfall, shading emphasises the driest and wettest regions respectively

about 200 inches a year. An annual rainfall of over 40 inches is, however, rare in South Africa, and in fact 90 per cent of the whole country receives less than 30 inches per year. Roughly half of South Africa can be classed as arid or semi-arid. During the last thirty years South Africa has become increasingly aware of the limited nature of her water resources on which her agricultural and industrial development vitally depends. It has been calculated that the entire run-off from South African rivers for one year could be contained in the reservoir of Lake Mead on the Colorado river in the United States, but only about one-tenth of South Africa's rainfall ever reaches her rivers. In only a small corner of South Africa can rain be expected in all months of the year—along part of the south coast. Elsewhere rainfall is markedly seasonal in its incidence—85 per cent of South Africa has mainly summer rainfall.

The *western coastal strip* (a. Fig. 82) is the driest region of South Africa, though a relatively cool one. Throughout the year it comes under the influence of mTs air blowing off the Atlantic and over the cool Benguela current, the latter increasing the stability of the air (see Port Nolloth, Table 25). The distinctive feature of the *south-west Cape region* (b. Fig. 82) is the winter rainfall, brought by air-masses of modified mP type. The rainfall is greatly accentuated on the mountain ranges, with corresponding rain-shadow effects in the intervening valleys and on the Little Karroo (see Cape Town, Table 25). The *southern coastal belt* (c. Fig. 82) is the only region of South Africa in which the rainfall is fairly equally distributed throughout the year. In winter it is brought by the mP air-masses which move along the coast from the Cape at this time of year. In summer the rain derives from mT air-masses of Indian Ocean origin (see Port Elizabeth, Table 25). Along the *eastern coastal belt* (d. Fig. 82) rain falls in every month, but there is a pronounced concentration in the summer, brought by moist air-masses from the Indian Ocean (see Durban, Table 25).

The rainfall over the interior plateau of South Africa varies from over 40 inches in the Lesotho highlands to less than 3 inches around the lower Orange river. The rain is confined to the summer months, while the winter is a season of drought. The *western interior* (e. Fig. 82) comprises the vast semi-arid heart of the sub-continent, which climatically continues northward as the Kalahari in Botswana. Complete drought prevails from May to September usually, when subsiding cT air is dominant. In the summer a weakening of the local anticyclonic conditions occasionally allows moist air to penetrate from the north and north-east

Table 25

Precipitation (inches) at selected stations in South Africa

Station	Alt. (feet)	J	F	M	A	M	J	J	A	S	O	N	D	Total
Port Nolloth	23	0·1	0·1	0·2	0·2	0·3	0·3	0·3	0·3	0·2	0·1	0·1	0·1	2·3
Cape Town	40	0·7	0·6	0·9	1·9	3·7	4·3	3·7	3·3	2·3	1·6	1·1	0·8	24·7
Port Elizabeth	176	1·2	1·3	1·8	1·8	2·4	1·8	1·9	2·0	2·3	2·2	2·2	1·7	22·7
Durban	16	4·3	4·8	5·1	3·0	2·0	1·3	1·1	1·5	2·8	4·3	4·8	4·7	39·7
Upington	2,641	0·6	1·0	1·7	0·7	0·5	0·4	0·1	0·1	0·1	0·3	0·4	0·5	6·1
Oudtshoorn	1,099	0·4	0·5	1·0	0·8	0·8	0·4	0·7	0·6	0·9	0·8	1·2	0·8	8·9
Kimberley	3,927	2·4	2·5	3·1	1·5	0·7	0·2	0·2	0·3	0·6	1·0	1·6	2·0	16·1
Johannesburg	5,463	4·5	4·3	3·5	1·5	1·0	0·3	0·3	0·3	0·9	2·2	4·2	4·9	27·9

(see Upington and Oudtshoorn, Table 24). In the *central interior* (f. Fig. 82) aridity is less extreme (see Kimberley, Table 25).

The *High Veld and Lesotho highlands* (g. Fig. 82) lie east of the 20-inch isohyet. From this minimum rainfall increases eastward to 30 inches around Maseru at the foot of the Lesotho highlands, and to 75 inches at the crest of the Drakensberg. On the High Veld the winter drought period generally lasts through June, July and August, when the region is dominated by cT air; for the rest of the year rain in varying amounts is brought by disturbances of both tropical and mid-latitude origin. The barrier of the Drakensberg cuts off the South-East Trades; for most of the time the High Veld and Lesotho lie above the shallow layers of maritime air affecting the Natal margins. The seasonal summer rain of the High Veld is now known not to be a monsoon effect.

Rainfall characteristics

On the High Veld the rainfall is mainly associated with thunderstorms, due partly to the convectional instability of air-masses passing over the hot land surface. This area is known to be one of the most thundery in the world. One characteristic of the resultant rainfall is its intensity. On the Witwatersrand, for instance, about one-quarter of the rain falls in showers depositing more than one inch at a time. This characteristic also applies to the east coast belt where the rain liberated by the mT air is also concentrated in short periods. In March 1940 Eshowe, the capital of Zululand, experienced no less than 23 inches in 36 hours, and though this is exceptional, it serves to emphasise that rainfall concentrated in this way can do much damage by flooding and soil erosion; it is also very wasteful of water. Another aspect of the rainfall of South Africa, especially important for agriculture, is its reliability. In general it appears that the rainfall is most reliable in areas where it is heaviest, and conversely least reliable in the drier parts. This explains the necessity for irrigation over so much of South Africa, and it also shows how precarious farming can be in areas where rainfall amounts are marginal. There are, too, few parts of South Africa which never experience drought; the interior and parts of the High Veld seem to be most prone to this.

The effectiveness of the rainfall must also be considered. This is especially important in the summer rainfall zone, where temperatures—and therefore evaporation losses—are highest at the time of the rain. Figures for evaporation from an open water tank vary from about 50 to 110 inches per year in different parts of South Africa. Very few parts have the necessary rainfall to offset such potential losses, but, of course, the figures are misleading to some extent, since the natural ground surface is never continuously wet. Few measurements of evaporation losses from various types of ground surface have yet been made; and the same applies to transpiration losses from crops. Experiments at Pretoria showed that maize growing on a gentle slope there needed 25–35 inches of rain per year; of this about 50 per cent was used by the crop, and about 35 per cent lost by evaporation, most of the remaining 15 per cent being accounted for by run-off and percolation.

VEGETATION

The principal vegetation zones stand out clearly on Fig. 83; most extensive is the vegetation of the semi-arid zones—the Karroo and desert scrub. Secondly, and most important from the viewpoint of farming, there are the several grassland types, principally on the High Veld. Smaller areas are occupied by the maquis of the Cape, the savanna or tree veld of the east and north-east, and the various forest types. It should be emphasised that changes of vegetation between one zone and the next often occur very gradually: the grassland of the High Veld, for instance, grades imperceptibly west into the semi-desert. The extensive areas classed as semi-desert serve to emphasise how inadequate rainfall is over much of South Africa. It must also be remembered that the vegetation has been greatly modified by human interference: the temperate evergreen forest, which now occupies only a fraction of 1 per cent of the total area, was undoubtedly more widespread before the arrival of the Bantu or Europeans; the Cape maquis has been much thinned and impoverished by goats; and large areas of the Veld are still subject to regular burning.

Grassland generally occupies the land over 4,000 feet with more than 15 inches of rain annually. Tree growth is restricted by the relatively low winter temperatures, for here the frost period may be 120–180 days. The principal species, occupying 60 per cent of the area, is the 'red grass', so called from its brownish colour as it dries out in autumn after the rains. According to the particular variety, it attains a height of 1 to 3 feet; and it is recognised as one of the best pasture grasses in South Africa. The main problem for stock rearing on the High Veld is the lack of rainfall outside the period October–March. Grass growth is limited to this period of

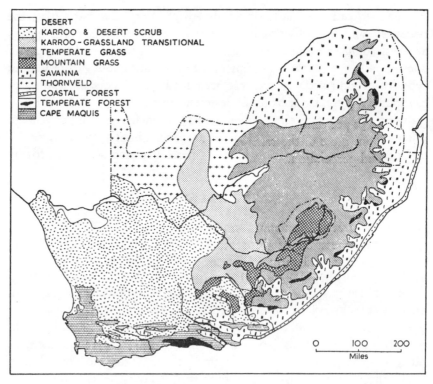

DESERT
KARROO & DESERT SCRUB
KARROO - GRASSLAND TRANSITIONAL
TEMPERATE GRASS
MOUNTAIN GRASS
SAVANNA
THORNVELD
COASTAL FOREST
TEMPERATE FOREST
CAPE MAQUIS

0   100   200
Miles

Figure 83 *The vegetation of South Africa*

summer rain, and grasses quickly lose their nutritional value in the winter. Provision of supplementary winter feed for animals is thus of vital importance for successful stock rearing. To encourage grass growth at the beginning of the rains, removal of dead grass is essential. To do this, farmers often resort to veld burning, a practice which may be very injurious if the land is thereby laid bare to heavy rain showers.

The typical Karroo vegetation of western Cape Province consists of small scattered shrubs and bushes, varying in height from a few inches to 2 or 3 feet according to the degree of aridity, but all possessing great resistance to drought. A few coarse grasses may cover the spaces between them, but much bare land is apparent, and is in fact becoming more widespread with overgrazing. As a pastoral area the Karroo is only fit for sheep, and the maximum carrying capacity of good Karroo has been estimated at no more than six sheep per acre.

Southwards the Karroo grades into the Cape maquis, also of limited pastoral value except for sheep and goats; and goats are exceedingly destructive. The maquis consists of drought-resisting evergreen shrubs, grasses only appearing on some of the wetter parts. It should be noted that the map (Fig. 83) is inevitably generalised, and cannot show the many changes of vegetation associated with the individual Cape Ranges.

The savanna in South Africa is generally known as bushveld. It is found mostly in areas below 4,000 feet, and with at least 15 inches of rain annually; again, a gradual transition is effected both to the higher grass-land and to the Karroo and maquis in the south. The density and type of tree growth vary greatly. All varieties of savanna are represented from open woodland at one extreme to grassland with only scattered trees at the other. Both evergreen and deciduous trees occur.

SOILS

There is a great variety of soils, arising from variations of relief and rain-fall, and from the fact that temperatures in sub-tropical regions are often critical for certain soil-forming processes. Both podsolic and lateritic soils occur in South Africa. The strong relief associated with the various escarpments and the dissection of the coastal margins have given rise to many immature soils. In such areas parent rock type is often the principal determinant of soil character. Soils are also closely related to parent rock in the case of certain areas of volcanic and intrusive rocks—as in the Transvaal bushveld, or in the areas of upper Karroo basalts.

Few South African soils have an adequate humus content. This is mainly because of the limited vegetation cover over the western two-thirds of the country, including the Cape region, and the leaching in the wetter areas; but it is also the result of such practices as mono-culture and overgrazing. In most areas under crops, fertilisers and some form of crop rotation are much needed to combat deficiencies in the soil.

Lateritic soils occur in areas with more than 20 inches of rain, and are better developed with more than 35 inches, combined with annual average temperatures of over 65°F. Under natural conditions these soils support grassland and occasional forest; cultivation succeeds well initially, but thereafter the soils become quickly exhausted and liable to erosion.

The High Veld is characterised by fairly acid podsolic soils, often low in humus content; but in certain areas of dolerite outcrops the soil improves to a black clay, excellent for maize. Black clays are also associated with the igneous rocks of the Bushveld Basin; in fact, accumulated minerals probably make them the most potentially fertile soils of South Africa, but unfortunately the rainfall is precariously low. Soils of the Cape region tend to be podsolic, generally immature and lacking in humus. Probably the best are the mildly acid loams associated with the Bokkeveld shales.

The soils of South Africa, like those of all other countries with seasonal rainfall occurring in heavy and spasmodic showers, are extremely vulnerable to erosion. In the 1930's South Africa became known as one of the most severely eroded countries in the world. Numerous physical and economic factors contributed to this. Undulating or broken relief is characteristic of areas outside the Great Escarpment, and of those parts of the plateaux dissected by rivers; on the numerous steep slopes run-off is rapid and its erosive power considerable. Rain falling in torrential showers after dry periods when the soil hardens also encourages rapid run-off. In the drier parts vegetation is too sparse to have much binding effect on the soil. Man has contributed to the problem by many agricultural malpractices. In the pioneer days the European settlers thought little about such matters, with the result that pastures became dust-bowls, and arable land was gashed by gullying. The heavy rains washed away soil that in periods of drought had been laid bare by overstocking or unsuccessful cultivation. Veld-burning was another injurious practice, not yet eliminated in fact, while the spread of maize monoculture in the 1920's was a major factor in soil deterioration over large areas and the onset of appalling soil erosion in the 1930's. In the African areas overstocking and uncontrolled grazing have always represented the greatest menace to the soils because these practices are so widespread; cultivated land is less extensive, but is often characterised by severe gully erosion, leaving steep ridges of bare red soil.

The general situation today is far better than it was up to World War II. With the appreciation of the scale on which valuable land was then being destroyed, and the simultaneous realisation that South African agriculture had to be intensified and expanded, the government intervened, beginning with the Forest and Veld Conservation Act of 1941. Since then the improvement of agriculture, aided by agricultural research stations and the universities which have made intensive studies of soils, crop rotations, grassland management, etc., has gone far to remedy the situation in many areas. Better farming techniques, greater use of machinery and fertilisers, and diversification of farming now play their part in soil conservation. On the other hand, the problem of erosion still remains acute in the Native Reserves.

41

Farming

'South Africans rightly regard the land and its potential development as the most important economic feature of their country' (J. H. WELLINGTON). Many reasons, chief among them the expansion of the population and the growth of agriculturally non-productive urban centres, have made it imperative to expand the national food supply. It is estimated that a quarter of the European population and three-quarters of the African are directly engaged in agriculture. Yet in recent years agriculture has accounted for only one-seventh of the national income. South Africans are fully aware that agriculture in their country labours under many natural disadvantages. At present no more than 7 per cent of the land is cultivated. Large areas suffer from deficiency or irregularity of rainfall, and nearly all parts experience seasonal drought. The better-watered land is often hilly and liable to soil erosion; the soils themselves are commonly poor. Underground water supplies are sometimes too saline for safe use, while highly variable river régimes and unsuitable topography limit the opportunities for irrigation agriculture. In addition to these problems the farmer must contend with a variety of crop diseases and insect pests.

Farms vary greatly in size, from the vast 10,000-acre ranches in north-western Cape Province to farms of less than 100 acres in areas of intensive agriculture near towns or on irrigated land. Arising from the limitations of the environment, and, in particular, low rainfall, pastoral farming has always been the most characteristic form of land-use and has always provided a major share of the agricultural income. It is reckoned that 80 per cent of South Africa is suited only to pastoralism, and in many parts pastoralism of a very limited nature. *Sheep rearing* is most wide-spread, since it is best adapted to semi-arid conditions. About three-quarters of the sheep are merinos, introduced in 1789 and bred almost entirely for their wool. South Africa is well known as one of the five great wool-producing countries of the world, and wool usually takes second place (after gold) in the export trade. Back in 1867, before the mining era, wool furnished three-quarters of South Africa's exports. The best conditions for sheep rearing, both in respect of the carrying capacity of the pasture and the yield of wool, are found on the High Veld. The Karroo, although the pasture it provides is inferior, is an even more extensive area of sheep farming. Over 80 per cent of the annual wool clip comes from Cape Province and the Orange Free State. In contrast, Natal and most of the Transvaal have few sheep.

The distribution of *cattle* is more limited, as most of the western interior is ruled out by aridity. Tsetse fly is a restrictive factor only in Zululand. The greatest concentrations of cattle are in the east, where large numbers are native-owned and of poor quality. Beef cattle are the most widespread, whereas dairy cattle are not found in the drier parts or in the warmer low-lying regions of the east and north. Cattle kept primarily for fresh milk are concentrated around the main urban areas such as the Witwatersrand or the Cape lowlands. Natal, however, lacks any area of intensive fresh-milk production, in spite of the existence of Durban, partly because of the warm climate and partly because much of the land is devoted to Native Reserves, or with various forms of monoculture, especially for sugar around Durban. More important than fresh milk in South Africa is the production of cream and butterfat; dairy cattle kept for these purposes are more widely distributed. The best grazing land, as for sheep, is the High Veld, but even here the winter drought is a serious problem, making it necessary to supply extra feed when the grass dries up.

Until about 1900 South Africa was a mainly pastoral country, although in the nineteenth century two crops of outstanding importance were introduced—maize and sugar-cane. Since 1900 arable farming has expanded; today the Republic is the principal crop-producing country of southern Africa. Several events stimulated this expansion of arable farming—the two world wars, demonstrating the need for greater self-sufficiency in food production; the world economic depression of the early 1930's, which led to the South African Government's first measures to improve and stabilise agriculture (for example, in the construction of the first major irrigation projects and the introduction of protective tariffs); and, above all, the expansion of urban population associated with the growth of industry. The years since World War II have seen great changes in agriculture in the European-farming areas, particularly in mechanisation (over 120,000 tractors in 1958 compared with 6,000 in

1937) and the improvement of soils, crops and livestock. At the same time it must be stressed that only a very small proportion of the total land area is under crops at present—5 per cent or about 23 million acres—and that because of the adverse physical environment it is unlikely that this figure will ever be raised to more than 7 or 8 per cent, even taking into account the several ambitious irrigation projects being contemplated.

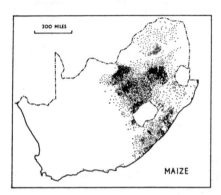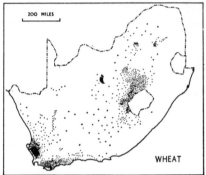

Figure 84 *Maize and wheat production in the Republic of South Africa.*
1 dot represents about 5,000 bags of 200 lb. each. The total volume
of maize produced is more than five times that of wheat

The most important cereal grown in South Africa is *maize,* principal food crop of the Africans and occupying 10 million acres on European farms. It is found almost entirely within the summer rainfall region of the east, and by far the larger part is concentrated in the 'maize triangle' on the High Veld (see page 483 and Fig. 84). *Wheat* (Fig. 84) is grown much less extensively (3 million acres). Only the winter rainfall area of the south-west is really suitable for wheat, but it is also found in many more marginal areas. The main reason is that wheat is subsidised and protected by tariffs in order to maintain home production; wheat is one of the few farm products whose output falls behind the Republic's needs.

Sugar-cane is concentrated in Natal, where at present the sugar industry is a prosperous one, in spite of the fact that the climate is distinctly marginal for the crop. *Fruit* is generally the fifth most important export of South Africa, the greater part being sent to Britain. The large September–October shipments of citrus fruit arrive in Britain at a time when there is little competition from other fruit-producing areas. Citrus fruits are produced under a wide variety of conditions in several eastern parts of

South Africa (Fig. 85). All are below 4,000 feet in frost-free areas, and irrigation is essential. The northern Transvaal is a major producing area, though most of the fruit is shipped from Cape Town since it must reach the British market as quickly as possible. Deciduous fruits are concentrated in the south and south-west, where average winter temperatures are usually, but not always, low enough to maintain a necessary dormant period for the trees, but where summers are warm and sunny with little risk of late frost.

A distinguishing feature of agriculture in the south-western Cape is the *vine* (Fig. 85), which flourishes in the typical Mediterranean climate, with irrigation in the interior valleys. The export of wines is gradually being built up in spite of the costs of transport to Europe, competition with European wines and a certain lingering prejudice against South African wines and spirits. Table grapes, raisins and sultanas make an important contribution to fruit exports.

FARMING REGIONS (Fig. 86)

A. THE HIGH VELD This is the most important area of European farming in South Africa. The land undulates gently between 4,000 and 6,000 feet; rainfall is normally between 20 and 30 inches and long droughts are uncommon in the rainy season, though some irregularity is apparent. It is, however, an area of summer rainfall, and therefore subject to heavy evaporation losses. Average temperatures vary from about 45°F in July to 70°F in January. Most of the High Veld is in pasture, but it also contains over three-quarters of all the arable land in the Republic. The natural grasses provide excellent sheep pasture. Most of the sheep are merinos, bred for their wool and brought here in the early nineteenth century by the original Boer settlers. Both beef and dairy cattle are also kept, with the emphasis on the latter; milk production for the cities of the Rand is important. The chief problem for stock-rearing on the High Veld is the supply of winter feed, and increasing attention is now being paid to fodder crops such as lucerne.

The outstanding crop of the High Veld is maize. It is concentrated in the so-called 'maize triangle', whose corners are approximately provided by Mafeking, Carolina and Ladybrand. This is a zone where a number of relatively favourable conditions for maize are combined, among them sufficient rainfall, flat land, and soils which are not highly fertile but above average for South Africa. Soil types range from black clays on dolerite

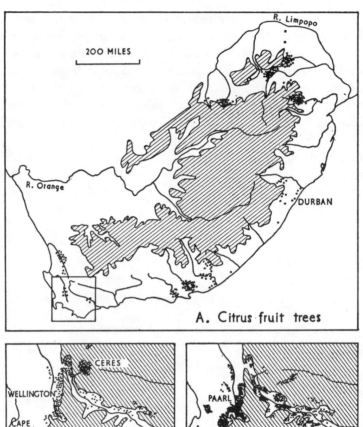

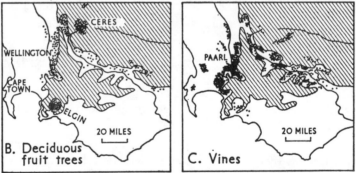

Figure 85 *Fruit and vine growing in South Africa*

A. 1 dot = 20,000 citrus trees. Land over 4,000 feet shaded

B. The south-western Cape
   1 dot = 20,000 deciduous trees. Land over 1,000 feet shaded

C. The south-western Cape
   1 dot = 250,000 vines. Land over 1,000 feet shaded

The area covered by B and C is indicated by the rectangle on A. For other place-names in the south-western Cape region, see Figure 87 outcrops to sandy loams. The maize triangle produces about two-thirds of the Republic's maize. The term 'maize triangle' is, however, misleading in two respects: maize actually occupies no more than 15 per cent of the area (much of the rest being pasture), and the original system of maize monoculture which became so prevalent in the 1920's, is gradually being replaced by more mixed farming and crop rotation. In the past, successive crops of maize without the application of fertilisers quickly led to soil exhaustion. Even today yields of maize are comparatively low (on average only one quarter of the yield common in Argentina) unless expensive fertilisers are used. The main maize-collecting centres are Kroonstad and Bethlehem; a considerable part of the maize

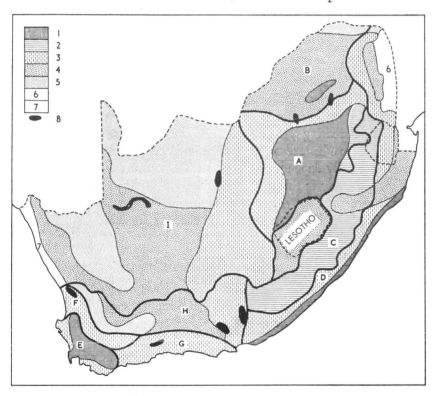

Figure 86 *Land classification and major land-use regions of South Africa* (adapted from J. H. Wellington, 1955 and 1932)

1. Intensive arable. 2. Intensive pastoral. 3. Semi-intensive arable and pastoral 4. Extensive pastoral and arable. 5. Ultra-extensive pastoral. 6. Game Reserve 7. Desert. 8. Major irrigated areas

The letters refer to regions described in the text

crop is exported (value £44 million in 1963) since production is now nearly twice the level of domestic consumption. Other cereals are less important. Wheat is grown as a winter crop—about 30 per cent of the Republic's wheat production; oats and potatoes occupy small areas. On the western margins, where rainfall is less than 20 inches, kaffir corn is found.

Around the built-up area of the Witwatersrand there is a zone of intensive farming—market gardening, dairying, etc. Fresh vegetables for the Rand and other urban areas are also supplied from irrigated land in the Vaal valley to the south and in the Transvaal Bushveld Basin to the north.

B. THE TRANSVAAL BUSHVELD The complex topography of this area has already been noted, but there are also wide areas of flat land, such as the Springbok Flats. As regards climate, the relatively low elevation (average 3,000 feet) and northerly location mean generally warm conditions and freedom from frost; rainfall is seasonal and low, many areas having less than 20 inches, much of which is in any case lost by evaporation. The drier parts are only really suited to extensive cattle grazing. Stock rearing is in fact the main aspect of farming in the region; considerable areas have also been constituted Native Reserves. Cultivation of crops generally depends on irrigation. Cotton, maize and tobacco are grown successively in this way. The Transvaal is the largest producer of tobacco in the Republic, the best-quality leaf coming from the Rustenburg district. Citrus orchards are grouped in three main areas:

1. Around and east of Rustenburg, using water from the Hartebeestpoort Dam on the River Crocodile, and from the River Hex.

2. South of Pietersburg, using tributaries of the River Olifants; the Zebediela Estates on the north-eastern Springbok Flats are probably the world's largest single citrus grove with one million trees planted.

3. Around Nelspruit, on the River Crocodile of the eastern Transvaal lowveld.

There are possibilities of further extending cultivation of sub-tropical crops with irrigation in the northern Transvaal, but the water supply is definitely limited—the majority of streams are not perennial in flow—and communications will have to be improved.

C. THE EASTERN UPLANDS The parts of South Africa lying east of the Great Escarpment, between Swaziland in the north and the Great Fish river in the south, can be conveniently treated in two divisions: the

Eastern Uplands lying above 2,000 feet and the Coastal Region below 2,000 feet. In the Eastern Uplands there are several physical limitations on agriculture. Much of the relief is dissected by the steeply graded rivers, the only reasonably flat areas being in the Midlands of Natal at 2,000–3,000 feet north and south of Pietermaritzburg, and in some river basins, e.g. around Ladysmith. The rainfall is more reliable than in many other parts of South Africa, and generally 30 inches or more, but the winter drought period may be as much as four months in the interior. Soils are often leached and easily eroded. These limitations singly or in combination make large parts of this region unfavourable for arable farming, which together with the poor network of communications explains why the area has less than one-tenth of the cropland of South Africa in spite of the relatively high rainfall. Large areas are also taken up by Native Reserves (see p. 524), where the Africans keep great numbers of poor-quality cattle and engage only in limited subsistence agriculture. On the European farms beef and dairy cattle are most important, utilising the natural tall grasses; some very successful attempts have been made to improve the pasture by introducing new grasses. Maize and kaffir corn are the principal crops. A product peculiar to this area of South Africa is wattle bark, which is used for tanning. The wattle trees are grown either on plantations or on private farms, at elevations between 2,000 and 4,000 feet.

D. THE EASTERN COASTAL REGION Sub-tropical temperatures prevail throughout the year (65°–75°F average), and the rainfall of some parts exceeds 40 inches. There are, nevertheless, pockets of drier conditions where hill ranges cause rain-shadow effects, and the rainfall may also be erratic. The relief is more subdued than in the adjacent Eastern Uplands, but does not warrant the term 'coastal plain'. Native Reserves again occupy considerable areas. The main aspect of European agriculture is the cultivation of tropical cash crops. Sugar-cane first planted in 1847 occupies by far the greatest area of cultivated land, in a belt stretching for roughly 100 miles from Durban to Eshowe, the capital of Zululand. From the coast to about 20 miles inland the low rounded hills are covered with cane growing up to 8 feet tall. Climatic conditions are distinctly marginal for sugar-cane: rather low temperatures, with some risk of frost in interior valleys, plus a rainfall which is rather undependable and on the low side for sugar, are the chief problems. Consumption of sugar in the Republic is rising, but there is nevertheless an increasing surplus for export. Exports in 1950 only amounted to 89,000 tons, but by 1962 had reached 552,000 tons, out of 1,100,000 tons produced. Crops other than sugar occupy far smaller areas. Cotton growing is increasing in the northern parts, while citrus orchards are located chiefly in the Durban–Pietermaritzburg area and in the Mooi valley.

E. THE CAPE REGION (Fig. 87) The unique feature of this region is a winter rainfall (10 to 30 inches) sufficient for arable farming. The region lies outside the major Cape Ranges, extending from the mouth of the Great Berg river in the north to Cape Agulhas in the south, and inland to the foot of the Drakenstein Mountains, 30 miles east of Cape Town.

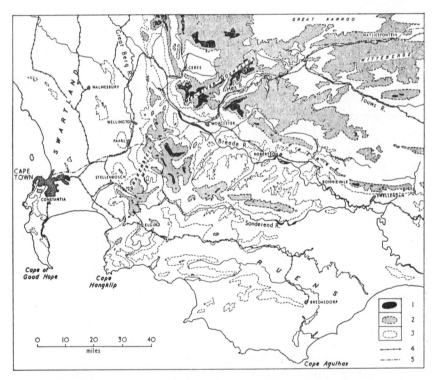

Figure 87 *The south-western Cape region*
1. Land over 5,000 feet. 2. Land over 3,000 feet. 3. Land over 1,000 feet.
4. Main railways. 5. The main road from Cape Town to the interior via Paarl, du Toits Kloof, and Worcester
The highest point on the map is 7,386 feet, near the north-eastern end of the Hex River Mountains

South Africa House

11 A typical Zulu kraal in northern Natal, showing the traditional round huts, and an enclosure for cattle. Part of a second kraal can be seen on the right beyond the track

South African Information Service

12 (A) A typical wine farm in Cape Province, South Africa

12 (B) A vineyard in the Paarl Valley. The vines are trellised to facilitate cultivation and to protect the grapes from the sun

South African Information Service

Most of the land consists of rolling hills below 1,000 feet; apart from the Drakenstein Mountains themselves (which exceed 5,000 feet) there are few hills which exceed 3,000 feet. This is the part of South Africa which was first settled by Europeans. The Dutch colonists in the seventeenth century established wheat farming and vineyards, and these have remained the principal features of the agriculture. More wheat is grown here than in any other parts of South Africa, especially on the gently undulating areas of Swartland northwards from Cape Town to the Great Berg river, and the Ruens between Bredasdorp and Swellendam in the south. Yields, however, are low (about half those commonly obtained in the USA) and reflect the poverty of the soil. The wheat is usually grown in rotation with oats and other cereals. Sheep farming is successfully practised, sometimes using stubble or fallow lands; the natural pasture is too poor for cattle. But on the lowlands immediately north of Cape Town more intensive mixed farming is found, with dairy cattle based on old-established and improved pastures, and on fodder crops. Nearly half of Cape Town's milk is supplied within a radius of 20 miles from the city.

The principal vine-growing areas are shown on Fig. 85. The distinction between those west of the main Cape Ranges, and those of the drier interior and the Breede valley where irrigation is essential, is clearly seen. The first Cape wine was pressed by Jan van Riebeeck in 1659. He made 4 gallons. The vintage today is about 70 million gallons. In the early years vine growing was concentrated in the vicinity of Cape Town, especially in the Constantia valley. In the early eighteenth century it spread to the foot of the Drakenstein Mountains. Centres such as Stellenbosch, Paarl and Wellington came into being, and vineyards adorned the mountain slopes and valleys where rainfall was sufficient (Plates 12A-B). Later, viticulture moved over the mountains to the valley of the Breede river flowing past Worcester and Bonnievale, an area included under the next regional heading because of its greater aridity. Irrigation for vineyards becomes essential when the rainfall drops much below 20 inches.

A relatively new development in the Cape region is olive growing. The main olive-growing district today is found around Wellington, Paarl and Stellenbosch, well away from the sea, with at least 10 inches of rainfall, and with the lowest mean monthly temperatures below 54°F. Although a species of wild olive is indigenous to South Africa, and climatic conditions in the south-west are broadly comparable with the main olive-growing regions of the Mediterranean, commercial olive growing dates only from 1935.

F. THE DRY SOUTH-WEST The rain-shadow effect of the mountains separating this region from the previous one means that most crops, including the vine, can only be grown with irrigation. Fortunately the region contains several large rivers which draw on ground water in the dry season and are therefore perennial—the Olifants, Breede, Hex, the rivers draining the Ceres valley, and others. Due to the need for irrigation, only the flat valley floors can be cultivated. Orchards and vineyards are most important, producing citrus and deciduous fruits, grapes, wines and brandy. Specialities include peaches from Elgin and Ceres, and pears from Ceres and the Hex valley. The Hex valley produces half the Republic's exports of table grapes. Some tobacco is grown, together with winter crops of oats and barley. The unirrigated land generally provides only poor sheep grazing, though some of the lower mountain slopes have been used for government forestry plantations.

The several small towns in the region, including Clanwilliam, Worcester, Robertson and others already mentioned, are primarily concerned with fruit packing and drying, and the manufacture of wines and spirits. The region is well placed for export through Cape Town.

G. THE SOUTHERN COASTAL REGION From the Breede river in the west to Port Elizabeth in the east there is a narrow coastal strip lying south of the Langeberge and Outeniqua Mountains which receives rain all the year round, amounting to 20 or 25 inches in most parts, and up to 50 inches on the southward-facing slopes of the mountains. In this region we can also include the lower Gamtoos valley which opens out between Port Elizabeth and Humansdorp. A great variety is apparent in the pattern of land-use; grass grows well in the relatively humid conditions, and both sheep and cattle are found. The main crops are oats and potatoes, followed by wheat; fruit orchards are deciduous (apples and pears particularly) and also citrus trees on the rich alluvial floor of the Gamtoos valley. This valley is intensively cultivated and possseses the most valued land of the region.

H. THE KARROO Under this heading are included the Great and Little Karroo, together with several of the Cape Ranges such as the Swartberge and Witteberge. The northern limit of the region is provided by the

Great Escarpment; eastward the Great Fish river is a convenient boundary though there is actually a gradual transition to regions (c) and (d). The climate is generally semi-arid: rainfall is less than 15 inches and in parts less than 10 inches; consequently, irrigation is essential for agriculture. Stream flow is generally intermittent, so that storage dams are required. In this way the waters of the Great Fish (with the Grassridge Dam), Sundays (with the Van Rynevelds Dam and Lake Mentz), Olifants, Dwyka, Gamka and Touws rivers have been utilised (Fig. 88). The irrigated valley floors support citrus orchards in the case of the Great Fish and lower Sundays rivers; there are considerable problems here of rapid silting of the reservoirs; four reservoirs built 1920–5 ten years later showed losses in storage capacity of 43, 33, 25 and 14 per cent. Also it is important to avoid letting the alkali content of the water become too high as a result of evaporation in the reservoirs. Other crops grown on the irrigated land include lucerne, tobacco and also grapes. Oudtshoorn is the centre of intensive farming in the Olifants valley. Apart from the irrigable land, the Karroo is useful only as grazing for sheep and goats. The carrying capacity of the Karroo shrubs is very low—one sheep per 10 acres in many parts—so that farms here are large (up to 10,000 acres). The animals are kept for their wool and mohair.

(I) THE DRY PLATEAU REGIONS The Great Escarpment provides a physical boundary to the south and west; eastward this region merges gradually into the High Veld. No rigid limit can therefore be drawn in this direction, though from the point of view of land-use the 20-inch isohyet provides a convenient dividing line, west of which agriculture is generally dependent on irrigation. Rainfall decreases steadily to the west and north-west: Kimberley 16 inches, Carnarvon 8 inches, Pella 3 inches. Furthermore, the rainfall is unreliable, with long periods of drought, and some years of practically no rainfall at all in places. Most farms rely on bore-holes to provide water for domestic use and for their livestock. Extensive pastoralism is the characteristic form of land use. Cattle find sparse grazing in the east, but elsewhere sheep are most numerous, and indeed represent the sole interest of some farmers. Everywhere the carrying capacity of the land for animals is low. In the west 20 acres may be needed to sustain each sheep. Consequently, farms are often of great size—40,000 acres or more in some cases.

Entering the region from the east, however, are several rivers of considerable size. The chief ones are the Orange and Vaal, which bring water from the wetter regions of the High Veld and the Lesotho high-lands, and possess régimes that, with storage reservoirs, can provide for irrigation (Fig. 88). The River Orange even in its lower course is a peren-nial stream, though its flow is greatly reduced by evaporation and rela-tively little reaches the Atlantic. Above Aughrabies Falls there are stretches of alluvium upstream for about 150 miles which provide suitable land for irrigation. The Buchuberg Dam, 50 miles north-west of Prieska, pro-vides storage to even out fluctuations in the river's flow. Completed in 1934, it has been provided with under-sluices to prevent rapid accumula-tion of silt in the reservoir. So far, about 36,000 acres have been irrigated; about half the land produces crops of lucerne and wheat. Vegetables, maize and fruit occupy smaller areas.

Another important irrigation project, commenced in 1934, is the Vaal–Hartz scheme, just north of Kimberley. Water storage is provided by the Vaaldam (south of Johannesburg); water from this flows down the river for 360 miles before being diverted by a weir and system of canals on to the area between the Vaal and its minor tributary the Hartz. The total available land here is 91,000 acres, of which about three-quarters have so far been irrigated. The soils have proved rather poor, with an underlying lime stratum which promotes waterlogging. The main crops are lucerne, groundnuts, peas and wheat.

Two smaller schemes should be mentioned briefly. One uses water from the Riet river (south of Kimberley) which is held up by the Kalk-fontein Dam, second only in storage capacity to the Vaaldam, to irrigate about 20,000 acres for lucerne, cereals and potatoes. The second is the smaller and old-established system of the Zak River Estates, 150 miles south-west of Prieska, where wheat is sown as the floodwaters of the river, diverted into shallow earth basins, subside.

THE ORANGE RIVER DEVELOPMENT SCHEME (Fig. 88)

The largest existing irrigation and water supply undertakings in South Africa are located in the Vaal Basin, in which the available water re-sources are approaching full utilisation. The Orange river, South Africa's largest, which annually discharges about 11·5 milliard cubic metres into the sea, is now to be harnessed in the boldest long-term project on which the Republic has yet embarked. The project will span thirty years, is to cost more than $560 million, and will eventually bring under new irrigation some 750,000 acres, equivalent to 3 per cent of the total cultivated area. Another aspect of the scheme is the generation of hydro-electricity (200 MW), though this is small compared with the Republic's coal-fired power stations.

The key structure is to be the Hendrik Verwoerd Dam at Doornpoort, about 20 miles below the Caledon confluence. Initially 225 feet high, and

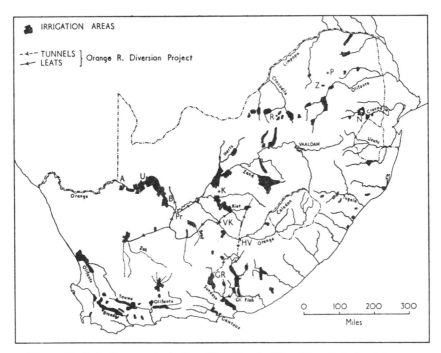

Figure 88 *Irrigation areas in the Republic of South Africa.* Not all the land shown in black is actually in use: the units shown are Administrative areas. Some are government schemes; others are private or municipal schemes

A Aughrabies Falls, B Buchuberg, GR Graaff Reinet, HV Hendrik Verwoerd Dam, K Kimberley, N Nelspruit, P Pietersburg, Pr Prieska, R Rustenburg, U Upington, VK Van der Kloof Dam, Z Zebediela Estates

subsequently to be raised in stages, this dam will impound water for diversion to areas north and south of the river. Northward, a pipeline will take water to the Kaffir river for irrigation, to Bloemfontein and to the Modder valley. But the southern diversion is to be more far-reaching, for, by means of a 51-mile tunnel, water will be led into a headstream of the Great Fish river. The irrigation schemes of the Great Fish and Sundays river valleys have already been mentioned in discussing land-use region

(H). These schemes have proved rather disappointing because of variable river flow arising from erratic rainfall, and because of the high load content of the rivers which is quickly silting up the dams. Measures to reduce the load by controlling soil erosion in the upper reaches are, furthermore, having an adverse effect on the level of water run-off. By the tunnel, about 10 per cent of the flow of the Orange will be brought into the area; there will be a link canal from the Fish river at Cookhouse conducting water to Lake Mentz and the lower Sundays valley, and a 32-mile tunnel from the Grassridge Dam on the upper Fish to Graaff Reinet on the upper Sundays. The extra water will augment the irrigable area to over 500,000 acres in these valleys, and provide a useful surplus for the expanding industrial area around Port Elizabeth.

Eighty miles below the Hendrik Verwoerd Dam the River Orange will pass into the Van der Kloof Dam (depth 270 feet), from which water will be distributed over a vast area of the interior plateau. One canal is to lead to the Brak valley near De Aar, and thence westward to the Zak river, whose small but primitive irrigation scheme has already been mentioned. A branch from this canal will take water to Prieska, under the Orange river by siphon, and into the Witsand area of the southern Kalahari. The third major dam will be just above the Vaal confluence, to control water distribution along the Orange valley to Prieska. At each dam there will be hydro-electric stations; but the largest of these will be at the remote and desolate Aughrabies Falls, where the river plunges 475 feet.

Crops to be grown on the newly irrigated areas will range from lucerne, maize and wheat to fruit and vegetables. The production of lucerne hay and the wider distribution of water will enable sheep farming and wool production to be greatly expanded. The Republic may even become self-sufficient in cotton and wheat.

Although irrigation projects of this magnitude are spectacular and challenging, it must not be forgotten that in many other ways the Republic of South Africa is endeavouring to increase its agricultural potential. The greater use of fertilisers, the more widespread adoption of crop rotations, measures to control soil erosion, improvements to stock and pasture, and the selection of crops capable of yielding high returns per acre on valuable irrigated land, are amongst the ways in which increased agricultural production can be achieved. Expansion of food production is essential for the Republic in view of the increasing size of the urban population, and the possible doubling of the total population by the end of this century; yet much has already been achieved, for whereas at the beginning of the century South Africa was unable to feed herself, today she produces nearly all her food requirements.

THE FISHING INDUSTRY

The fishing industry makes a vital contribution to South Africa's food supply, and to agriculture in general by providing fishmeal fertilisers and feed-stuffs. Most of the fresh fish is caught by trawlers, based mainly on Cape Town, but also at Mossel Bay, Port Elizabeth and East London. By contrast, only 15 per cent of the inshore catch is for fresh or frozen fish; 55 per cent is taken for meal and oil, and 21 per cent for the canneries. The inshore fisheries provide about seven-tenths of the total catch; trawlers three-tenths. The most important fishing ground for both trawlers and inshore fishing is off the west coast, particularly between latitude 33° and the Cape of Good Hope, where the continental shelf is up to 50 miles wide, washed by the cool waters of the Benguela 'current'. The Agulhas Bank, off the south coast, is up to 120 miles wide, but trawling is to some extent impeded here by rock and coral on the sea floor. There is no important trawling ground off the Natal coast. The South African fishing industry could be expanded without difficulty—the total catch has already built up from 22,000 tons in 1939 to about one million tons in 1961 so that South Africa now has the second largest fishing industry in the southern hemisphere—and could supply a much-needed protein addition to the diet of the Africans. It is unfortunate, however, that many Bantu tribes still maintain a prejudice against eating fish.

42

Mining

South Africa is the fortunate possessor of one of the richest mineral areas in the world. Today the Republic alone is responsible for nearly half of Africa's total mineral production by value, while it leads the world in the output of gold, chrome, gem diamonds and platinum, and is the world's third uranium producer.

GOLD MINING

South Africa now supplies two-thirds of the world's gold. Gold was first discovered in the Archaean rocks near Johannesburg in 1853, but the main period of gold mining began in 1886, when, two years after gold-bearing 'reefs' or conglomerates were located in the Witwatersrand System (see p. 462), the Witwatersrand area (or 'Rand') was proclaimed a Public Diggings. Within the next few years bore-holes showed that the gold reef was not just a surface deposit. It was soon found that the gold content of the ore varied considerably from place to place, and even within individual mines, and that it was often low compared with other gold fields, but advances in extraction techniques and the availability of cheap labour have enabled mining of relatively low-grade ores to be profitable. Johannesburg today is the centre of the most concentrated mining area in the world, the key point in a great crescent that stretches 100 miles eastward and the same distance to the west before it sweeps under the Vaal river another 100 miles into the Orange Free State. Strung out along this semicircle are seven major gold fields with over sixty main producers. Each working day more than 20,000 Europeans and 200,000 Africans descend the shafts to bring out the conglomerate containing the gold.

The geological structure of the Witwatersrand gold fields is complex. The Witwatersrand System lies near the base of the Pre-Cambrian sedimentary formations, all of which have been folded and faulted, and parts later subjected to erosion. Fig. 89 shows the present outcrops of the System, and arrows indicate the directions in which it is dipping. Until recently it had not been economical to mine at depths much in excess of 8,500 feet, but there are now four mines working at more than 9,500 feet, and the new Western Deep Levels mine plans to win gold from 12,500

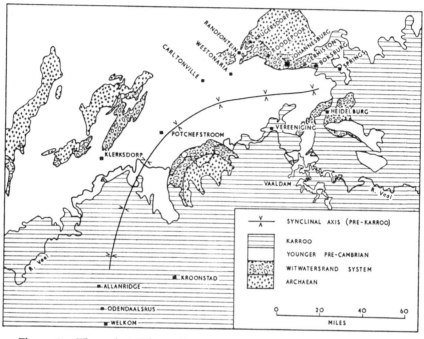

Figure 89 *The geological basis of gold-mining in South Africa.* As the surface outcrops of the Witwatersrand System have now been worked out, it is necessary to determine areas where the System is concealed by later strata but does not lie at excessive depths. In areas where Archaean rocks outcrop at the surface, the Witwatersrand System has clearly been eroded away

feet. At such depths temperatures are high (109°F at 9,000 feet in the Crown Mine), problems of ground pressure, ventilation and dust control are considerable, and haulage of the ore to the surface is costly. Of the gold produced on the Rand since 1887, about half has come from the area known as the Central Rand, roughly between Boksburg and Roodepoort, but since 1920 production here has declined, while the chief mining area shifted first to the east (Springs–Heidelburg) and more recently to the

west (Randfontein–Klerksdorp). The latter district now includes the richest
mine of the Rand yet opened, at West Driefontein, and also the deepest–
Western Deep Levels opened in 1962.

*Table 26   Changes in the location of gold production (% of total output)
in South Africa*

Year	Central Rand	Far East Rand	West Rand	Far West Rand	Klerksdorp	Orange Free State	Others
1895	87	5	5	—	—	—	3
1916	67	24	9	—	—	—	—
1941	35	51	11	2	—	—	I
1956	19	28	5	17	8	20	3

One of the obvious problems faced by any gold mine is the exhaustion
of the ore. Already many mines in the Central Rand have closed down,
such as the Ferreira Deep, opened 1902, closed 1929; and between
February and May 1962 no less than eight mines closed in the East Rand.
The productive life of a mine, however, depends not only on geology,
but on the economic factors which determine the profitability of working
—the price of gold, the cost of extraction and the value of any by-
products obtained. So far, new mines have been opening at a rate faster
than the old ones have been declining, so that the level of gold production
is rising, exceeding $840 million in 1963. The gold-mining companies
have been active in exploration and the opening of new mines, in spite
of the high costs involved—$73 million to open Western Deep Levels,
for instance. Western Deep Levels has an estimated life of 60 years.

An event of the highest importance in recent gold-mining history, and
one which ranks equally with the initial discovery of gold in Africa, has
been the opening and development of an entirely new gold field in the
Orange Free State, south of the River Vaal. This is an area where the
Pre-Cambrian gold-bearing formations are entirely buried by the Karroo
System. The presence of the Witwatersrand System deep below the
surface had long been suspected—in fact it was confirmed by boring in
1934—but thorough exploration has been a slow and costly business.
Nearly 600 diamond-drill bore-holes have been sunk at great cost. The
first gold was produced in 1951; the Orange Free State is now responsible
for nearly one-third of the Republic's production, and the proportion is
likely to rise still further in the near future.

Table 27 Production of gold (in millions of fine ounces)

Year	Orange Free State	Transvaal	Total
1930	—	10·7	10·7
1953	0·4	11·5	11·9
1957	3·8	13·3	17·0
1963	9·2	18·2	27·4

It seems probable that much of the gold ore in the Orange Free State lies at shallower depths (not more than 5,000 feet) than in the Rand, but reef values are more irregular, and temperatures are higher because of the blanketing effect of the Karroo strata. It is thought that production from the Orange Free State will reach its maximum about 1970, and should not begin to show any decline until 1990. A similar forecast has been made for the newly developing Klerksdorp gold field in the Transvaal.

Power supply to the mines is provided by several thermal electric stations, using conveniently local coal. The gold mines account for about 80 per cent of the electricity consumed on the Rand. The Orange Free State gold fields are supplied by a thermal electric station (capacity 300 MW) built at Vierfontein near the Vaal river.

Certain problems are common to all the mines, apart from those of possible exhaustion of the ore and depth of working. Considerable quantities of water are needed not only in the refining processes but also in the mines, where the air must be saturated to control dust from the drills. Furthermore, the mining population living in the vicinity consumes even more water than is used in the mines. In the case of the Rand the mines can make use of underground water which must be pumped from the workings, but in the Orange Free State mines this water is too saline to be usable. The major requirements of the mining areas are drawn·from the Vaaldam on the River Vaal. It is particularly unfortunate that the Witwatersrand is a watershed region, and only the Vaal to the south can supply sufficient water. Furthermore, although the Vaaldam can now (since it was raised another 20 feet in 1956) provide 620 million gallons per day, it has to supply not only the gold mines and the towns of the mining areas, but also irrigation schemes down river (for which the Vaaldam was partly designed) and the rapidly expanding industries which have grown up around the mines. It is estimated that if the present rate of industrial growth is maintained the water supply available from the Vaal river and its tributaries will be wholly absorbed by 1975. One possible solution is that the mines and industry will have to use the available water more efficiently; another is to bring additional water, by pipeline, perhaps first to the Orange Free State mining area, from the Caledon river to the south (see also Chapter 45, Lesotho).

Another major problem facing the mines is labour supply. Even though the mines have by increased efficiency reduced their labour requirements by over 50,000 since 1946, they are still running below capacity due to labour shortage. There are at present 400,000 Africans and 49,000 Europeans employed in gold mining. Wages paid to Africans are low (the average is 10–20 per cent of those paid to Europeans), and limited by legislation; only with the present low wage structure can the gold be mined profitably. The labour supply is drawn from various parts of southern Africa, but especially from the Native Reserves in the Republic, and from Lesotho and Moçambique. Migration from the Reserves to work in the mines is ensured by overpopulation and low incomes from agriculture in these areas. Thus the mines depend on migrant labour, constantly changing and therefore inefficient, and because of low wages and the exclusion of skilled jobs by the operation of the colour bar the African has little incentive to improve his position. The African workers are housed in 'compounds' near the mines; only in the new Orange Free State mines have attempts been made to provide better living conditions, with the hope of attracting a more permanent and stable labour force than is available on the Rand.

The changes in the economy and settlement of South Africa which the mining of gold has brought about are tremendous. Before 1886 the South African economy was based chiefly on agriculture, and settlement was largely peripheral. It is true that the inland towns of both Pretoria and Bloemfontein were founded by the Boers after the Great Trek of 1836, but the Witwatersrand until 1886 was open veld country. Gold played the same part, relatively, in the emergence of South Africa as an economic power as coal did in Great Britain. It proved the most effective means for obtaining surplus wealth with which to purchase from abroad the capital instruments which South Africa so sorely required in order to open up its vast territories and to span them with modern means of communication. Gold has been primarily responsible for the development of southern Africa's biggest concentration of population and industry. The population of Johannesburg and its suburbs alone now exceeds 1 million. In the Orange Free State gold fields the towns are newer and smaller, but growing at a phenomenal rate. Welkom, the chief town with a population of 103,000, including African mine workers, in 1961, did not exist in 1946; Odendaalsrus, where Europeans numbered 483 in 1946, had by 1961 a total of 27,500. In the West Rand there are the new towns of Westonaria (26,500) and Carletonville (51,000), while Klerksdorp has grown from a town of 18,000 in 1946 to 43,000 in 1960. The development of the Witwatersrand gold field has also been responsible for largely determining the present pattern of communications in the interior of South Africa.

The importance of gold mining to the national economy today can hardly be overestimated. It has been reckoned that, directly or indirectly, gold mining affects the lives of well over half the Republic's population. Export of bullion in 1963 amounted to $960 million, without which the Republic would not be able to purchase many of the capital and consumer goods at present imported. The gold mines spend about $280 million a year internally, mainly on purchases of machinery and electric power produced by other South African industries, and distribute about $210 million a year in wages. Internal expenditure on such a scale, together with the fact that the demand for gold is almost unaffected by changes in world economic conditions, mean that gold is a vital stabilising factor in the Republic's economy. Even during periods of economic depression the gold mines continue to spend internally since their product remains saleable, thereby giving a measure of protection to certain other industries in the Republic. On the other hand, the gold mines themselves have experienced rising costs of production not compensated by advances in the price of gold. The dollar price has remained fixed since 1934, and the devaluation of sterling in 1949 has been more than outweighed by the rise in working costs since.

URANIUM MINING

The gold-bearing reefs of the Witwatersrand System contain small amounts of uranium and thorium. Unfortunately, the concentrations are low—about $\frac{1}{2}$ lb. of uranium oxide per ton of ore (equivalent to about one-quarter the yield of the North American ores). But the reserves are immense—they probably represent the world's largest accessible source of uranium, and not only can the uranium be extracted from gold ores currently being mined, but also from the waste material deposited in earlier years from the gold mines. With British and American help, new processes have been designed to extract the uranium profitably: the first

extractor plant was set up in 1949 on the Far West Rand. Today there
are twenty-three gold mines, including seven in the Orange Free State,
which produce uranium; some indeed, such as Randfontein or Dominion
Reefs, now find uranium more profitable than gold. Production in 1958
was valued at $148 million, falling to $103 million in 1962. Uranium production is of great importance to the gold-mining industry, for it has
substantially increased working profits, and has also made it possible to
consider working reefs for gold and uranium together which were of too
low value in gold alone. Most of the uranium is exported to the USA
and Britain; in view of South Africa's abundance of cheap coal, it seems
unlikely that any nuclear power station would be a paying proposition.

DIAMOND MINING

Until diamonds were discovered in South-West Africa in 1908, and later
in other parts of the continent, notably the Congo, Angola, Tanganyika
and Sierra Leone, the Republic was virtually the only source of diamonds
in the world. It was also the discovery of diamonds that made available
much of the capital necessary to open up the gold fields later. The history
of diamonds in South Africa begins with a small boy playing on the banks
of the Orange river, who in 1867 chose a 21¾-carat diamond for a play-
thing. Diamonds were later discovered not only in alluvial deposits but in
volcanic pipes or necks of late Cretaceous–early Tertiary age. These
pipes became the sites of gigantic excavations. An American tourist landing at Kimberley airport said that the city looked as though it had just
survived a nuclear attack, having seen the cratered landscape in the
slanting light of a setting sun. The 'Big Hole' at Kimberley, supposedly
the largest man-made hole on earth, is three-quarters of a mile wide and
1,400 feet deep. One hundred and fifty pipes have now been discovered
and worked, including those at Kimberley (1870), Koffiefontein (1875),
and the Premier Mine (east of Pretoria) opened in 1902. The Premier is
the greatest of all diamond mines, yielding in 1905 the world's largest
diamond, the Cullinan, weighing 1½ lb. The De Beers Company has since
1888 owned practically all the workings, so that systematic mining is
possible, now mostly underground. Of the total production at present,
about 60 per cent by value (85 per cent by weight) are diamonds for
industrial use in drills, cutting tools, etc. Alluvial diamonds come from the
Vaal valley west of Kimberley, from the south-west Transvaal and from
the coast region from the Olifants river northward to Luderitz (the last

area, falling largely within South-West Africa, is considered in Chapter 47). There has been rapid expansion of production since the war. Diamond sales rose from $80 million in 1946 to $260 million in 1962. Production is carefully controlled, and marketing agreements are concluded with other African producers.

COAL MINING

Ninety-seven per cent of Africa's total coal reserves are thought to be located in the Republic. The reserves are immense, and at the present rate of production would last for at least 2,000 years. The coal seams occur in the Karroo System (the richest are in the middle Ecca beds). The main producing areas are:

1. the Witbank–Middleburg district in the Transvaal, only 80 miles east of Johannesburg and the Rand, producing about 19 million tons a year;

2. the Springs–Heidelburg, Ermelo–Breyten, Vereeniging, and other smaller producers; the first and third of these lie even closer to the Rand than those in group 1. Production in 1961 from this group was about 18 million tons. The Cornelia colliery near Vereeniging is the biggest single producer in the southern hemisphere;

3. the North Natal coal field (around Newcastle, Dundee and Vryheid), producing under 7 million tons in 1961.

Three features common to all the coal fields have made mining relatively simple: the seams are generally horizontal, the depth of working is generally small (maximum 200 feet in the Transvaal, and 700 feet in Natal), and there are no important seams thinner than 4 feet (6 to 15 feet is the usual range). In Natal, however, the coal-bearing strata have been invaded by dolerite intrusions, which have not only detrimentally altered the coal in some cases, but make shaft-sinking costly owing to their hardness, and render the workings liable to collapse. In spite of these difficulties the proportion of machine-mined coal in Natal is 75 per cent, while in the Transvaal and Vereeniging fields the proportion is no less than 97 per cent. South African coal is the cheapest in the world to produce, not only because of the ideal conditions for mechanisation but also because of the availability of cheap African labour. However, since practically all distribution must be by rail, the price to the consumer is often largely made up of freight charges. Rail transport merely from Witbank to Johannesburg adds from 40 to 80 per cent on the price of a

ton of coal at the pit-head. The proximity of coal to the Rand mining and
industrial area is thus a great advantage.

About one-quarter of South Africa's coal output is used for the generation of electricity—the cheapest thermal electricity in the world because
of the low price of coal. The other major purchaser of coal, together with
coke produced at the coal fields, is the iron and steel industry. It is unfortunate that reserves of coking coal in the Republic are not great, and
that the best-quality coking coal is not found in the Transvaal, where
most of the iron and steel industry is established, but in Natal. About
half of Natal's output is coking coal. A small amount of coal is exported,
but in recent years no more than 2 per cent of total output. The bunkering
of ships at Durban (mainly steam coal from north Natal, 150 miles
distant) has practically ceased as nearly all vessels now use oil.

OTHER MINERALS

It is impossible here to mention all the other minerals which the Republic
possesses and mines. Output of each of the following has been valued at
more than £3 million annually in recent years: asbestos, copper, iron ore
and pyrites, manganese and chrome. Over 60 per cent of the chrome
output is purchased by the USA. The Republic is also the world's largest
producer of platinum (from Rustenburg in Transvaal), and has immense
reserves of titanium and vanadium. It is, in fact, one of the few countries
in the world which possesses within its boundaries all the minerals needed
for steel-alloy production, including immense reserves of iron ore.

Table 28   *Value of minerals produced, £ Million*

	1938	1950	1955	1962
Gold	51·7	144·8	182·7	318·3
Fissionable materials	—	—	30·0	36·9
Coal	4·7	14·8	17·3	32·8
Diamonds	3·5	14·4	12·4	17·9
Asbestos	0·4	3·6	7·0	13·3
Copper	0·5	5·7	13·5	9·4
Total, including others not named:	63·8	196·7	288·4	474·4

Note: Sterling was devalued in 1949

43

Manufacturing, Transport and Trade

MANUFACTURING

Within the last 100 years the economy of South Africa has passed through two phases and into a third phase. A landscape in which the ox-wagon and the sheep-farm, maize crops and vineyards were the most characteristic features was transformed by gold and diamond discoveries and by the coming of the railway. Mining became the most important aspect of the economy, and gold and diamonds provided the foreign exchange necessary for the import of manufactured goods. Next, stimulated by World War I, manufacturing tentatively began to spread; by 1939 there were 10,000 manufacturing concerns of various sizes in the country, and their rate of increase since then, carrying with it demands for capital and labour, has caused what can only be described as an industrial revolution. Today there is more capital sunk in secondary industries than in all the mines together. Employment in industry has increased more than four-fold since 1930, and the following figures show even more vividly the way in which manufacturing has come to dominate the Republic's economy:

Table 29   The National Income of the Republic of South Africa (£ million)

	1918	1928	1938	1948	1958
Agriculture, forestry and fishing	36·9	49·2	43·9	128·9	244·3
Mining	34·7	50·3	73·2	88·5	256·8
Manufacturing	16·4	35·8	65·8	182·0	487·5
Trade	26·6	42·4	51·8	133·3	248·3
Other	56·3	92·6	138·9	310·5	751·2
Total	170·9	270·3	373·6	843·2	1,988·1

Note: Sterling was devalued in 1949

Industrialisation is helping greatly to provide the Republic with a sounder economy than it formerly possessed; as already observed, agriculture is in many respects precarious and distinctly limited, whilst it must not be forgotten that world demand for the rarer minerals is unpredictable and that eventually many mineral deposits will be exhausted. The present high level of gold production, for instance, is unlikely to last more than another fifty years.

Fuel and power

Coal is the chief fuel and source of power in the Republic. The part it has played in the development of the iron and steel industry will be described later. Other industries, together with the mines, depend chiefly on electrical power, which in turn is at present almost wholly produced from coal. The total capacity of electric power stations is now over 5,200 MW, for South Africa uses nearly twice as much electricity as all the rest of Africa combined. Industry purchases about 18 per cent of the electricity generated, the railways 6 per cent and the mines 53 per cent.

Up to 1954 all the Republic's liquid-fuel requirements were imported, but in that year an oil refinery was opened at Durban with a capacity of $1\frac{1}{2}$ million tons, reducing the need for imports of refined fuel by one-half; and in 1955 production began at the SASOL oil-from-coal plant at Sasolburg, Orange Free State. This plant uses local low-grade coal, and is now producing about 10 per cent of the Republic's petrol requirements, plus other fuels and by-products. It has been designed particularly to serve the Rand conurbations and to eliminate the costs of transport of liquid fuel from the coast to the Rand. Much money has been invested in the project: 1960 was the first year in which a profit was made. SASOL will encourage greater use of diesel-electric traction on the railways—a great advantage for regions where water is scarce—and will in this way be more efficient than any extended electrification of the railways based on coal-burning power stations situated at a distance from the coal fields. In 1963 a second major oil refinery was built at Durban, with a capacity double the first; another smaller one is being built at Cape Town.

Water supply for industry

Apart from agriculture, manufacturing industry is the largest consumer of water in South Africa, far exceeding the mines, the towns or the railways. Industry, too, is concentrated in relatively small areas: three-quarters of the Republic's industrial output comes from the Cape Town, Port Elizabeth–Uitenhage, Durban–Pinetown and South Transvaal areas. It is in the last of these four areas that the problem of water shortage is most acute, for here are concentrated most of the mines, 40 per cent of the white population, 20 per cent of the African population and about one-third of the Republic's industries, including most of the iron and steel industry. The needs of the steel industry and power stations are particularly large; the steel works at Vanderbijl Park alone uses 9 million gallons a day, the new Vierfontein power station 8 million gallons a day and the SASOL oil-from-coal plant about 10 million gallons a day. The Vaal river and its tributaries are the chief source of supply for the South Transvaal industrial region, but industrial water requirements are increasing at such a rate that the next two decades may witness problems of acute water shortage. Already the National Resources Development Council has recommended that no new industries requiring large amounts of water should be established in the Vaal Basin.

The iron and steel industry

The iron and steel industry provides the basic raw material for one of the main groups of manufacturing industry in the Republic, that concerned with engineering and machinery. Steel consumption has increased enormously since the 1930's; nevertheless, the Republic can now produce nearly all her steel requirements, and produce steel in the Rand area at lower cost than that of imported steel which must travel by rail from the coast. Production of steel has increased from less than half a million tons before the war to 2·64 million tons in 1962. Development has taken place in three main areas:

1. PRETORIA The first blast furnace here was built in 1917; an integrated iron and steel works was opened in 1934 by ISCOR (South African Iron and Steel Industrial Corporation Ltd., which produces 90 per cent of the Republic's steel). Most of the iron ore is brought by rail from Thabazimbi, in the Crocodile valley, where high-grade haematite is mined. ISCOR produces 85 per cent of its coke requirements at Pretoria, drawing on low-grade coking coal from Witbank which it mixes with high-grade coking coal from Natal. The remainder of the coke is purchased from independent Natal producers. Limestone for flux, etc., is

neither plentiful nor conveniently situated in the Transvaal; it is worked at Marble Hall and Taungs. Requirements of other minerals—manganese, chrome, flourspar, vanadium, etc.—are met from the Transvaal with the exception of manganese, which is produced at Postmasburg, west of Kimberley. Capacity of the steel plant is about 1·1 million tons.

2. THE RAND Steelworks only are located here, depending on steel scrap, and pig iron produced by ISCOR. Development began in 1911.

3. VEREENIGING Steel works opened in 1913 were also based on scrap, and pig iron from Natal. The most important development, however, was the establishment in 1943 here of ISCOR's most modern integrated iron and steel works—at Vanderbijl Park—complete with coke ovens, blast furnaces, rolling mills, and with a capacity of 1·25 million tons. The raw materials are drawn generally from the sources which supply Pretoria, but the site is superior in several respects. Water from the Vaaldam is close at hand (whereas water for Pretoria has to be pumped over the Rand from Vaaldam); electricity is produced by local power stations using local coal; and it is well situated to supply not only the Rand industrial area just to the north but also the newly developing areas of the Orange Free State to the south and the Far West Rand.

4. NATAL Newcastle produces pig iron, all of which is sold to the Rand and Vereeniging steel works. Coke is provided by the Vryheid collieries; iron ore is either locally obtained from the Coal Measures or brought from Manganore (near Postmasburg) and Thabazimbi. The Newcastle pig-iron producers are hampered by the distance from the markets for pig iron (principally the Rand steel works) and consequent high transport costs.

The general location of the main iron and steel works in the Republic is clearly determined not only by the location of raw materials and essential services, including water supply, but also by the situation of the markets for which the steel is destined. Cost of transport is the chief locational factor, and it is the one reason why South African steel can be sold on the Rand at prices so far below those for imported steel.

Other manufacturing industries

Manufacturing industry dates back to the early days of European settlement in the Cape region, when local flour mills, tanneries, distilleries, wagon works, etc., were first established. Later, the development of mining stimulated the growth of other industries such as the chemical industry making explosives for the mines and also fertilisers for agriculture. Eventually the revenue obtained from the sale of minerals and the impact of two world wars, which stressed the need for home production of essential goods, prompted the huge growth of manufacturing industry in the last three or four decades. The principal industries, after iron and steel, are:

1. Food processing (28 per cent of annual gross output)
2. Engineering and metal working (27 per cent)
3. Textile and clothing industry (13 per cent)
4. Chemical industry (13 per cent)

About two-thirds of all the raw materials used in these concerns are now home produced, the development of the steel industry having played an important part in this.

1. THE FOOD-PROCESSING INDUSTRY A great variety of products is dealt with. Flour and grain milling is most important, followed by sugar refining. The fruit-canning industry is expanding rapidly, and over three-quarters of its production is exported; it is concentrated in the south-western Cape region and to a lesser extent near other major fruit-growing areas.

2. ENGINEERING AND METAL WORKING Products from this group of industries range from heavy machinery, locomotives and farm equipment to steel tubing, corrugated iron and wire products. Also included are the ship repairing and vehicle-assembly industries. It is estimated that the Republic can now supply 80 per cent of its own industrial plant, such as equipment for the steel, chemical or mining industries. The greater part of the engineering and metal works are located on or near the Rand, close to the markets for the products, not only taking advantage of power and transport facilities, but also enjoying a measure of protection against similar imported products, since the distance from the coast adds transport costs to imported goods.

3. TEXTILES AND CLOTHING The clothing industry, using chiefly Coloured and Indian labour, accounts for about half the output of this

group. Most of the raw materials for it are imported. South Africa's cotton and rayon industry has only developed recently (the first integrated spinning and weaving mill was opened in 1947), but expansion of this side of the textile industry took place rapidly, in spite of the fact that South Africa is only a small cotton producer. The woollen textile industry is in contrast based entirely on home wool production, though it is smaller than the cotton textile industry which supplies industrial fabrics as well as the clothing trade.

4. CHEMICAL INDUSTRY Manufacture of explosives and fertilisers was the dominant aspect until World War II, but there has since been considerable expansion and diversification, based on the wide range of raw materials available, especially coal, salt, phosphates and pyrites. The development of uranium extraction called for large quantities of sulphuric acid and other chemicals; the new SASOL plant also needs sulphuric acid, and in turn supplies ammonium sulphate to the fertiliser industry. Fisons in 1959 completed a £2½ million fertiliser plant at Sasolburg. SASOL is also to be the base for a synthetic-rubber industry, the first in Africa. But the main centre of the chemical industry remains in the Modderfontein–Klipfontein area, north-east of Johannesburg, dominated by explosives and insecticide factories.

These and other South African industries are concentrated into four regions. In order of importance these are the South Transvaal (including the Rand), the Cape Town, Durban and Port Elizabeth districts. Location at a major port is an advantage for any industry requiring imported raw materials, and it also takes advantage of the available market for the goods in the port area. *Durban* (pop. 660,000) has the benefit not only of possessing South Africa's largest harbour but of being the nearest port in the Republic to the Rand. Moreover, it is an area where water is not scarce, in contrast to the Rand. Shipbuilding is important here, and also chemical works. The two major oil refineries have already been noted. *Cape Town* (pop. 746,000) is noted for industries connected with textiles, clothing and food processing; the British Motor Corporation has a vehicle-assembly plant here, and a major oil refinery is under construction. *Port Elizabeth* (pop. 274,000) is the main centre of the footwear industry and tire manufacture, and was chosen by both Ford and General Motors (1924 and 1926) as the site for the first motor-assembly plants in South Africa.

The Witwatersrand area was, until the 1930's, dominated by mining, but since then has been transformed into the greatest industrial region of the Republic, responsible for 40 per cent of the gross manufacturing output. The region extends from Randfontein to Springs, a distance of over 60 miles (Fig. 90). Its industrial development has been mainly in response to the demands of the local market created by the mines and the mining population, and so far has been concentrated in the Central and East

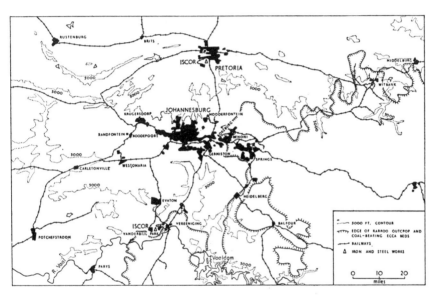

Figure 90 *The Witwatersrand conurbation and adjacent mining and industrial centres.* Three of South Africa's largest coal-mining centres are shown— Vereeniging, Witbank, and Middleburg. The sites of ISCOR steel works at Pretoria and Vanderbijl Park are indicated. Notice how a dozen main railways converge on the Rand

Rand, since it has followed the pattern of mining activity in which these two areas have in turn been dominant. The Central Rand, including *Johannesburg* (pop. 1,221,000) and *Germiston* (pop. 214,000), has major engineering industries, most of them supplying mining equipment; the clothing industry is second in importance to engineering, attracted by the large local population. Johannesburg is the world's chief diamond-cutting centre. On the Eastern Rand industrial development is more recent, especially at *Springs* (pop. 135,000), where railway facilities are good and there is plenty of suitable land. The Western Rand has little

industrial development yet; it is more distant from the sources of many
raw materials such as steel, and it is likely that the opening of the Klerksdorp
and Orange Free State gold fields will now attract industry that once
might have favoured the Western Rand.

Some of the problems which the Witwatersrand faces in its industrial
development have already been indicated: the shortage of water, arising
partly from its watershed position, and its inland location, 300 miles from
the coast. Its location handicaps any industries needing imported raw
materials (e.g. the clothing industry), but also helps to protect certain
other industries from foreign competition. The rapidity of industrialisation on the Rand has led to temporary shortages of iron and steel, and
of power. These are economic problems, but there are also social problems. Although the African population here has doubled since before the
war, shortage of labour is acute, intensified by the competition for labour
between mining and manufacturing. The policy of racial segregation also
raises difficulties, not least of which is the frequent distance of residence
from place of work and the inadequate transport facilities for the workers.

The future rate of expansion of manufacturing industry is uncertain.
A wide range of raw materials and an ample supply of electric power
from coal are available in South Africa, together with an abundant,
though often wastefully used, labour supply. Furthermore, there is a
large potential market for manufactured goods in southern Africa, even
though at present the purchasing power of most of the working population is very low. Probably the chief limitation on further industrial
development in certain areas will be shortage of water. Natal, however,
has a good deal of water potentially available for industrial purposes. A
second cause for concern is the shortage of high-grade coking coal to
support the expanding iron and steel industry. Nevertheless it is certain
that in the more distant future the Republic's economy will rest even
more strongly on industry, in view of the eventual decline in the mining
of gold and other minerals.

TRANSPORT AND TRADE

Transport

South Africa's change from wagon wheels to rails, macadamised roads
and aircraft is a fascinating story. For 200 years after the first arrival of
European settlers at the Cape the trails of ox-drawn wagons alone linked

the coastal centres with their hinterland. Families moved from one district to another in what was probably the most versatile vehicle in the world—the ox-wagon. Long after the great railway boom in England, South Africa's population was too insignificant, her industries too unimportant, her agriculture too pastoral to warrant the great expenditure of railway construction.

Railway construction dates back to 1859, when the building of a line between Cape Town and Wellington was begun. Extension of the railway net quickly followed the diamond and later gold discoveries; Kimberley was linked to both Cape Town and Port Elizabeth by 1885, and the Witwatersrand to all major ports by the turn of the century. By 1910 the track mileage was 7,500. Today it is 13,600 miles, mostly 3 feet 6 inches gauge. The adoption of this narrow gauge dates from the 1870's when the railways were first negotiating the difficult country of the Cape Mountains and Natal, and it still seriously restricts railway capacity.

The Republic now possesses two-thirds of Africa's total railway mileage, a reflection on the state of economic development here as compared with the rest of the continent. The plateau nature of much of South Africa has been an advantage for railway construction; on the other hand, the bounding escarpments and dissected marginal zones have presented great difficulties to the railway engineer, which are only now being gradually overcome at heavy cost. There is no direct rail connection yet between Durban and East London, and Durban itself has only one rail link with the interior. Goods traffic provides over 85 per cent of the railways' revenue, the main items being agricultural produce and minerals (especially coal, coke and iron ore). Since the bulk of the freight either comes from, or is moving to, the southern Transvaal, there is considerable railway congestion in this area and on the lines linking it to the various ports. The first section to be electrified was on the main Durban line in 1926; now 11 per cent of the total track is electrified. The first diesel-electric locomotives were introduced in 1958, and it is expected that they will be of most use in areas where water is short but traffic not sufficient to warrant electrification.

In the virtual absence of navigable waterways the railways are responsible for the distribution of most raw materials and manufactured goods in South Africa. Railway tariff policies have also played an important part in industrial location. In the interests of the national economy, unusually low rates are quoted for raw materials, so that industry is encouraged to develop at the markets for the finished goods. Cost per mile generally decreases with distance, so that the long haul of certain raw materials (necessary in a few cases, e.g. manganese from Postmasburg to Pretoria) is not such a disadvantage as it might seem.

A comprehensive network of roads has been built up in the Republic, covering all the more populous areas. National trunk roads with bitumen surface, however, only total 4,400 miles, and a great many main roads remain unsurfaced. This is partly due to the fact that most heavy goods traffic moves by rail.

Ports and trade

South Africa is not well endowed with naturally sheltered harbours; nevertheless, its three major ports are now among the largest and most modern in Africa. Nearly half the total cargo landed or shipped (11 million tons in 1963) is dealt with by *Durban*, the nearest port in the Republic of South Africa to the southern Transvaal. Durban Bay on which it stands is large and well protected by sandspits. Its size has permitted a spacious layout of the various quays, but the entrance is narrow and would be only a few feet deep without dredging. A minimum depth of 50 feet is now maintained. Major port activities include shipments of coal and manganese ore, sugar, oil bunkering of ships and the import of liquid fuels and machinery.

Cape Town handles 4·5 million tons, less than a quarter of the Republic's trade, but is more important than Durban in bunkering. The docks have been built out into Table Bay which before the construction of the breakwater in 1860 afforded no protection from north-westerly winter gales. Following the rebuilding of the harbour in 1937–40, Cape Town has now the largest dock area of any port in southern Africa, and it also possesses the largest graving dock (opened 1945) in the southern hemisphere. Its export trade is concerned mainly with fruit and other agricultural produce.

Port Elizabeth extends for several miles along the open shores of Algoa Bay, with even less natural protection than Cape Town. The city is built on a bluff running along the edge of the sea, so that many of its streets are steeply graded. The main breakwater enclosing the harbour on the east and south dates from 1927; a new quay built in 1935 can accommodate the largest vessels visiting South Africa. Wool and fruit are the chief outgoing items. *East London* is a much smaller river port, handling similar cargo to Port Elizabeth, but greatly handicapped by silting and the narrowness of the estuary.

An interesting feature of the Republic's trade is the relatively small variation in the tonnage of incoming traffic at these four ports, due mainly to manipulation of railway rates. Of the imports, the largest single item in every case is liquid fuel. On the other hand, tonnage of exports varies greatly, Durban handling nine times as much as East London and three times as much as Cape Town. The port of *Lourenço Marques* has been dealt with in Chapter 38; it handles about one-sixth of the Republic's trade. The proportion has been controlled by international agreement since 1910, for Lourenço Marques is 100 miles nearer the Rand than Durban. Table 30 shows the principal imports and exports of the Republic.

Table 30

Exports, 1963		Imports, 1963	
	(£ million)		
Gold	(No official figures)	Metals, machinery, vehicles, etc.	284·2
Fissionable materials	33·5	Textiles and clothing	92·5
Wool	57·9	Petroleum, etc.	45·6
Diamonds, cut and uncut	43·0	Chemicals and fertilisers	31·6
Fruit	35·2	Food, drink and tobacco	34·8
Maize	44·2	Others	143·9
Asbestos	12·1		
Machinery and vehicles	10·9		
Others and re-exports	258·2		

Nearly half of all exports are destined for the United Kingdom (but only 29 per cent if gold bullion is excluded). The USA purchases a high proportion of the gold output, but only 7 per cent of other exports. Rhodesia, Zambia and Malawi are the next best customers to the United Kingdom for non-bullion exports, taking 13 per cent of the total in 1964, while other African countries took a further 4 per cent. The level of trade between South Africa and Rhodesia increased sharply in 1966 after the imposition by other countries of sanctions on Rhodesia.

44

Population and Settlement

The population of the Republic of South Africa is now over 17 million, of which nearly 12 million are African, and just over 3 million are White. A map of general population distribution shows a definite concentration in certain zones. First, in the eastern half of the country with more humid conditions favouring agriculture; secondly, in the southern Transvaal mining and industrial area, where nearly 3 million people (including half the White population) are clustered; and thirdly, in the coastal regions, particularly around the chief ports. This broad picture, however, is complicated by the contrasts in distribution of the component racial groups (Fig. 91). Thus, for example, two-fifths of the Africans live in areas demarcated as Native Reserves, and the Coloured people are mostly found in Cape Province, while the Asians are concentrated in parts of Natal.

Table 31   Density of population per sq. mile, 1960

	Cape Province	Natal	Transvaal	Orange Free State
White	3·6	10·1	13·3	5·5
African (Bantu)	10·7	63·8	41·7	21·5
Asian	0·1	11·7	0·6	—
Coloured	4·7	1·3	0·9	0·5

Source: Census of the Union of South Africa, September 1960

Over the last few decades the proportion of the population living in towns has shown a steady increase. About 45 per cent of the total population is now classed as urban,* but the proportion of White South

* Urban areas officially comprise 'towns, villages having some form of local urban government, and those which, though having no local form of government, are considered urban in character'.

Africans living in towns has now reached 80 per cent, compared with 68 per cent in 1936. The African population is also becoming increasingly urbanised as a result of the attraction of industry—27 per cent is now classed as urban, a marked rise from the corresponding figure of 17 per cent for 1936. Johannesburg, the largest city, with its suburbs contained a quarter of a million Africans in 1936; by 1945 the number had reached 400,000 and today the figure is over 600,000. Africans have been pouring into this and other cities and towns in such a torrent that in the 1960 Census Pretoria was the only important settlement to keep its White majority (Table 32).

Table 32   Population of towns over 200.000 by racial groups (1960)

Metropolitan area	White	African	Coloured	Asian	Total
Johannesburg	398,517	626,366	58,555	27,467	1,110,905
Cape Town	286,418	66,241	384,408	8,727	745,789
Durban	195,418	206,318	26,979	231,219	659,934
Pretoria	207,202	199,890	7,452	8,046	422,590
Port Elizabeth	94,804	113,833	61,460	4,083	274,180
Germiston	86,156	120,920	4,184	2,382	213,642

Source: Census of the Union of South Africa, September 1960

THE EUROPEANS   Although the two Boer Republics and the two British colonies were united in 1910, differences of language, religion and culture are still strongly marked: the present Dutch community has a distinct language of its own, known as Afrikaans, and the majority of 'Afrikaners' are members of the Dutch Reformed Church.

Partly reflecting the course of history, the English-speaking South Africans are today concentrated in Natal, in the area of Cape Town and other urban centres of the south, and, as a result of the later development of mining and industry, in the southern Transvaal (Fig. 91). The proportion of British South Africans classed as urban is particularly high—about 90 per cent. The Afrikaners in the Republic number about 1·75 million (cf. English-speaking South Africans 1·25 million), and nearly one-third of them are classed as rural: in fact, Afrikaners account for over 80 per cent of the European rural population. However, this situation is gradually changing, as, in recent years, more Afrikaners move into the towns; furthermore, the birth rate among Afrikaners is higher than that of the British South Africans, so that the Afrikaner element is steadily increasing.

There is thus a sharp cleavage in the European community; the

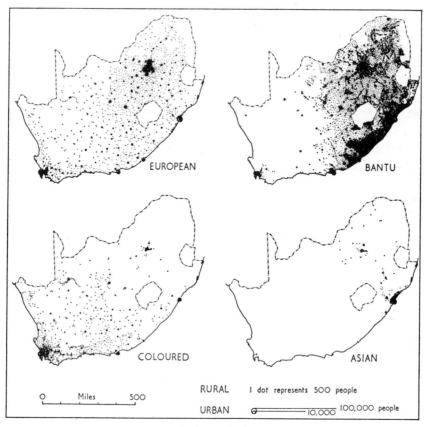

Figure 91 *The distribution of the principal ethnic groups in the Republic of South Africa*

Afrikaners are in the majority, and form the dominant political party. But it is the British South Africans who chiefly control industry, the mines and commerce, whereas many of the Afrikaners have remained on the land, or entered the professions or government service. It is estimated that only one-tenth of the Republic's invested capital is Afrikaner; and it is the Afrikaners who make up most of the class known as the 'poor whites'—those whose standard of living has, for various reasons, not kept up with the general betterment of the European community as a whole.

THE AFRICANS The great majority of the Africans in South Africa are referred to as Bantu (or, in South African official publications, as 'natives'). Most of them are to be found in the eastern half of the Republic (Fig. 91), and over one-third in the Reserve areas of Natal and the Transkei alone. They do not represent the indigenous inhabitants of South Africa. Before the arrival of both Europeans and Bantu-speaking Africans, southern Africa was only thinly peopled with primitive nomads— Hottentots and Bushmen. At about the same time that the Dutch were extending their settlements eastward and north-eastward from the Cape, Bantu-speaking Africans were migrating southward from East Africa, mainly into the warmer, more humid areas of southern Africa, and eventually as far as the area of the Great Kei river, where they encountered Dutch colonists. Present-day Afrikaners thus maintain that their ancestors, and not the Africans, had prior claim to the southern and western parts of the Republic.

Originally the Africans were organised in tribes, living in small villages or 'kraals'. They were pastoralists and shifting cultivators; grazing areas were held in common, though cultivated lands were often controlled by particular families. The only resemblance to this situation today is in the Native Reserves, where 43 per cent of the Africans are found. The rest of the Africans now live in towns (27 per cent) or on European-owned farms (30 per cent). Outside the Native Reserves, which will be considered in more detail later (p. 524), Africans are not permitted to buy land, nor even to own their own homes in the towns. Only in the Reserves has some sort of tribal organisation been maintained, but even here most of the younger men are absent for long periods, working in the mines, factories or on European-owned farms in order to pay taxes and provide part of the subsistence for their families in the Reserves. This system of migrant labour is the main cause of the break-up of the tribes; it is also partly responsible for the deterioration of agriculture in the Reserves. The increase in the numbers of Africans living in the towns has already been noted: the 1960 Census showed 3·5 million, compared with 1·7 million in 1936, and only 600,000 at the beginning of the century. Urbanisation is in fact proceeding at a slightly faster rate among Africans than Europeans: in 1936 Africans made up 38 per cent of the urban population of South Africa, whereas by 1960 the proportion had risen to 45 per cent.

THE ASIANS Equal to only 3 per cent of the total population, this is South Africa's smallest racial group of significance. Ninety-seven per cent of the Asians in the Republic are Indian speaking. With the development by the British of sugar plantations in Natal in the mid-

nineteenth century it was found that the local African population did not
provide a suitable or sufficient labour supply. Permission was gained to
bring over Indians, the first of whom arrived in 1860. The initial period
of contract was for five years; after ten years they were given a choice of
free passage back to India, or a grant of land in Natal. Many, naturally
considering the conditions of poverty and land-pressure in their homeland, chose the latter. Soon the Indians spread to other occupations, as
small farmers, traders or factory workers. Today most of the sugar-
plantation labourers are in fact Africans. With lower standards of living
the Indians were easily able to undercut the European settlers in many
fields, and they began to expand into other parts of South Africa. In 1896
free entry of Indians was prohibited; nevertheless, their natural rate of
increase was such that their numbers rose from 123,000 in 1904 to 461,000
in 1960. The excess of births over deaths today is 28·5 per 1,000 for the
Asians compared with only 16·4 for the Europeans. Attempts were
made from 1911 onwards to induce Indians to return to India, but without much success, since in most cases their standard of living in South
Africa is immeasurably superior to what they could achieve in their
homeland. At the present day most of the Indians are South-African born.
There are relatively few of them outside Natal—virtually none in the
Orange Free State—due mainly to legislation prohibiting their free
movement in the Republic. Nearly half the Indian population is in
Durban and Pietermaritzburg, and another quarter in other large towns
of Natal (Fig. 91).

The presence of the Indian community greatly aggravates South
Africa's racial problems, and while South Africa was a member of the
Commonwealth was a principal cause of friction between her and India,
for White racial discrimination against Indians is as strong as that against
the Africans.

THE COLOURED Numbering 1·25 million, this community forms the
principal ethnic group in western Cape Province (half the Coloured
live within 200 miles of Cape Town); within the whole area of Cape
Province 88 per cent of the total Coloured population of the Republic is
found (Fig. 91). There are almost as many Coloured living in Cape Town
as there are Africans in Johannesburg (see Table 32). The Population
Registration Act of 1950 classified as 'Coloured' all those persons who
did not fall within the four principal ethnic groups—White, native
(African), Asian and Cape Malay. The Cape Malays number only about

65,000, and have often been included within the Coloured group. The Coloured have relatively little Negro blood; they are mainly the result of mixing between Europeans, the indigenous pre-Bantu peoples of the Cape (Bushmen, Hottentots, etc.), and various immigrant Asians, including Malays.

Officially, the Coloured group also includes the few remaining relatively pure-blooded Bushmen and Hottentots of the interior parts of Cape Province. According to a recent survey, only about twenty Bushmen remain in Cape Province and a handful in south-east Transvaal. Elsewhere in the Republic they are extinct.

The economic role of the Coloured is generally to provide unskilled labour for farming or industry in western Cape Province. Traditionally they also included many craftsmen, such as builders or carpenters, but the numbers of these are declining, and nearly 90 per cent are classed as unskilled today. The living standards of the Coloured are generally low; though the birth rate at 50 per 1,000 is higher even than that of the Asians, the death rate is also relatively high, and the infant mortality rate is four times that of the Europeans and twice that of the Asians.

The Republic's present racial policy distinguishes Coloureds sharply from Whites; they are represented in Parliament only by Europeans. Their economic position appears to be steadily deteriorating.

Several distinctive racial groups have thus been thrown together in South Africa. Their distributions overlap, so that the overall pattern of population is complex. But within individual towns or cities there is a definite geographical separation of the residential areas, a separation which the government of South Africa is concerned to maintain and extend. Characteristic of the east of Cape Province, where European, African (here the Xhosa) and Coloured peoples intermingle, is the town of Alice.

Throughout its one hundred years of existence, the European population of Alice has increased only slightly (391 Europeans in 1875 and 750 in 1950). The European residential area, with tarred tree-lined streets, electric light, piped water supply, and other urban amenities, provides a striking contrast to the 'location' areas where Coloured and Native urban inhabitants live. The majority of the Coloured community is housed in a sub-economic housing estate of some 24 houses on the western hill, apart from the European residential area. Overcrowding is rife, as over 200 people live in these tiny 2–3 roomed houses. The rest of the urban community of 365 lives in houses and shacks in the European area of the town. A recent survey carried out among Coloured wage earners reveals a very low standard of living, the average wage being only about £1 10s a week. The native urban community lives mainly in the location of Ntselemanzi on the eastern slopes of Black Hill. The population of Ntselemanzi is 907 which includes 24 Coloureds.

Individual dwellings vary from the square European type of house and oblong, oval, and square huts to the traditional round hut. . . . Roofs are of thatch or of corrugated iron, thatching reeds, roofing timbers and poles being obtained from the pine and wattle plantations on the nearby Amatola mountains. The huts are of wattle and daub, or sun-dried mud bricks, the exterior often being worked attractively with a simple rectangular pattern. Windows are very small and there is often only one room in which all the family activities are carried out. Fortunately the brilliant sun permits many of these activities to be carried on out of doors for much of the year.[3]

In striking contrast to small market towns such as Alice are the great cities of the Republic, the products of European industry and initiative. Johannesburg, known to Africans as Goli, the city of gold, and to the back-country Afrikaners as the Duiwelstad, the Devil's city, is the largest city in Africa after Cairo and Alexandria. Seventy years ago there was hardly a building in Johannesburg, and ten years before that the Voortrekkers grazed their oxen where modern buildings now stand. In September 1886 gold was struck in the Main Reef. Today Johannesburg (Plate 11B) is a vast city of skyscrapers, immense blocks of flats and luxury hotels; though its main streets are wide, traffic congestion is acute, reflecting the rapidity of its commercial growth. Parts of the city and its outskirts are occupied by the huge waste dumps of the mines, great heaps of gleaming white sand marking the course of the golden ridge.

Segregation of the races is maintained as far as possible. Africans live in 'locations' such as Orlando or Alexandra, the shanty towns of the suburbs, except for the mine workers who are housed in 'compounds' or hostels, and the servants in white households.

RACIAL POLICY

'The uniqueness of the South African situation lies in the attempts to achieve for [the] four widely different cultural groups an adjustment to, and a pattern for peaceful co-existence in, a marginal environment.'[4] It is the policy of the present South African Government to introduce gradual separation of the main racial groups. This is the policy of 'apartheid', meaning the separate development of the races in South Africa, so far as their economic interdependence will allow. The reasons for the adoption of this policy are several, but the two chief ones are first to ensure the survival of a 'White South Africa' (districts where more than 40 per cent of the population is European are now relatively few), and secondly to allow the Bantu and other non-European groups to develop their own areas, with greater opportunities for advancement than are at present available in a mixed society. It is, however, recognised that total separation of the races is impracticable, because of the dependence of South Africa's economy on non-White labour for agriculture and industry. It is hoped that 'apartheid' will make possible greater control over the system of migrant labour which has harmed both the urban and rural economy.

Apartheid faces its greatest problems in the large industrial centres, particularly those of the Witwatersrand. The development of industry has been primarily responsible for increasing urbanisation of both Europeans and Africans, the general effect of which is to increase the economic integration of the two main groups—a process exactly opposed to the policy of apartheid.

In 1955 the Tomlinson Commission[5] put forward a plan for development of separate Bantu areas (including the present Native Reserves). The various proposals discussed in its report included the following:

1. More efficient use should be made of the native lands than is the case at present; native farmers should be helped to improve their land and stock, and soil erosion brought under control.

2. Irrigation should be developed where possible, and cash crops introduced.

3. Industries should be established within the Bantu areas. (This proposal was later rejected by the government in favour of developing industries on the margins of the Bantu Reserves, but within the European areas.)

4. The removal of all Africans (a relatively small number outside Cape Town, in fact) eventually from part of western Cape Province, where only Europeans and Coloureds should be allowed to remain.

On the basis of these and other proposals, the Tomlinson Commission considered that the Bantu Reserves could support 8 million people, with only partial dependence on labour migration, compared with the present 3·6 million population of the Reserves. But even if this is possible, it does not take into account the rate of increase of the African population.

So far only some of the Tomlinson proposals (including 1, 2 and 4 above) have been accepted by the South African Government.

Native Reserves (Fig. 92)

The idea of a permanent home for the majority of the African population originated in the Native Land Act of 1913. A series of reserved areas was demarcated, mostly in the east, amounting to 13 per cent of the total area of the Republic of South Africa. The Transkei, recently granted a measure of internal self-government, is the largest, accounting for about a quarter of the total Reserve area and lying between the Natal border and the Great Kei river. Zululand, the second largest Reserve, represents about 14 per cent of the Reserve area, and various districts in north-east Transvaal another 14 per cent. Here and elsewhere the pattern of the smaller Reserves becomes highly confused and fragmented, because they are arranged on an ethnic basis which does not allow a reasonable geographical grouping without the addition of large areas in White possession. The total population of the Reserves is 4,760,000, which represents only two-fifths of the total African population, but a population density very much higher than the average for the Republic. Densities of up to 200 per sq. mile are recorded in parts of Natal, indicating extreme population pressure, for native agriculture in the Reserves is generally backward and often neglected. The natives live in kraals, clusters of circular huts with conical thatched roofs and walls of mud bricks (Plate 11). A few huts are now square in plan and some have roofs of corrugated iron. Beside the kraals are the enclosures for cattle, consisting of aloe or thorn hedges.

Traditional systems of cultivation and grazing, combined with frequently poor soils, erratic rainfall, or unsuitable terrain, result in low production per person and low productivity per acre of cultivated land. Large numbers of cattle are kept, many more than the land can naturally support, so that the pasture becomes impoverished, the animals suffer in turn, yields of milk fall and everywhere clear signs of soil erosion, active or incipient, are to be seen. About 12 per cent of the Reserve area is under crops, mostly maize. The women usually work the maize patches, using

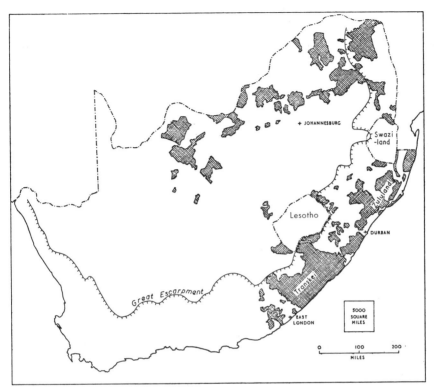

Figure 92 *Native Reserves and Purchase Areas in the Republic of South Africa*

simple implements and ox-drawn ploughs. Crop rotation is virtually unknown, and few Africans practise manuring. Consequently, yields are low (in the case of maize, less than one-third the yield obtained on European farms) and the land becomes exhausted. The traditional remedy was to allow the exhausted land to lie fallow for a period and to cultivate a new area, but with the big increase in the African population in the last forty years, and the delimitation of Reserve areas, this is no longer possible on any significant scale. It is therefore not surprising that the fertility of the land is steadily declining.

The majority of the Africans in the Reserves subsist on a poor diet, which leads to malnutrition, and encourages disease and a high rate of infant mortality. At present the Reserves are dependent on imported food to maintain their present population, and it is estimated that agriculture in the Reserves provides less than half the income of African families living there. As a result of these factors, and also the incidence of taxation, labour migration is an economic necessity for the African; but, as already pointed out, the exodus of young men from the Reserves to earn wages in the mines, factories or on European farms means that agriculture in the Reserves suffers in turn. To improve the situation, farming methods must be radically reformed. Cattle must be limited, and their value not measured simply in numbers. The soil must be conserved and its fertility restored. But if these reforms were achieved, and productivity increased, employment off the land would have to be found for the surplus population. Yet today there is virtually no industry in the Reserves. One small factory on the outskirts of Umtata, the capital of the Transkei, produces furniture and coffins. If ever the Reserves, or 'Bantustans' as they will become under the policy of apartheid, are to stand on their own feet economically, industry as well as agriculture will have to be fostered.

Labour problems

Cheap African labour is vital to the South African economy. In 1961, the average annual wage of the African was $530, compared with $800 for the Asians, and $2,650 for White persons. In recent years the numbers of Africans employed by various sections of the economy have been approximately:

agriculture	750,000
mining	550,000
industry	650,000

A great part of the labour is migrant: from the Reserves to the industrial areas or the European farms, or from outside the Republic (especially from Lesotho and Moçambique). It is reckoned that about one-sixth of all Africans in the Republic are absent from their home areas as labourers, and that there are also over 750,000 Africans resident in the Republic who were born outside it—37 per cent from Lesotho, 26 per cent from Moçambique and 20 per cent from Rhodesia and Malawi. These are attracted to the Republic by the possibility of earning wages, which however low they may be are in fact higher than those available at home. The migrants from the Reserves in the Republic are forced out by population pressure and the necessity to earn a wage to support their families.

Paradoxical as it may seem, both mining and industry in the Republic are suffering from acute labour shortage. This is due to the rapidity of expansion in the manufacturing industries, and competition for labour between the mines and industry. The mines and industry are doing all they can to attract more labour, but this, of course, is leading to further urbanisation of the Africans, and conflicts with the policy of apartheid which seeks to limit the number of Africans moving into the towns. The operation of the colour bar in industry sets aside the more skilled and better-paid jobs for Europeans: hence, the prospects for the African (or Coloured) are very limited, which in turn means lack of incentive and inefficiency. The generally low wages paid out to non-Europeans also react on industrial development by limiting purchasing power and therefore the internal market for many of the manufactured goods.

In the towns the majority of Africans are housed in 'locations', the mine 'compounds' and in the shanty suburbs. The acute housing shortage has led to conditions of gross overcrowding. The government is attempting to reorganise the distribution of urban Africans and to segregate them in defined areas to a greater extent than at present. Thus the population of Sophiatown, a native suburb to the west of Johannesburg, has recently been moved to a new location further south-west. This redistribution of the urban natives usually results in their being moved farther from their place of work; this in turn, with the present inadequate transport facilities, often causes great hardship for the workers and also lowers industrial efficiency.

FUTURE TRENDS

Since the beginning of the century the population of South Africa has been growing rapidly. The increase applies generally to all sections of the community, though some sections are expanding more rapidly than others (Table 33). There have been various attempts to predict the rate of expansion of South Africa's population in the future; compared with the 1960 figure of 15·8 million, the forecast for the year 2000 ranges from 24 million to 31 million.

Other trends that seem likely to continue in the near future have already been mentioned. The shrinkage of 'White South Africa' is likely to proceed still further as the proportion of non-Europeans rises in most parts of the Republic, unless apartheid is more rigorously applied. Further urbanisation of all sections of the community is likely to continue also as industry expands; and if standards of living among the non-White

Table 33

Vital statistics (per 1,000 population), 1952–62

Year	EUROPEAN			ASIAN			COLOURED		
	Births	Deaths	Excess births over deaths	Births	Deaths	Excess births over deaths	Births	Deaths	Excess births over deaths
1952	25·9	8·6	17·3	36·0	10·9	25·1	47·8	19·9	27·9
1957	24·8	8·5	16·3	31·3	8·9	22·4	47·7	16·3	31·4
1962	24·5	9·0	15·5	38·6	7·4	31·2	47·5	15·1	32·4

No comparable figures are available for the Africans. In the period 1936–56 the increase in numbers of Africans was 29 per cent, compared with 37 per cent for Europeans, 54 per cent for Coloureds and 91 per cent for Asians, but part of these increases for Europeans and Africans is due to immigration.

community are raised at all it is possible that the death rate may be reduced more rapidly than the birth rate.

Table 34   Increase in the population of the Republic of South Africa, 1921-60

	1921		1960	
	Population	% of total	Population	% of total
European	1,521,000	21·9	3,088,492	19·4
African	4,697,000	67·8	10,806,488	68·2
Asian	164,000	2·4	477,125	3·0
Coloured	545,000	7·9	1,509,258	9·4
Total	6,927,000	100·0	15,881,363	100·0

Lesotho and Swaziland

Within southern Africa prior to 1966 there were three British Protectorates which came under the control of the Commonwealth Relations Office in London; they were governed under the direction of the British High Commissioner resident in South Africa. Two of these Protectorates, Basutoland and Bechuanaland, achieved independence in 1966, and were renamed Lesotho and Botswana respectively. Botswana, which borders the Republic of South Africa on the north-west, is dealt with in Chapter 47.

Lesotho (11,700 sq. miles), the size of Belgium, has been aptly described as an island surrounded by an ocean of South African territory; Swaziland (6,700 sq. miles), smaller in area and not yet independent in 1966, is partially surrounded by the Republic, but has a 60-mile stretch of frontier with Moçambique. All three territories are closely linked economically with the Republic; most of their exports pass to or through it (wholly in the case of Lesotho), and they all (especially Lesotho) contribute to the Republic's economy by supplying migrant labour.

LESOTHO

Nearly all parts of the country exceed 5,000 feet in height, and in the east the mountains rise to over 11,000 feet, the greatest elevation in South Africa (Fig. 93). The western parts are a continuation of the High Veld plateau surface of the Orange Free State, but eastward as the ground rises the topography becomes more broken and eventually mountainous in character. The basal geological stratum is Karroo sandstone, which is overlain by a horizontally layered mass of Karroo lavas some 4,000 feet thick. Strong erosive action has sculptured this elevated country into a network of mountain ranges and ravines. Here are to be found the head-streams of the Orange river, and many of those of the Caledon, which explains the vital interest of the Republic of South Africa in this mountainous country. Rainfall is adequate for agriculture—25 inches at Maseru, rising to over 75 inches on the crests of the Drakensberg; the well-watered nature of Basutoland is a refreshing contrast to the aridity of so much of South Africa. Most of the rain falls in the summer months, often in torrential showers, but even in winter droughts are rarely prolonged. On the higher ground there is widespread winter-snow cover, and temperatures are often below zero.

The lower valleys provide areas of rich friable black or brown soil, which with similarly fertile areas in the western strip form the agricultural wealth of the country. The mountain slopes constitute the main grazing areas, clothed in sweet veld up to 8,000 feet, and a less palatable sour veld at higher levels. At 10,000 feet and over a tundra-like vegetation prevails. The chief scourges of Africa, the mosquito and the tsetse fly, are absent.

Against such a background it is at first surprising to learn of the poverty of the country and the formidable economic problems it faces. Almost the entire population consists of Africans—639,000 in the 1956 Census; Europeans number less than 2,000, being mainly government officials, missionaries or traders. There are no large towns; the population of Maseru the capital is only 6,500. Since such a large part of the country is mountainous and thus not available for cultivation, the population is concentrated in the west, where density exceeds that of any of the Native Reserves in the Republic, and there is thus considerable pressure on the cultivable land. There are no industries of significance in Lesotho; agriculture is the mainstay of the economy, while the Africans supplement their income by emigrating for periods to the mining and industrial centres of the Republic. It is estimated that about 154,000 Basuto, a number equal to two-fifths of the adult male population, are at present absent from their homeland, earning money to buy wives, and slaking the thirst for adventures once assuaged by tribal wars and migrations. Their womenfolk, and the remaining men and boys, carry on the traditional way of life, based on the keeping of sheep and cattle, and the cultivation of maize, millet, beans and a little wheat. Wool and mohair provide Lesotho's only sizeable export, but production of food crops, and in particular maize, is insufficient to meet the country's needs. Arable land amounts to only 13 per cent of the total area, and because of the mountainous nature of so much of the terrain is capable of little expansion. Even grazing land is scarce; by transhumance, pastures up to 9,000 feet are regularly occupied in the summer months.

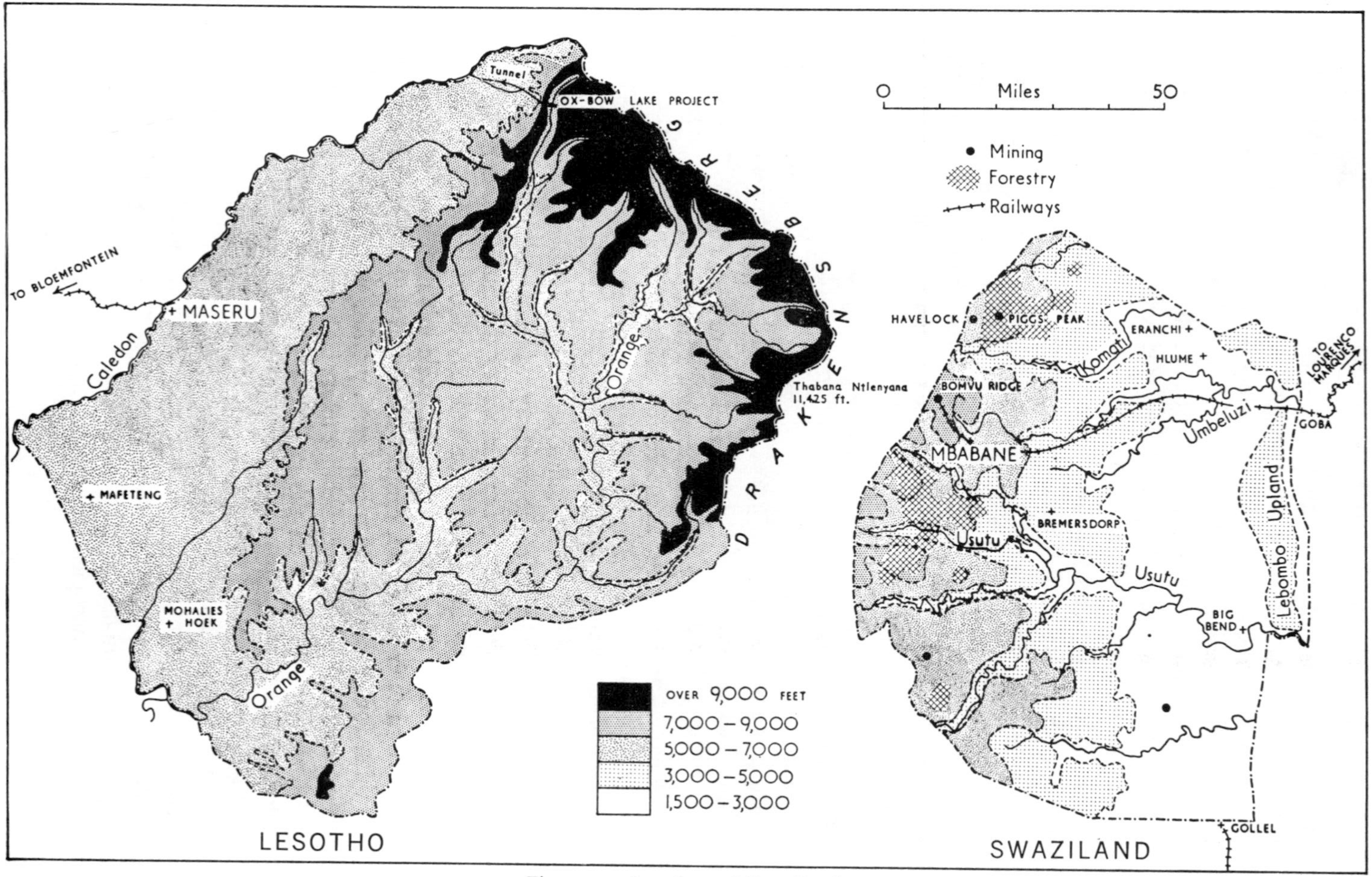

Figure 93 *Lesotho and Swaziland*

The main problem for agriculture in Lesotho is that of soil erosion. The frequently torrential rains combined with the high incidence of steeply sloping land lead to widespread gully erosion. In 1935 it was estimated that 10 per cent of the arable land was threatened, but since then great progress has been made in attempts to control erosion, under grants from the British Government. Terracing of hill slopes, construction of dams and other measures have now protected most of the western lowland areas and foothills. In the uplands, where erosion is brought on primarily by overgrazing, the main problem lies in persuading the Basuto to reduce numbers of stock. There are more than thirty cattle and 110 sheep per sq. mile.

No mineral resources of value have yet been discovered, though a private company has recently been prospecting for diamonds in the north. Thin coal seams, of little significance, occur in some of the Karroo beds.

Lesotho's rivers are not yet utilised for irrigation or power generation on any significant scale. The amount of land topographically suitable for irrigation agriculture is distinctly limited. Nevertheless, the country is of great importance to the Republic in connection with the use of the Orange–Caledon rivers for irrigation and industrial water supply in the Orange Free State. A scheme to produce hydro-electricity and to regulate the flow of the Caledon river has been proposed. It involves the construction of a dam in the extreme north of Lesotho on one of the tributaries of the River Orange (Fig. 93). Known as the Ox-Bow Lake scheme, it would supply water through a tunnel leading west into a tributary valley of the Caledon 4,000 feet below the dam, and when complete could have a generating capacity of 90 MW. In 1959 the cost was estimated at over $40 million, many times the value of Lesotho's total exports. The electricity produced could be used to establish local textile or clothing industries in Lesotho, which in turn could absorb some of the country's surplus labour. Water could be led by gravity to the Witwatersrand or Orange Free State gold fields.

Transport within Lesotho is greatly hampered by topography. The territory possesses but one mile of railway (the eastern end of the Bloemfontein–Maseru line), and no more than 400 miles of main road, entirely in the west. The principal tracks in the eastern mountains are only suitable for four-wheel-drive vehicles. Transport here is very largely by pack animals.

SWAZILAND

The remaining member of the High Commission Territories, Swaziland is known as one of the most beautiful parts of South Africa. Green, timbered and mostly well watered, its broken landscape contrasts sharply with the monotonous farmland of the adjacent Transvaal. The Drakensberg ring it round on the west, and it is this barrier that has preserved the country's political entity through the vicissitudes of the past century. Poised between the Republic and Moçambique, it is a country whose inhabitants are keenly alive to their external relations. With a population of 8,000 Europeans and 270,000 Africans, it has far greater potentialities for economic development than either Lesotho or Botswana. Unlike Lesotho, it depends to a minor extent on labour migration to the Transvaal—only about 8,000 Swazis are absent from their homeland in this way. The economic development of the country has so far been principally retarded by the fact that it lies off the main lines of communication in southern Africa. Until 1964 there were no railways in Swaziland, though railways run from its southern and eastern borders to Durban and Lourenço Marques respectively. On the other hand, it possesses a greatly superior network of roads to Lesotho.

The country can be divided into four north–south belts (Fig. 93): *The High Veld* in the west lies between 3,500 and 6,000 feet. Rainfall is considerable here, from 45 to 75 inches a year (Mbabane 55 inches). The country is dissected, and many areas are unsuitable for cultivation. Soil erosion is a serious problem for arable farming; the main aspects of land-use are sheep grazing and forestry. *The Middle Veld*, between 1,300 and 2,700 feet, is separated from the High Veld by a marked escarpment. It is an area of tall grassland, where there are considerable potentialities for the development of stock rearing, and the cultivation of maize and various sub-tropical crops. Rainfall averages 30 to 40 inches a year. *The Low Veld*, between 500 and 1,000 feet, is a drier region (20 to 30 inches annually), so that successful cultivation of crops depends largely on irrigation. There is, however, much good cattle pastur here. *The Lebombo Range* in the east rises to 2,700 feet.

The greater part of Swaziland is at present devoted to pastoral farming, with cattle rather more numerous than sheep or goats, though an important aspect is the wintering of sheep from the Transvaal. Where rainfall is sufficient crops of maize, kaffir corn, cotton and tobacco are grown. But there are considerable prospects for extending irrigation agriculture.

Swaziland fortunately possesses several sizeable perennial streams. The lower Usutu river, for instance, has an average annual discharge greater than that of the Vaal at Vaaldam in the Republic. So far the chief area of irrigation are on the Usutu river at Big Bend and west of Bremersdorp, and around Eranchi and Hlume in the north-east using water from the Komati river. Crops of rice, citrus and other tropical fruits, and sugarcane are grown. Sugar mills have been built at Big Bend and Mhlume. A recent most important development concerns the newly forested area covering 150 sq. miles of hilly country around the Usutu river south of Mbabane (Fig. 93). A pulp mill completed in 1961 by Courtaulds is the adjunct to this man-made forest. Its output of pulp, destined for the European market, is to build up to 100,000 tons a year, which at present market prices is worth about $11 million. Farther north the Pigg's Peak plantations cover only a slightly smaller area.

Swaziland also has mineral resources capable of further development. The principal minerals are associated with the Archaean granite which underlies most of the country. Asbestos is at present the outstanding product: the mines at Pigg's Peak (Fig. 93) represent one of the world's major sources. The Havelock Mine here forms a great scar in the heart of the mountains, visible for miles, and is the focus of a small modern settlement in the High Veld, with tarred roads and street lighting contrasting strangely with the dirt tracks of the surrounding country. From the mine the crysolite is taken in buckets along an aerial cableway to Barberton in the Transvaal, and thence by rail to Lourenço Marques.

A little coal, including anthracite, is worked in the east and south-east. However, much more important than either asbestos or coal are the iron-ore deposits at Bomvu Ridge, north-west of Mbabane, whose exploitation has far-reaching implications for Swaziland's economy. The Anglo-American Corporation of South Africa is financing intensive exploitation of the ore (the iron content is 65 per cent) and the construction of a 140-mile railway, Swaziland's first, via the capital Mbabane (pop. 8,400) to Lourenço Marques, whence the ore is being shipped to Japan. The railway (opened in 1964) has cost $25 million, and the iron-ore contract will be worth $110 million to Swaziland, spread over ten years. The significance of such figures can be readily appreciated when they are compared with the pre-1964 level of exports—$21 million in 1962. Of this, asbestos accounted for one-third. But the railway will be of inestimable benefit to Swaziland, providing for the first time efficient transport facilities from the interior to the outside world.

References

1 J. H. Wellington, *Southern Africa: a geographical study* (Cambridge, 1955, 2 vols.), p. 39
2 L. C. King, *South African scenery* (London, 1963, 3rd ed.)
3 N. C. Pollock, 'The town of Alice, Cape Province', *Geography*, 39 (1954), 176–82
4 K. Buchanan in *The Changing World*, ed. W. G. East and A. E. Moodie (London, 1956), 768
5 Summary of the Report of the Commission for the socio-economic development of the Bantu areas within the Union of South Africa (Pretoria, 1956)

Selected Bibliography

Basutoland, Bechuanaland Protectorate and Swaziland. Report of an Economic Survey Mission (H.M.S.O., London, 1960)
M. M. Cole, *South Africa* (London, 1961)
W. J. Talbot, *Swartland and Sandveld* (Cape Town, 1947)

H. C. Brookfield, 'Some geographical implications of the apartheid and partnership policies in southern Africa', *Trans. Inst. Brit. Geogr.*, 23 (1957), 225–47
H. C. Brookfield and M. A. Tatham, 'The distribution of racial groups in Durban', *Geog. Rev.*, 47 (1957), 44–65
K. Buchanan and N. Hurwitz, 'The Asiatic immigrant community in the Union of South Africa', *Geog. Rev.*, 39 (1949), 440–9
K. Buchanan and N. Hurwitz, 'The Coloured community in the Union of South Africa', *Geog. Rev.*, 40 (1950), 397–414
K. Buchanan and N. Hurwitz, 'Land use in Natal', *Econ. Geog.*, 27 (1951), 222–37
M. M. Cole, 'The growth and development of the South African citrus industry', *Geography*, 39 (1954), 102–13
M. M. Cole, 'The Witwatersrand conurbation: a watershed mining and industrial region', *Trans. Inst. Brit. Geogr.*, 23 (1957), 249–65
T. J. D. Fair, 'Durban—its sphere of influence as a regional capital', *S. Afr. Geog. Journ.*, 31 (1949), 77–92
T. J. D. Fair, 'Agricultural regions and the European rural farm population of Natal', *S. Afr. Geog. Journ.*, 34 (1952), 3–19
H. J. R. Henderson, 'The dairying industry in South Africa', *Trans. Inst. Brit. Geogr.*, 28 (1960), 237–52
L. H. Impey, 'The olive industry in South Africa', *S. Afr. Geog. Journ.*, 44 (1962), 34–49
S. P. Jackson, 'Climates of southern Africa', *S. Afr. Geog. Journ.*, 33 (1951), 17–37
J. H. Moolman, 'The Orange River, South Africa', *Geog. Rev.*, 36 (1946), 653–74

D. L. Niddrie, 'Uranium from the Union of South Africa', *Geography*, 40 (1955), 193–4

D. R. Petterson, 'The Witwatersrand: a unique gold mining community', *Econ. Geog.*, 27 (1951), 209–21

B. R. Schulze, 'The climate of South Africa according to Thornthwaite's rational classification', *S. Afr. Geog. Journ.*, 40 (1958), 31–53

P. Scott, 'Otter-trawl fisheries of South Africa', *Geog. Rev.*, 39 (1949), 529–51

P. Scott, 'Inshore fisheries of South Africa', *Econ. Geog.*, 27 (1951), 123–47

P. Scott, 'The Witwatersrand goldfield', *Geog. Rev.*, 41 (1951), 561–89

P. Scott, 'The iron and steel industry of South Africa', *Geography*, 36 (1951), 137–49

P. Scott, 'The development of the northern Natal coalfields', *S. Afr. Geog. Journ.*, 33 (1951), 53–68

P. Scott, 'The Orange Free State goldfield', *Geography*, 39 (1954), 13–20

P. Scott, 'Some functional aspects of Cape Town', *Econ. Geog.*, 30 (1954), 347–63

J. H. Wellington, 'The evolution of the Orange River basin', *S. Afr. Geog. Journ.*, 40 (1958), 3–30

G. Whittington, 'Developments in southern African diamond production', *Geography*, 48 (1963), 194–6

O. Williams, 'The power sources and fuel supplies of the secondary industries of Natal', *S. Afr. Geog. Journ.*, 41 (1959), 31–40

O. Williams, 'Sugar growing and processing in the Union of South Africa', *Econ. Geog.*, 35 (1959), 356–66

J. B. McI. Daniel, 'Some government measures to improve African agriculture in Swaziland', *Geog. Journ.*, 132 (1966), 506–15

P. Scott, 'Mineral development in Swaziland', *Econ. Geog.*, 26 (1950), 196–213

P. Scott, 'Land policy and the native population of Swaziland', *Geog. Journ.*, 117, (1951), 435–47

P. Scott, 'Transhumance between the Transvaal and Swaziland', *Geography*, 40 (1955), 50–2

B. S. Young, 'Projected hydro-electric schemes in Basutoland', *Journ. of Geog.*, 60 (1961), 225–30

PART XI

South-Western Africa

Two major physiographical units command our attention in this sector of Africa: the Kalahari Basin and the line of uplands extending from South-West Africa into Angola. Politically these fall within Botswana (formerly Bechuanaland Protectorate), South-West Africa and Angola. The northern and north-eastern parts of Angola strictly should be considered with the rest of the Congo Basin; similarly the northern parts of the Kalahari fall within the upper Zambezi catchment and therefore merit inclusion in Part IX; but, as elsewhere in Africa, a rigid adherence to physiographic limits which so often conflict with political divisions is obviously impracticable.

46

Physical Geography

STRUCTURE AND RELIEF

The belt of highland extending from the lower Orange river northward
to Angola is built largely of Pre-Cambrian rocks: either the Archaean
granite-gneiss complex or the later Pre-Cambrian sedimentary formations. Bordering the highland in eastern Namaqualand and north-eastern
Angola, Kárroo sediments outcrop. The solid rocks of the highland belt
disappear gently eastward beneath the sands of the Kalahari Basin, and
apart from isolated minor outcrops the older formations are not again
seen until they rise on the far side of the Kalahari in Zambia, Rhodesia or
the Transvaal. The Kalahari sands are reddish in colour where not leached;
they probably reach a thickness of 300 feet in a few places. Their precise
origin is unknown, but it is likely that they have been derived by former
river action from Karroo sandstones, and have later been redistributed by
wind action in dry periods. On the western side of the South-West
African-Angolan highlands the coastlands are in places underlain by
Cretaceous and Tertiary marine sediments, most significant around
Benguela and Luanda (Fig. 67).

PHYSICAL REGIONS

A number of major relief regions can be distinguished in South-Western
Africa (Fig. 68). THE COASTLANDS, lying generally below 1,500 feet, extend
from the mouth of the Orange northward for 1,600 miles to the Congo
estuary. The southern portion, between the Orange and Cunene rivers,
is known as the Namib desert, and is not crossed by any permanent
streams. In Angola the coastlands are broadest in the north, up to 120
miles wide in the Luanda region; in the south of Angola they are characteristically barren and arid. There are no perennial streams of any size

between the Cunene and the Catumbela. Behind the coastlands rises the Great Escarpment, the westward-facing rim of the highlands. Between the Orange river and the Erongo Mountains (north-east of Walvis Bay), it is a well-defined feature reaching 5,000 feet; it is also imposing north of the Cunene, attaining 7,500 feet at Sá da Bandeira and 8,600 feet north of the Benguela railway. Elsewhere it is less distinct, either due to the activity of river erosion in the wetter north of Angola or to the lack of any resistant sedimentary strata to cap the granite-gneiss in the northern parts of South-West Africa.

THE HIGHLANDS OF SOUTH-WEST AFRICA are limited by the line of the Great Escarpment in the west, and comprise a series of mountains and plateaux reaching 8,144 feet in the Khomas highlands near Windhoek, and more than 5,000 feet over considerable areas. Eastward the elevation gradually drops to 3,000 feet on the Kalahari border. Over most of Namaqualand the underlying rocks are gently dipping quartzites and limestones, producing extensive plateaux. In the Khomas highlands a much more rugged topography is apparent. Over the northern parts the granite-gneiss surface is lower, and, except for inselberge, more evenly cut, declining not only eastward to the Kalahari but also westward to merge with the Namib coastlands.

THE ANGOLA HIGHLANDS may be considered in three subdivisions. In the south the Serra da Chela continues the line of the South-West African highlands, broken by the transverse valleys of the lower Cunene and Coroca. With a capping of Pre-Cambrian quartzite, the Serra da Chela rises to 7,500 feet in the Humpata plateau around Sá da Bandeira. In the centre of Angola lies the Bié plateau. The escarpment crest continues from Sá da Bandeira north-eastward to the Benguela railway (which crosses it at 6,075 feet near Villa Robert Williams); beyond the railway it climbs to 8,563 feet, the highest point in Angola. Most of the Bié plateau lies, however, at 5,000–6,000 feet. With its summer rainfall of up to 60 inches, several major rivers originate here—the Cunene, the Cubango (Okovango); farther east the Cuando and upper Zambezi tributaries; and on the northern side the Kasai and the Cuanza. In northern Angola the Luanda uplands are much lower and dissected by many broad valleys. The maximum elevation is 4,900 feet (near Duque de Bragança), and there are several plateaux at various heights between 1,500 and 3,500 feet. The Great Escarpment is no longer present as a definite feature; indeed, the Cuanza and other streams have pushed back the watershed between the Atlantic and Congo drainage until it lies up to 300 miles from the coast.

THE KALAHARI BASIN occupies the heart of the sub-continent of southern Africa—no less than one-third of its area in fact—and extends from the Orange river to the headstreams of the Zambezi. It cannot be described as a lowland: with a minimum elevation generally of 3,000 feet (2,500 feet near Upington on the Orange), 'plateau' would be a more correct description. The fact that the floor is almost completely mantled with sand has already been noted. It is probably the largest continuous expanse of sand in the world. Yet the Kalahari is not a true desert, for, except in a few small areas, the sand is not now mobile but fixed by grass, shrub or tree growth. Only in the sense that it lacks surface water can the Kalahari be termed a desert. Parts of the Kalahari are traversed by permanent streams originating outside it, such as the Cunene in the north-west, the Cuando and upper Zambezi in the north-east, and the Orange. But there are also three major basins of interior drainage within the Kalahari: the small Etosha Pan in the north-west, the Okovango–Makarikari area in the north and the Molopo–Nossob area in the south. The last two of these three basins occupy, in fact, most of the Kalahari. The Molopo–Nossob System undoubtedly once drained to the Orange, but under present climatic conditions the Molopo does not flow west of long. 22°45' (it last reached this point in 1893), and the Nossob has not been known to reach the Molopo. The main distinction between this part of the Kalahari and the Okovango–Makarikari Basin farther north lies in the greater rainfall of the north, and the fact that the Okovango system drains an area with up to 50 inches rainfall. At the Botswana border the average annual flow of the Okovango is no less than 13 billion cubic metres: it is 150 yards wide and up to 17 feet deep. Farther downstream it splits up into a maze of reed-choked channels (Fig. 94), where much of its flow evaporates. Some water used to find its way to 'Lake' Ngami (which Livingstone reported as a shallow lake in 1849, but which has been generally dry since 1925, with grass and thorn trees growing on its floor). Most excess water now drains by the Botletle river to Lake Dow, and in flood this may overflow in turn to the Makarikari depression. North of the Okovango swamp is another marshy area crossed by the sluggish Linyanti (known in Angola as the Cuando). This river is now a tributary of the Zambezi, but formerly used to drain to the Mababe depression (3,040 feet). It is possible that in the geological future the Okovango may also be diverted to the Linyanti swamps and become a Zambezi tributary too (see Chapter 3, p. 45).

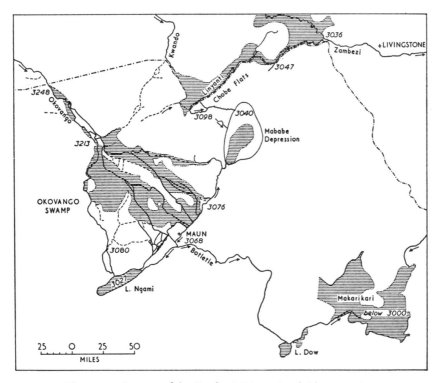

Figure 94 *Swamps of the Zambezi, Linyanti and Okovango rivers*

At one time schemes were proposed to divert the Zambezi for irrigation purposes into the Makarikari depression by way of the Mababe and Botletle channel, but such schemes are now wholly abandoned. Even if Kariba did not demand maintenance of the middle Zambezi's existing discharge it is estimated that evaporation losses in the swamp area would absorb and waste more than half the Zambezi's mean flow.

CLIMATE

Spanning latitudes 6° to 28°S, and ranging in height from sea-level to over 8,500 feet, it is clear that there will be great differences of climate in South-Western Africa. Along the coast from the Orange river to

Moçamedes is one of the most arid regions of Africa, yet a comparatively cool one. Inland, the southern Kalahari can only be termed semi-arid in comparison, yet it is the hottest part of southern Africa in the summer. Farther north, the Angolan highlands are relatively cool for their latitude as a result of their elevation, and they are also favoured with considerable summer rainfall. In the Congo district of northern Angola the climate becomes warmer and more humid, until the 'equatorial' climate of the Congo Basin proper is reached.

Throughout this region climatic statistics are unfortunately meagre, and commonly based on short-term records, especially in Angola. Maps of temperature and rainfall should accordingly be used with caution.

The variation of temperature with altitude has just been noted. In spite of its position within 13° of the equator, the Bié plateau has moderate temperatures (e.g. Caconda at 5,200 feet has a mean of 67°F), with an annual range of about 10°. Windhoek, at a slightly higher elevation (5,500 feet) and 10° farther south in latitude, has the same mean temperature, but a range of 20°: it lies in a drier and less cloudy region so that summer temperatures may be high (January mean 74°) with day temperatures up to 110°. On the coastlands the effect of the cool Benguela current is strongly marked, especially in South-West Africa and southern Angola. Coastal stations show a small temperature range: at Walvis Bay, for instance, the annual range is only 10°F, and at Moçamedes, farther north, 14°F. At Walvis Bay the mean land temperature is 62°F, compared with a mean sea temperature of 59°F. In northern Angola the influence of the Benguela current diminishes: at Luanda the mean land temperature has increased to 75°F, though the annual range of only 12°F is still small.

There are few records available for the Kalahari, but it is known that both annual and diurnal temperature ranges are large, and that some very high temperatures are experienced in summer. The mean temperature of the warmest month (November) at Francistown is 77°F; at Maun, in the Okovango swamp area, it is 80°F. The annual range is 20°.

For present or potential land-use, rainfall is a more critical element in climate (Fig. 95). The coast is the most arid part. As far north as Moçamedes no coastal station records an annual average greater than 3 inches, and many areas experience practically no rain. This is the Namib desert. The rain that does occur occasionally is irregular in incidence and amount —an isolated shower followed by several years' drought. The subsident character of the mT air, and the cooling effect of the Benguela current on the lower layers of the air, are responsible for the aridity, which becomes

Table 35

Temperature and rainfall at selected stations

Station	Alt. (feet)		J	F	M	A	M	J	J	A	S	O	N	D	Year	Temp. range
Luanda	194	Temp. °F	78	80	80	80	77	72	69	68	71	75	77	78	76	12
		Rain in.	1·0	1·4	3·0	4·6	0·5	0·1	0·1	0·1	0·1	0·2	1·1	0·8	12·7	
Moçamedes	10	T.	72	75	76	74	68	64	61	62	63	67	69	70	68	15
		R.	0·3	0·4	0·7	0·5	0·1	0·1	0·1	0·1	0·1	0·1	0·1	0·1	2·1	
Windhoek	5,669	T.	74	72	69	66	60	56	55	60	65	71	71	74	66	19
		R.	3·0	2·9	3·1	1·6	0·3	0·1	0·1	0·1	0·1	0·4	0·9	1·9	14·3	
Francistown	3,600	T.	76	75	73	70	63	57	58	62	70	76	77	76	69	20
		R.	4·2	3·1	2·8	0·7	0·2	0·1	0·1	0·1	0·1	0·9	2·2	3·4	17·7	

most extreme along the actual coastline. The same factors, however, encourage fog formation and perhaps slight drizzle. Walvis Bay experiences fog on an average of fifty-five days per year, and a mean annual rainfall of 0·3 inches.

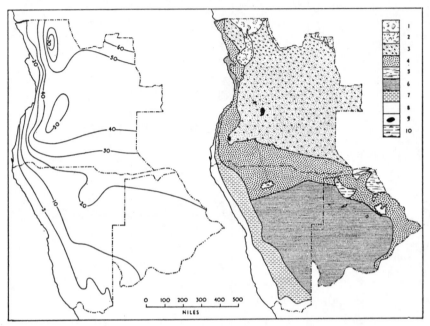

Figure 95 *South-Western Africa:* mean annual rainfall (inches) and vegetation. There are many areas for which detailed information is lacking; these maps should therefore be regarded as provisional only

1. Rain forest. 2. Forest-savanna mosaic. 3. Moist savanna. 4. Dry savanna. 5. Dry deciduous forest. 6. Wooded and grass steppe. 7. Semi-desert. 8. Desert. 9. Montane. 10. Swamp

North of Moçamedes, rainfall gradually increases, the cooling effect of the Benguela current diminishes and fog becomes less frequent. At Luanda the total annual rainfall averages 13 inches, of which 12 inches fall in the half-year November to April. At the Congo estuary the rainfall has increased to 27 inches. All coastal Angola experiences highly variable rainfall, for the ITC is usually aligned parallel with the coast but at unpredictably variable distances from it in different years. Moçamedes had 12 inches in 1933-4, less than 1 inch in 1937-8.

In the Kalahari the annual rainfall varies from 5 inches in the south to over 20 inches in the north (Maun 17 inches; Lealui, in Barotseland,

32 inches). The rainfall is, however, restricted to the summer, and periods of drought are prolonged (at Maun an average of only 2 inches falls between April and October). The rainfall is also erratic, and occurs in thunder showers.

On the South-West African highlands rainfall amounts are as low as or lower than the Kalahari in equivalent latitudes (Keetmanshoop 5 inches, Windhoek 14 inches, Tsumeb 22 inches). More than 80 per cent falls in the summer half-year. North of the South-West African border, and inland from the coast, rainfall increases rapidly, though a summer concentration is maintained. At Sá da Bandeira the total is 36 inches; at Nova Lisboa, on the Bié plateau, 59 inches; and at Carmona, in the north, 73 inches—a gradual transition to the humid conditions of the Congo Basin.

VEGETATION (Fig. 95)

In response to variations in climate and in degree of alteration by man, the vegetation ranges from tropical forest to savanna in central Angola; with increasing dryness the savanna thins and is replaced by Karroo and desert shrub associations. In the valleys and on west-facing slopes in northern Angola true rain forest is encountered, but on moving south to the Luanda, Bié and Humpata uplands, the forest thins to become open grassland with patches of woodland, the latter usually representing remnants of a formerly more extensive forest cover. On the drier coastlands from Luanda southward, and on the lower parts of the escarpment, poor scrub vegetation occurs, the country becoming gradually more barren towards the Moçamedes region where true desert conditions commence. In the Namib desert only small bushes survive on mist or occasional drizzle, with a few acacias and tamarisk along the normally dry stream courses. Eastward the desert passes into poor grassland, improving with increasing rainfall until the better pastures of the Windhoek region, or the savanna country of Ovamboland, are reached. The Kalahari vegetation varies generally from poor grassland in the south, through an extensive area of mixed thorn forest (with abundant acacias) and coarse grass, to open forest of *Mopani* and *Brachystegia* in the upper Zambezi area of the north. Smaller areas are occupied by swamp vegetation (Okovango, Linyanti, etc.), and by open grassland of moderate pastoral value, as in the floodplain areas of Barotseland or around the Etosha and Makarikari depressions.

47

Botswana and
South-West Africa

BOTSWANA

With an area slightly larger than that of France, this is a vast sprawling and dry country, large parts of which are still incompletely known. It covers 300,000 sq. miles, and there is almost exactly one inhabitant to each of them. It was proclaimed a British Protectorate in 1885; ten years later the southern part, including the capital Mafeking, was transferred to Cape Colony, which subsequently became part of the Union of South Africa. For sixty years the country was administered from Mafeking (pop. 35,000), an arrangement which was both demoralising and inconvenient, especially after the secession of South Africa from the Commonwealth. Independence was achieved in 1966. The capital is Gaberones (pop. 6,000).

The population of Botswana in the 1964 census was 543,105, of whom only 3,921 were Europeans and 3,909 Coloured or Asian. Life and development gravitate mainly to the railway running along the eastern flank, where the towns of Lobatsi, Gaberones and Francistown are located. Most of the Africans live on tribal Reserves in the east. Reserves (Fig. 96) account for about half the area of the territory, but vast areas of them are only thinly inhabited. The largest Reserve is that of the Bamangwato (pop. 109,000; capital Serowe) with a population density of 2·5 per sq. mile, while in contrast the Bamalete Reserve, near Lobatsi and Gaberones, supports 44 persons per sq. mile. Labour migration is an important feature; it is reckoned that one in every five adult males is absent at any given time in South Africa, Rhodesia or Zambia, and that they remit to the territory about £500,000 annually in wages or savings.

The Africans in the Reserves are village dwellers, dependent on their cattle and a little cultivation. With uncertain and low rainfall, and often poor sandy soils, few crops are possible. Most arable land is planted for basic food crops such as maize and kaffir corn; there is a small surplus of the latter for export, but maize is a marginal crop except in the south-east, and, because of low yields, production is insufficient. Altogether, though, only 0·2 per cent of the total area is cultivated. Much more important to the African are his cattle. As elsewhere in Africa, they are regarded as a form of wealth and investment, even though their quality is poor. Since social prestige is proportional to numbers of cattle owned, it is not surprising to learn that on average there are five beasts per person. Overgrazing, with its consequences of grassland deterioration and soil erosion, is only too prevalent. Nevertheless, it is on the African's cattle that the economy of Botswana rests. Over 80 per cent of exports consist of live cattle, hides and skins, or carcasses from the Lobatsi abattoir.

There are very few European farms in Botswana. They are found only in the east, for instance in the Tuli block along the Limpopo, and in the Tati concession around Francistown. In some cases irrigation of sub-tropical crops and citrus orchards has begun on a small scale; a new dam has just been completed near Lobatsi.

WATER RESOURCES AND LIVESTOCK

The limiting factor in practically every aspect of economic development in Botswana is water shortage. Rainfall of no more than 25 inches is concentrated at a time of the year when evaporation losses are highest, and the Kalahari sands absorb water so efficiently that there is little surface moisture. Apart from the Linyanti and Limpopo rivers on the border, the Okovango is the only large concentrated source of surface water in the territory. Underground water exists in strata beneath the sands, and is tapped by some bore-holes, but little is yet known about its amount and rate of recharge. In the years 1946–60 the government sank 851 bore-holes at a cost of nearly £1 million, of which only 490 were successful. So far as irrigation is concerned, the Limpopo provides water for a few very small schemes (as already mentioned); the Okovango (Fig. 94) has much greater potential and several schemes for its utilisation have been discussed.[1] The swamp area, with a surface gradient of 1 inch per mile and sufficient water annually to flood it to a depth of 3 feet, presents ideal hydrographic conditions for drainage and irrigation agriculture, but such developments would be highly expensive and the location very remote from all present lines of communication. Much more information is needed, too, on the soils and their suitability for irrigation.

Botswana is at present primarily a cattle-ranching country and likely to remain so. Vast areas of grassland are unused, because of distance from the railway in the east, the lack of roads, and, above all, shortage of drinking water. Writing in 1951, Debenham reported that

> these broad Crown lands, with no population to speak of except primitive hunters, are producing next to nothing in a world short of meat. Even Livingstone, a hundred years ago, recognised that if only there were water available, this would be ranching land. Grass there is in profusion in the rainy season, and many edible shrubs in the dry season. The question is: can water be obtained from below, in sufficient quantity and at reasonable expense, to maintain stock? There is no tsetse fly, and as yet hardly any cattle disease.[2]

(It should be noted, incidentally, that much of the Okovango swamp is afflicted with tsetse.) Wild animal life in large areas of northern Botswana is abundant and varied, reinforcing the opinion that it is potentially good cattle country. If, however, cattle ranching is to be expanded, certain problems apart from water supply will have to be faced. The question of winter-feed supplies must be examined, for when the rains are deficient, as frequently happens, the natural grass growth is reduced in summer, leaving little edible material for the dry season. Grazing will have to be strictly controlled. In the light sandy soils any overstocking, even for a few weeks, could begin a dust-bowl and serious erosion. Around some water-holes this has already happened.

It is possible that some areas will never support more than one animal for every 50 acres. The expense of fencing will have to be faced so that stock can be moved from one large paddock to another the moment there are signs of overgrazing. Then the quality of the cattle must be improved. At present there is no selective breeding, and the African tends to hold on to large numbers of ageing animals. But, provided these and other problems are dealt with, the livestock industry of Botswana can be expected to extend considerably in the future.

Although mining in Botswana has a history of over a century, only one mine was working in 1966: this was at Ootse, near Lobatsi, which produces some 17,000 tons of manganese annually. Asbestos was also mined in 1965, but production has temporarily ceased. Total output of these two minerals in 1965 was valued at about $550,000. Large coal reserves exist on or near the railway at Mamabula and west of Palapye; opencast mining would be possible and, in view of the distance from Wankie or Witbank, prices might be competitive. The cost of opening such a mine, however, might well be about $3 million.

Until the last few years the Lobatsi abattoir provided the only industry in Botswana; industrial development on any significant scale is unlikely, but the territory now has a tannery, soap and bone-meal factories and a creamery.

THE BUSHMEN

The indigenous pre-Bantu peoples of the Kalahari are the Bushmen, primitive hunters and gatherers, of whom only about 5,000 now remain in Botswana. As will be mentioned in the next chapter, more are found in the north-eastern corner of South-West Africa. In a recent penetrating study of the Bushmen, Elizabeth Marshall Thomas describes them in these terms:

> The Bushmen are one of the most primitive peoples living on earth. Bushmen make the . . . tools they use from wood and bone, grass and fibre, the things of the veld. They dig roots and pick berries to eat because they have no crops. The desert is too dry for anything but desert plants to grow naturally, and Bushmen, who quickly consume all the wild food available in one place, cannot stay anywhere long enough to tend crops or wait for them to grow.
>
> There is not enough water to water livestock, and for this reason Bushmen have no domestic animals. Most of their groups do not even have dogs. Instead of herding, Bushmen hunt wild antelope. . . . Hunting is very difficult, for travel in the veld is thirsty and rigorous and the antelope are clever, but as often as not the Bushmen hunters shoot one [with poisoned arrows] and then they use it all. Most of the meat is dried to preserve it, causing it to last at least a few weeks. . . .

In order to live as they do, Bushmen must travel through the veld, changing their abode every few days in search of food. Because of their way of life, they do not need villages to live in . . . making [only] small domes of grass for themselves, just a little shade for their heads, grass which the wind soon blows away. Sometimes they do not even bother with this, but push little sticks into the ground to mark their places. They sleep beside the sticks and arrange their few possessions around them, symbols of their homes.

The Bushmen, together with the Hottentot peoples, are known to have lived in South Africa long before the Bantus came. But during the waves of the early Bantu migrations . . . the Bushmen yielded their land to the stronger newcomers, and most of them were either killed, enslaved or driven farther and farther back into the most remote parts of the country, where the Bantu people and their livestock could not live.[3]

SOUTH-WEST AFRICA

This territory came under German control in 1892. In the following years up to World War I the Germans were responsible for the first phase of economic development, with investment in ports, railways, mines and ranching. The Caprivi strip in the north-east was acquired in 1893 as an outlet to the Zambezi, but no use was ever made of it, since the river here is of no practical value for navigation, and Rhodes blocked Germany's attempt to link up with her East African colonies. In 1915 South-West Africa was conquered by South African forces; in 1920 it became a Mandated Territory, and later a Trusteeship Territory, administered by South Africa for the United Nations. It is, in practice, now a fifth province of the Republic of South Africa. Walvis Bay and nearly 400 sq. miles around it is an enclave of sovereign South African territory.

Many varied elements make up the population of this country, whose area is 317,800 sq. miles, two-thirds the size of South Africa. The White peoples, numbering 74,000, comprise Afrikaners (60 per cent), Germans (30 per cent) and British (10 per cent). There are 24,000 Coloured. Of the Africans, the Bantu tribes total 428,000; originally cattle herders, many now work on White farms or in the mines and towns. The indigenous inhabitants are Hottentots (30,000) and Bushmen (about 12,000); the former live mostly in Reserves (Fig. 96) in the south, keeping flocks of sheep and goats, while the Bushmen, primitive hunters and gatherers, have retreated north and north-east to the Kalahari border. The most densely populated area in South-West Africa is Ovamboland (in the north), with about 200,000 Bantu. Elsewhere, apart from the towns, population densities are less than one per sq. mile. Overall, the population is increasing at an average annual rate of 2·9 per cent (compare South Africa—2·4 per cent); between 1921 and 1964 the population has more than doubled. As in the Republic of South Africa, government is entirely in the hands of the White settlers, here numbering 14 per cent of the total population.

The country is divided into two major administrative areas: the tribal

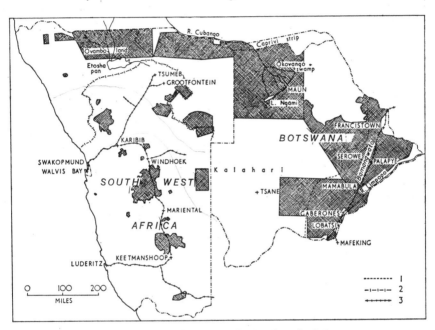

Figure 96 *Botswana and South-West Africa.* The shaded areas represent Native Reserves

1. Western limit crops and livestock zone in Botswana. 2. Northern limit of the Police Zone in South-West Africa. 3. Railways

Reserves in the north and north-east, and the Police Zone (about three-quarters of the country) where European law is enforced and the land largely European-owned. The capital is *Windhoek* (pop. 43,000), a fast-growing modern town with an expanding industrial area, but still retaining clear signs of its German ancestry.

THE ECONOMY

The dual nature of the economy is clear cut; commercial livestock rearing, mining, and fishing are almost entirely in the hands of the Europeans, while the Bantu provide most of the cheap labour on which these enterprises rest.

PASTORAL ACTIVITIES   For climatic reasons farming is largely concerned with livestock as in Bechuanaland. In the south sheep farming is the only practicable form of land-use. Most of the sheep are karakuls, introduced to South-West Africa by German settlers in 1907. The country is now the largest producer of karakul pelts in the world, to the value of £6 million in 1962. The pelts, known as 'Persian lamb', are taken from day-old lambs; the ewes thus do not have to support many young and can survive in unusually arid conditions. In the central uplands, around Windhoek and Rehoboth, cattle as well as karakul sheep are raised. This area has adequate pasture, with 10–14 inches of summer rain. Farther north, cattle replace sheep entirely. The European-owned cattle are usually dual-purpose (i.e. dairy and beef) animals. Native-owned cattle are mostly to be found in Ovamboland and are commercially unimportant.

CROP GROWING   In South-West Africa this is limited to the north and north-central area, and is always subsidiary to pastoral farming. The Africans grow limited crops of maize, groundnuts, millet or kaffir corn for subsistence only. Virtually the only area of European mixed farming is around Tsumeb and Grootfontein, where water from springs is available. The first major irrigation scheme of about 7,000 acres is being developed from the Hardap Dam, not far from Mariental on the Fish river, which flows in summer.

THE FISHING INDUSTRY   This is an important facet of the economy, based on the cool waters of the Benguela current. Lobster, pilchards and white fish caught are annually valued at more than £10 million. The fishing fleet is centred on Luderitz and Walvis Bay; both ports have important fish-canning industries and Walvis Bay a metal-can factory. *Walvis Bay* (pop. 17,000) is now exporting half a million tons of fish products a year, apart from other cargo.

MINERALS are the most valuable aspect of the economy, especially diamonds. The alluvial diamond fields of the southern Namib, near the mouth of the Orange river, are so rich that entry to the area is prohibited. Discovered in 1908, these coastal deposits are now worked exclusively by the De Beers (Oppenheimer) Diamond Corporation, producing £23 million worth in 1963. Offshore, in the 3 miles of territorial waters, sea-floor deposits of sand and gravel are now being sifted for diamonds, from the estuary of the Olifants river in South Africa to Luderitz Bay. In the vicinity of Plumpudding Island is thought to lie one of the world's richest diamond reserves. Ninety per cent of South-West Africa's current diamond production is of gem stones. A very different mining venture is located at Tsumeb, where production of lead, copper, zinc and germanium is controlled by the American Newmont Mining Company (value of output £10 million in 1963). New copper and lead smelters were installed in 1962 and 1963 respectively. *Tsumeb*, where copper mining began in 1908, is now a modern town like Windhoek, and has a population of 7,000.

COMMUNICATIONS A great contrast is seen between the pattern of communications in South-West Africa and Botswana. South-West Africa is served by part of South Africa's comprehensive rail network, linking Tsumeb, Windhoek and the chief ports to South Africa via Upington. Diesel locomotives are overcoming water-shortage problems while after the completion of the Cunene hydro-electric project below the Ruacana Falls, the Tsumeb–Windhoek line is to be electrified. A system of well-maintained roads links every town of importance in South-West Africa, whereas Botswana as yet has not even a single satisfactory east–west road. These differences between the two territories are to be explained by German investment in South-West Africa during the years 1892 to 1915, by the revenue obtained from mining production in subsequent years, and by considerable expenditure on the development of the territory by the government of the Republic of South Africa. In 1964, a Five-Year Plan was instituted, entailing expenditure of £75 million. Of this, completion of the Cunene project will absorb £25 million, additional roads about £20 million, and a system of water storage dams and canals in densely populated Ovamboland about £12 million. Injection of capital on this scale will bolster the economy of the territory still further, and it is hoped that the net national income per capita will double in the next 15 to 20 years.

48

Angola

Slightly greater in size than the Republic of South Africa, and fourteen times the size of Portugal, Angola is Portugal's largest overseas territory (481,300 sq. miles), with 300,000 white settlers. Its capital, *Luanda*, founded in 1575 (pop. 200,000) is Portugal's third largest city, and claims to be the oldest European settlement in Africa south of the Sahara. The coastline of Angola was explored by Diogo Cão in 1482-3, as far south as Porto Alexandre. For three and a half centuries thereafter Angola was known mainly as a source of slaves, large numbers of whom were shipped across to Brazil. By 1836, when the slave trade was finally abolished, the African population had been drastically reduced; this is one of the principal reasons why the present population is no more than 4·9 million, and why the territory has one of the lowest population densities (less than ten per sq. mile) in *Afrique Noire*. It was not until after the Berlin Conference of 1885 that the Portuguese took a renewed interest in this part of Africa. Until then, all Portuguese settlements had been coastal ones—. Luanda, Benguela (founded 1617) and Moçamedes (founded 1839) being the largest—but now the Portuguese began to develop the interior, with railways leading to the uplands from the ports. The Bié Plateau, because of its elevation, has been most attractive for European settlement. The Benguela railway was commenced in 1903, and Nova Lisboa, at 5,600 feet, was chosen in 1927 as the future site for the capital of the colony, though the transfer from Luanda has yet to take place. Other principal settlements which developed on the plateaux included Silva Porto, and Sá da Bandeira with its railway down to Moçamedes. The Bié plateau and the Luanda uplands farther north are today the areas of relatively dense rural population, while vast areas in the south and east are virtually uninhabited.

The present agricultural economy of Angola is based on two main crops, coffee and maize, and a number of less-important ones.

Coffee About 13 per cent of Africa's coffee comes from Angola. Between 1953 and 1957 Angola came second only to the Ivory Coast in production, but was subsequently ousted from second place by Uganda. Angolan coffee has also been the most valuable export of the Portuguese currency area. The crop was introduced in 1837 around Luanda, and later in the Porto Amboim district. It is now grown in many areas of northern Angola (Fig. 97) as far south as the Benguela railway, but four-fifths of the production is from areas north of the Cuanza river, particularly around Carmona. Rainfall in the coffee areas is usually 50 inches or more, while winter temperatures are not normally below 50°F. In the north the uplands between 1,000 and 3,000 feet are favoured, but higher plantings are becoming more common south of the Cuanza river, with some new estates on the Bié plateau at nearly 5,000 feet. The tropical red earths prevalent over much of north-central Angola produce very good crops of coffee when properly cared for, though in the hands of speculators, anxious to obtain quick profits while a coffee boom lasts, they quickly deteriorate. About two-thirds of the crop is grown by Portuguese farmers. The area under coffee has expanded very rapidly: before World War II it was less than 200,000 acres, by 1945 it had spread to 300,000 acres, and most recent estimates indicate over 600,000 acres. At the same time coffee has risen to become Angola's staple product. Whereas coffee exports in 1938 were valued at only £400,000, or 11 per cent of total exports in that year, coffee now provides two-fifths of Angola's exports—£20 million in 1959. The situation is indeed reminiscent of Brazil in the 1920's, and there are many other interesting comparisons with this country. In spite of the great increase in trade consequent on the coffee boom, especially trade with the United States, and the great increase in revenue which has been used to finance many development plans, including new roads, railways and port modernisation, the Angolan economy today still is a very vulnerable one. Fluctuations in world coffee prices, or failure of the coffee harvest, could well herald disaster. The danger sign was apparent in 1959 when, by International Agreement to deal with the mounting surplus of coffee in the world, Angola agreed to limit her coffee exports to a figure set at 10 per cent below the 1956 level.

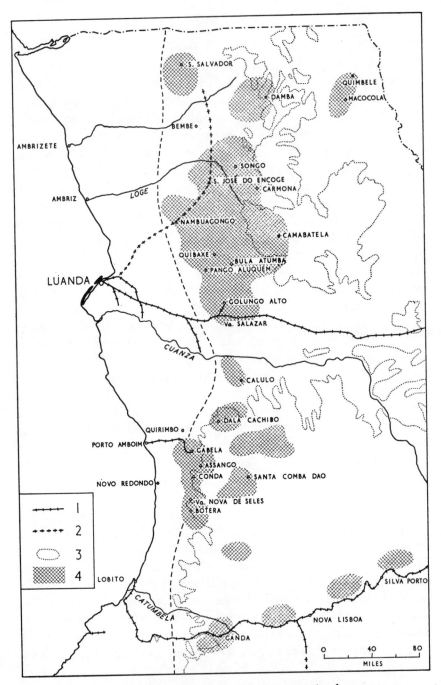

Figure 97 *Coffee regions of north-western Angola*

1. Railways. 2. Railways projected or under construction. 3. Land over 3,000 feet. 4. Main coffee-growing areas

The towns and villages shown are coffee collecting centres. The broken line running roughly parallel with the coast represents approximately the 40-inch rainfall isohyet

Along with the coffee boom has come the expansion of many towns, both old and new. Luanda, the capital, is a port handling three-quarters of the coffee trade; a new railway to the Congo frontier in the north is being built not only to handle the coffee but for strategic reasons. There is now a new road from Luanda to Carmona, centre of the northern coffee region, a town whose white population has multiplied tenfold in the last decade. Other settlements connected with coffee are the four secondary ports of Ambriz, Ambrizete, Porto Amboim and Novo Redondo. All are open roadsteads, where ships are loaded by surf-boat or lighter. Porto Amboim's handling facilities were recently improved, but its traffic has tended to decline, since its local railway to Gabela is steeply graded, with many sharp curves.

Maize is the principal food crop of Angola, grown almost entirely by Africans, and occupying the largest area of any crop. Probably over three-quarters is grown on the Bié plateau. Production fluctuates considerably from year to year; in some good years up to half the crop has been exported. Other African food crops include beans, groundnuts and cassava. The coffee boom has had its effect even on these basic food crops, for both Africans and Portuguese have been quick to appreciate the profits obtainable from growing coffee instead of subsistence crops.

Of the less important cash crops, *sugar-cane* is grown on irrigated plantations in the coastal valleys near Benguela, Porto Amboim and Luanda. *Sisal* production is increasing, and now amounts to 10 per cent of Africa's total. Since so much of Angola's export trade consists of shipments of coffee, maize, beans, etc., in sacks, fibre crops are of great importance. Recently the Companhia União Fabril established a 75,000-acre plantation in the M'bridge valley (north-western Angola) to be devoted mainly to fibre crops for sacking. Cotton occupies about the same area as fibre crops. In the lower Cuanza valley, Angola's first major irrigation scheme is developed, based on the Cambambe Dam (1962). Both food and cash crops are being produced.

African agriculture in the remoter parts is largely for subsistence and based on shifting cultivation. In recent years the Administration has begun to tackle the problem of improving African agriculture, and is attempting to replace shifting cultivation by fixed settlements. Several settlement schemes are under way (Fig. 98), the largest of about 20,000 acres in the Loge valley west of Carmona, with others at Damba (also in Congo Province) and at Caconda (south of Nova Lisboa). So far the African response has been disappointing—less than 10 per cent of the land at Loge valley has been taken up and planted to coffee, oil-palms and food crops. Cattle are much less important in Angola than elsewhere in South-Western Africa. They number about 1·25 million, and are found almost entirely in the south. The southern limit of tsetse fly is represented approximately by the Benguela railway.

SETTLEMENT SCHEMES (Fig. 98)

Since World War II three major settlement schemes for Portuguese have been started. Angola, even more than Moçambique, is a convenient out-let for the surplus rural population of Portugal; since 1945 over 200,000 white settlers have arrived. There are new colonies at Forte Roçadas, on the middle Cunene, soon to be tapped by a branch railway from Sá da

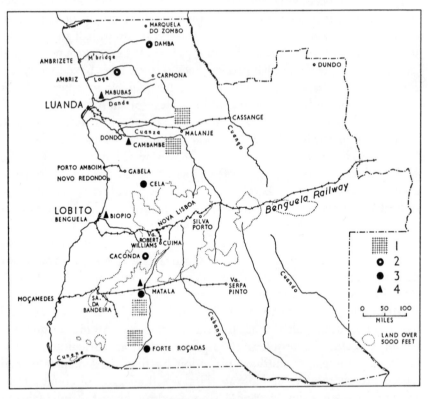

Figure 98 *Angola*

1. Irrigation schemes. 2. African settlement schemes. 3. European settlement schemes. 4. Hydro-electric installations

Bandeira; at Matala, on the upper Cunene, already connected by rail to
Sá da Bandeira; and at Cela. The Matala scheme is based on irrigation
from the Cunene Dam; it is planned to settle about 8,000 eventually, but
in 1962 the total was a little more than 1,000. The settlement at Cela, north
of the Bié plateau, was founded in 1952, since when no less than $22
million has been spent on it. Until very recently no white settler has been
allowed to use African labour, and this, together with the poor road connection to Luanda, 250 miles away, has been one of the main reasons why
the scheme has not been a success. The total number of settlers scattered in
a dozen villages over 12,000 acres is no more than 2,500 at present, and the
years 1954–60 saw about 100 families leave. The soils and climatic conditions were new to the settlers and with inadequate equipment and labour
they produced only limited crops of maize, beans and rice. The government has now admitted that African labour will be necessary, and that the
settlers must pay larger deposits, for it is clear that the scheme is proving
much more costly than anticipated.

MINERALS AND POWER

Though the Angolan economy rests heavily on coffee, the mineral
resources of the country provide a subsidiary support. Diamonds, both
gem stones and industrial, have been mined near the frontier in the
north-east at Dundo since 1917, and represent the second most valuable
product of Angola. Manganese ore is worked at several places along the
Luanda–Malanje railway; copper is mined in many other localities, the
chief being Mavoio, near Maquela do Zombo in the north. Though
reserves are small, these mines supply nearly half of Portgual's copper
needs. Production of iron ore has expanded greatly in recent years (1957—
104,000 tons; 1966—900,000 tons), partly because of the loss of Goa,
formerly Portugal's chief iron-ore supplier, and partly because of the
opening in 1961 of a new steel works near Lisbon. Cuima, at the end of a
branch diverging from the Benguela railway at Villa Robert Williams,
has hitherto been the chief iron-mining centre, but its place has now been
taken by Cassinga which in 1966 produced about 500,000 tons of high-
grade (64 per cent average) ore. Production is to be greatly expanded in
the next few years, and a new 50-mile railway is under construction to
provide transport.

In a country which lacks usable coal the discovery of oil near Luanda in
1955 was of great significance. The oilfields produced nearly 1 million tons

in 1963. A new refinery completed here in 1958 has a capacity for handling 650,000 tons of crude oil, enough for Angola's current needs. Angola's other power requirements are supplied by various hydro-electric installations. The principal ones in operation are at Biopio, on the Catumbela river near Lobito, at Mabubas, on the Dande river near Luanda, and at Matala, completed 1959, on the upper Cunene. Another, finished in 1962 and very much larger, has been constructed at Cambambe on the Cuanza river, and illustrates how rapid development has sometimes been badly planned, for only half its present capacity of 260 MW is being taken up (mostly transmitted to Luanda), while its potential is about 550 MW.

COMMUNICATIONS AND TOWNS

The two largest towns of Angola are *Luanda*, the capital (pop. 200,000), and *Lobito* (pop. 80,000), both major ports. The part played by Luanda in the Angolan coffee trade has been mentioned. Lobito is the maize port, and also the terminus of the Benguela railway. Since the last war it has been handling an increasing bulk of traffic from the Katanga: cargo has grown from 210,000 tons in 1938 (mostly of domestic origin) to 1·6 million tons in 1961 when about half the traffic was derived from the Congo. So far, however, Lobito has never been overloaded in comparison with Beira on the other side of the continent. The port of Lobito (Fig. 78) has grown up entirely since 1903, when construction of the Benguela railway began. It has an ideal situation behind a northward-growing sandspit; the wide approach channel makes pilotage unnecessary. Its potential cargo capacity has been raised to 3·5 million tons, and even this is by no means the limit. Between 1952 and 1960 manganese ore from Katanga was the most bulky commodity. Other minerals handled included up to one-quarter of the copper and one-half of the zinc produced by Katanga. In the period 1960–2, when Katanga seceded from the rest of the Congo, practically all Katangan copper used the Lobito outlet.

The Benguela railway was completed through to the Katanga in 1928, built by a British engineer, Sir Robert Williams, and owned, curiously, by Tanganyika Concessions Ltd., in which Belgians hold 41 per cent of the shares. Its capacity is probably 2 million tons; in 1963 it carried 500,000 tons of freight from Katanga (mostly minerals) and nearly 1 million tons originating in Angola. The climb up the escarpment (Plate 13) to Villa Robert Williams at 5,700 feet involves gradients of 1 in 40, which force a reduction of the maximum load per locomotive by two-thirds; fuel and

Galitzine & Partners

13 A freight train on the Benguela railway descending the Great Escarpment in Angola. The railway, completed from Lobito to Katanga in 1928, descends over 5,000 feet in this section

14 (A) Tobacco harvesting near Salisbury, Rhodesia

14 (B) The port of Beira, Moçambique, which handles the greater part of Rhodesia's trade. Copper, chromite and tobacco are the principal exports, for its hinterland includes Zambia as well as Rhodesia

water are other problems. The journey to Elisabethville, which is as far from Lobito as Istanbul is from London, takes four days for passengers and twice as long for freight.

Recently the Portuguese have been extending other railways. From the old fishing port of Moçamedes, now being equipped with a new harbour capable of handling 100,000-ton iron-ore carriers, one can reach Vila Serpa Pinto crossing the Cunene at the Matala Dam. Another link from Luanda to the northern frontier is under construction. There is an efficient internal air service.

FUTURE PROSPECTS

The future of Angola is very much in the balance. If political stability can be maintained there are many possibilities for further development, though it will not be rapid, for Portugal herself is not a rich country. Lack of adequate communications and the small size of the population will seriously retard development. Potentially, Angola is fairly well endowed; there are good farming lands awaiting utilisation, there are minerals and there is hydro-electric power. The economy today is precarious because of excessive reliance on the sale of coffee. Diversification of Angola's agriculture, forced on Brazil thirty years ago, is urgent but need not be difficult. The unique colonial policy of the Portuguese has already been mentioned in connection with Portugal's other major African territory, Moçambique. Like Moçambique, Angola is administered from Lisbon through a Governor-General, and is treated as a province of Portugal. There has been no racial discrimination, and about 30,000 Africans are 'assimilados' or 'civilised', compared with about 5,000 only in Moçambique. The Portuguese have encouraged white immigration and further 'assimilation' of the Africans. They hope that an African Brazil is in the making. But it must be remembered that Brazil took 300 years to evolve to its present form. Also Brazil claimed her independence from Portugal 150 years ago—a part of the Brazilian story which Portugal does not wish to see repeated in Angola. Ostensibly the Portuguese hope by encouraging white immigration to establish a truly mixed society; but in fact, as many have pointed out, they are threatening to create a 'Portuguese Algeria'. Between 1945 and 1961 the white population has increased fivefold, while the corresponding increase for the Africans has only been 10 per cent. The proportion of mixed blood has, if anything, shown a tendency to decline relatively. Thus

increased white immigration is serving to divide the country more
rigidly into black and white, between whom there is growing economic
competition. And without African co-operation it is clear that the
economic development of Angola can never be advanced.

References

1 J. H. Wellington, 'Zambezi–Okovango development projects', *Geog. Rev.*, 39
  (1949), 552–67
  J. H. Wellington, 'A new development scheme for the Okovango delta,
  northern Kalahari', *Geog. Journ.*, 113 (1949), 62–9
2 F. Debenham, 'Livingstone's Africa and future development', *Geography*, 36
  (1951), 107–11
3 E. M. Thomas, *The harmless people* (London, 1959)

Selected Bibliography

Basutoland, Bechuanaland Protectorate and Swaziland. Report of an Economic Survey
  Mission (H.M.S.O., London, 1960)
F. Debenham, *Kalahari Sand* (London, 1953)
D. Randall, *Factors of economic development and the Okovango delta* (Chicago, 1957)

F. Debenham, 'Journey in Thirstland: in search of water in Bechuanaland', *Geog.
  Rev.*, 41 (1951), 464–9
F. Debenham, 'The Kalahari today', *Geog. Journ.*, 118 (1952), 12–23
E. J. Wayland, 'More about the Kalahari', *Geog. Journ.*, 119 (1953), 49–56

H. K. Airy Shaw, 'The vegetation of Angola', *Journ. Ecology*, 35 (1947), 23–48
I. S. Van Dongen, 'Coffee trade, coffee regions and coffee ports in Angola', *Econ.
  Geog.*, 37 (1961), 320–46
W. A. Hance and I. S. Van Dongen, 'The port of Lobito and the Benguela
  railway', *Geog. Rev.*, 46 (1956), 460–87
R. J. Houk, 'Recent developments in the Portuguese Congo', *Geog. Rev.*, 48
  (1958), 201–21
P. B. Stone, 'New development in south Angola', *S. Afr. Geog. Journ.*, 39 (1957),
  55–60
H. F. Varian, 'The geography of the Benguela railway', *Geog. Journ.*, 78 (1931),
  497–523
G. Whittington, 'Iron mining in Angola', *Geography*, 49 (1964), 418–19
D. S. Whittlesey, 'Geographic provinces of Angola', *Geog. Rev.*, 14 (1924), 113–26

PART XII

Equatorial Africa

Bisected by the equator, the Congo Basin is one of the most clearly defined drainage units in the continent of Africa. The River Congo is not the longest river in Africa, but it has by far the greatest discharge on reaching the sea, for it drains an area over most of which the annual precipitation exceeds 50 inches. The Congo was the last of the great African rivers to be explored, and all European settlement and economic development of the Congo interior dates back for less than a century. Equatorial Africa, however, includes not only the Congo Basin but also adjacent regions to the west which share with the Congo a humid tropical environment, but whose outlook is towards the Atlantic. Here settlements along the coast were founded by the Portuguese nearly four centuries before Stanley's great journey down the Congo river. Today in equatorial Africa colonial rule only remains in a few small areas—Cabinda (Portuguese), Spanish Guinea and the Spanish and Portuguese off-shore islands of Fernando Poo, Principe, São Tomé and Annobon. The rest of the area politically consists of self-governing states—the Republic of the Congo (Kinshasa)*, the Congo Republic (Brazzaville)†, Gabon, the Cameroun Republic, the Central African Republic and the Republic of Rwanda and the Kingdom of Burundi‡. Thus an area which has a considerable measure of geographical unity is now split by political frontiers into seven or more parts. Economically, the Congo (Kinshasa) is the most advanced part; figures for the value of exports from equatorial Africa in 1959 show that out of a total of $700 million, over three-

* Former Belgian Congo; Leopoldville was renamed Kinshasa in 1966.
† Former Moyen Congo, of French Equatorial Africa.
‡ Former Ruanda-Urundi, included in Chapter 50 since until 1960 they were administered jointly as an integral part of the Belgian Congo; physiographically, their place is with East Africa.

quarters originated in the (then) Belgian Congo, the most valuable section being minerals from Katanga Province. The Congo (Kinshasa) also has the distinction of being Africa's second largest country (905,000 sq. miles).

49

The Land and its People

Although a distinct hydrographic unit, the Congo Basin (Fig. 99) must be regarded as no more than a slight depression in the African continental platform. The floor of the basin, between 1,000 and 1,700 feet, rises almost imperceptibly to the series of uplands and plateaux forming the rim. The River Congo, whose upper section is known as the Lualaba, follows a course curving through the northern part of the basin before cutting abruptly through the Crystal Mountains in a gorge up to 1,600 feet deep. This is the only outlet of the basin to the sea; its development by the overflow of the Quaternary Congo lake was described in Chapter 3. Through the gorge between Stanley Pool and Matadi the river tumbles over thirty-two cataracts, dropping altogether 850 feet. In contrast, from Stanley Pool upstream to Stanleyville, the river's gradient is only 6 inches per mile. In this section the river flows slowly in a shallow and braided channel, the width of the channels amounting to 9 miles in one place. In these regions shadowed by the great tropical forest the land surface is flat and monotonous.

The floor of the Congo Basin is an area of Pliocene and Quaternary alluvium deposited in the old lake or during the stages of its draining. Remnants of the former lake can be seen in Lakes Tumba and Leopold II, together with extensive swamp areas in what has been aptly described as the sump of the basin. The alluvial floor is enclosed by outcrops of pre-Tertiary rocks, whose edge is represented by a low but well-marked break of slope, roughly elliptical in shape, which the rivers cross in rapids or falls—the Archduchesse Stephanie rapids at Kikwit on the Kwilu, at Charlesville on the Kasai, Stanley Falls on the Congo and above Zongo on the Ubangi, to name a few. In the south and east of the basin several higher breaks of slope appear, associated with variations in rock resistance, and marked, for instance, by the falls above Kindu on the Lualaba, or on the Uele and Bomu before these join to form the Ubangi.

The basin is surrounded by uplands and plateaux (Fig. 99). The Bié plateau of Angola, described in a previous chapter, continues eastward, dropping gradually to the Katanga plateau at 3,000–4,000 feet. This in turn is essentially a continuation of the plateau of Zambia (see Chapter 34). In north and central Katanga, however, the plateau has been fractured; downfaulted areas contain the swamp-filled depressions and lakes of Bangweulu, Mweru and the Lualaba north of Bukama. Intervening horsts such as the Kundelunga massif rise to 6,000 feet. Along the east of the Congo Basin the rampart of the Western Rift Valley Highlands reaches more than 10,000 feet in places, towering over Lakes Tanganyika, Kivu and Edward in imposing fault-scarps. Certain volcanoes in north Rwanda attain 14,000 feet. A curious feature is the drainage of Lake Tanganyika, which itself receives the overflow of Lake Kivu by a volcanic accident, into the Congo Basin via the Lukuga gorge through the Rift Valley Highlands.

The watershed with the Nile is not well defined, consisting of undulating bush-covered plateaux at 3,000–4,000 feet. Occupying the divide between the Nile, Chad and Congo drainage are the Bongo Mountains (4,600 feet). Westward, the land declines until, at a point only 2,000 feet high, the Chad drainage approaches to within 60 miles of the Ubangi at Fort Possel. Imperceptibly the ground rises again to the Yadé plateau (4,500 feet) in north Cameroun. On this plateau in the north-west stands part of the great volcanic chain of the Cameroon Mountains. These reach their greatest elevation in the still-active Mount Cameroon itself (13,350 feet), particularly impressive since it is isolated and situated on the coast, though usually swathed in cloud. The volcanic chain continues out to sea as a series of partly submerged peaks, from Fernando Poo to Annobon.

The watershed between the Congo Basin and the Atlantic drainage of such rivers as the Ogooué and Nyong comprises a series of highly dissected plateaux usually attaining 2,000–3,000 feet, but reaching a maximum of 5,165 feet in the Chaillu Mountains of central Gabon. These plateaux rise abruptly behind the coastal plains; their edges are known in northern Gabon as the Crystal Mountains, and in the south as the Mayombé Mountains. The coastal plains vary considerably in width. In the north around Douala and Edea there is a wide alluvial embayment,

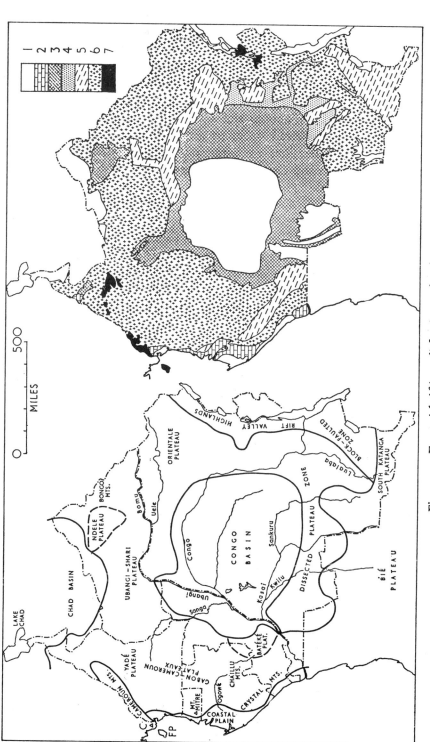

Figure 99 *Equatorial Africa: relief regions and geology*

1. Quaternary. 2. Tertiary and Mesozoic marine. 3. Tertiary, Cretaceous and Jurassic continental. 4. Karroo. 5. Katanga System (Pre-Cambrian). 6. Other Pre-Cambrian. 7. Post-Karroo Volcanics

C Cameroon Mountain, FP Fernando Poo

and another similarly broadens out behind Libreville, with the Ogooué pursuing a sluggish course across it in mangrove-lined channels; but in parts of Spanish Guinea the coastal plain virtually disappears. Mount Mitre, for example, rises to 4,000 feet within 15 miles of the coast. The coastline itself is generally smooth and sandy from Cape Lopez to the Congo estuary, and sheltered openings are lacking. North of Cape Lopez, in contrast, identations are numerous, including the excellent harbours of the Gabon and Cameroun estuaries.

GEOLOGY

Archaean crystalline rocks (Fig. 99) form the foundation of the Congo Basin, and also outcrop as part of the rim, from Angola to Cameroun, and thence eastward along the 'Guinea ridge'. Lying unconformably on these basement rocks are sedimentaries, of upper Pre-Cambrian age and of great economic importance because of the minerals occurring in them. Known as the Katanga System, and partly contemporaneous with the Transvaal System of South Africa, they outcrop principally on the eastern side of the Congo Basin, from the Katanga plateau to the Sudan border. In the Congo Basin itself, but largely concealed by more recent deposits, there are Karroo beds (Permo-Triassic here), useful for the coal seams at some horizons. In the Jurassic and Cretaceous these Karroo beds were buried by river-borne and wind-blown deposits, known as the Lubilash beds; some of the river gravels are rich in diamonds. Meanwhile, on the Atlantic coast, marine sediments accumulated, now forming the foundation of the coastal plains around the Congo estuary, Libreville and Douala.

The Tertiary history of the Congo Basin was one of alternating periods of denudation, slight warping and deposition in the basin centre. The main period of sub-aerial denudation produced the extensive Miocene planation surface, and downwarping of the pre-Tertiary rocks produced the present shallow basin, though a depression in the Pre-Cambrian basement must have existed here since at least the Permian. The Tertiary period saw continuing marine deposition on the coastlands, and also the commencement of the volcanic activity which produced the Cameroon mountain chain.

CLIMATE

Though there is a certain homogeneity of climate in equatorial Africa, the great extent of the area must be remembered: it is half the size of the

USA and variations of climate are to be expected. Differences arise owing to varying distance from the equator, distance from the Atlantic Ocean and varying altitude. The floor of the Congo Basin lies at over 1,000 feet, with consequent benefit to the climate in contrast to the Amazon Basin on the opposite side of the Atlantic.

Over most of equatorial Africa the climate is monotonous in that seasonal variations of temperature are slight: the mean monthly range is 8°F at Kinshasa, 4°F at Douala. Only on the Katanga plateau, more than 10° south of the equator, does a relatively cool season appear (see Lubumbashi, Table 36). Because of the amount of cloud, temperatures are never so high as, for instance, in the Kalahari farther south during the summer, and mean monthly figures rarely rise above 80°F. At Kinshasa, on average, two out of every three days have overcast skies with little or no sunshine. Humidity is the most unpleasant feature—81 per cent mean daily relative humidity at Kinshasa, with even higher figures recorded from the interior or the lower Congo valley.

Total annual rainfall (Fig. 100) varies from as little as 30 inches at Banana on the Congo estuary, to over 400 inches on Mount Cameroon. Fifty to seventy inches is a more normal figure. The relative dryness of the coast near Banana and in Cabinda represents a continuation of the coastal dry zone of Angola and the influence of the last traces of the Benguela current. From the Congo estuary northward along the coast there is a remarkably rapid increase in rainfall—Loango 48 inches, Mayoumba 62 inches, Libreville 99 inches.

Most of the rainfall is convectional or frontal, and reflects the extreme instability of the prevalent mE air. Thunderstorms occur almost daily on the equator, and frequently in the hot season in more distant zones. At Jadotville, in Katanga, the average number of thunderstorms (taken over a four-year period) was 129 in the months from October to April, and two for the rest of the year. On the equator there is no dry season in the interior, but only two periods of lesser rainfall between the overhead passages of the ITC (see Kisangani, Table 36). About latitude 3° north or south a short dry season begins to appear; a period of lesser rainfall in the wet season is maintained (see Kinshasa, Table 1). Farther north or south the dry season expands so as to shorten and eventually to eliminate the lesser of the two rainy seasons (see Lubumbashi, latitude 12°S, or Ngaoundéré on the Yadé plateau, latitude 7°N, Table 36).

In the rift valley area to the east the equatorial climate is modified by altitude and by the presence of large lakes. The latter exert a cooling

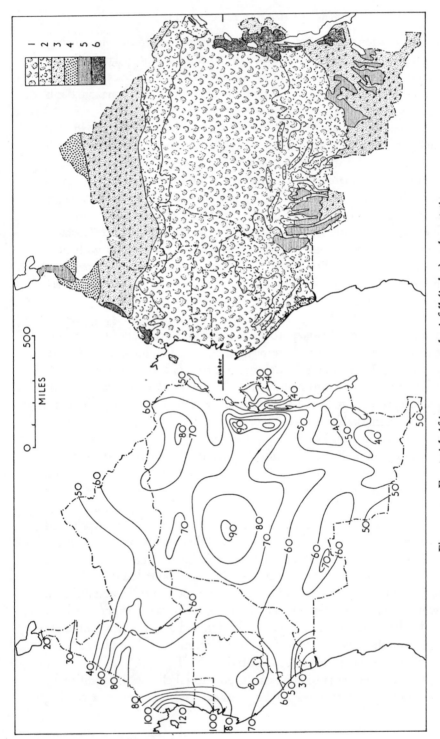

Figure 100 *Equatorial Africa: mean annual rainfall (inches) and vegetation*

1. Rain forest. 2. Forest-savanna mosaic. 3. Moist savanna. 4. Dry savanna. 5. Grass steppe. 6. Montane

effect on the lands immediately next to them and also reduce the seasonal range of temperature still further. The Rwanda–Burundi plateau is thus cooler (see Nyundo, Table 36), and the peaks which rise above it have greater rainfall—100 inches at 8,000 feet, compared with 50 inches at 5,000 feet. The rainfall at high altitudes is frequently finer and more continuous. On the Rift Valley Highlands a decrease of rainfall is noticeable above 8,000 feet.

VEGETATION (Fig. 100)

Rain forest occupies the lower ground of the basin and the Congo–Atlantic watershed up to about 2,500 feet, with the exception of areas either cleared for cultivation or where the soil will not support forest (e.g. highly laterised soils, or sandy river deposits). The border of the forest is not clearly defined, there being a gradual transition through country possessing a forest-savanna mosaic, representing partial destruction of a former forest cover by fire. Tongues of forest also penetrate far up the river valleys into the neighbouring savanna zone. The true forest is mainly evergreen and possesses a great number of species (see Chapter 6). Deciduous species appear on its margins.

The extent to which the forest has been disturbed by man cannot be precisely determined. The long-continued native practice of shifting cultivation may have affected very large areas of equatorial Africa. The length of time elapsing between successive clearings of the same patch of ground will determine the extent to which the forest can regenerate itself; well-developed secondary forest usually has denser undergrowth than the original forest and may contain species originally introduced by the natives, such as the oil-palm. In many areas, however, intervals between cultivation are short, and the regular burning of the vegetation results in the replacement of forest by savanna. The soils also suffer in this process; burning hardens the lateritic soils, exposure of the soil accelerates leaching and destruction of the forest also removes the primary source of organic material for the soil. The development of European agriculture in the last hundred years has further assisted in the deforestation of large areas. The Belgians, for instance, introduced compulsory cultivation of food-crops and encouraged African cash crops.

The forest area is shrinking, that of the savanna expanding. Recent maps indicate that only about half of equatorial Africa is under rain forest, and even this does not allow for areas of cultivation within the

Table 36 Temperature and rainfall for selected stations in equatorial Africa

Station	Alt. (feet)		J	F	M	A	M	J	J	A	S	O	N	D	Year	Temp. range
Ngaoundéré	3,575	Temp. °F	70	71	70	72	72	73	73	71	71	70	72	69	71	4
		Rain in.	0·3	0·	2·8	5·6	11·6	15·8	14·0	11·2	7·9	6·3	0·1	0·3	75·9	
Banana	7	T.	78	78	79	79	77	74	70	70	72	76	79	79	76	9
		R.	1·1	6·6	6·0	5·5	4·2	0	0	0	0·1	0·4	3·7	2·7	30·3	
Kisangani	1,370	T.	78	78	78	79	78	77	75	75	76	77	76	77	77	4
		R.	2·1	3·3	7·0	6·2	5·4	4·5	5·2	6·5	7·2	8·6	7·8	3·3	67·1	
Lubumbashi	4,035	T.	71	72	71	69	65	61	61	65	71	75	74	72	69	14
		R.	10·5	9·6	8·4	2·2	0·2	0	0	0·1	0·1	1·2	5·9	10·6	48·7	
Nyundo (Rwanda)	6,168	T.	65	66	65	65	64	64	64	65	65	65	64	65	65	2
		R.	4·1	4·6	7·2	7·4	4·6	2·5	1·0	2·6	4·7	5·8	4·3	4·5	53·3	

For Douala, Libreville and Kinshasa, see Table 1

forest. The savanna occupies a zone of varying width to the north and south of the forest, in which a three- to six-month dry season is normally experienced. At such times of the year the savanna grasses become brown and parched, while the trees shed their leaves, except for the gallery forest along water-courses. The grasses vary in density and height with the soil character. Old lateritic soils support only short grass (3–4 feet) with many bare patches, whereas alluvial silts or organic soils near the forest margin often support the elephant grass up to 16 feet high. Practically the whole of Katanga is covered by various forms of savanna. In the south, open *Brachystegia* woodland, broken by grassy 'dembos' along streams or in marshy areas, continues from Zambia; in the northern half of Katanga the high plateau tops support short grass, with savanna woodland on slopes below 5,000 feet, and tracts of elephant grass in the valley bottoms.

POPULATION AND SETTLEMENT

The total population, on an area of 1·5 million sq. miles, approaches 25 million. This figure includes a variety of racial and linguistic groups of which the largest is the Bantu (though this term itself covers many different tribes and different languages). One of the larger Bantu tribes is the Fang, who live in Gabon and south Cameroun. The Bantu, who were probably not the first inhabitants of equatorial Africa but arrived there before the dawn of recorded history, are found in both the forest and savanna areas. In the forest their settlements are usually in clearings by the rivers and are moved periodically as new areas are used for cultivation. Shifting agriculture, fishing and gathering forest products provide the basis of the economy; in the savanna cattle are kept in some open areas relatively free from the tsetse fly of the surrounding bush.

The original inhabitants of equatorial Africa, not discovered by white man until 1865, are the Pygmies. The name Pygmy comes from a Greek word meaning 'a cubit tall'. They originally inhabited open country, but have been driven deeper and deeper into the forest by more active tribes such as the Bantu. Thus they have managed to retain their physical peculiarities and their traditional nomadic way of life, but their numbers are few and are probably declining. The Pygmies subsist entirely on hunting and collecting, together with some simple barter trade with neighbouring Bantu. Pygmies depend on the Bantu for certain foods, such as plantains, in return for which they hunt and fish for the Bantu who are in many areas more or less their masters. Although in these respects they are backward, in others, such as in their construction of daring rope bridges made solely from twisted vines to cross rivers, they are remarkably ingenious, considering the primitive methods at their disposal.

In the north and east of the Congo Basin live a people distinct from the Bantu or Negro: these are the Hamites, who came into the area from the Nile Basin and Ethiopia about 400 years ago. In Rwanda and Burundi they comprise the Watutsi, a tall, aristocratic people making up 15 per cent of the population. They are primarily shepherds and cattle folk, who brought with them their big-horned Ankole cattle. From the fifteenth century onwards they became the rulers over the ordinary Bantu, who in this area are devoted to agriculture. Burundi is still ruled by the Watutsi, but when Rwanda gained its independence in 1962 the Bantu (here known as the Bahutu) overthrew their traditional Watutsi overlords, many of whom fled into Tanganyika.

The latest arrivals in equatorial Africa before European settlers were the Arabs (Semites). They entered from the east as traders and slaveseekers. Practically no pure-bred Arabs now remain, but their influence on culture, dress and buildings can still be clearly seen in Rwanda, Burundi and some eastern parts of the Congo. The men still wear the traditional Moslem robes, profess the tenets of Islam and even occasionally go on pilgrimage to Mecca.

No precise census has yet been taken in any of the countries comprising equatorial Africa; it is thought that official figures underestimate by 10 per cent or more. However, the general distribution of population is fairly clear. At the one extreme there are Rwanda and Burundi, the most densely peopled countries in Africa with an average of 225 persons per sq. mile; while at the other, almost half the Congo Basin has less than one inhabitant per sq. mile. The average for the two Congo republics, Cameroun and Gabon, varies between four and twenty per sq. mile, but, like all averages, these figures conceal the fact that the great majority of the people are clustered in villages or in the towns. The towns of the Congo (Kinshasa) with more than 1,000 persons each, numbering about 170, in fact contain one-eighth of the total population. All, however, were planned and built by the Belgians, for before the arrival of the white man the Bantu nowhere built settlements larger or more complex than their agricultural villages. The concentration of people in Rwanda and Burundi is unique in tropical Africa, and the more extraordinary when one learns that half the population of these tiny countries lives on but a quarter of their total area—resulting in densities locally exceeding 1,000 per sq. mile—and that nearly all the people (about 98 per cent) live in scattered rural dwellings.

The European population is naturally concentrated in the towns. The six largest towns of the Congo (Kinshasa) contain half the Europeans of the country; three of them (*Lubumbashi*, pop. 184,000, *Jadotville*, pop. 75,000 and *Kolwezi*, pop. 47,000) are in the Katanga mining area. By far the largest town in equatorial Africa is *Kinshasa*, with nearly 1,000,000 inhabitants, including about 20,000 Europeans, in 1966. Facing it across the river is *Brazzaville*, the former capital of the French Congo, with 145,000 inhabitants. Farther upstream the main port outlet of the Central African Republic, *Bangui*, has about 80,000.

In their part of equatorial Africa the Belgians made great progress in improving tropical living conditions and disproving the myth that white people cannot successfully colonise the humid tropics. Disease, not the climate, was the root of the problem. In 1910 the death rate amongst Europeans living in the Congo was 32 per 1,000. By 1930 this had been brought down dramatically to 13 per 1,000. In 1959 it was only 3·4 per 1,000.

50

The former Belgian Territories

THE REPUBLIC OF THE CONGO (KINSHASA)*

Thé River Congo, which every minute discharges 3 million cubic metres of water into the Atlantic and colours it with mud for more than 30 miles off-shore, is the main artery of the Republic. Along its 2,500-mile course to the sea it receives on both sides the waters of countless tributaries, some of them major rivers themselves, such as the Ubangi, which is as long as the Danube.

The early history of the country was outlined in Part II; after Stanley's return to Europe the territory was acquired by King Leopold II of Belgium, and in 1907 it became a Belgian colony. The slave trade, initiated by the Portuguese on the west coast and subsequently extended into the eastern Congo by Arabs from the opposite side of the continent, was replaced in the nineteenth century by interest in other local commodities—ivory, wild rubber and palm-oil. In 1900 the chief product of the Congo Free State, as it was then known, was wild rubber. Until 1910, in fact, the Congo supplied nearly 40 per cent of the world's rubber. The years 1913–14, however, saw a rapid decline in the wild-rubber industry as the new plantations of South-East Asia came into production. But whereas these years were disastrous for the rubber industry of Brazil, in the case of the Congo the decline of wild rubber was hardly noticed, for this was the time of the momentous discoveries of mineral riches in the south-east of the Congo Basin. Today the Congo is noted as a major world source of cobalt, copper, diamonds and uranium; with the exception of diamonds, these are mostly obtained in Katanga Province.

* To avoid repetition of this cumbersome term the Territory will be referred to simply as the 'Congo' in this chapter. Up to mid-1960 it was known as the Belgian Congo.

In the years following World War II particularly, Belgian investment in the Congo was on a tremendous scale, and development proceeded rapidly, for the Congo, though nearly eighty times the size of Belgium and nearly 1 million sq. miles in area, was Belgium's only overseas territory. Belgian colonial policy remained, however, distinct from that of certain other European powers in Africa; no attempt was made to develop any form of local government, or to advance the political status of the African. Until 1960 neither the Congolese nor the Europeans resident in the Congo had any voting rights. In theory there was no colour bar, though the towns were in practice divided into European and African sectors, and the Africans were barred from certain higher professions and occupations. Few Congolese ever travelled outside the country. The years leading up to the calamitous events of 1960 saw the first signs of discontent, developing with unprecedented rapidity into a situation which the Belgians could no longer control, representing as they did less than 1 per cent of the population. In July 1960 Belgian administration came abruptly to an end; the Congo became formally independent; and a period of anarchy ensued. The European population in the next seven months was virtually halved as many of the Belgians fled the country. Certain parts of the Congo, however, remained relatively stable, one of which was southern Katanga, the province which immediately broke away from the rest of the Congo. Its independence was never recognised by the central Congolese government at Leopoldville (Kinshasa), and subsequently, after a period of hostilities, reunification of the Congo was achieved.

It is of vital importance to take account of these political upheavals in any consideration of the Congolese economy. Agriculture and communications were disrupted over wide areas; famine and disease returned on a scale unknown for many decades; and the finances of the Congo fell into a critical state. The situation in Katanga was less serious; by 1963 the mines were working again at full capacity. Probably about three-quarters of the European population remained. In 1959 nearly 65 per cent of the total Congolese revenue came from Katanga's mineral production, and it was clear that the Congo could never regain its former economic position or prosperity unless Katanga was reunited with it. It will be many years before the whole economy can once again be built up to the impressive level achieved by the Belgians in the later years of their administration, or before foreign investment again plays its essential part in the development of the area.

During their last fifty years of administration the Belgians effected great improvements in many aspects of agriculture in the Congo, devoting much time and money to research. Experimental stations were established to study the cultivation of rubber, coffee, oil-palms and other crops, and to deal with pest control, seed selection and other techniques, especially under the guidance of INEAC (Institut National pour l'Etude Agronomique du Congo Belge), founded in 1933 and later to become one of the world's leading tropical research institutes. The area under effective cultivation was also greatly increased, partly as a result of the policy brought in during the 1930's of compulsory cultivation by Africans of both cash crops and food crops. Such crops were produced under the supervision of the local administrator, and were collected periodically, usually weekly in the case of foodstuffs. It was particularly necessary to step up food production in an endeavour to supply the mining areas and expanding towns of the Congo.

In the 1950's, the Belgians began introducing 'paysannats', schemes for organising African shifting cultivation. Basically, they involved dividing land into strips whose fields were cultivated for perhaps three years and then allowed to revert to bush for 15–20 years. By 1958, about 200,000 Africans were working in paysannats, producing sizeable quantities of maize, cotton, and rice, in spite of the limited scale of operations. However, in most other parts of the Congo, more primitive forms of shifting agriculture are the rule, for land is abundant relative to the population. After choosing a new plot the Africans clear and burn the vegetation (producing valuable ash and destroying many insect pests), and cultivate the patch intensively for perhaps three to five years. The menfolk generally assist in the initial task of clearing, while the women are often responsible for the subsequent cultivation.* Implements are simple—an axe, a hoe, a knife and a rake represent the usual range. The main food crops vary somewhat from one region to another, but cassava is most widespread. Introduced to Africa by the Portuguese, its cultivation is simple, but it quickly exhausts the soil. Its root provides flour for bread. Maize occupies a smaller area; it is often put in as a snatch crop to be grown and harvested before the cassava is ready. In the drier savanna

* An account of the system of shifting agriculture employed by the Fang will be found in Chapter 51.

areas the staple food is often millet. Rice is cultivated mainly in the eastern provinces, to which it was brought by Arabs from East Africa. Sometimes a surplus is produced for sale to the towns. Also representing a basic food crop in the east are bananas. Many other minor crops are grown, but in spite of this the African often suffers from famine as a result perhaps of the failure of one crop before another is ripe, or of not storing sufficient to tide him over a lean period. Starvation of many thousands was a tragic feature of the anarchic situation which prevailed immediately after independence, with crops destroyed or never harvested.

African cash crops (Fig. 101)

Of the cash crops raised by Africans three are most important—cotton, coffee and the oil-palm. Cotton is the most extensive, occupying about one-eighth of Africa's total cotton area (910,000 acres in 1959). Its production is almost entirely in the hands of Africans, who sell it to European-owned ginneries. About 20 per cent is consumed in the cloth mills at Leopoldville, apart from exports which normally realise about £10 million. As it thrives in areas with a regular dry season its cultivation is concentrated in the savanna zones. Coffee is grown both by Africans and on European plantations. Of a rather scattered production, the most valuable part is in the eastern highlands and Orientale, where Arab influence remains. Total coffee acreage in 1959 was 207,000, yielding about 12 per cent of Africa's coffee production. The oil-palm is indigenous to western tropical Africa, growing in rainforest areas with little or no dry season. The Africans tend wild trees and plant additional ones near their villages, but there are also important European plantations which will be described later. Oil-palm products are the Congo's most valuable export after minerals, being valued at £18 million in 1958, with the Congo the world's second largest producer (after Nigeria). About half the African plantings are in the provinces of Leopoldville and Equateur, concentrated near the rivers which are used for transport.

European cash crops (Fig. 101)

European agriculture takes two main forms—the large plantations leased to companies such as Huileries du Congo (a subsidiary of Unilever), and the farms of a few private European settlers, mainly found in regions of

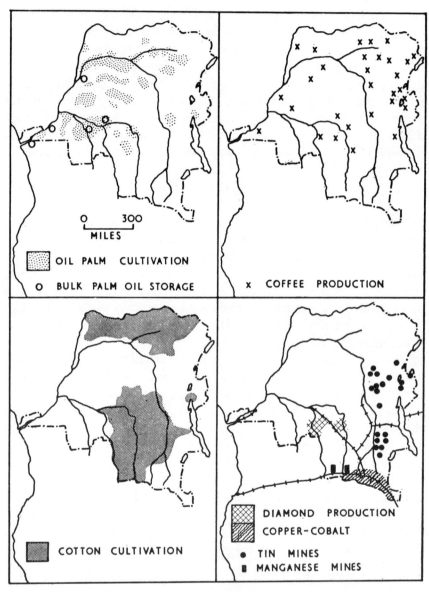

Figure 101 Distribution of crop and mineral production in the Congo (Kinshasa), Rwanda and Burundi. Main railways are indicated on the diagram showing minerals

more pleasant climate such as the Kivu or Katanga uplands. The plantations are concerned chiefly with coffee, rubber and oil-palms. Rubber growing has developed afresh since the 1930's, with the first plantings of *Hevea Braziliensis* coming into production in 1938. The acreage devoted to rubber reached 200,000 in 1960, concentrated in the western half of the Congo and yielding nearly 2 per cent of the world's natural rubber.

The oil-palm is indigenous to tropical Africa within latitudes 10° north and south. The tree cannot have too much rain—it flourishes in 200 inches or more—but it does require at least 60 inches with no marked dry season. The principal oil-palm plantations are those of Unilever, whose concession dates from 1911, when a convention was signed between the Belgian Government and Lever Brothers Ltd. to establish plantations and set up oil mills in the Congo. The first Viscount Leverhulme obtained a total concession of 1·75 million acres. The actual plantations today cover altogether about 160,000 acres, whilst an additional area of 250,000 acres containing wild oil-palms has been regularly harvested. The largest individual concession is Lusanga (205,000 acres) with headquarters at Leverville near Kikwit. Smaller ones are at Brabanta near Port Francqui and Flandria near Mbandaka (formerly Coquilhatville). Five others are on or near the middle Congo and one is in north-east Kivu. Both plantations and oil mills are located on or near navigable rivers. The principal mills are at Kinshasa, Leverville, Alberta and Elisabetha (both on the middle Congo), and Brabanta. The numbers of Africans employed have risen from about 30,000 in 1951 to over 50,000 in 1961. Unilever have provided houses for practically all their workers, clustered in neat villages provided with shops, schools and hospitals. Unilever's current investment in the Congo amounts to no less than $64 million, seriously jeopardised by the political crises since 1960. Although some of the northern plantations were badly affected by the disorders of 1960–2 and river traffic impeded, the 1960 production was valued at $19 million.

Other trees in the rain forest are of little commercial importance at present. Lumbering touches only a minute fraction of the forest, and production is mainly for local uses. The greater part of the forest interior is remote; there are no pure stands of timber; and many of the varieties are obscure. The only area where timber extraction is of more than local significance is in Bas-Congo (Mayombé), and in the adjacent Portuguese enclave of Cabinda (see page 602).

Most parts of the Congo are afflicted with tsetse fly. Southern Katanga is an exception, and consequently one of the few regions where livestock are found in numbers.

MINING AND POWER SUPPLIES (Fig. 102)

The richly mineralised zone of the Zambian Copperbelt continues across the frontier into Katanga. Of this copper-rich area much the larger part lies in the Congo, where it was first investigated in 1892. Today the Katangan–Zambian Copperbelt furnishes 18 per cent of the world's copper—11 per cent from Zambia and 7 per cent from the Congo. Working in Katanga began in 1906, though there was little output until the arrival of the railway (from Northern Rhodesia) in 1910. In 1906 mineral rights over 8,000 sq. miles were granted by King Leopold to the Union Minière du Haut Katanga, a company formed by Belgian and British interests. Copper production increased rapidly after World War I. Indeed, for a few years in the 1920's the Union Minière was producing more copper than any other single company in the world, but it was soon overtaken by the rapid expansion of North American, North Rhodesian and Chilean sources.

The deposits chiefly worked are high-grade oxidised ores containing 6 to 8 per cent copper and various subsidiary minerals such as cobalt and, occurring in Pre-Cambrian schists, quartzites and dolomites. Most of the mines are opencast, with the ore dug out mechanically along huge benches. They are grouped in three areas today:

(a) around Elisabethville. Close by is the 'Star of the Congo' mine, fabulously rich when first opened

(b) around Jadotville and Kambove (Plate 15)

(c) around Kolwezi, which now yields 80 per cent of the Katanga copper, in addition to nearly all the cobalt.

Minerals are often worked in conjunction with one another: copper and cobalt are obtained together at Kolwezi, while at Kipushi the range of subsidiaries produced with copper includes lead, zinc, germanium and cadmium.

Owing to the great distances of the area from the coasts of Africa, and consequent high cost of rail haulage, the ore must be smelted at the mines. The amount of reduction accomplished can be judged from the fact that ore production, all minerals, exceeds 10 million tons a year, but the total weight exported from Katanga is little more than half a million tons. The first copper smelter was built at Elisabethville in 1911, depending on

15 Copper mines and smelting works of the Union Minière at Jadotville in Katanga

16 (A) Oil derrick in the Niger delta. An artificial bay is dredged out of the bank
to protect the drilling rig from swift river currents

16 (B) Takoradi harbour, Ghana. This artificial deep-water harbour, Ghana's
first, was created in 1928 and enlarged in 1953

Aerofilms Library

wood fuel and imported coal, but the first electrolytic copper refinery was not in operation until 1929 at Jadotville. Today hydro-electricity supplies most of the power. To produce 1 ton of electrolytic copper, 99·95 per cent pure, requires up to 2,500 kwh, and for 1 ton of cobalt as

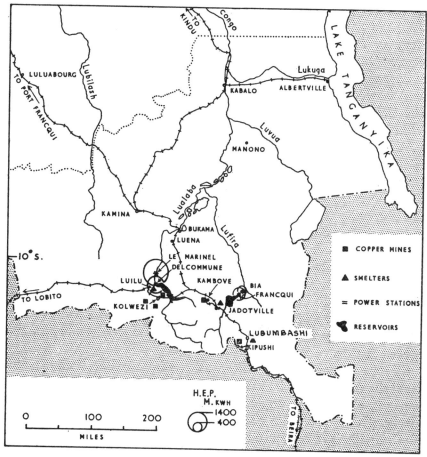

Figure 102 *Katanga: mines, power stations, and rail links*

much as 10,000 kwh. The first big hydro-electric plant was the 'Francqui' on the upper Lufira river, opened in 1936 (Fig. 102). The main development of hydro-electricity has, however, come since the last war, culminating with 'Delcommune' and 'Le Marinel' on the upper Lualaba in 1951 and 1956 respectively. The latest, and one of the world's most modern electrolytic smelters, costing $5·6 million, was opened at Luilu in 1960. This alone can produce annually 100,000 tons of copper and 1,750 tons of cobalt. At Kambove a vast new concentrator capable of handling 0·75 million tons of ore a year came into operation in 1961. Not only are the refining facilities being constantly improved and expanded, but new mines are being opened, the latest of which are at Fungureme and Kakanda.

Mineral production in Katanga has not been greatly affected by the events of 1961-2. By April 1963 normal activity was reported in all sectors. Output figures for copper were only slightly down (1962—295,200 tons, 1963—269,900 tons), while the output for 1960 (300,680 tons) showed a 7 per cent increase over 1959, and 27 per cent over 1958. The Union Minière remained a Belgian Limited Company until 1965, when the Congolese government took over control. Labour supply for the mines was a problem in the early days, for Katanga was then sparsely populated (average less than 5 per sq. mile). In January 1963 the Union Minière employed 23,250 workers. The labour force has been mainly permanent since 1930, except for some recruits from Rwanda and Burundi. The workers live in well-planned villages, a striking contrast to the compounds of the Rand.

Minerals other than copper, produced in smaller quantities in Katanga, are nevertheless of great strategic importance. The Katanga produces 60 per cent of the world's cobalt (7,400 tons in 1963). This is probably one of the world's largest cobalt deposits, the metal being closely associated with the copper ore. The mines, also owned by the Union Minière, are in the Kolwezi district. The chief cobalt reducer, at Shituru, was opened in 1945.

Of even greater strategic value are the radium and uranium deposits. Until about 1950 every atomic weapon was made basically from Katanga uranium, and Katanga produced over half the non-communist world's supply of this metal. The ore was discovered almost by accident near Elisabethville in 1913, and at Shinkolobwe in 1915. A mine at Shinkolobwe was opened in 1922, at first opencast but later underground. The ore was sent to Belgium for refining; it was found to have a metal content of 1 to 4 per cent compared with 0·02 per cent of the South African variety. Until the late 1930's, when the first studies of atomic fission were made, there was little demand for uranium, and the mine closed down for several years. It was reopened in 1943; production figures were kept secret but in 1957 appear to have been about half of South Africa's output. Reserves may not be extensive, for the Shinkolobwe Mine closed down in 1961. Radium, however, is still being produced.

Many other minerals are produced in Katanga. Manganese ore is the bulkiest (316,000 tons exported in 1962), with zinc concentrates (167,000 tons in 1962) coming second. The new zinc smelter at Kolwezi is reducing the bulk of the latter. Tin is mined in several more northern areas of Katanga, between Busanga and Manono, by companies including the Union Minière (total 1960 production = 9,000 tons of concentrate, 3,400 tons of smelted tin). Rare minerals produced also include silver and gold. Finally in Katanga the two small coal fields of Luena and Lukuga should be noted. Reserves in the Karroo beds are considerable and seams are thick, but the coal has a high ash content, up to 30 per cent. Output is less than one-tenth of that at Wankie in Rhodesia.

Katanga should not be thought of as the only province of the Congo with mineral wealth. Kasai, the neighbouring province to the west, is famed as the world's biggest source of industrial diamonds, producing over two-thirds of the world's total in normal years (15,000,000 carats in 1959, compared with 2,800,000 from South Africa). The extent of the Kasai diamond fields was revealed in 1909: they are equivalent in area to the whole of Rhodesia. The diamond-bearing rocks are Jurassic conglomerates, ancient river deposits. In contrast to the diamonds produced by South or South-West Africa, only a small fraction (4 per cent) of Kasai's output is of gem stones.

POWER

Hydro-electric stations on the Congo's headwaters in Katanga have been mentioned, these being so far the only installations operating in the Congo. The enormous water power potential of the lower Congo has not yet been utilised. Below Kinshasa this largest of African rivers by volume pours down cataracts for a vertical distance of 850 feet. In 1957 a possible site for a hydro-electric installation was inspected at Inga valley. A Swedish plan involved simply drawing off water from the river through a tunnel into the neighbouring Inga valley to produce about 1,500 MW. No reservoir would be needed, as the discharge of the lower Congo, unlike that of any other major African river, fluctuates relatively little throughout the year (from 850,000 to 2,365,000 cusecs). The scheme was estimated to cost $300 million and was approved by the Belgian Government at the end of 1957, actual construction to begin in 1960 or 1961. With the changed political situation the scheme must be regarded as indefinitely postponed. The power was not destined to supply Katanga, up to 1,000 miles distant, but an aluminium industry (proposed capacity

500,000 tons), and other subsidiaries such as wood-pulp industries, near Matadi. Bauxite was to be imported from Guiana or Ghana. Alternatively, there was the possibility of refining certain concentrates from Katanga before shipment abroad, particularly uranium ore.

COMMUNICATIONS AND PORT FACILITIES

There is only one important ocean terminal in the Congo—Matadi. Until mid-1960 this port handled as much traffic as it could cope with, amounting to more than half the total exports by weight, and 80 per cent of the imports of the Congo. Owing to the volume of traffic and the fact that nearly all of it had to use the single-track Matadi–Leopoldville railway, this outlet represented a most serious bottleneck, yet use of the outlet was officially encouraged since the whole route to it lay within Belgian territory; special low freight rates were offered as an inducement in the face of competition from other routes and non-Belgian ports. From mid-1960 to 1963 Matadi ceased to receive any Katanga traffic, and other traffic was greatly reduced. In more normal years about 40 per cent of Matadi's exports by volume consist of vegetable oils, fats and oil seeds; minerals, of which copper accounts for half by bulk, make up about 25 per cent. The largest group of imports comprises petroleum and petroleum products (about 40 per cent of the total). Much more mineral traffic from Katanga uses the Lobito outlet than Matadi. Approximately 60 per cent of the total bulk of minerals is exported from Lobito, compared with 25 per cent from Matadi and 15 per cent from Beira. Taking Katangan copper alone, 45 per cent is shipped from Matadi, compared with 22 per cent from Lobito and 33 per cent from Beira.

Without any doubt the most important railway in the Congo is that linking Matadi with Kinshasa. A single-track line, reconstructed in 1932 to a maximum gradient of 1 in 60, it has by far the highest density of traffic of any Congo railway. If the Inga power scheme is ever carried through this line will certainly be electrified with great benefit. The other main railways of the Congo serve Katanga. The line to Port Francqui was opened in 1928; that through Angola to Lobito in 1931. In 1956 the Kamina–Kabalo line was completed to give a through connection from Elisabethville to Lake Tanganyika, whence a ferry and the East African railways can convey cargo to Dar es Salaam. Southern Katanga has therefore four major rail routes converging on it—a network of railways which could only have been justified by the mineral wealth present here.

Many of them have been relaid in recent years, and the electrification of the 200-mile Lubumbashi-Kolwezi section represents the first such venture in tropical Africa. To move from Katanga to Matadi freight uses the railway to Port Francqui, the Kasai and Congo rivers to Kinshasa, and then a second rail journey. A rail link from Port Francqui to Kinshasa has often been considered, for it would reinforce Matadi's position and save two trans-shipment points. On the other hand, it would involve much expensive bridging, the route would be 440 miles longer than that to Lobito, and would inevitably mean higher freight rates compared with the existing rail-water route.

Table 37   Railways in the Republic of the Congo (Kinshasa)

	Track mileage	Proportion of total traffic	Relative density of traffic
Matadi-Kinshasa	270	29 %	100 (base)
Katanga (to Port Francqui, Dilolo, Kabongo)	1,588	60 %	39
Eastern provinces (Kisangani–Ponthierville, Kindu–Albertville, Kabongo–Kabalo)	521	6 %	12
Others	667	5 %	4

When King Leopold of Belgium first acquired the Congo the vast natural network of waterways was considered the greatest asset of the region. Water transport is still important, but less so than formerly. Of all the freight traffic converging on Matadi before independence, 40 per cent of the total freight mileage was by water, whilst nearly 60 per cent was by rail. The Congo and its tributaries have, in fact, several inherent disadvantages for shipping. They are obstructed by falls and rapids, to circumvent which railways are needed, with associated trans-shipment points. For much of their courses the rivers are shallow, beset with sandbanks and, in the case of tributaries, subject to changes in level. In the whole region only 1,650 miles of waterway have a minimum depth of 4 feet, and another 4,000 miles of 3 feet. Shallow-draft stern-wheelers predominate, but with recent increases in traffic such improvements as diesel engines, radar and the use of mirrors on corners are being introduced. But journeys are still slow: from Kinshasa to Kisangani takes a week upstream, or five days down. A new menace to river traffic is the water hyacinth weed.

Road transport is scarcely developed other than locally. Officially, road mileage is 85,000, but this is clearly optimistic, and very little consists of all-weather roads (Plate 13A). Wash-outs, flooding and insecure bridges still make journeys from the capital to Lubumbashi (formerly Elisabeth-ville), the second town of the Congo, very hazardous by road. Ferries replace bridges on the wider rivers. On the Congo itself Kisangani (formerly Stanleyville) is the lowest bridging point.

The port of *Matadi* up to 1960 handled roughly two-thirds of the Congo's trade, about 2 million tons of cargo a year, but by 1962 this had declined to only 1 million tons. Its site, on the south shore of the lower Congo, was determined by the need for providing it with a rail link to Kinshasa which did not bridge the Congo nor pass through non-Congolese territory. One hundred miles from the sea, the first pier was built here in 1890, and deep-water berths provided in 1933. Access is not easy, owing to the sharp bends of the river downstream, the strong currents and whirlpools and shifting sand-banks. Nor is there much room for the port itself, the land behind rising steeply. Seven miles downriver is the separate petroleum terminal of Ango-Ango, with its pipeline to Kinshasa. Most of the cargo exported from Matadi is of agricultural and forest products: a large proportion of the Katanga minerals has always favoured Lobito, with its all-rail connection.

Kinshasa, the Congo's principal river port, actually handles more cargo than Matadi, for whereas the latter has no industries of importance, Kinshasa is a major consuming and manufacturing centre. River traffic up to 1960 exceeded 1·5 million tons a year (1962, 855,000 tons), of which about one-quarter was absorbed by the textile, food-processing and wood-working factories. The port has major petroleum and palm-oil storage facilities. A little traffic crosses the river to Brazzaville to utilise the railway to Pointe-Noire; before 1960 a minor amount of Katangan copper travelled by this route (28,000 tons in 1959).

Kisangani and *Port Francqui* stand at heads of navigation on the Congo and Kasai rivers. Each handles about 400,000 tons of cargo a year.

RWANDA AND BURUNDI

Belgium acquired a mandate over these two small countries, each no bigger than Belgium and formerly part of German East Africa. From

1925 to 1960 they were administered as part of the Belgian Congo (the justification for including them in this chapter). In 1962 they were granted independence, Rwanda as a republic and Burundi as a kingdom. The countries are, as already noted, the most densely populated in tropical Africa, with 5 million inhabitants. In Burundi the Watutsi until recently formed the ruling class, and in Rwanda their power was curtailed.

Figure 103 *Rwanda and Burundi*. Shaded areas represent land over 6,000 feet. Note the complex drainage pattern, resulting from eastward tilting of the plateau between the highlands and Lake Victoria (to which the Kagera now flows). Also shown is the main road linking the respective capitals of Bujumbura and Kigali

Both countries may be divided into three physical regions, running from north to south (Fig. 103). In the west there is the rift valley floor, containing Lakes Kivu and Tanganyika, connected by the Ruzizi river. Rising sharply along the east of the rift are high mountains, reaching 8,000 to 9,000 feet in many places, and 14,000 feet in northern Rwanda, where there are volcanoes, two of them active. East of the mountain crest the land drops more gently towards Uganda; there are extensive plateaux at around 5,000 and 6,000 feet, with rivers such as the Kagera draining to Lake Victoria. Thus although the countries are small, their landscape is a varied one and the scenery attractive. In the mountains, 'foothills of rough lava lead up to hazy blue cones; . . . [elsewhere, there are] green hills terraced right to the summit, and fertile valleys where cows and goats graze between fields of millet. Rich bean crops grow on steep beds, and there are acres and acres of pyrethrum, scrubby lavender-like plants with white daisy flowers.'[1]

The people live in traditional beehive-shaped huts, built of poles and mud bricks, with thatched roofs.

As only about two-fifths of the land can be cropped, the amount of cultivated land works out at no more than 1 acre per person. In such overcrowded conditions it is not surprising that many areas are suffering severely from soil erosion and overgrazing. Most of the cultivation is undertaken by the Bahutu. Their main food crops are cassava, plaintains, beans and sweet potatoes. The rich volcanic soils sustain the main cash crop of coffee, which occupies about 100,000 acres. Cotton and oil-palms are cultivated in the rift valley lowlands. Cattle are the main concern of the Watutsi, the tall pastoral people who invaded the area some four centuries ago. Cattle, reckoned as a form of wealth, are kept in large numbers, giving rise to serious overgrazing. Except in the rift valley lowlands there is practically no tsetse fly. The cattle are of little commercial value and use land that could often better be devoted to crops.

Mining and industry are generally unimportant. There is minor production of tin and tungsten ores, mainly from northern Rwanda. Small hydro-electric plants at Bujumbura (Usumbura), Kisenyi and Taruka (near the tin mines) have a total capacity of less than 4,000 kw. The chief towns and respective capitals of Rwanda and Burundi are Kigali and Bujumbura. Bujumbura is a port of 50,000 inhabitants at the head of Lake Tanganyika, and is the only town with any significant manufacturing activities; there are small factories concerned with clothing, tea processing and brick and tile making. Because of overcrowding on the land and the lack of employment opportunities, many thousands of the Rwanda and Rundi people seek work on the cotton and coffee farms in neighbouring Uganda. To some extent the migration is seasonal, but there are also many who have permanently taken up residence in Uganda, having acquired a piece of land there.

51

North-western Equatorial Africa

Comprising Gabon, the Republic of the Congo (Brazzaville), the Central African Republic, the Cameroun Republic, Spanish Guinea, the Portuguese islands in the Gulf of Guinea, and Cabinda (Fig. 104)

THE FORMER FRENCH TERRITORIES

Starting from a coastal settlement on the Gabon river in 1839, and the establishment of Libreville in 1848, the French gradually extended their control over various parts of the Atlantic coastlands between Spanish Guinea and the Portuguese settlements near the Congo mouth. Penetration inland was slow; the outstanding figure in the exploration of the interior was de Brazza, who investigated the Ogooué Basin in the 1870's and claimed the north shore of the Congo river at Stanley Pool in 1880— later to become the site of Brazzaville. In the next few years the territory between the Atlantic and the line of the Congo–Ubangi rivers came to be known as the French Congo. French claims were extended northward; eventually the whole vast area stretching for nearly 2,000 miles as far north as the Tibesti highlands in the Sahara came under a unified administration, and after 1934 became the single colony of French Equatorial Africa. In many respects the colony deserved its description as the 'Cinderella of the French Empire', for the French devoted far more attention to the development of their western and northern colonies in Africa.

In 1960 the four territories comprising French Equatorial Africa chose to become independent member states of the French Community, with representation in the French Senate. Their new names, population figures and areas are given in Table 38.

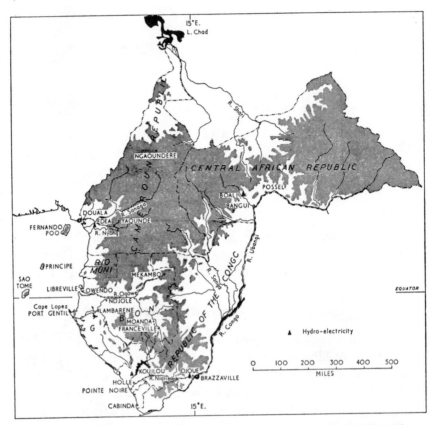

Figure 104 *North-western equatorial Africa.* Land over 1,500 feet shaded. The only railways run inland from the ports of Douala, Libreville and Pointe Noire

Table 38

	Former name	Area (sq. miles)	Population, 1965
Gabon	Gabon	103,100	463,000
Congo (Brazzaville)	Moyen Congo	132,100	826,000
Central African Republic	Oubangui-Shari	238,200	1,352,000
Chad (see Chap. 21)	Tchad	495,800	3,307,000

The average population density is less than five per sq. mile, while Brazzaville is the only town of more than 100,000. These four states formed a Customs Union in 1959, and in 1960 agreed to adopt a common economic and defence policy.

GABON

Though it is the smallest and most sparsely populated country of the three, it is incomparably the wealthiest. Gabon achieves the unusual distinction for a young underdeveloped country of balancing both her budget and her overseas payments, and her economy is likely to expand considerably in the next few years. Gabon's most famous resident was Dr. Albert Schweitzer, in charge of his village medical centre at Lambaréné.

Physically the country consists mostly of densely forested plateaux, lying mostly between 2,000 and 3,000 feet and descending in steps to a relatively narrow coastal plain (Fig. 104). The latter is underlain by sedimentary rocks; most of the uplands are built of the Archaean Crystalline Basement, though the Batéké plateau in the south-east is of sandstone, supporting only open savanna. Rainfall is heavy in all parts, reaching 150 inches on the northern border with Spanish Guinea, and nowhere less than 60 inches.

At present timber is the most valuable resource, and until 1960, when she was surpassed by Ghana, Gabon was Africa's foremost exporter of wood and wood products. The forest which covers three-quarters of the country yields a variety of both hard and soft woods, but limba, and okoumé, a particular species of softwood used for plywood, are in most demand. The principal problems of extraction concern the scattered distribution of any one species, typical of the equatorial forest, and the large capital outlay involved in applying heavy logging machinery to wide areas of forest. One okoumé tree to the acre is common. Since timber cutting is exceeding natural regeneration rates, reafforestation is being undertaken, and although the newly planted trees may take fifty years to mature, the concentration of particular species in the plantations will eventually effect great savings. Sawmills and plywood factories are located at Libreville and Port Gentil.

Since the first successful drillings in 1955 petroleum has risen in importance to become Gabon's second export. Concessions have been leased in the Port Gentil area to North American, Dutch and French companies. A pipeline links the six currently producing fields to a tanker terminal at Cape Lopez. Production in 1963 reached 1 million tons. Petroleum deposits of any size are of great significance to sub-Saharan Africa, and those of Gabon in particular possess a greater variety of oil grades than the Saharan fields.

Vast deposits of manganese ore have been discovered at Moanda, downstream from Franceville on the Ogooué. Here a Franco-American corporation is undertaking their extraction and export via Pointe Noire in the neighbouring republic of Congo (Brazzaville), now that a combined rail and cable way across the Chaillu Mountains has been completed at a cost of $28 million. Gabon is now fifth largest world producer of manganese. An even more ambitious project concerns the tapping of major iron-ore deposits at Mekambo in the north-east, which involves a 400-mile railway to the Gabon estuary. Finally, mining of uranium ore, just north of Moanda, began in 1961.

However, timber, petroleum and mining activities concern only a small proportion of Gabon's population. Agriculture is the mainstay of the scattered rural population, and until quite recently was largely in the hands of primitive subsistence cultivators. Only in a very few areas of equatorial Africa did the French succeed in improving this situation and introducing cash crops, principally by setting up experimental farms and demonstrating more modern techniques of cultivation. The following account is of the traditional native agriculture associated with the more remote parts of interior Gabon. L. Martrou describes the activities of one of the larger tribes, the Fang, and although his account dates from 1909 it is still applicable to many parts of equatorial Africa.[2]

The Fang are a Bantu community inhabiting a region of rain forest around the middle Ogooué valley and Ndjole. The Fang live 'by the devastation of the forest—gathering and cultivation—and by fishing and hunting'. The forest provides various tree fruits, and also rubber, ebony and mahogany which the Fang sell to trading posts. The longer of the two dry seasons (August–September) is the time for river fishing when the waters have fallen, and is usually followed by the hunting season when wild animals such as wart hogs, monkeys or porcupines are caught. But the main part of their subsistence depends on cultivation. Towards the end of January the Fang

'go into the forest and find a favourable place, settle in common the respective limits of each plantation, and the work of cutting the thick-growing underbrush begins. The underbrush once cleared away, the men cut down the big trees. . . . In the beginning of March (the short dry season), the branches of the trees are chopped up in pieces and burned, and soon, in place of the great forest, there remain only the big trunks lying on the ground. In this ground, covered with ashes, the women place banana plants, stalks of manioc [cassava] and seeds of gourds.'

In the subsequent rainy season, April and May, the plants ripen rapidly. After harvesting, the ground is again cleared of weeds and replanted in the drier period of early August before the fishing season begins.

'The Fang know absolutely nothing of intensive cultivation. With their primitive agriculture, they need immense stretches to support the smallest group of human beings. Every year, new sections of virgin forest fall under their destructive axes. . . . Moreover, the Fang, since they have no thought of remaining permanently, do not plant fruit trees even where they would succeed very well, for at the time when these trees would be in full bearing, the planters would be far away and . . . would not profit from their work.'

The length of stay in any one village varies, but the average duration of a village is five or six years.

In only a few parts of Gabon has cash-crop agriculture yet been developed. Cacao was first grown near Libreville in 1887, and in 1960 was the country's third most valuable export. A small amount of coffee is produced, and the cultivation of oil-palms is to be considerably expanded, especially when a Unilever plantation near Lambaréné is fully developed. But, overall, agriculture in Gabon is still backward, methods of cultivation primitive and crop yields low.

One of the chief hindrances to the development of Gabon's interior is lack of adequate transport facilities. Swamps, rugged mountains and dense forests have retarded modern road construction, while there are yet no railways other than the cable and rail link from the manganese mines to the Congo (Brazzaville). But the Mekambo railway when completed will serve to open up much new country for lumbering and farming, as well as handling valuable iron ore. The Mekambo railway will terminate at *Libreville*, the capital (pop. 30,000) and principal port. The amount of traffic handled at the port has greatly increased since World War II, from 75,000 tons in 1947 to well over 300,000 tons today. Soon, however, the port of Libreville will be superseded by a new deepwater harbour at Owendo, 12 miles to the south. *Port Gentil* (pop. 20,000) has not lagged far behind. Gabon's future economic prospects seem bright. The one serious handicap may prove to be shortage of labour

to carry through the various development projects, arising from the
smallness of the population.

THE REPUBLIC OF THE CONGO
(BRAZZAVILLE)

Much larger than Gabon, and with twice the population, this territory is
poorly defined in terms of physical geography (Fig. 104). The larger part
consists of flat swampy valleys and low divides descending east and south-
east to the Congo river. The area between longitude 16° and the Ubangi
river is in fact one vast swamp, with rivers such as the Sanga winding slug-
gishly across it. The higher ground towards the Gabon frontier is known
as the Batéké plateau, reaching 2,700 feet. South of this the valleys of the
Niari and Kouilou descend more rapidly to a narrow coastal plain sand-
wiched between the frontiers of Gabon and Cabinda. Like Gabon, the
climate is everywhere tropical and humid. Rainfall at Pointe Noire, the
driest part near the Kouilou estuary, is 48 inches per annum; at Brazzaville, on the shore of Stanley Pool, at an elevation of 1,000 feet it is
58 inches, while on the uplands farther north it approaches 70 inches.
Two-thirds of the country is under rain forest or swamp vegetation.
Only in the extreme north, and in parts of the south where the forest has
been cleared, does grassland with scattered trees become dominant.

Most of the population of the Republic is to be found in the south,
especially in the region between Brazzaville and Pointe Noire. These two
towns are the largest, *Pointe Noire* being the new capital (pop. 60,000)
and major seaport, while *Brazzaville* (pop. 145,000) is an important river
port. Both owe their commercial development to the French. Away
from these relatively modern centres the native village is the largest unit
of settlement. The main tribes are the Fang (see the section on Gabon),
the Batéké and the Bakota, all living in the southern half of the country.
The Bakota are a more sedentary people than the Fang, possessing somewhat larger and more permanent villages. The northern half of the
Republic is very thinly inhabited, with an average of less than three
persons per sq. mile.

African agriculture follows the same primitive pattern found in most
parts of equatorial Africa. Cassava and plantains are the main food crops,
maize and beans are secondary. Shifting cultivation prevails. A few
villages attempt some limited production of cash crops—a little coffee on

the uplands which emerge here and there through the forest; cacao, which was introduced in the 1930's following its success in West Africa; groundnuts, mainly on the Batéké plateau; while in the rain-forest areas wild-rubber trees and oil-palms are tended. Much more important are the government-assisted projects in the Niari valley, where experimental planting of sugar-cane, groundnuts, and several food crops have proved very successful.

In the national economy timber holds first place, as in Gabon, and provides as much as two-thirds of all exports by value. But unlike Gabon the Congo Republic has few mineral resources. Since 1937 there has been very minor production of lead and zinc at Mfouati, midway along the Brazzaville–Pointe Noire railway. Phosphate deposits at Holle are more substantial but await exploitation. Oil was located in 1959 at Pointe Indienne (near Pointe Noire) in small quantities (1961 production— 103,000 tons).

There are considerable possibilities for hydro-electric power development. At present only the small Djoué scheme near Brazzaville is working, and it is significant that so far the expected industry has failed to materialise, half the plant's capacity standing idle. But already a much larger scheme is in hand on the Kouilou river (Fig. 104). When the 410-foot-high dam is completed a reservoir twice the size of Lake Geneva will be created, its outflow capable of providing 820 MW of electric power. This is destined to supply future metallurgical and electro-chemical industries at Pointe Noire, to which manganese ore is already being railed for shipment from Gabon. *Pointe Noire* is developing rapidly, for not only does it handle nearly all the trade from the Republic, but also manganese from Gabon and some timber from Cabinda to the south. Its cargo traffic amounted to 690,000 tons in 1961, compared with only 98,000 tons in 1938. The railway to Brazzaville was opened in 1934, and proved highly expensive to construct, both in materials (there are ninety-two bridges in 320 miles) and human lives; only since 1945 has it begun to carry enough traffic to justify its existence.

Apart from the southern region around Pointe Noire, Brazzaville and their connecting railway, modern forms of transport are not yet available. The Congo and Ubangi rivers form the only link with the northern two-thirds of the country, where development will undoubtedly be exceedingly slow.

THE CENTRAL AFRICAN REPUBLIC

Lying astride the divide between the Ubangi river and the Chad Basin, this is topographically a monotonous area, with vast expanses of gently undulating grassland, diversified only by occasional rocky eminences and the strips of gallery forest fringing water-courses. Imperceptibly the country rises to the Yadé plateau on the Cameroun border at 4,600 feet (Fig. 104), and to similar heights on the Dar Challa plateau near the Sudan border, where bolder granite massifs rise out of a surrounding sandstone cover. The low central divide between the Ubangi and Shari rivers north of Possel is only 600 feet above the Ubangi and has formed an important north–south trade route in the past. Rainfall decreases from 69 inches at Bangui to 42 inches at Fort Archambault in the north where the régime is strongly seasonal.

Agriculture is the basis of the economy. Cotton is the chief cash crop, with coffee as a subsidiary, the two together accounting for three-quarters of the Republic's exports, though they are produced from only 0·3 per cent of the total area. Over vast areas only occasional primitive shifting cultivation is found, while the prevalence of tsetse fly precludes livestock except in the northern areas. The overall population density is only five persons per sq. mile, approximately the same as for Gabon and the Congo Republic (Brazzaville).

There are no significant mineral resources; the chief source of alluvial diamonds became largely exhausted in 1955 and production subsequently has fallen by one-third, now accounting for less than 10 per cent of exports. There is a small hydro–electric installation at Boali near Bangui. *Bangui* is the capital (pop. 78,000), established by the French in 1889. It represents the only real outlet for the country's trade, but it is over 900 miles from the sea, and the Ubangi river on which it stands has a very irregular flow and is shallow in the dry season. New port facilities are being constructed and river dredging undertaken, but these are only a partial answer to the country's transport problems which arise from its interior location. The situation is such that even air transport is at present regularly in use to export part of the cotton on which the Republic so heavily depends.

THE CAMEROUN REPUBLIC

Germany established a Protectorate here after the Berlin Conference, and exploited the natural agricultural resources, such as wild rubber and the oil-palm, as well as developing banana and other plantations. The area was occupied by Britain and France in the First World War, subsequently being divided into two mandates: the British Cameroons of 30,000 sq. miles, and the French Cameroons of 166,000 sq. miles. In 1946 these became United Nations Trusteeship territories under the same British and French rule. Independence was granted to the French Cameroons in 1960; the northern part of the British Cameroons is now integrated with the Federation of Nigeria. The present Republic (1965 pop. 5·2 million) comprises the former French territory and the southern part of the former British area (total area 183,000 sq. miles).

Behind the large delta region of the Sanaga, Nyong and other rivers there is an abrupt rise on to the plateau country (Fig. 104). In the eastern half of the territory the bush-covered plateau undulates at around 2,000–3,000 feet, rising gently to 4,000 feet in the Yadé plateau. In the north-western areas the relief becomes more mountainous, with deep valleys and abrupt escarpments, until the volcanic chain of the Cameroon Mountains is reached, with peaks touching 7,000 feet. Rainfall is extremely heavy on the coastlands and the Cameroon Mountains (Douala 158 inches), but over most of the plateau averages 60 to 80 inches. In the extreme north it diminishes rapidly to 30 inches. There is thus a wide variety of climate in the Republic, while vegetation ranges from moist tropical forest in the south to open savanna grassland in the north.

The higher country of the north is largely free from tsetse fly, and cattle rearing is consequently important here. In the south, and particularly on the Yaoundé plateau and the coastal lowlands, the production of tropical cash crops is the main activity. The French considerably extended the plantation agriculture begun by the Germans, with bananas, cacao, coffee and oil-palms as the chief concern. Cacao accounts for about 38 per cent of all exports, coffee about 20 per cent. The French moved the capital to *Yaoundé* (pop. 92,000) on the plateau, and built a railway to link it with the port of *Douala*. The latter, however, remains the chief town (pop. 130,000) and centre of commerce. Its port facilities, handling a million tons of traffic, more than any other port north of Matadi in equatorial Africa, have been much improved since World War II. There is now a railway bridge over the Wouri estuary at Douala, linking the formerly separate railways to Yaoundé on the one hand and N'Kongsamba on the other. A hydro-electric station (160 MW) was completed in 1956 near Edea, 40 miles from Douala, on the Sanaga river, and an aluminium industry established (1962 output—57,000 tons). The smelter refines imported alumina at present, but there are prospects of eventually using local bauxite. There is minor production of tin and titanium ore from Mayo Darlé in the extreme north-west.

PORTUGUESE AND SPANISH POSSESSIONS

CABINDA This curious enclave of Portuguese territory, the size of Luxembourg, originated by exchange; it was ceded to Portugal as token compensation for the handing over of the region of the Congo mouth to Belgium at the end of the last century. It is administered as a province of Angola, and possesses a population of about 50,000, including 2,000 Portuguese and 'assimilated'. For long it has been a remote and undeveloped backwater, with no railway and little economic activity. Its cover of dense tropical forest, however, is now being appreciated as more of an asset than an impediment, for since World War II intensive exploitation of the forest has begun, and this has brought about a general revival of the economy. In the decade 1948–58 wood exports, mostly tola and limba, have increased fourfold to 74,000 tons a year. The principal port of shipment is Cabinda (pop. 12,000) on a large but shallow north-facing bay. Cabinda has a few coffee and cocoa plantations, and oil-palms, but lack of labour is holding back their development. In recent years phosphate deposits have been investigated, while prospecting for oil is in progress.

SPANISH GUINEA Spanish possessions in equatorial Africa consist of Rio Muni (pop. 160,000) and the islands of Fernando Poo, Annobon, Corisco and Elobey. The islands represent some of the peaks of the submerged volcanic chain which runs south-west from Cameroon Mountain —the peak of Santa Isabel on Fernando Poo touches 9,348 feet. The mainland of Rio Muni (6,700 sq. miles) saw relatively little development until the last decade; extraction of timber and the cultivation of coffee and oil-palms are now the main interests. Bata is a lighterage port. Fernando Poo, separated from the administration of Spanish Guinea in 1959, has a population exceeding 60,000, including 23,000 contract labourers, chiefly from Nigeria, on only 800 sq. miles. At the lower levels its rain forest has been mostly cleared for cacao plantations, with coffee, tobacco and cotton at higher altitudes. Annobon, only 7 sq. miles, supports 1,400 people, chiefly by the production of palm produce, copra, coffee and cacao. Taking Spanish Guinea as a whole, coffee and cacao make up 28 and 42 per cent respectively of the export trade.

PORTUGUESE ISLANDS IN THE GULF OF GUINEA São Tomé and Principe are two islands in the chain between Annobon and Fernando Poo. Well watered and mountainous (São Tomé rises to 6,500 feet, and receives over 160 inches of rainfall on its south-western side), they were uninhabited when first discovered by the Portuguese in 1471. They were annexed by Portugal in 1522. On a combined area of only 370 sq. miles the population numbers no less than 64,000, of whom about 1,200 are Portuguese and 30,000 are contract labourers from Angola. The basis of the economy is the cultivation of cacao, coffee, coconuts and oil-palms. Coffee culture began in the nineteenth century, and the first exports of coffee date from 1832, but by 1890 coffee was overtaken by cacao as the foremost product. In 1961 exports were valued at £2 million, of which three-quarters was contributed by cacao.

References

1 F. Spencer Chapman, *Lightest Africa* (London, 1955), 163
2 L. Martrou, 'Le nomadisme des Fangs', *Revue de Géographie Annuelle*, 3 (1909), 497–524

Selected Bibliography

A. Schweitzer, *On the Edge of the Primeval Forest* (London, 1922)

R. E. Birchard, 'Copper in the Katanga region of the Belgian Congo', *Econ. Geog.*, 16 (1940), 429–36
W. A. Hance and I. S. Van Dongen, 'The port of Lobito and the Benguela railway', *Geog. Rev.*, 46 (1956), 460–87
W. A. Hance and I. S. Van Dongen, 'Matadi, focus of Belgian African transport', *Ann. Assoc. Am. Geogr.*, 48 (1958), 41–72

S. Lerat, 'Une région industrielle au coeur de l'Afrique: le Katanga meridional', *Cahiers d'Outre Mer*, 14 (1961), 435–42

J. F. Loung, 'Les Pygmées de la forêt de Mill', *Cahiers d'Outre Mer*, 12 (1959), 362–79

R. L. Pendleton, 'The Belgian Congo: impressions of a changing region', *Geog. Rev.*, 39 (1949), 371–400

G. T. Trewartha and W. Zelinsky, 'The population geography of Belgian Africa', *Ann. Assoc. Am. Geogr.*, 44 (1954), 163–93

A. C. Veatch, 'The evolution of the Congo Basin', *Geological Society of America*, Memoir No. 3 (1935)

G. G. Weigend, 'River ports and outports: Matadi and Banana', *Geog. Rev.*, 44 (1954), 430–2

S. Daveau, 'L'ile de São Tomé', *Cahiers d'Outre Mer*, 15 (1962:), 92–5

J. Denis, 'Pointe Noire', *Cahiers d'Outre Mer*, 8 (1955), 350–68

I. S. Van Dongen, 'La vie économique et les ports de l'enclave de Cabinda', *Cahiers d'Outre Mer*, 15 (1962), 5–24

M. Georges, 'La vie rurale chez les Banda (République Centrafricaine)', *Cahiers d'Outre Mer*, 16 (1963), 321–59

W. A. Hance and I. S. Van Dongen, 'Gabon and its main gateways', *Tijdschrift v. Econ. en Soc. Geog.*, 11 (1961), 286–95

D. Hilling, 'The changing economy of Gabon', *Geography*, 48 (1963), 155–65

H. Nicolai, 'Naissance d'une région en Afrique centrale', *Cahiers d'Outre Mer*, 17 (1964), 292–313

P. Vennetier, 'La navigation intérieure en Afrique noire: le réseau français Congo–Oubangui', *Cahiers d'Outre Mer*, 12 (1959), 321–48

P. Vennetier, 'Population et économie du Congo–Brazzaville', *Cahiers d'Outre Mer*, 15 (1962), 360–81

P. Vennetier, 'La Société Industrielle et Agricole du Niari (Congo–Brazzaville)', *Cahiers d'Outre Mer*, 16 (1963), 43–80

P. Vennetier, 'Les transports dans le nord du Congo–Brazzaville', *Cahiers d'Outre Mer*, 16 (1963), 126–32

PART XIII

West Africa

The features that distinguish West Africa as a region are chiefly political and commercial. The term includes all the territories within the hinterland of the 'West Coast' or 'Guinea Coast' from Cape Verde to the Camerouns, formerly the chief source of slaves for the American plantations and today of vegetable oils and oilseeds, cocoa, cotton, coffee and the ores of iron, aluminium and tin. Most modern states of West Africa are the heirs of European colonies, including the former Federation of French West Africa and the looser association of British West Africa (Nigeria, Ghana, Sierra Leone and the Gambia). Liberia was the creation of American philanthropic societies to found a home for former slaves. Portugal and Spain still maintain colonies in the mainland territory of Portuguese Guinea and in the Cape Verde Islands.

Since there is no winter, rainfall is the critical climatic factor in cultivation and an isohyet of 15 inches has conventionally been adopted as the northern limit of the 'settled' region, or 10 inches to mark the edge of the Sahara. In practice the limits of settlement, of cultivation or of the desert, are indefinite or change from year to year. The chief climatic distinction of the Sahara is irregularity of precipitation which is completely absent in some years. To the east the high plateaux of Adamawa and Cameroun oriented from north-east to south-west appear to offer a physical barrier, and interpose a narrow belt of montane shrubs and grassland amidst the east-west vegetation zones characteristic of West Africa. Yet this ignores the continuity of relief and drainage in the basin of Lake Chad to the north, and the fact that the Cross river in the lowlands to the south-west is the more important divide, being a minor faunal 'frontier' and the approximate western limit of peoples speaking 'semi-Bantu' languages. The limits of such features as the harmattan, the dry dust-laden air of the Sahara, or of the distinctive vegetation associations of the West African savannas which lack the *Brachystegias* or 'miombo' trees characteristic of East Africa all lie farther to the east.

52

Physical Geography

RELIEF AND GEOLOGY

West Africa consists of a number of plateau surfaces or plains chiefly at altitudes of approximately 600 to 1,000 feet, 1,500 to 2,000 feet and 3,000 to 4,000 feet above sea-level. These are interrupted by a number of higher small plateaux and of residual inselberge, including granite domes and quartzitic ridges similar to features widespread in central and East Africa. In the south-west (Fig. 106) are the great plateaux of the Futa Jallon and Guinea Highlands rising generally over 3,000 feet and including peaks such as Mount Bintemani in Sierra Leone (6,390 feet). In the south-east are the more extensive high plateaux of Cameroun and Adamawa

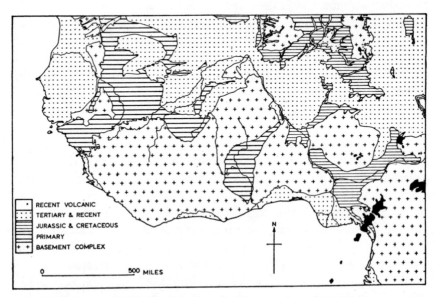

Figure 105 *The geology of West Africa and the southern Sahara*

associated with volcanic outpourings, and the enormous volcano of
Mount Cameroon (13,353 feet). About 120 miles to the north-west of
the Adamawa highlands across the Benue trough is the high plateau of
Jos, also associated with volcanoes, although all extinct. Surrounding
these plateaux are plains at about 1,500 to 2,000 feet above sea-level which
reach their greatest extent to the west of Jos in the plains of Hausaland
in northern Nigeria. Between them is the central low plateau of West
Africa, all below 1,500 feet above sea-level, interrupted by the broad
basin of the Volta and supporting numerous small plateau remnants
rising up to the general 2,000-foot level or in a few cases even higher.
To the north this plateau is limited by an east-to-west trough occupied
by Lake Chad, and the middle portions of the Niger and the Senegal.
To the south is the narrow coastal plain with the remarkably smooth
lagoon and sand-bar coast extending from Sherbro Island in Sierra Leone
in the west to the Niger delta in the east. This plain is narrowest in Liberia
and south-eastern Ghana. North of Sherbro Island is the drowned coast
consisting of the rias of the 'Rivières du Sud'; north of the Futa Jallon
extends the broad coastal plain of Senegambia forming the western end
of the Senegal-Niger trough.

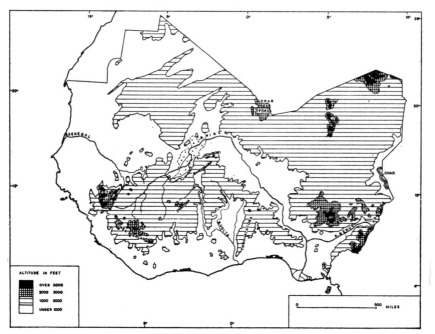

Figure 106 *The relief and drainage of West Africa and the southern Sahara*

The central low plateau is formed of the Pre-Cambrian granite, gneiss and schist of the Basement Complex (Fig. 105). The Basement Complex also appears in the Guinea Highlands and the Jos, Cameroun and Adamawa plateaux and to the north in the sub-Saharan plateaux. Elsewhere, what is in effect a great shield has been downwarped or downfaulted, and its surface covered by later sediments, chiefly Palaeozoic sandstones, Jurassic-Cretaceous sandstones, conglomerates and clays (Continental Intercalaire), Cretaceous chalky limestones (including shales and coal in south-eastern Nigeria) and Tertiary and Quaternary clays, gravels, sands and limestones. Lava flows of Cretaceous age or younger have occurred, chiefly in the east, the Jos plateau and the Cameroon Mountains and in the west in the Cape Verde peninsula. The sediments do not all occur at low altitudes. Palaeozoic sandstones are the chief material of the Futa Jallon plateaux with their escarpments and deeply dissected steep-sided valleys, although gabbros frequently form the peaks such as Mount Gangan (3,627 feet).

To the north-east sandstones appear again in the Bambuk and Manding Mountains of Mali and farther eastward in the high escarpments of Banfora and Bandiagara, in the Hombori Mountains and in the escarpment edges of the Volta Basin, notably Gambaga in northern Ghana and Mampong in the south. Saharan sands extend south of the middle Niger, into Senegal and Kano and Bornu Provinces in Nigeria. Different climatic distributions in the past led to the formation of dunes, now stabilised, south of the present Sahara. Another form of widespread superficial deposit is the capping of hydroxides of iron and aluminium frequently termed laterite. Most commonly iron hydroxides are dominant and the material has been described as an 'ironstone crust'. In many cases in West Africa laterite cappings formed in the past are now being denuded. Frequently they provide the level surfaces of great plateaux such as the Futa Jallon where they are referred to as 'bowé' (sing. 'bowal'). Laterite cappings in West Africa are thin-soiled and provide poor drainage conditions. They have been worked both for iron ores and for road stone.

DRAINAGE

The greater part of West Africa's drainage flows to the Atlantic (Fig. 106); yet the main watershed lies well to the south near the coast, particularly in the south-west where the Guinea Highlands and Futa Jallon are the sources of the Niger, Senegal and Gambia rivers. The headstreams of the

Senegal and Niger flow north-east towards the great northern east-to-west trough, where formerly the Niger entered a lake (Aroauane) lying south-west of Timbuktu and forming a centre of inland drainage (see Chapter 3). To the east a similar feature still exists in Lake Chad. Lake Araouane was drained when it spilled over its basin rim near Tosaye, its outflow cutting a gorge through the quartzitic ridge here, thus initiating the middle Niger.

Capture has also been a feature of West African river evolution. The Benue has cut back into the basin of the Logone river, capturing several tributaries and reducing the water supply to Lake Chad. Other notable captures have been of the headstreams of the Black Volta and Oti rivers, diverting former inland drainage southwards. Here, the shorter and more steeply graded streams flowing to the Atlantic have captured some inland-flowing rivers.

River régimes depend on the seasonal distribution of rainfall. Streams rising in the south frequently show double-flow maxima in contrast with the single-flow maximum of those rising farther north. The Niger, with its enormous length and great variety of sources, has a complex régime with a slight double maxima in its headstreams in August and September, a broad November to January peak near Timbuktu, levelled out by the low gradients and creeks of the former lacustrine basin (Fig. 7), and finally at least three maxima in August, September and March on the lower Niger supplied by:

1 The double maxima of local sources in August and September.
2 The lower, broader single maximum of the upper Niger source.

CLIMATE

Three air-masses exert most control over West Africa's climates:

1 The north-easterlies, generally cool and dry (cT type).
2 The south-westerlies, sometimes described as the 'Monsoon', generally warm and moist (mE type).
3 The equatorial easterlies, an upper airstream (cT type), at its lowest altitude above the junction of the north-easterlies and the south-westerlies, and frequently at ground-level when the south-westerlies have retreated southwards; cool and very dry.

The term 'harmattan' is used in West Africa when referring to a northerly or easterly cT airstream with very cool conditions (sometimes less than 50°F in the early morning) and a haze or mist of fine dust. It has been used with reference to both north-easterlies and to the equatorial easterlies, although the latter are generally associated with the lowest temperatures and the densest dust haze. Rainfall is provided by moisture from south-westerly mE airstreams and is at its heaviest at the point of maximum instability in the zone of contact between north-easterly and south-westerly air. Frontal disturbances are the most important factor in producing rainfall in West Africa and the movement of the ITC must be understood to appreciate the distribution of precipitation and, to some extent, of temperature.

Temperatures and humidity

Temperatures are rarely below 42°F, except in a few areas above 4,000 feet. The coast has more equable temperatures than the interior, warmer in January and cooler in July with generally lower means for the year (Table 39).

While interior temperatures are lowest when the sun is farthest south coastal temperatures, with the exception of occasional extreme spells in December or January, are lowest during the rainy season when cloudiness is at a maximum. Extremes occur when the ITC lies well to the south and the drier north-easterly or equatorial easterly cT air bring, in effect, continental conditions. Nowhere on the coast, however, are absolute maxima and minima comparable with those of the interior, nor humidities so low. Port Harcourt has high relative humidity and some rainfall in every month, but there are places such as Ibadan where there is a dry season of three months, but with high early-morning relative humidities and in consequence some condensation and moisture for plants.

Precipitation

Generally rainfall decreases inland from the southern coast and northward along the western coast. There are exceptions, however, to the expected pattern, notably in the 'dry belt' of south-eastern Ghana and southern Togo. These have been variously, but unsatisfactorily, explained as due to (1) parallelism of the coast and wind direction, (2) cold off-shore water from July to September, (3) deviation of the south-westerlies in

Table 39

Station	Alt. (feet)		J	F	M	A	M	J	J	A	S	O	N	D	Year	Temp. range
Dakar	131	Temp. °F T.	72	71	72	73	76	81	82	81	82	82	80	74	77	11
		Rain in. R.	—	—	—	—	—	0·7	3·5	10·0	5·2	1·5	0·1	0·3	21·3	
Freetown	223	T.	81	82	83	83	82	80	79	78	79	80	81	82	81	5
		R.	0·4	0·3	1·2	4·1	11·5	20·0	35·6	36·6	28·5	12·6	5·1	1·4	157·2	
Ouagadougou	991	T.	76	83	88	91	90	86	83	79	81	85	84	79	84	15
		R.	—	—	0·1	1·8	2·5	4·5	6·2	10·6	5·0	1·3	—	—	32·0	
Accra	60	T.	80	80	81	81	80	78	76	75	76	78	80	80	79	6
		R.	0·6	1·0	1·8	3·7	5·7	7·0	1·7	0·6	1·0	1·9	1·5	0·7	27·2	
Ibadan	745	T.	80	82	83	82	80	78	78	76	77	78	80	80	80	7
		R.	0·4	0·9	3·5	5·4	5·9	7·4	6·3	3·3	7·0	6·1	1·8	0·4	48·4	

this area as westerlies. The length of rainy season is more important than the rainfall totals in controlling plant distributions (Fig. 107). The area with more than seven months' rain has double maxima in almost all years with a brief drier period in August. At the beginning and end of the rains, downpours are extremely heavy. Axim in south-western Ghana has recorded 16·9 inches in 24 hours in June, and falls of 4 to 5 inches in 24 hours are common. Sudden squalls and thunderstorms accompany the heavy downpours which, although associated with frontal disturbances, frequently occur in the late afternoon or evening after the heat of the day.

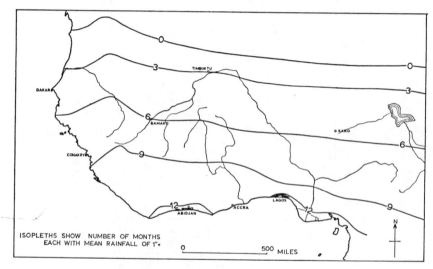

Figure 107 *The duration of the rainy season in West Africa*

Climatic regions

Broadly speaking five climatic types can be distinguished:

1. Sudanic with a single rainfall maximum, 10 to 40 inches of rainfall in three to seven months and temperature extremes only during the dry season.
2. Guinean with double rainfall maxima, over 40 inches of rainfall in more than seven months and equable temperatures.
3. Dry Guinean, similar to 2, but with only 25 to 35 inches of rainfall.
4. South-western with a single rainfall maximum and over 40 inches in more than seven months.

5. West Sudanic with more equable temperatures and higher humidities.

VEGETATION

The climax vegetation should consist of trees, tall and mainly evergreen where moisture is available all the year, and generally shorter and mainly deciduous where rainfall is seasonal. Although several trees shed leaves during the dry season there are others such as the 'Kad' (*Acacia albida*) which shed their leaves during the rains and are a source of fodder in dry periods. Natural grasslands may occur in areas of seasonal flooding or on cappings of impermeable material such as laterite, wherever soils are thin and drainage poor. Grassland, frequently termed 'savanna', is however, much more widespread, particularly in areas with a marked dry season, owing to the destruction of forest by cultivation and pastoralists. It reaches its greatest extent in the northern portions of the Guinean climatic region where, throughout West Africa, men appear to have removed forest most effectively, leaving only islands of tall trees on steep slopes or in valley bottoms.

Moist forest, rain forest

The few remaining areas of moist forest, chiefly in southern Nigeria and southern Ivory Coast, exhibit trees 120 feet or more in height with an almost continuous canopy. Some of these, such as African mahogany (*Khaya ivorensis*) and Iroko (*Chlorophora excelsa*), are valuable hardwoods, but only one tree of any species may occur to the acre. There may be as many as five strata with a poorly developed undergrowth. Cultivation breaks the canopy and encourages undergrowth. Oil-palms are an important secondary. On the coastal and estuarine fringes are stands of fresh-water swamp forest and mangrove forest—chiefly White Mangrove (*Avicennia nitida*) and Red Mangrove (*Rhizophora spp.*), of which *R. racemosa* is useful for pitprops and fuel.

Forest-savanna mosaic, 'derived savanna'

On its northern margins the moist forest has been degraded into the greatest extent of open perennial grassland in West Africa. Here climatic conditions permit the cultivation of almost all West African crops and here are the sites of several early West African states including that of the Oyo Yoruba.

Savanna, Guinea savanna

The main savanna zone consists only here and there of perennial grass-land. Mostly it is occupied by fire-resistant trees, chiefly 'doka' (*Isoberlinia spp.*) in the north and *Daniellia* and *Lophira* in the south, associated with coarse grasses. The trees have twisted branches and may be stunted by the annual burning, coppicing and pollarding. The *Brachystegia* so characteristic of this zone in east and south-eastern Africa is conspicuously absent in West Africa.

Relatively dry savanna, Sudan savanna

This zone consists of savanna plus trees, chiefly *Combretum, Terminalia* and *Acacia* species, but huge areas have been cleared or reduced to fallow grassland by the cultivators of the former great states of the Hausa and Mossi and of Mali. Baobabs are common, normally marking the site of a former or existing village. Typical relatively dry savanna has very mixed stands of trees and pure stands only occur under special physical conditions e.g. *Combretum* stands on thin ferruginous soils.

Steppe, Sahel

On the fringe of the Sahara—a zone in any case well suited to stock rearing during the rainy season because of the absence of tsetse fly and the abundance of the more tender annual grasses—the productivity of the land is frequently increased by annual burning of the vegetation. Thorn trees are common and extensive stands of *Acacia* and *Commiphora* species occur.

Montane grassland

At altitudes over 3,000 feet above sea-level in the Guinea Highlands and Futa Jallon in the west, and in the Jos plateau and Adamawa in the east, settlements of cultivators and pastoralists (chiefly Fulani) have reduced much of the former forest to grassland. The absence of tsetse fly and, in some areas, the infrequent occurrence of mosquitoes have no doubt been an encouragement to settlement. A distinct montane vegetation including grass and such plants as the giant lobelia is confined to heights above 6,000 feet and thus occurs only in the Cameroons.

SOILS

Soil-survey work in West Africa does not yet provide more than a broad picture of distributions, which divide acceptably into:

1. Grey or brown steppe soils, of the desert margins, often rich in organic matter, but in some cases saline and impermeable. Salts occurring at or near the surface are sometimes regarded as an advantage, for they may be in strong enough concentrations to be worked or provide a salt lick for livestock.

2. Ferruginous, mainly savanna, soils, commonly leached, ochre in colour with a long rainy season and red where the dry season is marked. Where drainage is poor, iron salts accumulate and concretions may occur. In some cases, as on level uplands, these may form massive cappings.

3. Ferrallitic soils, chiefly of the moist forest, frequently of great depth. Where forest is removed and the surface exposed to the sun or tramped down in pathways and market places, a hard impermeable clay may be formed. Ferrallite may become laterite and a new climax or 'paraclimax' of grass and shrubs replaces the forest. High temperatures usually last too short a time for the burning of vegetation to destroy humus or lead to hardening.

4. Other soils or special cases include alluvial soils, cultivated mainly in drier areas (they are avoided in wetter areas because of the dangers to health and flooding problems in valley bottoms); black soils, rich in organic matter, on former settlement sites; grey clays or 'firki' of flood-lands; 'poto-poto' or estuarine clays of the south-west, suitable for cultivation if flushed free of salt or sulphur; and 'tannes', the highly saline alluvium of the Senegalese estuaries.

53

Human Geography

PEOPLES

The 93 million people of West Africa live mainly in two zones: a northern or Sudanic and a coastward or Guinean. Neither zone is continuous, but consists of a number of widely separated nuclei the largest of which are in the east where Nigeria has 56 million. The Sudanic zone has population densities mostly of 25 to 50 per sq. mile rising to over 100 in the groundnut-producing areas of Senegal in the west and over 400 in the Kano permanent cultivation zone in the east. The Guinean zone has densities generally of 70 to 200 per sq. mile, but reaches over 800 in Iboland in south-eastern Nigeria and over 300 in Yorubaland (Fig. 108). It may be argued that the longer rainy season and more pro-

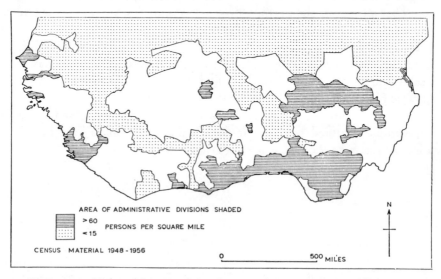

Figure 108 *High and low population densities of West Africa by administrative divisions*

ductive root crops of the Guinean zone account for the generally higher densities, whilst the Sudanic zone has ideal grain-growing conditions; this leaves between them a 'Middle Belt' of low population densities associated with thin soils, laterite and a high incidence of tsetse fly. But in fact, densities in each zone are too variable to justify any such conclusion. Islands of high density (over 200 sq. mile in northern Togo) exist in the 'middle belt', and many areas of low density have evidently been depopulated by warfare and slave raiding in the past.

Many of the more densely peopled nuclei correspond with groupings of distinctive communities, tribes or pre-colonial states. Low densities and woodland often correspond with the frontiers between them. The largest communities (Fig. 109) include the Hausa (6 million), Ibo (6 million), Yoruba (5·5 million), Malinke and Bambara (2 million) and Mossi (1·8 million). The Fulani (totalling 5 million) consist of a number of widely scattered communities, many of whom have close ties with other groups. Few of them today depend solely or even mainly on pastoralism for a living, although many of their traditions derive from a former life of nomadic stock rearing. During the last century many Fulani led a revolt against the rulers of Hausaland and adjacent kingdoms chiefly in

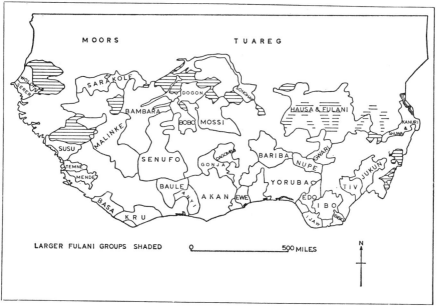

Figure 109 *The principal tribal communities of West Africa*

the Sudanic zone. Their success led to the formation of the two empires
of Sokoto and Gwandu ruled over by a Fulani aristocracy. The Hausa
created seven states each with a city, the earliest of which was founded
over a thousand years ago. Three of the cities—Kano, Katsina and Zaria
—are administrative and commercial centres. The Yoruba also lived
in city states but in the Guinean zone; they have the distinction of being
the most highly urbanised people in Africa. Forty per cent of the population of the Western Region of Nigeria, which has a majority of Yoruba,
were in settlements of 10,000 or more in 1952. Ibadan Province has an
urban proportion of 65 per cent.

The Ibo, another Guinean people, living in the present Eastern Region
of Nigeria, had no chiefs, and many of them lived in widely dispersed
hamlets and compounds. In their northern grasslands of the 'forest-
savanna mosaic', however, Ibo live in large agglommerations, many
of 10,000 or more. But such communities as Awka and Enugu Ezike
mostly lack streets and contain in effect a close-knit dispersal of compounds
and kitchen gardens within their confines. The Malinke created the great
empire of Mali in the centre of the West African Sudan, for long the
greatest military power west of Bornu, a major gold producer and
creator of a trans-Saharan trade from cities such as Timbuktu and Jenne.
The Mossi established a powerful state on the watershed between the
Volta and Niger. Other large groups of people include the Kanuri,
founders of the empire of Bornu in the east, the Wolof with their former
kingdom of Cayor in the west, and the Akan, creators of several states
including the great gold-producing power of Ashanti, formerly supplying
gold, kola nuts and ivory to the Sudanic states.

Non-African population

Of the non-Africans, Europeans and Americans number about 100,000
and Syrians, mostly retail traders, about 20,000; altogether some 0·1 per
cent of total population. Most of the Europeans are in the former French
territories, particularly in the great port of Dakar which contains
over 35,000 non-Africans. Few of the European planters who used to
grow coffee, cacao and bananas in the Ivory Coast and Guinea now
remain.

Agriculture is the mainstay of over three-quarters of the population and provides the greater part of overseas earnings. Tree cultivation is important for the production of such export crops as cocoa, coffee, palm-oil and kernels, and trees provide kola nuts, fruits and edible leaves for the internal market, but most cultivation is concerned with the growing of field crops by rotational bush fallow methods. In many parts of central Africa (and a very few parts of West Africa) true shifting cultivation involving the creation of new fields in woodland and the occasional shift of settlement still takes place. Most West African cultivators, however, maintain a nearly regular pattern of clearance and planting on land rarely more than ten years in fallow and frequently rested for only two to three years. Clearance involves the burning or pulling of grass and the cutting of trees, leaving the stumps in the ground. Refuse is heaped and burned. Pastoralists normally set fire to grass *in situ* in order to clear away coarse herbage and permit the growth of young, tender shoots.

Northern practice

The basis of the northern agricultural economy (Fig. 115) is grain, chiefly bulrush millets and sorghum or guinea-corn, mixed or grown in rotation with groundnuts, cotton, melons, various gourds, pulses and fonio or 'hungry rice'—a hardy grain often grown last in the rotation. Crops are normally planted in ridges and land may be under food or fibre plants for six years or even more before fallowing. The longer dry season of the north provides an annual rest, and in many areas Fulani pastoralists are invited to graze their cattle on the stubble and crop remains after harvest, thus providing manure. The chief northern export crops, groundnuts and cotton, are field crops and are thus grown as part of the normal rotation. Being annuals, their production is more easily controlled by growers in response to changes in market prices. Floodland cultivation is especially important in the north: chiefly sorghum, but also maize, sweet potatoes and rice. The Hausa specialise in growing onions by irrigation.

Southern practice

In the southern or Guinean areas there are two basic forms of agricultural practice (Fig. 115): the south-western, dependent on rice as a staple, and the south-eastern, dependent on the roots, cassava and yams as staples or with guinea corn or maize as co-dominants in cultivation. The divide between the two is approximately the Bandama river in the centre of the Ivory Coast. Rice in West Africa is mostly grown as an upland crop and rotated with groundnuts and fonio. Floodland rice cultivation with or without water control is becoming more common however, and has been encouraged by some governments as an alternative to flood cropping on steep hill slopes where soil erosion is feared. On the coast, in the estuaries of the south-western rias with their high tidal ranges, rice has been grown in polders for several centuries. Traditionally the rice is of African origin (*Oryza glaberrima*), but varieties of the Asian *O. sativa* have become increasingly popular. In the south-east yams are the chief traditional staple, but these require well-rested land, elaborate mounds and a trellis or support for the vine. Cassava is more easily grown; it will stay in the ground up to three years or more and all its root may be eaten since propagation is normally from stem cuttings. Cassava takes longer to prepare into flour, but is generally cheap and has good keeping qualities. With increasing popularity the plant is spreading, often at the expense of yams. In the wetter areas of the former rain forest, still distinguished by a fallow of woody plants rather than grasses, yams and cassava are commonly rotated with maize. Other crops include bananas or plantains, cocoyams, melons, peppers, tomatoes, pulses, pineapples and okra producing a sticky fruit used in stews. In southern Ghana cocoyams and plantains are the chief food crops, partly because of their value as shade plants for young cacao.

In the drier northern portions of the Guinean zone with their grass fallows, grains such as sorghum are often of equal importance with roots. In the drier areas of south-western Nigeria, southern Dahomey and Togo, maize is the staple and two crops a year may be grown on the same patch. Floodland is of less importance where the rains last nine months or more and several harvests are possible. Compound or kitchen-garden land is often a major resource, especially in overcrowded south-eastern Nigeria where compound land manured by household refuse supports permanent cultivation and often contains dense groves of oil-palms.

Export crops are chiefly perennials and include the oil-palm self-sown in the fallows, but today increasingly planted; cacao chiefly in Ghana, south-western Nigeria and the Ivory Coast; and coffee, chiefly in the Ivory Coast. Copra from coconut palms has a small importance, and so have piassava from Raphia palms, chiefly in Sierra Leone, and rubber from south-western Nigeria and Liberia. Perennial cropping admits little adjustment of area to offset any fluctuations in market prices; and, except where linked with shade plants in the early stages, it is divorced from food cropping. The cacao and coffee cultivators of West Africa have become dependent on food produced elsewhere in their country, or, to a small extent, imported from overseas.

Pastoralism

Livestock raising, chiefly of humped cattle, hairy sheep and goats, is generally divorced from agriculture because of the need to seek fresh pastures with the markedly seasonal distribution of rainfall. In the south, where rainy seasons are long, the grasses tend to be extremely coarse and the dangers of disease are greatest. Cattle concentrate in the Sahel and on uplands during the rains and on Sudanic croplands during the dry season. Most cultivators keep some small animals including goats, chickens and dwarf cattle. The Serer of Senegal practise a form of mixed farming, rotating pasture, groundnut and millet fields; attempts have been made to combine cattle keeping with cropping (especially in Mali and northern Nigeria) and to settle the Fulani pastoralists.

Other forms of production

Fresh-water fishing is widespread in West Africa and some governments have tried to develop fish farms; the chief inland fishing areas are the middle Niger and Lake Chad. Sea fishing is also widespread, but especially important in Senegal and Ghana, where motor-driven canoes, launches and trawlers are all used.

Gathering wild produce makes its most important contribution to the export economy in the south—oil-palm produce, kapok and formerly rubber—and to the internal economy in the north—mainly wild grains and fruits to supplement the limited resources possible where the growing season is short.

Mining for iron ore, antimony, gold and tin has long been practised in West Africa. Modern mining is chiefly for iron ores in Guinea, Sierra Leone and Liberia, bauxite in Guinea and Ghana, tin, coal and oil in Nigeria, diamonds in Sierra Leone and Ghana, manganese in Ghana and phosphates in Senegal.

Industrial development is extremely small, but has increased rapidly since independence, especially in Ghana, Nigeria and Senegal. The demand for local cloth has led to a revival of textile manufacturing, and modern enterprises include the treatment of ores and agricultural produce, bicycle and motor-vehicle assembly, brewing, packaging, plastics, tyres and remoulds, tobacco and cigarettes and ceramics. Hydro-electric power resources are immense, especially in the Guinean zone, and Nigeria is particularly fortunate in having coal and oil resources. Problems frequently include high transport and power costs, shortage of skilled labour and the difficulties of developing a local market.

TRANSPORT

Colonialism brought railways and feeder roads, replacing the old tracks between the Guinean and Sudanic zones and diverting trade from the trans-Saharan routes to the coast. The railways (Fig. 116) were built from deep-water harbours at Dakar (1885), Conakry (1900) and Freetown (1899); from estuarine and lagoon harbours at St. Louis (1885), Abidjan (1903) (formerly Port Bouet on the sand-bar), Lagos (1901) and Port Harcourt (1916); and from beaches at Sekondi-Takoradi (1901), Accra (1909), Lome (1902) and Cotonou (1900). Most lines are single track and the export of produce concentrated in a short harvest period in the north is frequently held up. Nigerian groundnuts often have to be stored for months in pyramids near the railway, despite the additional use of river transport from Baro on the Niger to Burutu. On the whole, river traffic is of only minor importance except on the middle and lower Niger, the Senegal and the Gambia, for most well-populated crop-producing areas are well away from large rivers. Régimes and shifting channels together with floating vegetation provide additional hazards. Road traffic is mainly on earth surfaces, but, as elsewhere in the world, it has proved an effective competitor to railways and most governments have large schemes for road improvement.

WAYS OF LIFE

1. A Sudanic agricultural people: the Hausa

The Hausa kingdoms (Fig. 109) owe their origins to the movement and settlement of a number of pastoral and agricultural peoples on the high plains of northern Nigeria, mostly between 2,000 and 2,400 feet above sea-level. To the west lies a great basin drained by the Sokoto river and containing extensive fadama or floodlands. Here the nineteenth-century Hausa capital of Sokoto was created by a Fulani nobility. To the east is the basin of Bornu with its 'Great Forest' which formerly marked the frontier zone; to the south-west, the high plateau of Jos with its crowded hill refuges occupied by pagan, i.e. non-Moslem, peoples; and to the south, lower hills and plateaux, mainly between 1,600 and 2,000 feet, and the great trough of the Niger.

On their high plains and in the Sokoto valley the Hausa built great walled cities, some of which like Kano became emporia for the trans-Saharan traffic. They also developed the art of metal working and several crafts, particularly the manufacture of cloth. The Hausa settlements consist of cities of 10,000 or more in population, most of these being major trading and administrative centres; small market towns of a few thousand population, and villages, usually of only a few hundred. Some of the larger towns like Kano are surrounded by a dispersal of individual compounds and small farm hamlets. Within 10 miles radius of the walls of Kano such dispersed settlement contains a population with a density of 1,300 per sq. mile, one of the highest in Africa for people mainly dependent on agriculture.

The chief crops are early and late varieties of pennisetum millet, sorghum or guinea corn, cotton, groundnuts, maize, sugar-cane and sweet potatoes—the last three being grown chiefly on floodland. Irrigation from streams and wells, using principally the shaduf or small bags pulled up by ropes, is used for high-value crops, mainly onions and rice. Manuring is important, particularly in the overcrowded 'closed farm' zone around Kano where even nightsoil collected from the city is applied.

The chief crops exported are groundnuts, which are the most important commodity carried on the Nigerian railways, and cotton. Groundnuts are grown chiefly on the sandy soils of northern Hausaland, and cotton on the rather heavier soils of Zaria Province in the south. Large quantities of cotton are also grown for the internal market. An additional important source of income lies in the profits of trading, for Hausa traders are renowned throughout the greater part of West Africa and form small colonies in many of the major cities.

2. A Guinean agricultural people: the Yoruba

Yorubaland is situated in south-western Nigeria and consists of the greater part of the plateaux (averaging between 1,000 and 2,000 feet above sea-level) lying south and west of the Niger, and their associated coastlands. Within Yorubaland there is an important ecological distinction between the savannas of the north and the rain forest to the south and east. Distinctive soil and vegetation conditions and differences in humidity combine to provide marked agricultural distinctions. Thus the rain forest with its ferrallitic soils, frequently very heavy on the level plateau tops, has a cultivation dominated by tree crops, particularly cacao trees, oil-palms and kolas. Some crops are confined to the rain forest, notably bananas or plantains, or are found outside it only in exceptionally humid situations. Again the fallow plants are distinctive, being mainly shrubs, many of which develop deep roots. Admittedly many important crops, such as yams, cassava and maize, are found in both vegetation zones, but the savannas have their distinctions, possessing sorghum and grass fallows, having fewer oil-palms, and those chiefly near streams, and depending only to a small extent on tree crops. There are therefore marked contrasts between these two portions of Yorubaland.

Traditionally the savannas were held mainly by the powerful Oyo Yoruba whose ruler was the federal head of all the Yoruba kingdoms, although religious authority resided in the forest at Ife. Today the wealthiest portion of Yorubaland is the cocoa belt extending in a crescent on the northern and western margins of the rain forest and focussing chiefly on the great city of Ibadan, the capital of the Western Region. The Yoruba are highly urbanised (p. 618), yet in many of the cities the majority of the men are farmers. Huge areas of cultivation extend around the cities and the journey to the farthest fields may be 10 miles or more. Farm settlements consisting of scattered compounds are occupied by some members of the Yoruba families for most of the year and by others for short periods when large numbers of labourers are needed, particularly when the fallows have to be cleared and when planting has to be done. Like the Hausa, the Yoruba are skilled weavers and noted craftsmen, particularly in the manufacture of gold ornaments. Many are traders and some trade merchandise as far away as Ghana. Cocoa has brought greater wealth to Yorubaland than to any other comparable area of Nigeria. Small cocoa-farming hamlets, each with its own closely situated 'plantation', are the chief feature of much of the rain-forest zone, and here food farming is of less importance than growing crops for sale. Large quantities of food are imported, chiefly from markets in the savannas where commercial yam cultivation has become highly profitable. Other areas specialise in cassava, rice and plantain cultivation for the growing urban markets. Foodstuffs imported from overseas are also of growing importance although still only making a small contribution to the diet, notably wheat, sugar, tinned milk, meat and fish.

3. A pastoral people: the Fulani

The Fulani-speaking peoples are the most widespread ethnic group in West Africa. Most of them live in the Sudanic and Sahelian zones or in uplands such as the Futa Jallon and Adamawa, either as nomadic or semi-nomadic pastoralists, as cultivators keeping some livestock, or as settled townsfolk. Most of the pastoral Fulani depend in part on cultivation, and some members of the family till small-holdings in which are planted quick-growing varieties of pennisetum millet and occasionally guinea corn, rice, beans and groundnuts.

The Inland Niger delta of Mali, lying south-west of Timbuktu (see also Chapter 21), provides within the Sahel enormous areas of floodland where dry-season grazing is possible and where livestock may find abundant drinking water. During the rainy season the Fulani of Mali move with their herds across the Sahelian plains where, in many cases, they depend on deep wells for water supplies, or farther northwards via the Tilemsi valley to the plateau of Adrar des Iforas whose slopes are better watered than the desert plains below. To the south of the Niger the plateaux have some permanent pools and occasional streams and extensive areas of good grazing land. In the dry season the Fulani move from these outlying pastures inwards to the Inland Niger delta, the heart of their former kingdom of Macina. In March, with low river levels, extensive areas of nutritious *Echinochloa* grass or 'borgu' are exposed and first cattle and later sheep take advantage of these annually renewed grazing lands. The dry season is therefore the time for the best feeding. It is also a time when all the Macina pastoralists meet one another and visit the traditional markets of the Niger valley to sell animal produce and purchase cloth, weapons and grain.

There is therefore a community of interests, but unfortunately there is too a conflict over land, for the borgu pastures are also suitable for conversion into rice fields or may be planted with floodland varieties of sorghum. Thus, although cultivators and pastoralists need one another's produce, they also want the same land and during the same season of declining water levels. The problems involved have not yet been solved. Attempts to make more intensive use of floodland for rice production involving water control, and attempts to increase productivity, are bringing changes in land use involving permanent occupation. Eventually these must bring a suitable division of the borgu area between the different groups.

54

The Commonwealth Countries

NIGERIA

The Federation of Nigeria (Fig. 110) is one of the largest African countries and the largest member of the British Commonwealth in Africa. With a total area of 373,000 sq. miles the Federation is four times as large as the United Kingdom or Ghana and almost twice the size of France. The population (1964) of 56 million is greater than that of either the United Kingdom or France and represents some 55 per cent of the total population of West Africa. Nigeria became independent in 1959 as a federation of three regions, with the capital at Lagos. The Southern Cameroons, formerly part of Nigeria, voted in the plebiscite of 1961 to join the Cameroun Republic (former French Cameroons). The present four regions—Northern, Eastern, Western and (after 1962) Mid-West—correspond only broadly to ethnic distributions (Fig. 109), the Northern being dominated by the Hausa and Fulani (9 million), the Eastern by the Ibo (6 million) and the Western by the Yoruba (5·5 million). Many Yoruba and Ibo live in the Northern Region and large numbers of Ibo live in the Western. Other large groups include the Kanuri (1·5 million, Northern Region), Tiv (1 million, Northern Region), Ibibio (1 million, Eastern Region), Bini (0·5 million, Mid-West Region) and Nupe (0·4 million, Northern Region). Some of the minority groups wanted new regions and the creation of the Mid-West Region, mainly Bini and Ibo, was approved by the Federal Government in 1962.

GEOGRAPHICAL REGIONS (Fig. 111)

Nigeria is subdivided by the great east-west trough of the Niger and Benue, the narrower Lower Niger valley and the delta, into the plateaux and high plains of the north, the south-western plateaux and the cuestas and smaller plateaux of the south-east.

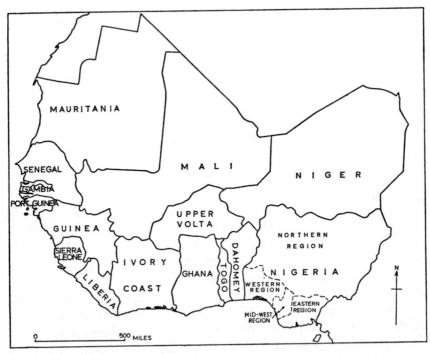

Figure 110 *The political divisions of West Africa and the southern Sahara*

THE NORTHERN HIGH PLAINS consist of Hausaland, mainly at about 2,000 feet above sea-level with broad shallow valleys containing 'fadama', or floodland, and the lower Sokoto plains drained by the Rima and its associated dallols, together with the plains of Bornu in the Chad Basin. Hausaland is mainly built of Basement Complex rocks overlain by sands whilst the plains of Sokoto and Bornu consist of sediments which, in the case of Sokoto, rise in the east to form a small escarpment overlooking Hausaland. The light sandy soils of former dunes, so widespread in the north, form good sites for settlement and are excellent for groundnut cultivation. The damper soils between the dunes support grains and vegetables. Farther south, notably in Zaria Province, the soils are heavier and cotton replaces groundnuts as the chief export crop. Lake Chad occupies a basin of inland drainage, although it is not itself at the lowest level and contains fresh, not brackish, water.

Above the northern high plains rises the Jos plateau with its steep escarpment on the south and west and with summits over 5,000 feet. The Jos plateau became a refuge for 'pagan' peoples fleeing from the raids of the Moslem Hausa. Population densities locally are over 200 per sq. mile on confined hill-top sites. In some cases a careful terrace cultivation using manures has been necessary to maintain productivity. Most of the original woodland of the plateau has been replaced by grass providing pasture for large herds of Fulani cattle, but the greatest resource is alluvial tin worked chiefly by draglines or hydraulic rams. To the east are the Biu plateau (over 2,000 feet), with thin soils and sparse population, and the Adamawa highlands rising to nearly 7,000 feet on the border. Here soils are often ferruginous and low yielding, but locally dense refugee populations have created terraces and apply manure to the land. The southern fringe of the high plains has some extremely broken relief with quartzitic ridges and numerous granite 'domes' or inselberge. Here and there are plains and basins where conditions are suitable for cultivation and population densities are low, for this is part of the 'Middle Belt'. Agriculturalists have entered from overcrowded areas, but adopt

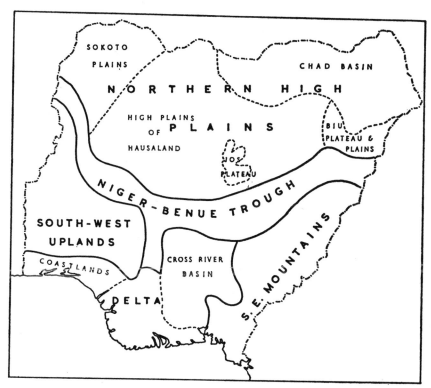

Figure III *The geographical regions of Nigeria*

extensive shifting-cultivation methods rather than the careful techniques of their homeland. The Northern Region government has tried to encourage better farming, notably on resettlement schemes such as that of Shendam.

THE NIGER–BENUE TROUGH of tectonic origin contains mainly Cretaceous sediments, the soils derived from which have been locally well cultivated, notably by the Nupe in the west, chiefly producing sorghum, yams, cotton and millet, and the Tiv in the east growing cassava, yams, sorghum and benniseed. Except at crossing points, densities of population near the rivers are low and the project to create a major navigable waterway may not need considerable re-location of population.

THE SOUTH-WESTERN UPLANDS, occupied mainly by the Yoruba, are mostly plains at 1,000 to 2,000 feet with the greatest heights in the extreme north-west and in the centre (Ekiti district) and lower plains to the south. Here and there they are interrupted by abrupt hills in outcrops of quartzite or granite. The northern half is mainly grassland and savanna woodland and the southern half high forest and woody plants in the fallows interspersed with oil-palms and cacao plantations. The watershed lies well to the north and most drainage flows directly to the sea, notably by the Ogun and Oshun rivers. The south-eastern cuestas of Awka and Udi-Awgu, the Ibo homeland, face eastward and are drained partly to the Niger by the Anambra and partly southward by the Imo river. Coal seams are exposed near the foot of the Udi escarpment and mined by adits.

THE NIGER DELTA AND THE SOUTH–EASTERN HILLS The Niger delta is one of the few sparsely populated deltas of the world, avoided by most Nigerians. Rainfall exceeds 100 inches in the year and there are extensive mangrove swamps. To the east are the lowlands of the Cross river flanking the plateaux of Obudu and the Oban hills. With overcrowding amongst the Ibo and Ibibio in the south-east (densities of over 600 per sq. mile, and locally even over 1,000), development of this region may help to relieve population pressure. At present it is chiefly the site of oil drilling (Plate 16A), a source of mangrove pit props and of fish. Some small attempts have been made to grow swamp rice in government schemes. The Nigerian coast is remarkably smooth and bars block or hinder navigation at the entrances to lagoons and river mouths.

Constant dredging is necessary at Lagos and shipping for Sapele, Warri, Burutu or Port Harcourt is limited in draught—generally depths vary between 10 and 20 feet.

THE ECONOMY

Nigeria's chief food resources are yams, cassava, cocoyams and plantains grown in the south and sorgham and bulrush millet grown in the north (Fig. 112). Of the principal exports four are southern (oil-palm produce, cocoa, rubber and timber), accounting for 63 per cent of total. Nevertheless, despite great distances from the coast, the Northern Region, mainly

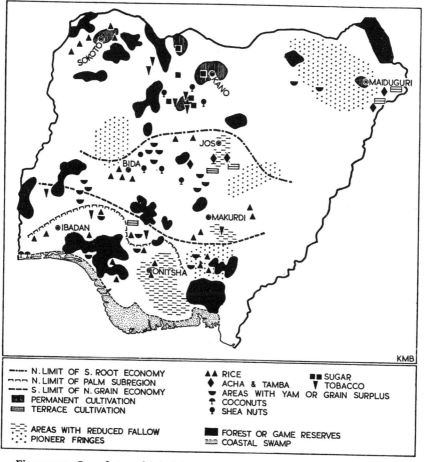

N. LIMIT OF S. ROOT ECONOMY	▲▲ RICE	■■ SUGAR
N. LIMIT OF PALM SUBREGION	◆ ACHA & TAMBA	▼ TOBACCO
S. LIMIT OF N. GRAIN ECONOMY	◣ AREAS WITH YAM OR GRAIN SURPLUS	
PERMANENT CULTIVATION	⚲ COCONUTS	
TERRACE CULTIVATION	⚲ SHEA NUTS	
AREAS WITH REDUCED FALLOW	■ FOREST OR GAME RESERVES	
PIONEER FRINGES	COASTAL SWAMP	

Figure 112 *Some factors of the subsistence crop economy in Nigeria* (by permission of K. M. Buchanan and J. C. Pugh)

with the help of flat freight rates for export produce, has become the second world producer of groundnuts and has in addition a considerable export of cotton, tin, benniseed and columbite. The Western Region produces almost all the cocoa, part of the timber and part of the oil-palm produce. It is easily the richest region both in total and per capita productivity and this is reflected in its increasing urbanism and its dense network of roads. The project to build a dam for a combined irrigation–waterway–hydro-electric power scheme on the Niger at Kainji in the Northern Region will serve mainly the Western Region which is the largest market for electricity and is also the chief market for the North's cattle, sheep and goats. The Mid-West Region produces all the rubber, a large part of the timber and part of the oil-palm produce. The Eastern Region despite its coastward location has been unable to realise the per capita wealth of the Mid-West and Western regions, although it is a major palm-oil and kernel exporter and West Africa's sole coal producer. Oil may be some help, for the greater part of Nigeria's oilfield appears to lie east of the Niger. However, much of the land in this region is badly overcrowded and gulleying, notably at Agulu, has cut some 300 feet deep into the soft sediments beneath the thin overworked soils.

Nigeria's main imports are machinery, textiles, motor vehicles and bicycles, and her principal trade is with the United Kingdom. In terms of per capita output Nigeria is poorly placed, and in terms of per capita exports she is one of the poorer countries of Africa, earning barely $11·2 per head in 1962 compared with $48 in Ghana, $56 in the Ivory Coast and $45 in Senegal. There is great scope for improvements, not only in agricultural productivity, but also in transport and marketing facilities.

With so large an area and unevenly distributed population, transport services and costs are of prime importance. Nigeria has the largest railway system in West Africa, with over 2,000 route miles extending northwards from Lagos and Port Harcourt to Hausaland and the Jos plateau and terminating near the northern border at Kaura Namoda and Nguru. A new railway from Jos to Maiduguri, the capital of Bornu Province, was completed in 1964. This should aid the economic development of this rather remote north-eastern corner. The Federation has a good road network, but only a small proportion possess tarred surfaces and the earth roads deteriorate badly during the wet season. The rivers are extensively used for navigation, but occasional rapids and reduction of depth during the dry season limit their value. In the wet season the Niger is navigable for 500 miles inland, as far as Jebba, and the Benue is navigable as far as Yola, near the border with Cameroun.

MINING AND MANUFACTURING

Nigeria is an important producer of *tin*, obtained from river gravels washed out of the granites of the Jos plateau. With an output of 10,500 tons, Nigeria was seventh world producer in 1961. These alluvial tin deposits are becoming exhausted and it is likely that more expensive shaft mining will eventually be introduced to work deep deposits within the granite. *Columbite*, formerly a waste product of the tin mining, is now used in the manufacture of special alloys for jet engines and gas turbines and Nigeria has become the world's major supplier. *Coal* is another mineral of importance. It is obtained from the Enugu coal field in eastern Nigeria and is sub-bituminous coal of Cretaceous age. These deposits are the only large reserves of West Africa. The annual output is now about 600,000 tons. After many years of prospecting, in 1958 *mineral oil* and *natural gas* in commercial quantities were found in the Niger delta. Since then more wells have been drilled and oil production is increasing rapidly. In 1965 13 million tons were exported. An oil refinery to process crude for the domestic market has been built at Port Harcourt, and a lubricating oil plant has been constructed at Apapa.

The oil and natural gas discoveries have notably affected the economy by leading to a shift from the use of Enugu coal in electricity manufacture, transport and industry to a cheaper and more efficient fuel; this is likely to stimulate further industrial development. Since the 1950's several manufacturing industries have become established: they include cement, textiles, timber and plywood, soap and margarine, tobacco and cigarettes, rubber and plastics, brewing and soft-drink manufacture, in addition to the usual processing of agricultural products such as cotton ginning, oil-seed pressing and cocoa preparation. No marked expansion of manufacturing is to be expected while the purchasing power of the people remains low. To this end the government strives to raise agricultural productivity, but it also devotes large sums to education and to the improvement and extension of communication, both necessary bases for expanding manufacturing industry.

TOWNS

The Federal capital and chief port is *Lagos* (pop. 665,000). It is built on an island connected by a bridge with the railway terminal on Iddo

Island. This in turn is linked by causeway with the suburbs of Ebute
Metta and Yaba on the mainland. Here the line of sand-bars is broken
by a dredged channel giving access to the open sea. The modern wharves
are opposite Lagos island at Apapa, where an industrial estate is developing
and where soap, drinks, textiles and foods are manufactured or processed.
Ibadan (pop. 1,000,000) is one of the largest cities in tropical Africa.
Little remains of the walls of the Yoruba 'camp' established about
1820, and the single-storey courtyard houses have been replaced by two-
storey mansions. The town is in the cocoa belt and a large part of the
population still depends on agriculture. Today Ibadan is the capital of
the Western Region, with Nigeria's largest university, and growing
manufactures of tobacco, bottling and canning, plastics and tires. Other
local market and administrative towns are Ogbomosho (pop. 320,000),
Ife and Abeokuta. Benin (pop. 54,000), capital of the Mid-West Region
and a walled city when the Portuguese arrived in 1485, is now an important
market for the local oil palm- and rubber-growing area.

Port Harcourt (pop. 72,000), the second port of Nigeria, was created
in 1916 to serve as the terminal of the railway from *Enugu* (pop. 63,000),
the capital of the Eastern Region and the centre of coal mining. In this
region the commercial towns are modern creations with the exception
of *Onitsha* (pop. 80,000) which has modern suburbs and is one of the
largest markets in Nigeria ('where anything can be bought, from an
elephant to an admiral's uniform') serving as a port on the mile-
wide Niger and ferry point connecting the two southern regions. On
the coast are the declining palm-oil ports of Degema, Bonny and
Calabar.

In the Northern Region, *Kaduna* (pop. 52,000) is the capital. It was
created by the British in 1917 and stands isolated from major population
centres on the fringe of the 'Middle Belt'. Textile mills have been established here. To the north are the major commercial centres of *Zaria*
(pop. 62,000) and *Kano* (pop. 295,000), the fourth largest city. Like other
Hausa cities, each is surrounded by high thick walls, and in addition has
British-created commercial and administrative suburbs, a quarter for
northern 'strangers' and a quarter, the 'sabon gari', for southerners.
Kano, standing in flat park-like country, is the centre of a permanent
farming district (see p. 623). Here and there are plots of guinea corn and
cotton, but overwhelmingly this is groundnut country, and great pyramids
of bagged groundnuts awaiting transport down the 700-mile single-line
railway to the coast are a common sight. In the west is the former Fulani

capital of *Sokoto* (pop. 52,000), centre of a floodland farming district producing sugar, onions and rice.

Regional diversity in Nigeria is very marked. With so large a country this may not be surprising, but these geographical divisions are reinforced by ethnic, tribal and religious divisions among the population. The single government of Britain was replaced in 1960 by a federal government that allowed greater powers to the regions, between whom there is great rivalry. The three southern regions are economically more advanced and more Westernised than the Moslem Northern Region, which for its own preservation is attempting to modify Islamic social codes, to welcome Western education (there are few literates, most of the clerical work being done by southerners), and to change a rigid feudal system into an elected parliamentary one. The large population of the Northern Region gives it a majority over the other regions combined, and theoretically makes it possible for it to control the Federal Parliament. Unrest came to a head with bloodshed in 1966, and the military took over the regional governments; federal government is largely in abeyance. Clearly, to keep the diverse parts of the Federation together in these early years in order to realise the great potentiality the future offers requires much wisdom, patience and tolerance.

GHANA

In 1957 the Gold Coast was the first West African territory to acquire independence after Liberia more than a century previously; it was renamed Ghana. Ghana is the second state of West Africa in terms of population, with 7·4 million people, and the wealthiest on a per capita basis (Fig. 117), with an estimated income in 1957 of $193 per head (compare Uganda, $56). At the same time Ghana is one of the smaller African countries (91,843 sq. miles, about the size of Uganda), and three-quarters of its population lives within half a day's motor journey of the capital, Accra. The people belong to more than 100 tribes, which vary in size from 2,000 to 250,000; some tribes are split by the frontiers which the British drew with little regard for ethnic considerations. As a whole, the population is relatively well educated. Ghana has indeed one of the highest adult literacy rates in Africa. The population is growing at a very high annual rate—over 3 per cent at present, but there is ample room for expansion. Apart from some congested areas in the south, the density rarely exceeds forty per sq. mile, and much of the central third of the country has less than twenty per square mile.

Three major relief divisions are normally distinguished: the coastal plains, the Ashanti low plateaux and the Volta Basin and plateaux (Fig. 113). To some extent these coincide with the threefold vegetation division of coastal savanna, rain forest and northern savanna. The COASTAL PLAINS west of Accra consist of hills and ridges all within 600 feet of sea-level, and fringed by a smooth shore west of Cape Three Points and by alternating bays and headlands to the east. On the coast east of Takoradi rainfall is less than 50 inches, but to the west it is higher (over 80 inches west of Axim) and rain forest is the climax vegetation. Even in these wetter areas, however, three months of the year are relatively dry. There are no good natural harbours, and until the completion of Takoradi in 1928 all goods had to be landed at surf ports. East of Accra stretch the Lower Volta or Accra Plains, characterised by a very low rainfall (as little as 30 inches) and a vegetation of scrub and grass. There is some market gardening on the moister fringes and cattle rearing on the grassland, for this dry area is free of tsetse fly. Future irrigation schemes may make this an important agricultural region. In the Volta delta coconut production and fishing are the principal activities. On the lower Volta river navigation is limited to vessels drawing less than 9 feet and motor launches can reach Kete Krachi.

To the north are the Akwapim hills, continued north-eastward as the Kpandu, Nkonya and Dutukpene highlands, and in Togoland and Dahomey as the Atacora Mountains. In Ghana these consist of a narrow belt of ridges and hills, mainly schists and quartzites, cut by the great gorge of the Volta.

THE ASHANTI LOW PLATEAUX are generally at about 1,000 feet, divided from one another by a number of north-east to south-west ridges. They form a series of basins within which are the chief cacao-growing settlements. To the north lie the plateaux, mainly granitic, of western Gonja, Wa and northern Mamprusi, which support the chief agricultural settlements of the savanna, and in Zuarungu are grossly overcrowded with more than 600 people per sq. mile. Groundnuts, yams, millet, cotton and tobacco are among the chief crops grown here.

To the east is the VOLTA BASIN with its high sandstone plateau fringe and outward-facing escarpments. Rainfall is less than 50 inches,

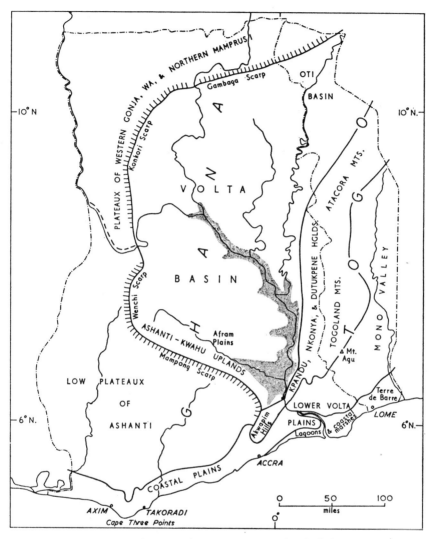

Figure 113 *Geographical regions of Ghana and Togo*. The shaded area represents the future Volta Dam reservoir

with a marked dry season. Soils on the sandstone give only low to moderate crop yields, but cattle are kept and supply meat for southern markets. The fringing uplands include the Ashanti-Kwahu uplands in the south, well watered and producing cacao and food crops in the valleys.

Cacao and timber

Although Ghana provides most of its own food needs, especially plantains, cocoyams, cassava, and sorghum, a large part of its wealth is derived from its export trade to which cacao contributes between 50 and 60 per cent, and timber about 10 per cent. Cacao planting began in the Akwapim hills more than a hundred years ago, and a second introduction was made in 1879 by a labourer Tetteh Quarshie, who returned from Fernando Poo and planted cacao trees in Mampong. Seedlings were distributed from the government botanical garden at Aburi in Akwapim and planting, often by 'companies' of farmers, spread north-westward. Cacao prefers well-drained areas with more than 50 inches of rain a year and the shortest possible dry season, and demands the shade of taller-growing trees, which also help to replenish the humus content of the soil when their leaves decay. It has been badly affected by several diseases, particularly swollen shoot which appeared as early as 1915. The older south-eastern plantations were affected first and migration of cacao planters north-westward was accelerated. No cure for swollen shoot has yet been found; the spread of swollen shoot has only been stopped by the ruthless destruction of diseased trees. Pre-war peak production was achieved in 1936 with 311,000 tons. From 1951 to 1959 annual production has fluctuated between 207,000 and 264,000 tons; the current level has reached the enormous figure of 600,000 tons, and Ghana remains the leading world exporter, although world prices have dropped through overproduction. Part of the labour force consists of some 250,000 seasonal workers from the Northern Territories and Upper Volta.

Timber is the second most valuable export, most of it coming from western Ashanti and the south-western area of high rainfall, and being exported via Takoradi where new timber wharves were opened in 1953 (Plate 16B). The rain forest is rich in hardwoods such as mahogany, odum (iroko), and sapele, for which there is a considerable demand. Today Ghana is Africa's leading timber exporter; exports of logs now exceed 35 million cubic feet (compare 1954 = 12·6 million cubic feet; and 1938 = 0·7 million cubic feet), while exports of sawn timber, plywood and veneers have risen to over 8·5 million cubic feet (compare 1954 = 5 million cubic feet, and 1938 = practically nil).

Ghana was in the past aptly named the Gold Coast, for during the last four centuries gold has been the country's leading mineral export, though the amount produced today is insignificant beside South Africa's contribution. The chief workings are in conglomerate near Tarkwa and Aboso, and in placer deposits in the sands and gravels of the southern rivers. Diamonds are also worked in alluvial deposits in the Birim and Bonsa valleys, both by large modern enterprises and by small family groups. Ghana is indeed second in the world only to the Congo Republic (Leopoldville) in the quantity of stones produced, but values are low, 70 per cent of the output being of industrial diamonds. Manganese ores occur at Nsuta near Takoradi, and bauxite is worked at Awaso near Dunkwa and Mount Ejuanema on the Mampong scarp. The largest deposit of bauxite discovered is at Yenahin west of Kumasi.

Table 40   *Mineral exports from Ghana ($£$ 000)*

	1953	1955	1957	1959	1961
Gold	9,460	9,050	9,794	11,200	10,750
Diamonds	3,920	5,530	8,980	8,660	7,149
Manganese	8,720	5,190	8,990	6,778	6,025
Bauxite	—	—	452	366	464

Even with the completion of the Volta River Scheme, Ghana will continue to be partly dependent on imported coal and oil for some of her electricity requirements. Other than wood and water power, Ghana has no fuel and power resources. Nevertheless, small-scale manufacturing industries are flourishing. Mills for extracting palm-oil and grinding corn, factories for preparing timber and metal working, and various repair trades have been established in the main towns for many years. More recently, canning and bottling industries, cigarette and soap manufacture, and general construction industries have been introduced. Today more than 25,000 people work in industrial establishments employing ten or more persons; taking smaller establishments into account, more people are employed in manufacturing than mining.

The Volta River Project (Fig. 113)

In 1962, work began on the construction of a 310-foot-high dam at Akosombo in the Volta gorge. The Akosombo dam wall was closed in 1964, and a lake formed behind it will extend for 200 miles and reach its top level by 1966. At Akosombo, up to 880 MW of electric power will be generated, plus 140 MW at Kpong in a later stage if desired. The electricity will be transmitted to Tema, where an aluminium smelter is being built; eventually, local bauxite will be used, but for the present the smelter will rely on imported alumina. About one-tenth of the power generated will be available for Ghana's rapidly growing towns and for new industries. A new navigable waterway will be created, although with·wider ferry crossings, and the lake will serve as a possible fishing ground. More than 80,000 people have been re-settled as a result of the creation of the lake. Water will be available for irrigation schemes in the dry south-east; these, it is planned, will produce rice and sugar, at present amongst Ghana's chief food imports. As Ghana is paying half the cost of the dam and power plant, and will have to meet loans on the remainder from the U.S.A., the United Kingdom and the International Bank, the country will have heavy financial commitments for some time, which her economy at present can ill afford. Already, the new port of Tema has cost £35 million, while the dam, power plant, transmission lines and smelter will cost about £120 million.

TOWNS AND PORTS

Accra is the capital of Ghana; with its new suburbs and the recently built port of Tema, it has a total population of half a million. Until Tema was completed, Ghana depended mainly on *Takoradi* (pop. 70,000) in the west, where an artificial deep-water harbour (Plate 16B) was created in 1928 and enlarged in 1953. The coast provides no natural site for a deep-water port, but poses the double obstacle of surf and sand. Vessels stand off-shore while the surf boats ferry cargoes to and fro. *Tema* lies 18 miles east of Accra (Fig. 114), and has been built with deep-water berths in connection with the new aluminium smelter. Despite handicaps, Accra has remained the capital and largest town, partly because its drier climate was more comfortable for residence and better suited to the use of transport animals

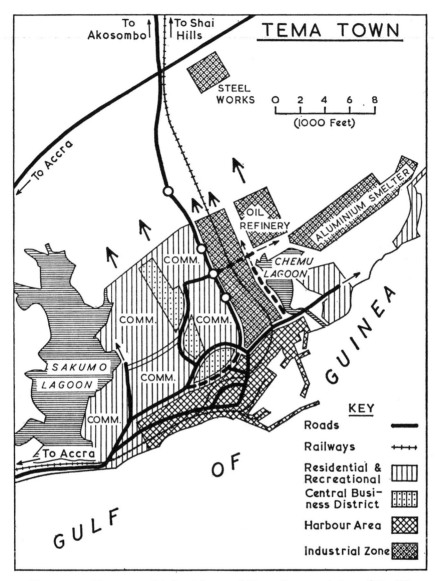

Figure 114 *The port and industrial area of Tema* (by permission of D. W. Hilling)

in the last century. In the 1920's it was conveniently near the main centres of cacao production, and became a railway terminal.

The largest inland town is *Kumasi* (pop. 190,000), the traditional capital of Ashanti, which was once the most powerful state west of the Togo-Atacora Mountains. Kumasi is now almost in the centre of the main cacao-growing areas, and a major focal point of Ghana's road system. Railways link it to both Accra and Takoradi. Other important towns include *Koforidua* (pop. 35,000), centre of the early cacao-producing districts in the south-east, and *Tamale* (pop. 40,000), the administrative centre of the Northern Territories.

Ghana's diversity of resources and relatively high level of educational achievement augur well for the future when the present overdependence on sales of cocoa has been ended, and when the loans on the Volta River Project have been paid off. High prices for cocoa after World War II brought a false sense of prosperity, and the insidious spread of swollen shoot has provided a warning against continued reliance on one crop. Development of forestry, expansion of food-crop cultivation, and the Volta River Project will collectively provide a wider base on which the economy may advance.

SIERRA LEONE

The independence of Sierra Leone came in 1961—later than that of either Ghana or Nigeria, partly because of slower economic progress and partly because of the social and political problems created by the presence of 80,000 'Creoles', descendants of freed slaves, amongst 2·5 million Africans. The area of the country is 28,000 sq. miles and the overall density of population at eighty per sq. mile is high for West Africa.

There is a broad contrast between the Coastal Plain about 50 miles in width and mostly under 400 feet in height, and the plateaux, hills and ridges to the east mainly at 1,000 to 2,000 feet above sea-level and fronting the Guinea highlands. The coast is divided by the Freetown or Colony Peninsula (Picket Hill 2,912 feet), composed of hard igneous rocks, into a northern estuarine swampland and a southern sandbar and lagoon-fringed swamp. The swamps consist of mangroves, badly drained sedge or better drained seasonally flooded grasslands. The Coastal Plain consists of low hills of metamorphic rocks, shales, sandstones and con-glomerates, supporting only a poorly developed rain forest. The highlands are chiefly of granite and schists and rise up to 6,390 feet in the dolerite peak of Bintimani in the Loma Mountains. The northern portions of the highlands support savanna and the north-eastern uplands have herds of Fulani-owned cattle.

THE ECONOMY

The lowland south-west and south of the country is better developed and more populous than the higher and severely dissected north and north-east. Soils are more fertile in the south, whereas in the north laterite soils are widespread. Moreover, communications are better developed in the south and include the railway from Freetown to Pendembu near the frontier with Liberia.

The chief foodstuff of Sierra Leone is rice, grown mostly on upland holdings in rotation with fonio and groundnuts. A little floodland rice was grown in polders in the north-west at the turn of the century, but extensive use of swamplands for rice cultivation came only after government encouragement. Both mangrove and inland fresh-water swamps are used and mechanisation has been introduced. Mangrove clearance is difficult and tidal ranges are less than in Guinea, consequently affording less satisfactory flushing and drainage. Costs have been high and people have been loth to leave the uplands for the swamps. Inland swamps have been easier to clear, but so far have given lower yields and are subject to heavy weed infestation. An important product of the swamps is piassava or the leaf stalks of Raphia palms, used for making brooms and brushes; Sierra Leone is the world's chief exporter of these. Other produce includes oil-palm kernels (the leading vegetable export product by value), coffee and cocoa, chiefly from the south-east in areas of former forest, and ginger chiefly from Bo, Moyamba and Bombali districts south-east of the Freetown Peninsula.

In the last thirty years Sierra Leone has become an important mineral exporter. In 1961 iron ore and diamonds together accounted for over 80 per cent of the export trade. *Iron ore* (52–69 per cent Fe) is mined near Marampa at Lunsar and taken by mineral railway to the ore port of Pepel in the Rokel estuary. Another larger deposit occurs farther inland in the Sula Mountains and probable reserves are estimated at about 100 million tons. By 1961 *diamonds* accounted for over half the value of exports. The diamonds are alluvial and occur in gravel beds beneath only 2–3 feet of overburden. The chief areas worked are in the south-east and east in the

Sewa and Moa river basins, especially in the Yengema district of Sefadu. *Chrome ore* is worked in the Hangha district near the eastern border and a little alluvial gold is won from eastern streams draining the Kambui schists. Platinum has been worked and ilmenite is known in the Freetown Peninsula, whilst occurrences of bauxite, molybdenum, corundum, rutile and lignite have also been established.

Freetown (pop. 128,000), the capital and port, founded in 1792, has the finest natural harbour in West Africa. Yet Freetown has grown only slowly and has little industry. Despite the variety of produce in its hinterland, the total output is small compared with that available for Lagos or Dakar, and the border with Guinea cuts Freetown off from access to the Upper Niger Basin, although the route is easier than from Conakry. *Bo* (pop. 20,000) is the second-largest town, a road and railway focus in the south-east.

GAMBIA

Gambia (3,977 sq. miles, pop. 315,000) is a narrow enclave of territory 290 miles long lying astride the lower and middle courses of the Gambia river. At the coast it is 12 miles wide, but inland the width is only 7 miles. It is, in fact, the product of its navigable highway which extends for vessels of 6 feet draught some 300 miles inland. Its capital and port of Bathurst has a very restricted hinterland, but one which is highly productive of groundnuts, for the cultivation of which some 10,000 'strange farmers' or seasonal immigrants annually join the colony's population.

The lowest lands are mangrove and reed swamps with, beyond, the 'banto faros' or seasonally submerged grasslands; the latter, where free of salt, can be used for rice growing. Land above floods consists of sand-hills and laterite and the sandstone plateau about 100 to 150 feet above the river. The sandy soils produce the groundnuts which provide over 90 per cent of the value of exports. Attempts to develop a mechanised rice scheme, poultry and fisheries schemes and ilmenite quarrying have all failed or proved little productive. *Bathurst* (pop. 28,000), built on an island barely above water-level, has a deep-water wharf but trade is limited. Gambia was the last British colony in West Africa to achieve independence (1965). It now has many problems to face, notably economic ones, for it needs financial aid just to maintain existing services. For the future, co-operation with Senegal which surrounds it will be imperative.

55

The French Community Countries

TOGO

The Republic of Togo was created from the French share of the former
German colony, the British portion having been absorbed by Ghana.
The Ewe tribe of the south numbering 700,000 are divided by the
frontier and their leaders have pressed for reunification. Various groups
have favoured the unification of the two Togos, or unity with Ghana.
With only 1·4 million inhabitants, Togo is the second smallest West
African state.

The territory of 22,000 sq. miles is 50 to 75 miles wide and 375 miles
long (Fig. 113). It consists in the south of a sand-bar and lagoon coast
fringing a low clay plateau known as the Terre de Barre, with farther
inland the low marshy plain of the Lama-Hollis depression. To the north
is the Mono valley rising to about 1,000 feet and divided from the Oti
Basin in the extreme north by the Togo-Atacora Mountains in which
Mount Agu reaches 3,366 feet.

The people of the northern savanna country are of Sudanic origin.
The most populous districts are in the south, where the people are
predominantly Negroid, depending mainly on cassava, maize and copra;
in the hill refuges of the Togo-Atacora Range, the people grow sorghum,
groundnuts and cotton. Densities of over 1,500 per sq. mile occur in some
of the hill cantons where peoples such as the Kabrai and Lamba depend
on manured terrace cultivation. Some resettlement has occurred in the
Mono Plains.

Togoland is thus essentially an agricultural country, growing enough
foodstuffs to feed its population, and exporting some coffee and cocoa
(from the south-eastern Togo Mountains and the coastlands), together
with palm produce, cotton and copra. There are practically no industries

except a small soap factory; all other manufactured goods have to be imported. Nevertheless, there is a favourable balance of trade. Deposits of bauxite, iron ore and phosphates are known to exist, but only the phosphates have so far been exploited. A North African mining company has obtained large concessions and commenced extraction near Hahotoe (1962 production: 360,000 tons). A short railway has been built to the coast at Kpeme (22 miles east of Lomé) where a washing plant and port facilities have been built. The new pier, nearly a mile long, allows handling of ships up to 20,000 tons.

Lomé (pop. 80,000), the capital, is a surf port handling about 110,000 tons of cargo annually, and has a small wharf for lighters. It is the terminus of the country's railways, the longest of which runs north to Blitta.

DAHOMEY

Geographically and economically Dahomey's situation is very similar to that of Togo with great length and little width (area 43,800 sq. miles), former tribal groups divided by frontiers, similar per capita export and revenue values and a problem of economic viability for its 2 million population, partially solved by French aid and by membership in the *Conseil de l'Entente*.

In the south are coastal sand-bars and lagoons, the fertile clayey Terre de Barre and the swampy plain of the Lama-Hollis depression. To the north are the fertile low plateaux of Parahoué, Abomey, Zagnanado and Ketou within the rain-forest belt where oil-palms flourish and orange groves have been introduced. Here are the chief concentrations of population and the centre of the former Fon state of Dahomey. North-wards again are the north-western table lands at about 1,000 feet above sea-level, drained by the Ouémé river and its tributaries. Here soils are lateritic and thin and population sparse. In the north-west are the Atacora Mountains. As in Togo, these are densely populated, particularly by the Somba who live in large fortified compounds. In the north-east is a small portion of the Niger valley.

Palm produce provides nearly 70 per cent of Dahomey's exports by value, grown chiefly in the south which also produces maize, cassava and copra. Groundnuts, coffee and cotton are minor exports chiefly from the tablelands and mountains. Iron and chrome ore deposits are known. *Cotonou* (pop. 70,000), the largest town, is a surf-port with a lighter wharf and the main centre of commerce. *Porto-Novo* (pop. 69,000), the capital, is a local railway and waterway focus with some external trade via Lagos.

IVORY COAST

Like the other countries of French West Africa, the Ivory Coast became independent in 1960, having been a member of the French Community from 1958. The Republic has an area of 123,200 sq. miles and a population (1964) of 3·5 million. It is now one of the most thriving states of West Africa. In French West Africa Senegal was for long the richest territory in export production, but since 1950 when the Vridi Canal was cut through the bar enclosing the Ebrié lagoon, making Abidjan a great port, the Ivory Coast has become a more important exporter, particularly of coffee, cocoa and timber. It is the chief member of the *Conseil de l'Entente* for which it provides some financial support and its port is the chief outlet for both the Upper Volta and Mali.

GEOGRAPHICAL REGIONS

Two distinctive regions may be discerned, the Low Plains and the Interior Plateaux, related to increasing elevation with increasing distance from the coast. *The Low Plains* extend inland 100 to 150 miles before attaining a height of 500 feet. In the west, the plain ends in cliffs some 200 feet high, but from Fresco eastward the coast has suffered recent submergence. It has also been smoothed by longshore drift and heavy surf which build up sand-bars and create extensive lagoons. These great sand-bars have prevented the development of good anchorages and ports and so have hindered the general economic development of the country. A canal cut through the sand-bar at Abidjan in 1904 had silted up by 1907 and the colony had to be content with open roadstead anchorages and lighter transhipment to wharfs on the bar. In 1936 the cutting of a new and bigger canal through the bar to the Ebrié Lagoon and Abidjan was begun. The war delayed the completion until 1950. This Vridi Canal is 1¾ miles long, 1,000 yards wide and the channel and lagoon give a 45-foot depth for shipping. The economic effect was immediate; trade increased threefold, a range of industries became attracted and Abidjan's population (24,000 in 1937) is now well over 200,000.

Pre-Cambrian rocks underlie most of the Ivory Coast, their gently undulating surface being somewhat monotonous although broken here and there by low hills. The climax vegetation of the Low Plains is rain forest, which extends farthest north on the eastern and western borders of the Republic. In the centre, in the Baoulé region drained by the Bandama river, the forest is at its narrowest—partly because of lower rainfall. The forest yields valuable timbers such as mahogany, and export crops of coffee, cocoa, oil-palm and bananas. The main subsistence crops are rice, yams and cassava. In the south-west population densities are very low and economic development has been slow. In the south-east, however, the Anyi, a people related to the Ashanti, created the former Kingdom of Sanwi and, with access to better communications, have encouraged the chief cocoa, coffee and timber developments.

The northern two-thirds of the Ivory Coast are occupied by the *Interior Plateaux*, at about 1,000 feet above sea-level rising to the Western Highlands with summits above 3,000 feet. Here the rain forest gives way to savanna; the soils are sandy or lateritic and much of the area is subject to the tsetse fly. This is part of the thinly populated, impoverished 'Middle Belt' of West Africa. The northern portion of the Ivory Coast is less important than the southern for export production except in the Massif of Man (attaining 4,000 feet) in the west, which is a major arabica coffee-producing region on the northern fringe of the rain forest.

THE ECONOMY

The Ivory Coast contains the dividing zone between rice and root crop staples (Fig. 115). Rice is the chief food crop in the south-west, with fonio or hungry rice as an important secondary, and yams and cassava are dominant in the east, with cocoyams and plantains of local importance especially in the cacao-growing areas. In the north, maize, sorghum and cotton are the chief crops both to the east and west. The dividing zone between rice and roots appears to be of social origin, although one may distinguish in the wetter areas of the coastlands between the single maxima with a better seasonal spread of rainfall of the east. Locally, however, such differences are of slight importance and rice and roots can both be grown throughout the wetter areas.

Coffee and cocoa account for 88 per cent of the value of exports. Both crops were grown on European plantations although there was some encouragement of African production in the 1930's. Since World War II the proportion of European production has declined, due partly to high costs and labour troubles, and African production dominates. Coffee is grown throughout the rain-forest zone; the robusta varieties, chiefly, which although producing a lower quality bean than arabica are better suited to the moist lowland conditions and preferred for the manufacture of 'instant' coffees. Cacao is confined chiefly to the south-east where in many cases it is grown in close association with coffee—cacao on hill tops or in valley bottoms and coffee on slopes.

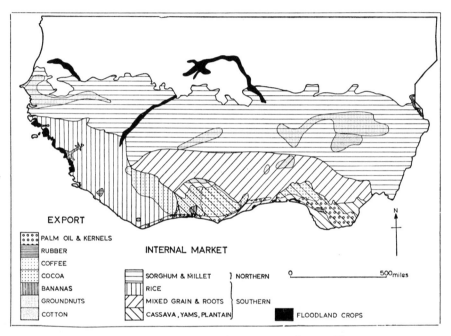

Figure 115 *The principal crop regions of West Africa*

Bananas, chiefly the small Chinese type, as in Guinea, are grown in the south-east and oil-palm kernels come mainly from Man and Sassandra. Cotton is important, especially in the north, and a small textile industry has begun at Bouaké (pop. 70,000), the largest town. Timber is cut mainly in the south-east with Abidjan the chief collecting centre. Bimbresso, to the west of Abidjan, has the first paper factory in inter-tropical Africa, using local wood pulp. A hydro-electric power scheme has been undertaken at Ayamé on the Bia river.

Abidjan is the capital and one of the great ports of West Africa, with a hinterland stretching as far north as the Niger and rapidly increasing productivity in its immediate vicinity. The city is situated on a peninsula with the African suburb of Adjamé to the north, and opposite, on the island of Petit Bassam, is another African suburb, Treichville, together with wharves and the industrial quarter. The numerous industries include the manufacture of margarine, soap, cocoa-butter, plywood, aluminium sheet and motor-vehicle assembly, fruit canning, brewing and saw-milling. An oil refinery was completed in 1965. With its great hinterland, its own varied resources and expanding economy, the Ivory Coast would seem to have the greatest potential of all the West African French Community states.

UPPER VOLTA

The area of the Republic is 105,900 sq. miles and the population (1966) 4·9 million. Overall population density is over 40 per sq. mile but many parts in the centre of the country have densities three and four times as great. Although none of the country is desert, there are many unproductive areas and considerable tracts are uninhabited. Much of the western part of the Republic is sandy and infertile, while, to the south-east, the valleys of the Volta rivers are tsetse infested.

The Upper Volta became independent in 1960, but as a very dependent member of the *Conseil de l'Entente*, the loose political federation of the Ivory Coast, Upper Volta, Dahomey and Niger. The Upper Volta is the poorest member, with the lowest budget revenue per capita and exports valued at only $1.50 per head. The main resource is the annual export of labour to the cacao and coffee plantations of the Ivory Coast and Ghana. This inland Sudanic state whose main centres are 500 miles or more from the coast (700 miles by rail) can produce little more than groundnuts and hides, the profit from which is mostly swallowed up by transport costs.

The *High Plains* at about 1,000 feet form the greater part of the country and are incised by the valleys of the Black, Red and White Volta rising near the north-western border. The *Central Plains* with their sandy or ferruginous soils are occupied by the Mossi, creators of the kingdoms of Yatenga and Ouagadougou which successively resisted the advances of Islam. Gourma to the north-east has outcrops of laterite and sandstone and is occupied mainly by pastoralists and a few isolated settlements of agriculturalists. The *South-western Plains* are occupied mainly by Lobi and Bobo cultivators with lower densities and the advantage of a rather longer rainy season. The Bobo area includes also the eastern extension of the Sikasso plateau terminated by the Banfora Escarpment where agriculture is confined to valley bottoms and the scarp foot zone.

Groundnuts and cattle are the chief exports of the Upper Volta, the main market being *Bobo Dioulasso* (pop. 52,000) which until 1954 was the terminal of the railway to Abidjan. Sorghum is the chief food crop of the south and bulrush millet of the north. Sisal, benniseed and cotton are also produced, but again mainly in the south. The Mossi area depends on its own food production and the remittances of its emigrant labour force—numbering about 150,000 annually. *Ouagadougou* (pop. 70,000), the capital and present railway terminal, is a traditional Mossi centre. Broadly the country is split politically between a Bobo-dominated south-west favouring federation with Mali and a Mossi-dominated centre and north-east favouring the present association with the Entente.

SENEGAL

French colonisation in Senegal dates from the beginning of the nineteenth century, and conquest was completed in 1887. In 1895 the Governor of Senegal became Governor-General of the French West African Federation with his capital at St. Louis, but seven years later Dakar became the Federal capital. In June 1960 Senegal and the former French Sudan became jointly independent as the Mali Federation, but three months later they separated. Subsequent disagreement led to a severance of trade relations and Dakar, the great port of Senegal, was cut off from its hinterland. Fortunately the political rift has since been healed. The area of the country is about 76,000 sq. miles and the population 3·5 million (1965).

GEOGRAPHICAL REGIONS

Senegal consists of great plains under 600 feet above sea-level incised by the broad valleys of the Senegal, Saloum, Gambia and Casamance rivers. North of the Gambia, stretching into central Senegal, is the *Ferlo 'desert'*. These plains, averaging only about 130 feet above sea-level, are extremely sandy, being remnants of a former southern extension of the Sahara. Water is scarce and settlement is sparse, confined mainly to villages situated beside old river valleys where wells can tap water near the surface. During the rains this area is grazed over by Fulani pastoralists. The French policy of providing bores to tap deep water supplies has helped pastoralists to keep larger herds and stay longer in the Ferlo; but this has also encouraged an invasion of Wolof groundnut culti-vators, for, except on thin, concretionary soils, the Ferlo is culti-vable so long as water is available for domestic use during the dry season.

To the west, between the coastal plains and the Ferlo, are the slightly lower and somewhat wetter *Western Plains*. This is an undulating area of argillaceous sandstones, in many places covered by older dune forma-tions. To the west the water table is nearer the surface than in the Ferlo and here most of the Wolof and Serer populations are concentrated in the former kingdoms of Cayor and Baol. The greatest groundnut-grow-ing region in the world has been developed here. Exports began before the middle of the last century, but the great expansion of production occurred with the construction of the railways, and the chief areas still lie along the Dakar-St. Louis railway and the lines to Kaolack and Kayes. During the last thirty years the construction of roads has spread ground-nut growing far beyond the railway zones. The principal area of production lies behind Dakar, around Kaolack, Diourbel and Thiès. Each year 30,000–40,000 'navétanes' or immigrant labourers, chiefly from Northern Senegal and Mali, arrive to help with the cultivation and harvest.

In the extreme north is the *Fouta*, the left-bank flood plain of the Senegal river (the Mauritanian bank is known as the Chemama, p. 260). This is inhabited mainly by the Tekrour ('Toucouleur') who once created a powerful state. It is a more fertile area than the sandy plains to the south. Cultivation depends on combining the floodland production of sorghum and maize with rainland groundnuts and bulrush millet. After the harvest nomadic Fulani graze their cattle here until the onset of the next year's floods. A small experimental rice and cotton scheme, comprising 2,500 acres at the edge of the flood plain, is established at Guédé, 80 miles above Richard-Toll. The Senegal itself is navigable for shallow-draught steamers from St. Louis to above Podor in time of flood.

The Coastlands The northern coast consists of the sand-bar Langue de Barbarie, which shelters St. Louis and the marshy Senegal estuary from the Atlantic and deflects the river mouth 15 miles to the south.

Salt is produced from the saline delta swamps and irrigated rice is grown within a large mechanised scheme to the south-west of Richard-Toll, at the head of the delta. South of the estuary is the smooth scrub-covered shoreline of Cayor with the marshy depressions or 'niayes' whose damp fringes are used for market gardening. The Cape Verde Peninsula consists of Quaternary volcanic remnants, 'Les Mamelles', and the Miocene basalts of Cape Manuel and Gorée together with the sands of the tombolo, and provides a sheltered site and deep harbour for Dakar, the capital and chief port. To the south is the 'Petite Cote' with rias and low cliffs of Recent sediments or of laterite. South of the enclave of Gambia is Casamance. Here rainfall is over 60 inches and behind the coastal mangrove swamps the oil-palm flourishes, rice, maize, yams and cassava are grown, and sisal and citrus fruits have been introduced.

THE ECONOMY

Bulrush millets and sorghum are the staple food, but imported rice and other foodstuffs provide over a third of present food needs, for groundnuts are planted at the expense of food crops. The annual export of groundnuts is of some 270,000 tons of shelled nuts, 160,000 tons of oilseed cake and 120,000 tons of groundnut oil. These account for over 90 per cent of the total value of exports. Minerals play little part in the economy. However, phosphates from the Pallo quarries near Thiés are finding a growing export market. Titanium (used in paint manufacture and in the alloying of steel) is obtained from titaniferous sands near the Saloum estuary. Limestone is quarried and used in cement manufacture at Rufisque, 15 miles east of Dakar.

St. Louis (pop. 48,000), the former capital, is on a small island in the Senegal river and is of declining importance as a result of the commercial competition of Dakar and the loss of its function as capital for Mauritania. Dakar (pop. 375,000) was first occupied in 1857 in order to develop a deep-water port, admirably sheltered from northerly winds. It is a great entrepôt and calling port on routes between Western Europe, South America and Africa. It has become the most industrialised city of West Africa. It has three groundnut-oil mills, a sugar refinery, fish canneries, and breweries, and manufactures soap, cordage, textiles, confectionery, chemicals and dyes. An oil refinery to process 750,000 tons of crude oil annually was completed in 1965. Kaolack (pop. 47,000) is the chief exporting port for groundnuts and has a modern salt works, but shipping is limited in draught by the depth of water at the Saloum entrance. Under a Four-Year Development Plan (1961–5) this entrance is being dredged deeper and port facilities improved. Substantial road improvements in the immediate hinterland of Dakar have also been completed.

56

Liberia and the Guinea Lands

LIBERIA

Liberia was founded as a settlement for North American ex-slaves. The American Colonisation Society first had responsibility for the government of the settlements until 1847. Liberia has been independent since then, but governed by the 'Americo-Liberians', descendants of former freed slaves who constitute less than 2 per cent of the population. The country was created by linking together a number of settlements founded from North America under the authority of one—Monrovia. The area of the Republic is 43,000 sq. miles and the population is probably about 2 million.

PHYSICAL REGIONS

Liberia has about 350 miles of coastline extending from the Ivory Coast in the east to Sierra Leone in the west. The coastal plain is 20 to 60 miles wide and supports savanna fringed by mangrove swamps. Outcrops of granite are associated with coastal promontories and hills, rising to 1,000 feet in Cape Mount at Robertsport. Sand-bars frequently hinder navigation at the mouths of estuaries. Inland there are forested hills rising to 600 feet, and then about 50 miles inland is a steep rise to the Interior Plateaux, 1,000 to 2,000 feet in height, much dissected and still largely unexplored. Despite lower rainfall (90 to 100 inches compared with 100 to 140 inches on the coast) a good deal of the plateaux is covered with rain forest, and shifting agriculture has taken less toll, probably due to a sparse population. Farther inland the grass-covered summits of the Guinea highlands rise to 4,500 feet.

Liberia is in the dollar area and 80 per cent of her exports go to the United States. The chief of these is rubber, mainly from the Firestone plantations at Harbel and near Webo on the eastern border. In 1945, Firestone produced 97 per cent of Liberia's exports by value, but since then other smaller plantations have been established and other products developed for export, including iron ore, fruit and a little cocoa and oil-palm produce. Iron ore (68 per cent Fe) has been quarried in the Bomi hills since the completion of the mineral railway in 1951. Other ore bodies are being developed in the Mano river district, in the Nimba Mountains and in the Bong hills, which should allow a total output of some 15 million tons a year after 1965, making Liberia one of the world's leading exporters. An additional source of income from overseas is from the registration of foreign shipping. Liberia's staple food crop is rice, chiefly grown on uplands, but there is a small rice import necessary to feed plantation and mine labour.

The physical geography draws attention to many points of comparison with Sierra Leone, but one principal difference that accounts for the greater development of Sierra Leone lies in communications (Fig. 116). The lack of communications has severely retarded economic development in Liberia. Rivers are obstructed by rapids; roads are few and mainly in the vicinity of Monrovia. The only railway connects the Bomi iron-ore mines with the harbour at Monrovia and a further mineral line is under construction to link the new iron mines in the Nimba Mountains, near the Ivory Coast border, with the coast.

Monrovia (pop. 80,000), the capital and chief port, is the only town of any size and is linked by road with the N'Zérékoré district of Guinea. It possesses a number of small factories (brick and tile, soap, acetylene, tire re-treading and a brewery). Its deep-water harbour on Bushrod Island was completed in 1948 as a Lend-Lease project by the United States and provides the only free port in West Africa.

THE REPUBLIC OF GUINEA

The Republic lies between Sierra Leone and Portuguese Guinea. It was formerly a French colony, but on attaining its independence in 1958

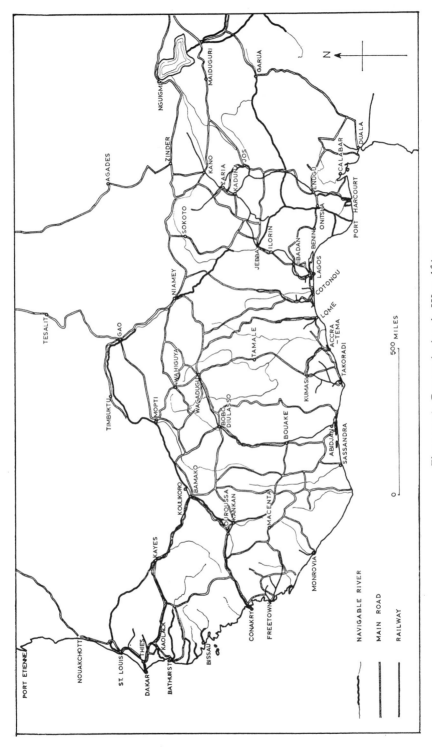

Figure 116 *Communications in West Africa*

decided to leave the French Community. The area is 106,000 sq. miles and the population (1965) 3·5 million. The Republic is notable in that it contains one of the largest areas of highland in West Africa. These mountains lie athwart the path of the rainbearing south-west winds, receive a heavy rainfall and start the Niger on its 2,600-mile course to the sea. Guinea is a poor state; her export trade amounts to little more than $11 per head of population and her Three-Year Development Plan of 1960 was modest and necessarily relied mainly on foreign capital.

GEOGRAPHICAL REGIONS

There are three major topographical divisions of Guinea: the Coastal Plain, the Futa Jallon-Guinea highlands, and the upper Niger Basin.

THE COASTAL PLAIN The coast differs from the east-west trending Ivory and Gold Coasts, already discussed, in that an absence of constant longshore drift does not favour the formation of sand-bars and lagoons. Instead, the coast has suffered recent submergence and rias have been formed. These muddy creeks and estuaries are now mangrove covered and flanked by marshes. Two rocky spurs, at Cape Verga and Conakry, break up the generally low coastline. Behind the mangrove swamps the coastal plain is 30-50 miles wide. It consists of sandy gravels washed down from the highlands and overlying old crystalline rocks. Here both rainfall and temperature are high (Conakry, 169 inches, mean annual temp. 81°F), but it is well populated. Rice and oil-palms are grown and there are some pineapple and banana plantations.

THE FUTA JALLON–GUINEA HIGHLANDS The main mass of the Futa Jallon consists of a remarkably level plateau of Lower Palaeozoic sandstone capped in places with a bare impervious ferruginous crust. The main surface, a little above 3,000 feet, is deeply incised by the trenches of the trellis-patterned drainage and has four higher areas rising to over 4,000 feet. To west and north the plateau edge consists of a series of fault steps, but to the east the slopes are gentler. One long north-to-south ridge includes the basalt peaks of Mont Gangan (3,627 feet) and the Kakoulima massif overlooking the coastal plain and separated from the main upland mass by a broad flat-floored valley. Much of this valley is drained by the Konkouré river which cuts westward through the ridge to the coast near Conakry. The upper highlands are well populated by Fulani who rear small Ndama cattle and adopt a semi-nomadic régime.

The Futa Jallon is continued to the south-east in the Guinea highlands. These consist of a series of north-east to south-west ridges in the crystalline rocks of the Basement Complex. They attain 5,695 feet in the Nimba Mountains on the border with Liberia. In contrast to the Futa Jallon there are few level surfaces, the hills are rounded and the lower slopes forested. These combined highlands form the watershed of West Africa; they provide the headstreams of the Niger, Senegal and Gambia rivers.

THE UPPER NIGER BASIN The north-east of Guinea comprises upland plains drained by the upper Niger and its tributaries flowing from the Futa Jallon-Guinea highlands. This plain consists of sandstones and granites with laterite cappings, mostly at about 1,000 feet. Rice is cultivated beside the rivers and cassava, yams and millets are grown. West of Siguiri in the Bouré district gold is worked in 'placer' deposits. Formerly this area was one of the chief sources of gold for the ancient empires of Ghana and Mali.

Rain forest in Guinea occurs along the fringe of the highlands especially in valley bottoms and on the coastal plain. Savanna prevails in the Niger Basin and grassland on the more densely populated uplands. Much of the original vegetation has been removed, especially on the coast where the mangrove swamps have been replaced in many areas by rice polders.

THE ECONOMY

Rice is the staple foodstuff grown in mangrove and freshwater swamps and as an upland crop. Other important food crops are fonio or 'hungry rice' (especially important on the poor soils of the Futa Jallon), sorghum, maize and plantains. The chief export crops are coffee, bananas, oil-palm kernels and fruits. Coffee is grown mainly in the Guinea highlands and Futa Jallon, and bananas in the coastal plain and in the valleys of the Futa Jallon. The banana industry is highly organised, located principally in the southern part of the coastal plain beside the railway. It concentrates on the production of the small sweet Canary Island or Chinese banana.

Guinea has an enormous reserve of *iron ore* (52 per cent Fe) in the Kaloum Peninsula at the tip of which is the port of Conakry (in 1961 production was 540,000 tons). *Bauxite* is worked on the Islands of Los (just off Conakry) and other deposits occur at Boké, Dabola and Kindia.

The production of alumina using Konkouré hydro-electric power (from the Kaleta Falls) began at Fria in 1960 and an eventual output of over 1 million tons a year is planned. *Diamonds* are now produced from the Beyla-Macenta district of the south-east.

Conakry (pop. 112,500), the capital and chief port, was built on Tombo Island and connected by causeway to the Kaloum Peninsula. The port is sheltered and has deep water, but remained unimportant because of the low productivity of the hinterland until iron-ore export began in 1952. Since then it has doubled its population and a number of industries—soap, fruit canning, plastics manufactures—have commenced. *Kankan* (pop. 29,000) on the navigable Milo tributary of the Niger is the terminus of the Republic's single railway from Conakry and is also a road focus and administrative centre.

PORTUGUESE GUINEA

This Portuguese colony was discovered by Nuño Tristâo in 1446. It covers nearly 14,000 sq. miles, has a population (1960) of 544,000 and comprises a rather monotonous lowland area nowhere attaining 1,000 feet and being mostly below 500 feet. The coastline has low peninsulas and rias with numerous off-shore islands. It is fringed by mangrove swamps and there is a high tidal range (spring tides of 19 feet at Bolama Island). Much of the colony comprises the lower courses and estuaries of sluggish meandering rivers. Three major ones are the Cacheu, Geba and Corubal, and each is navigable for about 100 miles. The only relief features are small cliffs of outcrops of laterite, except in the extreme south-east where broad grassy outliers of the Futa Jallon, rising to 700 feet, offer some variety. The south-west monsoon gives an annual rainfall of 80 to 100 inches along the coast, most of it falling within 6 months of the year. Inland, rainfall diminishes and the belt of rain forest behind the swampy coastlands gradually gives way to wooded savanna.

The economy depends mainly on the production of rice in the estuarine polders and groundnuts on the sandy soils of the inland plain. Palm kernels and a little copra are also exported. Most of the population lives in the coastlands, especially in the north where Bissau (6,000) is the chief port and the capital.

THE CAPE VERDE ISLANDS

The Cape Verde Islands, a Portuguese colony, lie 450 miles out in the Atlantic due west of St. Louis in Senegal. The ten major islands are of volcanic origin; the soils derived from the volcanic rocks are fertile and productive provided water is available. The islands lie in the Trade Wind Belt, here of Harmattan affinity and therefore dry. Rainfall is low, totalling 5-10 inches annually and falls in the late summer. Irrigation is necessary for successful agriculture. The area of the colony is 1,550 sq. miles and the population 201,000. Thus for mountainous islands the population density, at over 130 per sq. mile, is very high and the standard of living is low.

Local food production is limited and droughts may occur for up to three years. Famines have been frequent and there has been considerable emigration. Some irrigation is possible on São Tiago, the largest island, but several of the other islands are mostly wasteland or at best have only poor pasture. Exports consist of coffee, salt (from sea water), oilseeds, bananas and tunny. *Porto-Grande* (pop. 20,000) on São Vicente is a fuelling station on routes between South America and Europe. *Prais* (pop. 6,000) on São Tiago is the capital.

Selected Bibliography

R. J. Harrison Church, *West Africa* (London, 1963)

K. M. Buchanan and J. C. Pugh, *Land and People in Nigeria* (London, 1955)

T. E. Hilton, *Ghana population atlas* (Accra, 1960)

International Bank, *Economic development of Nigeria* (Baltimore, 1960)

J. Pouquet, *L'Afrique Occidentale Française. Paris,* 1954

A. B. Mountjoy, *Industrialisation and Under-developed Countries* (London, 1963) (esp. Ch. 8)

E. Huxley, *Four Guineas* (London, 1954)

R. W. Steel, 'Land and Population in British tropical Africa', *Geog.*, 40 (1955), 12–17

R. W. Steel, 'Some problems of population in British West Africa', in Steel and Fisher (eds.), *Geographical Essays on British Tropical Lands* (London, 1956), 17–50

R. J. Harrison Church, 'The transport pattern of British West Africa' in Steel and Fisher, *op. cit.*, 53–76

W. B. Morgan, 'Food imports of West Africa', *Econ. Geog.*, 39 (1963), 351–62

H. P. White, 'Ports of West Africa', *Tijdschrift v. Econ. en Soc. Geog.*, 50 (1959)

A. T. Grove, 'Soil erosion in Nigeria', in Steel and Fisher, *op. cit.*, 77–112

B. W. Hodder, 'Tin mining in the Jos Plateau', *Econ. Geog.*, 35 (1959), 109–22

R. Miller, 'The climate of Nigeria', *Geog.*, 37 (1952), 198–213

W. B. Morgan, 'Farming practice . . . in South-eastern Nigeria', *Geog. Journ.*, 121 (1955), 320–33

W. B. Morgan, 'Agriculture in Southern Nigeria', *Econ. Geog.*, 35 (1959), 138–50

H. P. White, 'New ports in Dahomey and Togo', *Geog.*, 46 (1961), 160–3

H. P. White, 'Dahomey: the geographical basis of an African state', *Tijdschrift v. Econ. en Soc. Geog.*, 57 (1966), 61–7

E. A. Boateng, 'Some recent changes in settlement in south-east Gold Coast', *Trans. Inst. Brit. Geogr.*, 21 (1955), 157–69

D. Hilling, 'Ghana's aluminium industry', *Tijdschrift v. Econ. en Soc. Geog.*, 55 (1964), 128–32

D. Hilling, 'Tema: the geography of a new port', *Geog.*, 51 (1966), 111–25

T. E. Hilton, 'Land planning and resettlement in northern Ghana', *Geog.*, 44 (1959), 227–40

T. H. Hilton, 'The changing Ivory Coast', *Geog.*, 50 (1965), 291–5

H. R. Jarrett, 'The urban geography of Freetown, Sierra Leone,' *Geog. Rev.*, 46 (1956), 334–54

H. R. Jarrett, 'The oil palm . . . in the economy of Sierra Leone', *Geog.*, 42 (1957), 50–9

J. Gallais, 'Riziculture de plaine en Haunte-Guinée', *Ann. de Géog.*, 68 (1959), 207–23

H. R. Jarrett, 'The geographical regions of the Gambia', *Scot. Geog. Mag.*, 66 (1950), 162–9

Y. Pehaut, 'L'Arachide au Sénégal', *Cahiers d'Outre Mer*, 14 (1961), 5–25

J. Janvier, 'L'Economie Senegalaise d'Aujourdhui', *Rev. Canadienne de Geog.*', 16 (1962), 13–19

H. Isnard, 'Agriculture et dévelopment en Afrique Occidentale', *Cahiers d'Outre Mer*, 16 (1963), 253–62

PART XIV

Conclusion

'Writing about modern Africa is like trying to sketch a galloping horse that is out of sight before you have sharpened your pencil' (Elspeth Huxley). It is the dynamic changes in African societies and economies that now compel the attention of the rest of the world. Everywhere throughout the continent changes are taking place: changes in society, institutions, ways of life, and locally, in the landscape. A great continent is being shaken out of its age-long lethargy. Within fifty years among many Africans there has been astounding progress: in half a century a jump from the Stone Age to the atomic era.

Despite the staggering advances, progress against backwardness, ignorance, poverty and undernutrition has a great way to go. We are only now at the beginning of the road. This century, particularly the last two decades, has revealed vividly the wealth, the variety and the personality of Africa to the rest of the world, yet much has still to be understood. It should now be clear that no assessment of Africa's standing and role in the modern world can overlook the many disadvantages that her geography displays. Physically, the greatest drawback is her lack of great alluvial plains; climatically, she suffers the penalties of the tropical environment: the poverty of widespread lateritic soils, fickle and unreliable rainfall over wide areas culminating in great deserts, the almost universal presence of predatory pests and debilitating diseases. In short, a harsh environment that is only now beginning to respond to the science, technology and capital brought in by the white man.

THE PROBLEMS OF THE TROPICAL ENVIRONMENT are paramount, and are only slowly being measured and comprehended by the world's scientists. It is upon the successful conquest of the tropical environment and its attendant disabilities that the full advance of Africa to levels of living, education and wealth already attained in the earlier developed continents hinges. The greatest development that would alter the character of much of tropical Africa would be the eradication of the tsetse fly.

Animals for draught purposes, improved agriculture with mixed farming, better diet and health for millions are the prizes for such an advance. The locust scourge, the worm diseases, malaria, and a multitude of endemic diseases have still to be conquered. The management of tropical soils, the breeding of better crops and animals for tropical climates still have a long way to go.

POPULATION PRESSURE is becoming marked in many parts of the continent. The white man has stamped out slaving and tribal warfare, while the introduction of better health measures and hygiene reduce death rates, particularly the infant mortality rate. We are witnessing the beginning of an astonishing population expansion that will build up to formidable proportions during the next two decades. Population structures are changing: African populations increasingly are becoming young populations with 40 to 50 per cent being under fifteen years of age. Growing numbers both retard and outpace economic development; pressure of population on the land may cause overstocking and over-grazing; unemployment in towns all too often leads to unrest and violence and support for extreme political views. A further symptom all over Africa is in growing urbanisation. The impact of the west and a money economy has undermined tribal authority. The values of the market place supersede the values of a kinship system, and the urban African gulping the heady wine of nationalism speeds the disintegration of an outmoded system before its replacement has been fashioned.

AGRARIAN PROBLEMS are pressing. Over much of the continent habitable lands are being destroyed through steadily increasing pressure of human and cattle populations, and by primitive and inadequate agricultural methods. Vast areas remain underdeveloped because of the need for capital to clear bush and establish water conservation projects. There is a crying need for land reform. One of the greatest obstacles to progressive native farming in Africa has been the system of land tenure. The general pattern that land is tribal and communal and allocated (often annually) by the elders stultifies innovation and discourages betterment. Many agricultural difficulties can be overcome if freehold is substituted for communal land tenure, title to land registered and the right to use land as a loan collateral conceded. A new and far more productive era in African farming is heralded by these means as Rhodesia, Ivory Coast and Kenya are now demonstrating.

It is imperative to raise African agricultural productivity, for until this occurs economic development introducing industrialisation can only have limited success. Africa is not underdeveloped because it has little manufacturing industry, but because its primary production is inefficient and inadequate. The raising of the productivity and efficiency of the one in turn stimulates and makes possible the expansion of the other. This suggests that, irrespective of future discoveries, the already known resources of Africa constitute great riches that have yet scarcely been

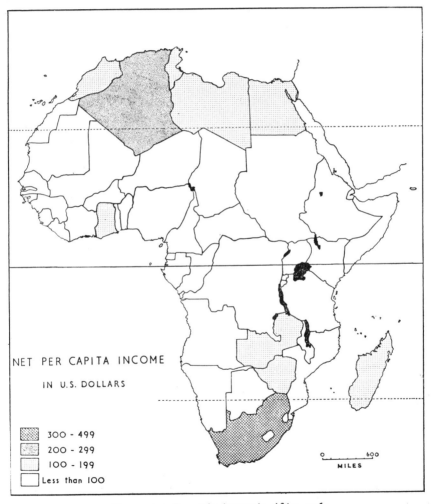

Figure 117 *Per capita income in Africa, 1962*

appreciated or developed. The initial physical disadvantages that the great continent possesses have retarded movement, knowledge and investment and only now is momentum being attained.

POLITICAL CHANGES also pose serious problems to the emergent African peoples. Independence has bred too many states, many of them small inland fragments of former large units, such as French West and French Equatorial Africa. No other continent is divided into so many separate states, and many of these new entities are politically weak and of doubtful economic viability. Thus their economic progress may be slow, which may lead to discontent and unrest.

ECONOMIC PROBLEMS Throughout the continent the dual character of the various economies has been demonstrated: the modern or revenue-producing sector, based upon a minority of the population and frequently run by the white man, and the much greater subsistence element affecting the mass of the people and contributing little towards investment for development and social services.

The modern sector of the economy in each country concerns itself with the production and export of a limited range of primary products or minerals. Cocoa provides Ghana with 65 per cent of her export revenue; cotton with 70 per cent of the value of Egypt's exports; cotton, coffee and sisal between them account for 60 per cent of East Africa's export revenue; and copper provides nearly 80 per cent by value of Zambia's exports. Because of this the economies of many African countries are vulnerable to the fluctuations in world prices of primary products. Such fluctuations of income have a number of adverse effects. The capacity to import capital goods and other growth-stimulating commodities is reduced, and taxable capacity becomes lowered; this in turn retards the development of social services and infrastructure of transport and utilities. Moreover, since the war, prices of primary products have lagged behind prices of manufactured goods, and the terms of trade between the developed and underdeveloped countries have grown disadvantageous to the latter. All this underlines the growing need for a greater diversity of economic development concurrent with a reduction of the subsistence sector of the economies.

Economic development in Africa aims at reducing the impoverished subsistence sectors of economies by vigorous measures of agrarian education and aid; and of diversifying economies by introducing manufacturing and service activities. These, however, will be limited both in scope and scale for an appreciable period, for local markets are small, skilled workers, managers and entrepreneurs are scarce, and the necessary infrastructure of utilities and services is yet inadequate. The tremendous investment required to bring about these changes cannot be produced by the African; of necessity there will be an increasing reliance upon loans, grants and commercial investment by the wealthier countries. It is only by such means that the great power and irrigation dams, railway, road and port extensions can be provided.

African development to date owes practically everything to the white man, mainly the European. The knowledge, skill, capital, enterprise and dynamic force have all come from outside the continent or from Europeans who have made it their home. It is the revenue created from their agriculture, industries and exports that is slowly lifting the standard of living of the African native. Whether the white man withdraws politically or not, he cannot withdraw economically—his involvement is too great and is reinforced by moral duty.

The pattern of African history has related the continent to Western Europe and although the one common denominator over most of Africa in recent decades has been the desire to be entirely free of colonial rule, the links with the West necessarily remain. Only in the Republic of South Africa has economic development progressed far enough to create a reasonable independence of external influence. Thus, all too often extremists having attained independence continue to agitate against 'neo-colonialism', for they find that the attainment of political freedom in no magical way releases them from close economic relationship and commercial dependence on the West. Egypt's trading pacts with the Soviet Bloc, the sales of Uganda cotton to India and the interest shown by Communist China in East Africa do not solve but underline the basic problem of chronic dependence upon external economic power.

Africa badly needs economic development and education; the one grows from the other, both are vastly expensive and will need much time. Given education, increasingly the black man will supplant the white man in administration, commerce and industry. Over most of the continent the days of the white man's use of cheap black labour are over; we are now seeing the uneasy transitional phase as power moves to the African majority. Here good sense and goodwill must prevail, for in the long run there can be no real economic or social progress until the problems of plural societies are solved, until racial harmony has been attained.

General Bibliography

Among recent publications or revisions of established texts dealing with Africa are

The Times Atlas of the World, Vol. IV (London, 1956)
United Nations, *Economic survey of Africa since 1950* (New York, 1959)
UNESCO, *A review of the natural resources of the African Continent* (Paris, 1963)
R. J. Harrison Church *et al.*, *Africa and the islands* (London, 1964)
W. Fitzgerald, *Africa, a social, economic and political geography* (London, 1961)
Lord Hailey, *An African survey* (London, 1956)
W. A. Hance, *African economic development* (New York, 1967)
W. A. Hance, *The geography of modern Africa* (New York and London, 1964)
G. H. T. Kimble, *Tropical Africa*, 2 vols. (New York, 1961)
A. B. Mountjoy, *Industrialisation and Under-developed countries* (London, 1963)
L. D. Stamp, *Africa, a study in tropical development* (London, 1957)
E. B. Worthington, *Science in the development of Africa* (London, 1958)

The most up-to-date contributions to the geography of Africa appear in the major geographical journals. A selected list of articles has been included at the end of each part. The abbreviations used are:

Geographical Journal (*Geog. Journ.*)
Geography (*Geog.*)
Transactions of the Institute of British Geographers (*Trans. Inst. Brit. Geogr.*)
Scottish Geographical Magazine (*Scot. Geog. Mag.*)
Geographical Review (*Geog. Rev.*)
Economic Geography (*Econ. Geog.*)
Annals of the Association of American Geographers (*Ann. Assoc. Am. Geogr.*)
South African Geographical Journal (*S. Afr. Geog. Journ.*)
Annales de Géographie (*Ann. de Géog.*)
Revue de Géographie Alpine (*Rev. Géog. Alpine*)
Tijdschrift voor Economische en Sociale Geografie (*Tijdschrift v. Econ. en Soc. Geog.*)

Index